Organic Reactions

Organic Reactions

VOLUME VIII

JOHN WILEY & SONS, INC.

NEW YORK · LONDON · SYDNEY

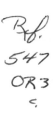

Library of Congress Catalog Card Number: 42–20265

PREFACE TO THE SERIES

In the course of nearly every program of research in organic chemistry the investigator finds it necessary to use several of the better-known synthetic reactions. To discover the optimum conditions for the application of even the most familiar one to a compound not previously subjected to the reaction often requires an extensive search of the literature; even then a series of experiments may be necessary. When the results of the investigation are published, the synthesis, which may have required months of work, is usually described without comment. The background of knowledge and experience gained in the literature search and experimentation is thus lost to those who subsequently have occasion to apply the general method. The student of preparative organic chemistry faces similar difficulties. The textbooks and laboratory manuals furnish numerous examples of the application of various syntheses, but only rarely do they convey an accurate conception of the scope and usefulness of the processes.

For many years American organic chemists have discussed these problems. The plan of compiling critical discussions of the more important reactions thus was evolved. The volumes of *Organic Reactions* are collections of chapters each devoted to a single reaction, or a definite phase of a reaction, of wide applicability. The authors have had experience with the processes surveyed. The subjects are presented from the preparative viewpoint, and particular attention is given to limitations, interfering influences, effects of structure, and the selection of experimental techniques. Each chapter includes several detailed procedures illustrating the significant modifications of the method. Most of these procedures have been found satisfactory by the author or one of the editors, but unlike those in *Organic Syntheses* they have not been subjected to careful testing in two or more laboratories. When all known examples of the reaction are not mentioned in the text, tables are given to list compounds which have been prepared by or subjected to the reaction. Every effort has been made to include in the tables all such compounds and references; however, because of the very nature of the reactions discussed and their frequent use as one of the several steps of syntheses in which not all of the intermediates have been isolated, some instances may well have been missed. Nevertheless, the investigator will be able

v

U. S

to use the tables and their accompanying bibliographies in place of most
or all of the literature search so often required.

Because of the systematic arrangement of the material in the chapters
and the entries in the tables, users of the books will be able to find information desired by reference to the table of contents of the appropriate
chapter. In the interest of economy the entries in the indices have been
kept to a minimum, and, in particular, the compounds listed in the tables
are not repeated in the indices.

The success of this publication, which will appear periodically, depends upon the cooperation of organic chemists and their willingness to
devote time and effort to the preparation of the chapters. They have
manifested their interest already by the almost unanimous acceptance
of invitations to contribute to the work. The editors will welcome their
continued interest and their suggestions for improvements in *Organic
Reactions*.

CONTENTS

SUBJECTS OF PREVIOUS VOLUMES

viii

CHAPTER 1

CATALYTIC HYDROGENATION OF ESTERS TO ALCOHOLS

The Late Homer Adkins

University of Wisconsin

CONTENTS

INTRODUCTION

In the presence of suitable catalysts, esters react with hydrogen to form alcohols according to the general equation

$$RCO_2R' + 2H_2 \rightleftarrows RCH_2OH + R'OH$$

The reaction is reversible, the relative concentrations of esters and alcohols at equilibrium being determined by the temperature and particularly by the pressure of hydrogen. For the representative case of n-octyl caprylate, in which the equation becomes

$$n\text{-}C_7H_{15}CO_2CH_2C_7H_{15}\text{-}n + 2H_2 \rightleftarrows 2\,n\text{-}C_7H_{15}CH_2OH$$

the concentration of the ester at equilibrium is about 80% at 140 p.s.i., 10% at 1200 p.s.i., and 1% at 4000 p.s.i. of hydrogen for reactions at 260°.[1] The higher the temperature, the higher is the concentration of ester at equilibrium. However, for pressures above 3000 p.s.i. and temperatures below 260° the amount of ester at equilibrium is so small that it is usually of little consequence.

The conversion of esters to alcohols may proceed either by hydrogenation,

$$\underset{\text{RCOR}'}{\overset{\text{O}}{\|}} + H_2 \rightleftarrows \underset{\overset{|}{\text{H}}}{\overset{\text{OH}}{|}}\text{RC—OR}' \rightleftarrows \overset{\text{O}}{\|}\text{RCH} + R'OH$$

$$\overset{\text{O}}{\|}\text{RCH} + H_2 \rightleftarrows RCH_2OH$$

or by hydrogenolysis,

$$\overset{\text{O}}{\|}\text{RCOR}' + H_2 \rightleftarrows \overset{\text{O}}{\|}\text{RCH} + R'OH \qquad \overset{\text{O}}{\|}\text{RCH} + H_2 \rightleftarrows RCH_2OH$$

There is no experimental basis for the choice of one hypothesis over the other. The distinction may not be significant, since the intermediate should be attached to the catalyst and so perhaps have no independent existence before it is converted to RCH_2OH. Use of the term hydrogenation in this chapter is a matter of convenience and does not imply a choice of mechanism.

Whereas the figures for the equilibrium concentration of ester cited above for n-octyl caprylate appear to be representative of the conversion of a variety of esters to alcohols,[1] the reversal of the hydrogenation of an

---

[1] Adkins and Burks, *J. Am. Chem. Soc.*, **70**, 4174 (1948).

ester such as ethyl laurate will give three new esters, i.e., dodecyl laurate, dodecyl acetate, and ethyl acetate. An even greater number of esters may result from the products of the hydrogenation of the ester of a dibasic acid, such as diethyl adipate.[2, 3]

Another side reaction not infrequently encountered is the formation

$$\underset{\|}{\overset{\text{O}}{}}$$

of significant amounts of esters of the type $RCOCH_2R$ from hydrogenations of esters of the type $RCO_2C_2H_5$ when a low pressure of hydrogen or other factors give a slow hydrogenation.[4] This reaction may be rationalized as the result of interaction of two aldehyde groups, adsorbed on the catalyst sufficiently close together to interact by a Tishchenko mechanism to give RCO_2CH_2R before hydrogenation of the aldehydes occurs. Alternatively, the RCO_2CH_2R type of ester may be produced slowly by alcoholysis of $RCO_2C_2H_5$ by RCH_2OH under the conditions existing in the reaction mixtures. Only with a few sugar lactones over a platinum catalyst has it been possible to hydrogenate an ester to an aldehyde[5, 6] without further hydrogenation to an alcohol.

The catalyst most suitable for the preparation of alcohols from esters by reaction with hydrogen under pressure is copper chromium oxide. The following discussion is concerned exclusively with this catalyst, except for the last section and its accompanying tables, in which certain other catalysts of limited usefulness are considered.

SCOPE AND LIMITATIONS

The yields of alcohols and glycols by hydrogenation of esters of monobasic and the higher dibasic acids free of complicating substituents (Tables I and IIB) are rather high, in many instances above 90%. In fact, with a pure sample of ester and a catalyst of good quality the hydrogenation of most such esters will lead to alcohols or glycols in yields above 95% at 250° under a pressure of 4000 p.s.i. Esters of dibasic acids with more than two carbon atoms separating the carbalkoxy groups give glycols in yields of above 95%. The yield from a succinate may be somewhat lower, i.e., 80–90%, since some hydrogenolysis is likely to take place with formation of an alcohol from the glycol. Diethyl oxalate gives a good yield of ethylene glycol but only with a

[2] Burks and Adkins, *J. Am. Chem. Soc.*, **62**, 3300 (1940).

[3] Lazier, Hill, and Amend, *Org. Syntheses*, **19**, 48 (1939); *Coll. Vol.* **2**, 325 (1943).

[4] Adkins, *Reactions of Hydrogen*, University of Wisconsin Press, 1937; *Ind. Eng. Chem.*, **32**, 1189 (1940).

[5] Glattfeld and Shamer, *J. Am. Chem. Soc.*, **49**, 2305 (1927); Glattfeld and Schnupff, *ibid.*, **57**, 2204 (1935).

[6] Adkins and Rice, unpublished data.

pressure much higher than normal. Malonic esters (Table IIA) constitute a special class, discussed below along with β-ketonic esters.

If a carbalkoxy group is located on an aromatic nucleus, the alcohol first formed can undergo hydrogenolysis with conversion of the CH_2OH group to a methyl group and water (Table IIA). This second step is an example of the debenzylation reaction (*Organic Reactions*, VII). If the

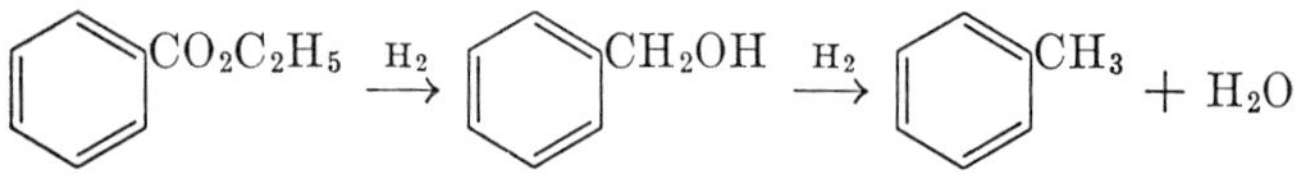

aromatic nucleus is naphthalene instead of benzene, another complication is introduced; one of the naphthalene rings can be hydrogenated, so that a methyltetralin is obtained by the hydrogenation of a carbalkoxynaphthalene. Fortunately the esters of these aromatic acids can be

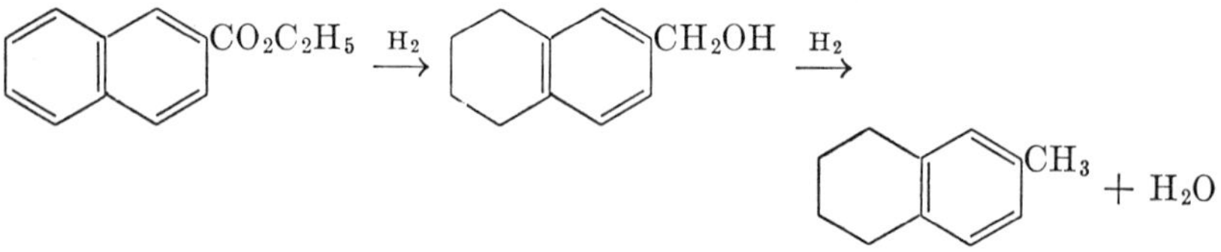

reduced at temperatures much lower than are required for esters of aliphatic acids. Ethyl benzoate undergoes hydrogenation at 125°, and ethyl 1-naphthoate even at 88°. This has made possible the preparation of carbinols from benzoic esters; the reductions are done in the temperature range 125–160°.[7] The use of a high ratio of catalyst to ester and limitation of the time of reaction permit the isolation of carbinols even from naphthoic esters.[8]

If a benzene nucleus is in the α position to the carbalkoxy group, the tendency towards hydrogenolysis is greatly reduced and the alcohol may be obtained in fairly good yield (80%) (Table IIIB). However, some hydrogenolysis of the CH_2OH group to a methyl group occurs, and a hydrocarbon may become the predominant product if the reaction is allowed to continue beyond the time when rate of hydrogen absorption falls off. The presence of two aromatic groups in the α position to the

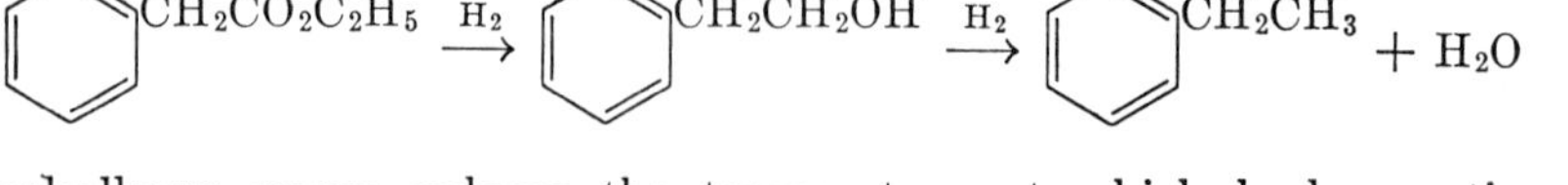

carbalkoxy group reduces the temperature at which hydrogenation takes place. Ethyl diphenylacetate is hydrogenated at a temperature (200°) that is 50° lower than would be required by an ester without a phenyl substituent.

[7] Mozingo and Folkers, *J. Am. Chem. Soc.*, **70**, 229 (1948).
[8] Adkins and Burgoyne, *J. Am. Chem. Soc.*, **71**, 3528 (1949).

α-Hydroxy esters are hydrogenated under milder conditions than most other esters. Ethyl benzilate is converted to the corresponding glycol in 77% yield at 125° within one hour with a 1:8 ratio of catalyst to ester. This temperature is 100° lower than would be required for an equal rate of hydrogenation for many esters. With a higher ratio of catalyst, five other α-hydroxy esters (Table IVA) have been hydrogenated to glycol, triol, or tetrol at 125°. The most striking case is the hydrogenation of diethyl tartrate to 1,2,3,4-butanetetrol without significant hydrogenolysis of the product.[9,10] 1,2-Glycols are more stable toward hydrogenolysis than 1,3-glycols or even 1,4-glycols so that good yields of 1,2-glycols can be obtained from α-hydroxy esters even at 200–250°.

Lactones can be hydrogenated to the corresponding glycols as recorded for γ-valerolactone in Table V. However, hydrogenolysis to an acid may also occur according to the following reaction.

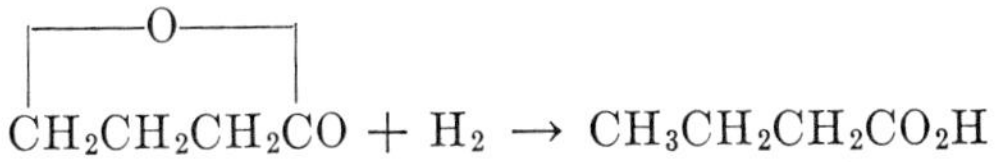

$$\overset{\lceil\text{----}O\text{----}\rceil}{CH_2CH_2CH_2CO} + H_2 \rightarrow CH_3CH_2CH_2CO_2H$$

If the reaction is run in an alcohol, the acid formed may be esterified and reduced to an alcohol, as shown for several lactones in Table V. Under more drastic conditions the hydrogenation of gluconolactone proceeds with hydrogenolysis of carbon-carbon as well as carbon-oxygen linkages and the formation of 1,3-propanediol and 1,2-ethanediol. No doubt the hydrogenation of lactones could be carried out in higher yields and with less hydrogenolysis than indicated by the data in Table V, if a higher ratio of catalyst to lactone were used.

Malonic esters, β-ketonic esters, and β-hydroxy esters undergo hydrogenolysis if hydrogenated at 250°, as is required with a 1 to 10 or 20 ratio of catalyst to ester (Tables IIA, IV, and VI). Typical formulations of these side reactions are as follows.

$$CH_3CHOHCH_2CO_2C_2H_5 \xrightarrow{H_2} CH_3CHOHCH_2CH_3 + CH_3CH_2CH_2CH_2OH$$

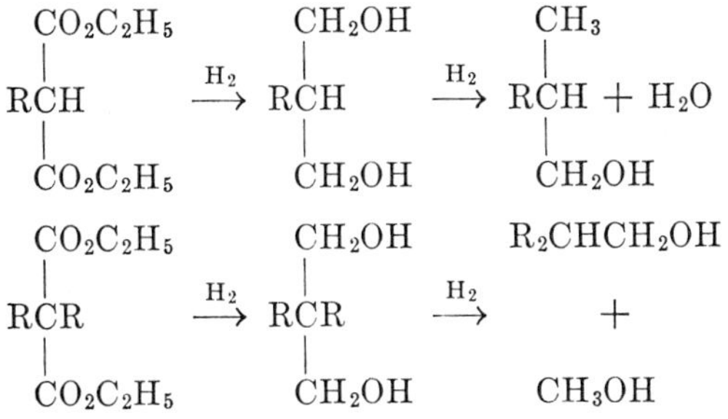

$$
\begin{array}{ccc}
CO_2C_2H_5 & CH_2OH & CH_3 \\
| & | & | \\
RCH & \xrightarrow{H_2} RCH & \xrightarrow{H_2} RCH + H_2O \\
| & | & | \\
CO_2C_2H_5 & CH_2OH & CH_2OH
\end{array}
$$

$$
\begin{array}{ccc}
CO_2C_2H_5 & CH_2OH & R_2CHCH_2OH \\
| & | & \\
RCR & \xrightarrow{H_2} RCR & \xrightarrow{H_2} + \\
| & | & \\
CO_2C_2H_5 & CH_2OH & CH_3OH
\end{array}
$$

[9] Adkins and Billica, *J. Am. Chem. Soc.*, **70**, 3121 (1948).
[10] Trenner and Bacher, *J. Am. Chem. Soc.*, **71**, 2352 (1949).

The glycol $RCHOHCH_2CH_2OH$ from a β-ketonic or β-hydroxy ester can undergo hydrogenolysis at either carbon-oxygen linkage so that isomeric alcohols are produced, i.e., $RCHOHCH_2CH_3$ and RCH_2CH_2-CH_2OH. A similar reaction takes place with a 1,3-glycol from malonic ester or a monosubstituted malonic ester, but only one alcohol, RCH-$(CH_3)CH_2OH$, is produced. As noted above, hydrogenolysis also occurs with glycols in which the hydroxyl groups are more distant from each other, but not to so great an extent.

With a disubstituted malonic ester, hydrogenolysis of a carbon-carbon linkage also occurs so that methanol and an alcohol, R_2CHCH_2OH, are obtained.

As in the aryl carbinols (p. 4), the hydrogenolysis of glycols may be avoided in large part if the hydrogenations are carried out with a high ratio of catalyst to ester.[9, 11] The use of as much catalyst as ester, or even more, makes it possible to hydrogenate esters at 80–150°. Under these conditions substituted malonates and β-hydroxy esters are converted to substituted glycols in yields of the order of 80%. The effectiveness of a high ratio of catalyst to ester in lowering the temperature required and thereby minimizing hydrogenolysis is illustrated by the hydrogenation of diethyl n-butylmalonate. With 95 g. of ester and 6 g. of catalyst, hydrogenation at 250° produces a 64% yield of 2-methyl-1-hexanol and a 26% yield of 1-hexanol. Thus hydrogenolysis occurs at both carbon-oxygen and carbon-carbon linkages. With 10 g. of ester and 15 g. of catalyst the hydrogenation goes as rapidly at 150° as at 250° with the lower proportion of catalyst. The only product is 2-(n-butyl)-1,3-propanediol. Similar observations have been made with other malonates and β-ketonic esters.

α-Amino esters are also readily hydrogenated to amino alcohols in good yields over copper chromium oxide. Most of these hydrogenations (Table VII) were carried out in alcohols at 175° or higher, so that alkylation of the amino group took place. However, it would appear that with a higher ratio of catalyst to ester the hydrogenations could be effected at 125° or lower without formation of secondary amines.

The hydrogenation of carbethoxy-substituted heterocyclic compounds (Table VIII) has not been very successful. Two or three carbethoxy-substituted pyrrolidines or pyrrolidones were converted to the corresponding alcohols in fair yields, but it appears that the use of a higher ratio of catalyst to ester and the lowering of the temperature of hydrogenation might yield significantly better results.

Hydrogenation has been carried out on esters of several different alcohols, e.g., methyl, ethyl, β-ethoxyethyl, n-butyl, sec-butyl, neopentyl,

[11] Mozingo and Folkers, J. Am. Chem. Soc., **70**, 227 (1948).

cyclohexyl, n-hexyl, 2-ethylbutyl, benzyl, hexahydrobenzyl, n-octyl, menthyl, and lauryl alcohols, and with esters of phenol and glycerol. The rates of hydrogenation of nine different esters of caproic acid were compared, but the variations in rate do not seem to be of great significance. As would be expected, the esters of alcohols or acids with alkyl substituents in the α or β position react more slowly than esters containing only unbranched chains. Glyceryl esters give water and propylene glycol as well as alcohols upon hydrogenation so that glycerides do not hydrogenate so rapidly as esters from which water is not formed. Benzyl esters form toluene and an acid upon hydrogenation, another example of the debenzylation reaction discussed in Volume VII. Phenyl esters furnish cyclohexanol and the alcohol corresponding to the acyl group in good yields.

The conditions required for the hydrogenation of carbalkoxy to carbinol groups are so drastic that almost any other unsaturated groups present in the molecule will be hydrogenated. Carbon-carbon double and triple bonds in open chains, carbon-nitrogen double and triple bonds, nitrogen-oxygen double bonds, carbon-oxygen double bonds, and carbon-carbon double bonds in furan, pyridine, and some benzene and naphthalene rings will be hydrogenated under the conditions usually used for conversion of esters to alcohols or glycols. Benzenoid nuclei in phenyl-substituted esters and pyrroloid nuclei are not hydrogenated and so appear in the alcohol or glycol unchanged after hydrogenation of

$$\text{an ester. An amide group} \quad -\overset{\displaystyle O}{\underset{\displaystyle }{\overset{\|}{C}}}-N\!\!< \quad \text{will also resist hydrogenation while}$$

a carbalkoxy group is being converted to a carbinol group. However, amides can be reduced to amines over copper chromium oxide.

If an ester contains halogen or sulfur, these constituents are removed by hydrogenolysis and deactivate the catalyst.

Esters containing a primary or secondary amino group are alkylated on the nitrogen if they are submitted to catalytic hydrogenation. Copper chromium oxide, like other hydrogenation catalysts, brings about reactions of the type:

$$RNH_2 + R'CH_2OH \rightarrow RNHCH_2R' + H_2O$$

$$R_2NH + R'CH_2OH \rightarrow R_2NCH_2R' + H_2O$$

This type of reaction may be useful in preparing secondary amines through hydrogenation of esters, amides, or imides, particularly in the case of pyrrolidines, piperidines, and hexahydroazepines.[12, 13]

[12] Paden and Adkins, *J. Am. Chem. Soc.*, **58**, 2491 (1936).
[13] Hill and Adkins, *J. Am. Chem. Soc.*, **60**, 1033 (1938).

THE COPPER CHROMIUM OXIDE CATALYST

Structure. Copper chromium oxide is an approximately equimolecular combination of cupric oxide and cupric chromite, i.e., $CuO \cdot CuCr_2O_4$. In addition, the most active varieties of this catalyst contain barium chromite and are sometimes referred to as barium-promoted copper chromium oxide.

P. W. Selwood,[14] on the basis of magnetic susceptibility measurements, has concluded that the catalyst "is not a simple copper chromite, nor is it a mechanical mixture of copper oxide and copper chromite. The catalyst is ferromagnetic at low temperatures and this property is not shown by the chromite, the copper oxide, or by mechanical mixtures of the two. Ferromagnetism is not shown by dispersed copper oxide." He felt that the term copper chromite for the catalyst "is definitely wrong and misleading as shown by Stroupe's X-ray work [15] and our own magnetic measurements." This conclusion is confirmed by the fact that the cupric chromite left after removal of the cupric oxide with an acid is inactive as a catalyst for hydrogenation of esters.

The catalyst is inactivated if, through excessive temperatures in the preparation or use of the catalyst, the cupric oxide reacts with cupric chromite to give cuprous chromite, $Cu_2Cr_2O_4$, and oxygen. However, the most frequent cause of inactivation of the catalyst is the reduction of the cupric oxide to copper. This is evidenced by a change in the color of the catalyst from black to a copper red. Such a deactivation of the catalyst is favored by the presence of water, acids, or ammonia in the reaction mixture. The reduction and inactivation of the catalyst may be minimized by precipitating barium (or strontium or calcium) chromate along with the basic copper ammonium chromate in the first step in the preparation of the catalyst.

The metallic copper in a red deactivated catalyst may be reoxidized to cupric oxide under mild conditions. In fact, a red deactivated catalyst is oxidized sufficiently in air at room temperature so that it again becomes black. According to Stroupe,[15] cuprous chromite may be reconverted to cupric oxide and cupric chromite by heating the deactivated catalyst in air at 600–700° for several hours. However, it is doubtful whether it is worth while in the laboratory to reactivate and use catalysts in which cupric oxide has been converted to cuprous chromite or metallic copper. Such reactivated catalysts are not nearly so active as good, fresh preparations.

[14] Selwood, Hill, and Boardman, *J. Am. Chem. Soc.*, **68**, 2055 (1946), and personal communications.

[15] Stroupe, *J. Am. Chem. Soc.*, **71**, 569 (1949).

Preparation. The catalyst may be made in a variety of ways, but the most satisfactory is the decomposition of basic copper ammonium chromate.[15a, 16–20] The chief reactions are the following.

$$2Cu(NO_3)_2 + Na_2Cr_2O_7 + 4NH_4OH$$
$$\downarrow 55°$$
$$2CuNH_4OHCrO_4 + 2NaNO_3 + 2NH_4NO_3 + H_2O$$
$$\downarrow 300°$$
$$CuO \cdot CuCr_2O_4 + N_2 + 5H_2O$$

In the preferred procedure,[16, 20] a solution (900 ml. at 80°) containing 260 g. of copper nitrate trihydrate and 31 g. of barium nitrate is poured with stirring into 900 ml. of a solution (at 25°) containing 178 g. of sodium dichromate dihydrate and 225 ml. of 28% ammonium hydroxide. The orange precipitate is collected on a filter, washed with 200 ml. of water in two portions, pressed and sucked as dry as possible, dried at 75–80° for twelve hours, and pulverized.

The product is decomposed in a three-necked 1-l. flask held in a Woods-metal bath at 350°. The flask is provided with a wide air condenser, a funnel for introducing a solid, and a stainless steel stirrer with a crescent blade 1.25 cm. wide and 10 cm. long, so shaped that it conforms to the bottom of the flask. The material to be decomposed is added through the funnel during a period of fifteen minutes with rapid stirring. The product is heated with stirring at a bath temperature of 350° for twenty minutes after all the material has been added. The temperature registered by a thermometer in the powder rises to perhaps 310° during the period of addition and then falls to about 278° during the subsequent twenty-minute period.

The product from the decomposition is leached by stirring for thirty minutes with 600 ml. of 10% acetic acid at room temperature. The residue is then washed with 600 ml. or more of water in 100-ml. portions, dried at 125° for twelve hours, and pulverized. The catalyst so obtained is brownish black and amounts to 160–170 g.

Evaluation of Catalyst. The quality of a sample of catalyst may be evaluated by hydrogenating 0.1 mole of methyl or ethyl laurate (previously freed of catalyst poisons by distillation from Raney nickel) with 5 g. of catalyst made up to 100 ml. with pure methanol or ethanol under 5000–6000 p.s.i. of hydrogen for three hours at 175°. A good sample of

[15a] Lazier and Arnold, *Org. Syntheses*, **19**, 31 (1939); *Coll. Vol.*, **2**, 142 (1943).

[16] Adkins, Burgoyne, and Schneider, *J. Am. Chem. Soc.*, **72**, 2626 (1950).

[17] Connor, Folkers, and Adkins, *J. Am. Chem. Soc.*, **54**, 1138 (1932).

[18] Calingaert and Edgar, *Ind. Eng. Chem.*, **26**, 878 (1934).

[19] Lazier, U. S. pat. 1,964,000 [*C. A.*, **28**, 5075 (1934)]; U. S. pat. 2,060,880 [*C. A.*, **31**, 711 (1937)].

[20] Riener, *J. Am. Chem. Soc.*, **71**, 1130 (1949), and personal communications.

copper chromium oxide will cause a drop in pressure corresponding to the apparent absorption of almost 0.2 mole of hydrogen with a conversion of more than 50% of the ester to dodecyl alcohol. The drop in pressure of hydrogen will be more than that which corresponds to the amount of ester hydrogenated, owing to adsorption of hydrogen by the catalyst.[16] However, a suitable drop in pressure may be taken as an indication of a sufficiently reactive catalyst. For example, a drop of 450–500 p.s.i. measured at 23°, under the conditions of test outlined above, in a reaction vessel where the drop in pressure per mole of hydrogen absorbed is 2600 p.s.i., indicates a first-class catalyst. The reliability of such a test depends upon precise observations of the pressure in the vessel after it has been shaken at room temperature but before it has been heated, and comparison with the pressure at room temperature after the completion of a three-hour reaction period at 175°. The test must, of course, be carried out in an assembly completely free of leaks.

EXPERIMENTAL CONDITIONS

Ester hydrogenations such as those summarized in Tables I–VIII are usually carried out under a pressure of 2000–6000 p.s.i. in a chrome-vanadium or stainless steel reaction vessel with a copper gasket and rocker-type agitation. The reaction vessels are readily fabricated or can be procured commercially in a variety of dimensions. It is important that a vessel have an adequate wall thickness of 0.5–0.75 in. for an internal diameter of 1.5–2.5 in. and that the length of the chamber be at least six times the internal diameter, if it is to be used in a rocker-type agitator. If agitation of the reactants is to be by stirring, a wider and shorter vessel is desirable. However, vessels with too large diameters are likely to present difficulties in obtaining an absolutely tight closure on continued use.

Safe practice in use of these pressure vessels requires: (1) a rupture disk designed to release at a 15–30% higher pressure than intended for the hydrogenation and attached as directly as possible to the vessel; (2) a barricade of masonry or 1/4-in. boiler plate surrounding the equipment; (3) controls and gauges outside the barricade for pressuring the vessel, observing the pressure, and releasing the pressure; and (4) rigid adherence to the rule that the enclosure is not to be entered while the vessel is being heated under pressure.

A means for securing an original pressure of at least 3000 p.s.i. and a temperature controller are essential for best results.

The rate of a catalytic hydrogenation is a function of several interdependent variables. Among the more important may be noted: ratio of catalyst to ester; activity of catalyst; purity of ester; temperature; and pressure of hydrogen. A deficiency in one of these factors sometimes may be compensated for by an excess in another factor. However, there are definite limits beyond which a higher temperature, for example, is not effective in taking care of deficiencies in quality of ester or catalyst or low pressure of hydrogen. Likewise, long periods of hydrogenation should not be used to make up for a deficiency in one of the five interdependent variables noted above. The course of the reaction should be followed by observations of pressure changes, and the time allowed should be based on these observations rather than on reaction times from the literature. Any factor that unduly prolongs the time required for completing a hydrogenation is very likely to result in poor yields of an inferior product. If hydrogenation does not proceed sufficiently rapidly under the usual conditions of temperature and pressure to complete the reaction within a few hours, then the ester, the catalyst, or the reaction vessel is contaminated with a catalyst poison. In this case, it is best to recover the ester from the reaction mixture and after purification submit it again to hydrogenation with fresh catalyst. Distillation of an ester from Raney nickel is often an effective method of purification.

A solvent is not usually necessary in carrying out the hydrogenation of an ester at 250°, since the original ester and the alcohol or glycol produced serve as a suitable reaction medium. However, a solvent is sometimes convenient in hydrogenating small quantities of ester, in order to minimize mechanical losses or to prevent a product from solidifying in the reaction vessel. Dioxane or an alcohol of two or more carbon atoms may be used. Since the critical temperatures for methanol and ethanol are about 240°, the observed pressure of hydrogen and ethanol at 250° will be about twice that at 25° as compared with a value of 1.8 for dioxane or other solvent not near its critical temperature. Ethanol as a solvent seems to give better yields than methanol at temperatures above about 200°, while below 200° methanol is somewhat preferable to ethanol. A reaction medium is almost always required for hydrogenation of esters at temperatures below 200° since the ratio of catalyst to ester required at these temperatures is so large that a good suspension of the catalyst cannot otherwise be obtained. Any basic or acidic impurities in the reaction medium are liable to deactivate the catalyst. Saturated hydrocarbons may be used as reaction media with the copper chromium oxide catalyst, although they seldom offer any advantage. Dioxane or the alcohols are solvents for any water produced in a hydrogenation and so prevent the formation of two liquid phases in the mixture.

Many of the yields reported in Tables I–VIII can doubtless be improved by conditions selected in the light of recent studies. In summary, the conditions most favorable to success are as follows: The pressure should be as high as can be obtained and used with standard high-pressure equipment. This is conducive to maximum rate and extent of hydrogenation. The original pressure should be high enough so that the maximum pressure when the temperature of reaction is reached is of the order of 6000 p.s.i. For a reaction temperature of 250° this would involve an initial pressure of about 3500 p.s.i. The pressure at the completion of the reaction should be 3000 p.s.i. or higher, measured at the temperature of reaction. For preparing alcohols and glycols stable to hydrogenolysis the hydrogenation may well be conducted at 250–260°, with one part of catalyst for each 10–20 parts of ester. The quality of ester and catalyst and their ratio should be such that all the ester reacts with hydrogen within one to eight hours. A much higher ratio of catalyst to ester should be used for preparing alcohols and glycols susceptible to hydrogenolysis at 200–250°, so that the ester may be hydrogenated within a few hours at a temperature of 80–160°. This is likely to require 1–1.5 parts of catalyst for one part of ester with methanol, ethanol, or dioxane as a reaction medium. The quality of catalyst, ester, and solvent should be such as to enable completion of hydrogenation within a few hours. In critical cases it may be necessary to run the hydrogenation in the vicinity of 100° in order to avoid as far as possible such undesired reactions as hydrogenation of unsaturated linkages, alkylation of amines, or hydrogenolysis of carbon-oxygen linkages.

TABULAR SURVEY OF ESTER HYDROGENATIONS CATALYZED BY COPPER CHROMIUM OXIDE

Tables I–VIII, in which the reported reactions are segregated according to a functional classification, summarize the literature through 1949. Within each group set off by a table title or sub-tabular heading, the entries are arranged first in order of increasing number of carbon atoms (exclusive of those present in N- or O-substituents) in the acid portion of the ester, and second in order of increasing branching.

Among the experimental data entered, the hydrogen pressure is least significant because there is no consistency in reporting this variable in the original papers, and the figure given may represent highest or lowest pressure used or their average. The most significant values would be the highest and lowest pressures observed at the temperature of reaction. The highest pressure reached is important since it determines the rate of reaction, whereas the pressure at the completion of the reaction will determine the extent of conversion if equilibrium is attained.

TABLE I

ESTERS OF MONOBASIC ACIDS (NON-AROMATIC HYDROCARBON SUBSTITUENTS ONLY)

Ester	Weight of Ester g.	Weight of Catalyst g.	Pressure p.s.i.	Temperature °C.	Time hr.	Product	Yield %	Reference
			Experimental Conditions					
Phenyl propionate	38	9	2200	250	19	1-Propanol	82	21
						Cyclohexanol	86	
Phenyl n-butyrate	33	8	2700	250	15	1-Butanol	81	21
						Cyclohexanol	98	
Ethyl valerate	35	5	3300	250	13	1-Pentanol	94	22
Ethyl α-methylbutyrate	15	3	3500	250	1.8	2-Methyl-1-butanol	97	23
Ethyl trimethylacetate	30	4	3300	250	1.5	Neopentyl alcohol	88	22
Methyl caproate	26	5	3700	250	2.2	1-Hexanol	92	24
Ethyl caproate	17	2	2700	225	7.5	1-Hexanol	62	24
n-Butyl caproate	34	5	3700	250	0.6	1-Hexanol	95	24
sec-Butyl caproate	21	2	2700	225	8	1-Hexanol	83	24
β-Ethoxyethyl caproate	23	2	2700	225	7	1-Hexanol	91	24
n-Hexyl caproate	24	2	2700	225	7.6	1-Hexanol	96	24
Cyclohexyl caproate	24	2	2700	225	3	1-Hexanol	Quant.	24
Hexahydrobenzyl caproate	25	2	2700	225	10	1-Hexanol	95	24
Lauryl caproate	34	2	2700	225	8.7	1-Hexanol	69	24
Ethyl β-methylvalerate	14	3	3700	250	1.5	3-Methyl-1-pentanol	90	23
Ethyl hexahydrobenzoate	39	5	4000	250	0.9	Cyclohexylcarbinol	97	24, 25
Ethyl cyclohexylacetate	40	5	2000	250	—	2-Cyclohexylethanol	94	26
Ethyl o-hexahydrobenzyl-hexahydrobenzoate	40	5	2000	250	—	o-Hexahydrobenzylcyclohexylcarbinol	74	26
Ethyl caprylate	34	5	2700	250	2	1-Octanol	94	24
Octyl caprylate	50	5	3980	260	0.7	1-Octanol	99	1
4-Methyloctyl 4-methyloctanoate	20	6	3500	250	2.2	4-Methyl-1-octanol	89	27
Methyl laurate	10	15	5000	150	13	1-Dodecanol	80	9
Ethyl laurate	30	3	3300	250	1.8	1-Dodecanol	98	22
Cocoanut oil	90	4	4500	285	6	Alcohols	88	28
Methyl n-hendecanoate	1.5	1	3000	250	6	1-Hendecanol	—	29
Ethyl α-ethylpelargonate	15	3	2500	250	0.8	2-Ethyl-1-nonanol	50	23
						Recovered acid	50	
Ethyl myristate	38	5	3300	250	2	1-Tetradecanol	98	22
Ethyl n-pentadecanoate	15	2.5	3000	250	6	1-Pentadecanol	85	29
Spermaceti	72	5	3700	250	2	1-Hexadecanol	97	24
Ethyl oleate	150	20	4900	250	2	Oleyl and stearyl alcohols	83	30
Butyl oleate	65	6.5	3000	250	—	1-Octadecanol	86	31
n-Butyl stearate	49	8	3700	250	11	1-Octadecanol	77	24

Note: References 21–51 are listed on p. 27.

TABLE II

Esters of Di- and Tetra-basic Acids (Non-Aromatic Hydrocarbon Substituents Only)

| | Experimental Conditions | | | | | | | |
Ester	Weight of Ester g.	Weight of Catalyst g.	Pressure p.s.i.	Temperature °C.	Time hr.	Product	Yield %	Reference
						A. Malonic Esters		
Diethyl malonate	10	15	5000	150	11	1,3-Propanediol	40	9
Diethyl malonate	32	6	4000	250	7.5	Ethyl propionate	—	24
						1-Propanol	—	
Diethyl methyl-malonate	10	15	5000	150	4.5	2-Methyl-1,3-propanediol	80	9
Diethyl ethoxymeth-ylenemalonate	10	15	5000	150	5	2-Methyl-1,3-propanediol	80	9
Diethyl ethyl-malonate	43	5	4000	250	2	2-Methyl-1-butanol	78	24
Diethyl ethyl-malonate	10	15	5000	150	6.5	2-Ethyl-1,3-propanediol	80	9
Diethyl ethyl-malonate	43	15	2500	250	8	2-Methyl-1-butanol	72	32
						1-Butanol	18	
Diethyl ethyl-malonate	28	8	5000	170	24	2-Ethyl-1,3-propanediol	49	11
Diethyl dimethyl-malonate	451	30	2500	250	4	Isobutyl alcohol	88	32
Diethyl n-propyl-malonate	10	15	5000	150	8	2-(n-Propyl)-1,3-propanediol	80	9
Diethyl methylethyl-malonate	246	15	2500	250	5	2-Methyl-1-butanol	80	32
Diethyl n-butyl-malonate	10	15	5000	150	9	2-(n-Butyl)-1,3-propanediol	80	9
Diethyl n-butyl-malonate	95	6	2500	250	9	2 Methyl-1-hexanol	64	32
						1-Hexanol	26	
Diethyl sec-butyl-malonate	53	12	5500	160	10	2-sec-Butyl-1,3-propanediol	24	11
Diethyl diethyl-malonate	108	10	2500	250	12	2-Ethyl-1-butanol	94	32
Diethyl methyliso-propylmalonate	308	20	2500	250	23	2,3-Dimethyl-1-butanol	—	32
Diethyl ethyl-n-butylmalonate	10	15	5000	150	13	2-Ethyl-2-(n-butyl)-1,3-propanediol	45	9
						Ethyl 2-hydroxymethyl-2-ethyl-n-caproate	28	
Tetraethyl propane-1,1,3,3-tetracarboxylate	166	17	4000	250	5	1,5-Pentanediol	90	33
Tetraethyl 2-methyl-propane-1,1,3,3-tetracarboxylate	65	7	4000	250	10	3-Methylpentane-1,5-diol	82	33
Diethyl n-heptyl-malonate	10	15	5000	150	11	2-(n-Heptyl)-1,3-propane-diol	80	9
Tetraethyl 2-propyl-propane-1,1,3,3-tetracarboxylate	40	4	4000	250	2	1-Hexanol	33	33
						3-Propyl-1,5-pentanediol	56	

Note: References 21–51 are listed on p. 27

TABLE II—*Continued*

ESTERS OF DI- AND TETRA-BASIC ACIDS (NON-AROMATIC HYDROCARBON SUBSTITUENTS ONLY)

	Experimental Conditions							
Ester	Weight of Ester g.	Weight of Catalyst g.	Pressure p.s.i.	Temperature °C.	Time hr.	Product	Yield %	Reference

A. Malonic Esters—Continued

Ester	Weight of Ester g.	Weight of Catalyst g.	Pressure p.s.i.	Temperature °C.	Time hr.	Product	Yield %	Reference
Diethyl isoamyl-ethylmalonate	77	10	2500	250	7	5-Methyl-2-ethyl-1-hexanol	91	32
Diethyl n-propyl-methylcarbinyl-ethylmalonate	212	15	2500	250	30	3-Methyl-2-ethyl-1-hexanol	80	32
Tetraethyl octane-3,3,6,6-tetra-carboxylate	100	8	4000	250	4	2,5-Diethyl-1,6-hexanediol	74	13

B. Esters of Dibasic Acids Other Than Malonic

Ester	Weight of Ester g.	Weight of Catalyst g.	Pressure p.s.i.	Temperature °C.	Time hr.	Product	Yield %	Reference
Diphenyl carbonate	35	5	2200	250	10	Methanol	75	21
						Cyclohexanol	82	
Diethyl succinate	10	15	5000	150	4	1,4-Butanediol	80	9
Diethyl succinate	77	7	3300	250	6.5	1,4-Butanediol	81	22
Diethyl glutarate	10	15	5000	150	10	1,5-Pentanediol	80	9
Di-n-butyl glutarate	49	7	3700	250	1.8	1,5-Pentanediol	92	24
Diethyl α-methyl-succinate	228	23	3700	250	1	2-Methyl-1,4-butanediol	72	33
Diethyl adipate	10	15	5000	150	12	1,6-Hexanediol	80	9
Diethyl adipate	34	2.5	2600	260	2.3	1,6-Hexanediol	—	2
Diethyl adipate	252	20	3000	255	2.5	1,6-Hexanediol	90	30
Diethyl α-isopropyl-succinate	100	10	3700	250	6.5	2-Isopropyl-1,4-butanediol	31	33
						Unchanged ester	12	
Diethyl hexahydro-phthalate	40	5	2000	250	—	Hexahydrophthalyl alcohol	40	26
						o-Methylhexahydrobenzyl alcohol	50	
Diethyl azelate	150	15	3000	270	4	1,9-Nonanediol	50	30
Diethyl sebacate	31	5	3700	250	1.7	1,10-Decanediol	94	24
Diethyl tetra-decanedioate	202	20	3700	250	4	1,14-Tetradecanediol	95	33

Note: References 21–51 are listed on p. 27.

TABLE III

ESTERS OF AROMATIC ACIDS

Ester	Weight of Ester g.	Weight of Catalyst g.	Pressure p.s.i.	Temperature °C.	Time hr.	Product	Yield %	Reference
		Experimental Conditions						
A. Esters with Carbalkoxy Group Attached to the Aromatic Nucleus								
Ethyl benzoate	50	7	5000	160	3	Benzyl alcohol	63	7
Ethyl benzoate	15	10	4500	125	5	Benzyl alcohol	65	8
Phenyl benzoate	40	9	2300	250	18	Toluene	69	21
						Cyclohexanol	87	
Methyl o-toluate	23	5	5300	160	2	o-Methylbenzyl alcohol	70	7
Methyl p-toluate	50	10	5300	130	11	p-Methylbenzyl alcohol	70	7
Ethyl 3,4-dimethyl-benzoate	89	10	5000	130	24	3,4-Dimethylbenzyl alcohol	64	7
Methyl p-isopropyl-benzoate	27	5	5000	160	8	p-Isopropylbenzyl alcohol	81	7
Ethyl 1-naphthoate	20	10	4500	88	3.5	1-Naphthylcarbinol	5	8
						1-Methylnaphthalene	35	
Methyl 2-naphthoate	19	10	4500	108	1.5	2-Naphthylcarbinol	35	8
Diethyl phthalate	40	5	2000	250	—	Phthalyl alcohol	9	26
						o-Methylbenzyl alcohol	14	
						o-Xylene	67	
Methyl salicylate	38	6	3700	250	6	o-Cresol	19	24
						2-Methylcyclohexanol	61	
Ethyl p-hydroxy-benzoate	50	10	5000	160	19	p-Hydroxybenzyl alcohol	60	7
Methyl o-methoxy-benzoate	36	5	5000	160	6	o-Methoxybenzyl alcohol	56	7
Methyl anisate	83	10	5000	140	23	Anisyl alcohol	89	7
Methyl veratrate	20	5	5300	155	4	3,4-Dimethoxybenzyl alcohol	86	7
B. Esters with Aryl Group Substituted in the α Position								
Ethyl phenylacetate	46	3	4000	250	1.8	Phenethyl alcohol	58	24
						Ethylbenzene	30	
Cyclohexyl phenyl-acetate	54	6	4000	250	0.5	Phenethyl alcohol	63	24
						Ethylbenzene	26	
Ethyl α-phenylpro-pionate	16	2	2500	250	3	2-Phenyl-1-propanol	16	23
						Isopropylbenzene	33	
Diethyl phenylmalonate	10	15	5000	150	1	2-Phenylpropane-1,3-diol	50	9
						2-Phenylethanol	32	
Diethyl phenylmalonate	71	10	2500	250	8	Ethylbenzene	71	32
						2-Phenylethanol	9	
Ethyl α-phenyl-butyrate	48	6	3700	250	0.6	2-Phenyl-1-butanol	78	24
Ethyl α-phenyl-butyrate	22	3	3500	250	1.3	2-Phenyl-1-butanol	61	23

Note: References 21–51 are listed on p. 27.

TABLE III—*Continued*

ESTERS OF AROMATIC ACIDS

	Experimental Conditions							
Ester	Weight of Ester g.	Weight of Catalyst g.	Pressure p.s.i.	Temperature °C.	Time hr.	Product	Yield %	Reference
B. Esters with Aryl Group Substituted in the α Position—Continued								
Ethyl α-phenyl-butyrate	96	8	2500	250	1.7	2-Phenyl-1-butanol	60	32
Menthyl α-phenyl-butyrate	42	6	2500	250	3	2-Phenyl-1-butanol	17	23
						sec-Butylbenzene	26	
Dimethyl α-phenyl-succinate	51	6	3700	250	6	3-Phenyl-1-butanol	67	24
						2-Phenyl-1,4-butane-diol	12	
Diethyl α-phenyl-succinate	38	4	3700	250	3	3-Phenyl-1-butanol	70	33
						2-Phenyl-1,4-butane-diol		
Methyl 1-naphthyl-acetate	20	20	4500	108	2	2-(1-Naphthyl)-ethanol	28	8
Ethyl 1-naphthyl-acetate	22	5	4500	190	3	2-(1-Tetrahydronaph-thyl)ethanol	77	8
						1-Ethyltetrahydronaph-thalene	17	
Ethyl diphenylacetate	40	5	2000	200	1	β,β-Diphenylethyl alcohol	58	26
						1,1-Diphenylethane	38	
C. Esters with Aryl Group Substituted in a Position Other Than α								
Ethyl β-phenyl-propionate	30	4	3700	250	1	3-Phenyl-1-propanol	93	24
Ethyl cinnamate	37	3	3300	250	9	3-Phenyl-1-propanol	83	22
Phenyl cinnamate	34	6	2200	250	11	3-Phenyl-1-propanol	81	21
Menthyl β-phenyl-butyrate	45	7	2500	250	2.6	3-Phenyl-1-butanol	73	23
Diethyl benzalmalo-nate	10	15	5000	150	5.5	2-Benzyl-1,3-propane-diol	80	9
Diethyl benzylmalo-nate	19	8	5000	160	6	2-Benzyl-1,3-propane-diol	26	11
Diethyl benzylmalo-nate	77	10	3000	250	8	2-Benzyl-1-propanol	68	32
						3-Phenyl-1-propanol	19	
Diethyl β-phenyl-glutarate	35	4	2250	250	1.5	3-Phenyl-1,5-pentane-diol	91	33
Ethyl α-ethyl-δ-phenylvalerate	11	2	2500	250	0.9	2-Ethyl-5-phenyl-1-pentanol	47	23
						Acid recovered	53	
Methyl β-(1-naph-thyl)propionate	21	10	4500	200	3	3-(Tetrahydro-1-naph-thyl)-1-propanol	89	8
Tetraethyl 2-phenyl-propane-1,1,3,3-tetracarboxylate	150	15	4000	250	7.5	3-Phenyl-1,5-pentane-diol	70	33
						3-Phenyl-1-propanol	27	
Ethyl γ-(1-naphthyl)-butyrate	24	5	4500	200	7	4-(Tetrahydro-1-naph-thyl)butanol	92	8
Ethyl γ-(2-naphthyl)-butyrate	24	5	4500	200	7	4-(Tetrahydro-2-naph-thyl)butanol	92	8, 35

Note: References 21–51 are listed on p. 27.

TABLE IV

Esters of Hydroxy and Alkoxy Acids

Ester	Weight of Ester g.	Weight of Catalyst g.	Pressure p.s.i.	Temperature °C.	Time hr.	Product	Yield %	Reference

Experimental Conditions

A. Hydroxyl Group in the α Position

Ester	Weight of Ester g.	Weight of Catalyst g.	Pressure p.s.i.	Temperature °C.	Time hr.	Product	Yield %	Reference
Ethyl lactate	10	15	5000	125	0.2	1,2-Propanediol	80	9
Ethyl lactate	30	5	4000	250	3.5	1,2-Propanediol	91	24
Butyl lactate	50	—	3000	225	2.0	1,2-Propanediol	81	23
Ethyl α-hydroxy-isobutyrate	10	15	5000	125	0.2	1,1-Dimethyl-1,2-ethanediol	80	9
Ethyl α-hydroxy-isobutyrate	340	20	2500	200	1.0	2-Methyl-1,2-propanediol	91	34
Diethyl malate	10	15	5000	150	3.0	1,2,4-Butanetriol	67	9
						1,4-Butanediol	20	
Dimethyl tartrate	4	2	5000	165	5	1,2,3,4-Butanetetrol	90	10
Diethyl tartrate	10	15	5000	125	9	1,2,3,4-Butanetetrol	80	9
Diethyl (+)-tartrate	4	2	5000	165		(+)-1,2,3,4-Butanetetrol	57	10
						(+,−)-1,2,3,4-Butanetetrol	39	
Diethyl α-hydroxy-β-methylsuccinate	102	10	4000	250	10	3-Methyl-1,2-butanediol	37	33
						2-Methyl-1,4-butanediol	25	
Ethyl citrate	150	12	9000	240	4.5	A trihydric alcohol	20	
Ethyl mandelate	10	15	5000	125	0.2	1-Phenyl-1,2-ethanediol	80	9
Ethyl mandelate	40	5	2000	250	—	2-Phenylethanol	70	26
						Ethylbenzene	13	
Ethyl benzilate	40	5	2000	125	1	1,1-Diphenyl-1,2-ethanediol	77	26

B. Hydroxyl or Alkoxyl Group in a Position Other Than α

Ester	Weight of Ester g.	Weight of Catalyst g.	Pressure p.s.i.	Temperature °C.	Time hr.	Product	Yield %	Reference
Ethyl β-ethoxypropionate	146	30	5000	170	23	3-Ethoxy-1-propanol	78	11
Ethyl β-hydroxybutyrate	40	6	4000	250	5	1- and 2-Butanol	55	24
Hexahydrobenzyl β-hydroxybutyrate	64	5	2500	250	6	1-Butanol	75	32
						2-Butanol		
Ethyl 2,2-dimethyl-3-hydroxybutyrate	34	4	3200	250	0.1	Isobutyl alcohol	98	22
Ethyl β-(4-hydroxycyclohexyl)propionate	57	—	3000	250	5	3-(4-Hydroxycyclohexyl)-1-propanol	93	36
Ethyl α-hexahydrobenzyl-β-hydroxybutyrate	47	5	2500	250	5	3-Cyclohexyl-1-propanol	96	32
Ethyl 12-hydroxystearate	—	16	3000	260	11	1,12-Octadecanediol	87	34
12-Hydroxystearin	4000	320	3000	260	7	1,12-Octadecanediol	—	28
Castor oil	200	16	3000	260	12	1,12-Octadecanediol	92	34

Note: References 21–51 are listed on p. 27.

TABLE V

LACTONES

Lactone	Weight of Lactone g.	Weight of Catalyst g.	Pressure p.s.i.	Temperature °C.	Time hr.	Product	Yield %	Reference
γ-Valerolactone	28	6	4000	250		1,4-Pentanediol	78	24
Gluconolactone	178	20	4500	250	2.5	1,2-Propanediol	21	37
						Ethylene glycol	9	
γ-Ethyl-γ-valerolactone	20	6	4000	250	3.5	4-Methyl-1-hexanol	80	27
o-Hydroxyphenoxyacetic acid lactone	19	6	2000	250	3.5	β-(o-Hydroxyphenoxy)-ethyl alcohol	77	21
γ-n-Butyl-γ-valerolactone	20	6	4000	250	2.8	4-Methyl-1-octanol	80	27
Coumarin	73	5	2000	250	0.7	γ-(o-Hydroxyphenyl)-propyl alcohol	90	38
Octahydrocoumarin	9	3	2000	250	4.5	γ-(2-Hydroxycyclohexyl)-propyl alcohol	50	38
γ-n-Amyl-γ-valerolactone	20	6	4000	250	3.5	4-Methyl-1-nonanol	84	27
6-Methylcoumarin	30	5	2000	250	1.5	2-(γ-Hydroxypropyl)-4-methylphenol	81	39
7-Methylcoumarin	29	5	2000	250	1	2-(γ-Hydroxypropyl)-5-methylphenol	76	39
4-Methyl-6-hydroxycoumarin	28	5	2000	250	4	4-Methyl-6-hydroxyhexahydrochroman	35	39
4,7-Dimethylcoumarin	35	5	2000	250	0.5	2-(γ-Hydroxy-sec-butyl)-5-methylphenol	80	39
γ-n-Hexyl-γ-valerolactone	20	6	4000	250	3.5	4-Methyl-1-decanol	85	27
7,8-Benzocoumarin	47	5	2000	250	3	2-(γ-Hydroxypropyl)-1-naphthol	31	39

Note: References 21–51 are listed on p. 27.

TABLE VI

ESTERS OF KETO ACIDS

Experimental Conditions

Ester	Weight of Ester g.	Weight of Catalyst g.	Pressure p.s.i.	Temperature °C.	Time hr.	Product	Yield %	Reference
A. Keto Group in the β Position								
Ethyl acetoacetate	10	15	5000	150	9	1,3-Butanediol	80	9
Ethyl acetoacetate	65	30	3700	170	9	1,3-Butanediol	30	11
Ethyl α,β-dioxo-butyrate	10	15	5000	100	4	1,2,3-Butanetriol	80	9
Diethyl acetone-dicarboxylate	10	15	5000	150	5	1,3,5-Pentanetriol	60	9
						Diethyl β-hydroxy-glutarate	12	
Ethyl ethylaceto-acetate	24	5	5000	168	11	2-Ethyl-1,3-butanediol	15	11
Ethyl ethylaceto-acetate	47	5	2500	250	5	Diethylcarbinylcarbinol	47	32
						1-Butanol	50	
Ethyl ethylaceto-acetate	10	15	5000	150	7	2-Ethyl-1,3-butanediol	80	9
Diethyl α-acetyl-succinate	144	15	4000	250	2	A lactone, $C_6H_{10}O_6$	20	33
						Glycols	40	
Ethyl α-methyl-β-ketovalerate	28	3	2500	250	8	1-Propanol	46	32
Diethyl α-acetyl-glutarate	139	14	3700	250	12	Glycols	50	33
						1,5-Pentanediol	—	
						2-Ethyl-1,5-pentanediol	—	
Ethyl α-n-butyl-acetoacetate	56	13	2500	250	26	2-Ethyl-1-butanol	21	32
						1-Hexanol	43	
Ethyl α-isopropyl-acetoacetate	52	5	2500	250	13	Isoamyl alcohol	60	32
						3-Methyl-2-ethyl-1-butanol	27	
Ethyl α,α-diethyl-acetoacetate	37	3	2500	250	8	Diethylcarbinylcarbinol	99	32
Ethyl isobutylidene-acetoacetate	43	—	4000	160	30	2-Isobutyl-1,3-butanediol	17	11
Ethyl α-benzoyl-acetate	10	15	5000	150	7	3-Phenyl-1-propanol	80	9
Diethyl α-butyl-α-acetylsuccinate	75	8	4000	250	1	2-n-Butyl-1,4-butanediol	93	33
Diethyl β-methyl-α,γ-diacetyl-glutarate	55	13	2500	250	16	A glycol	96	32
Diethyl α-acetyl-α-ethyladipate	46	5	4000	250	3	2-Ethyl-1,5-pentanediol	73	33
Ethyl α-benzylaceto-acetate	44	5	2500	250	5	3-Phenyl-1-propanol	89	32
Ethyl α,α-di-n-butyl-acetoacetate	49	3	2500	250	10	Di-n-butylcarbinyl-carbinol	99	32
Ethyl α-(phenethyl)-acetoacetate	47	5	2500	250	5	4-Phenyl-1-butanol	97	32
Diethyl α,γ-diacetyl-β-phenylglutarate	79	8	4000	250	8	2,4-Diethyl-3-phenyl-1,5-pentanediol	91	33
B. Keto Group in a Position Other Than β								
Ethyl levulinate	100	8	3700	250	4	1,4-Pentanediol	60	13
Ethyl δ-ketocaproate	67	8	3700	250	4	1,5-Hexanediol	85	13
Ethyl ε-ketoen-anthoate	56	8	3700	250	4	1,6-Heptanediol	82	13
Ethyl β-benzoyl-propionate	40	5	2200	250	—	4-Phenyl-1-butanol	94	26
Diethyl α-benzyl-α-acetylsuccinate	40	4	4000	250	1	3-Benzyl-1-butanol	39	33
						2-Benzyl-1,4-butanediol	34	
Ethyl o-benzoyl-benzoate	40	5	2000	250	—	o-Benzyltoluene	93	26

Note: References 21–51 are listed on p. 27.

TABLE VII

ESTERS OF AMINO ACIDS

	Experimental Conditions							
Ester	Weight of Ester g.	Weight of Catalyst g.	Pressure p.s.i.	Temperature °C.	Time hr.	Product	Yield %	Reference
A. Amino Group in the α Position								
Ethyl piperidinoacetate	10	15	5000	125	2.2	2-Piperidinoethanol	80	9
Ethyl piperidinoacetate	43	5	4000	250	2.0	2-Piperidinoethanol	82	40
Ethyl N-diethyl alaninate	—	—	3500	175	—	2-Diethylamino-1-propanol	63	41
Methyl (+,−)-leucinate in 1-butanol	8	15	3000	175	8	N-n-Butyl-(+,−)-leucinol hydrochloride	64	42
Methyl (+,−)-leucinate in dioxane	8	4	3600	175	5	(+,−)-Leucinol hydrochloride	74	43
Methyl (+,−)-leucinate in ethanol	8	10	3000	175	7	N,N-Diethyl-(+,−)-leucinol	83	42
Methyl (+,−)-leucinate in isobutyl alcohol	8	15	3000	175	16	N-Isobutyl-(+,−)-leucinol hydrochloride	56	42
Methyl (+,−)-leucinate in isopropyl alcohol	7	10	3000	175	16	N-Isopropyl-(+,−)-leucinol hydrochloride	64	42
Methyl (+,−)-leucinate in methanol	5	5	3000	175	7	N,N-Dimethyl-(+,−)-leucinol	—	43
Methyl (+,−)-leucinate in 1-propanol	9	15	3000	175	10	N-n-Propyl-(+,−)-leucinol hydrochloride	70	42
Methyl (+,−)-leucinate in 1-propanol	5	10	3000	250	12	N,N-Di-n-propyl-(+,−)-leucinol hydrochloride	26	42
Ethyl (−)-norleucinate in methanol	4	4	3600	175	7	N,N-Dimethyl-(+,−)-norleucinol	—	43
Ethyl N-acetyl-(−)-norleucinate in methanol	5	5	3600	175	6	N,N-Dimethyl-(+,−)-norleucinol	—	43
Methyl (+,−)-phenyl alaninate in methanol	6	10	3000	175	7	N,N-Dimethyl-(+,−)-phenyl alaninol	88	42
B. Amino Group in a Position Other Than α								
Ethyl β-piperidino-propionate	53	8	4000	250	11	Piperidine	—	24
						N-Ethyl- and propyl-piperidine	—	
						Ethyl propionate	—	
Ethyl γ-piperidino-butyrate	21	4	4000	240	1.5	γ-Piperidinopropanol	—	44
						4-Piperidino-1-butanol	62	
						1,4-Butanediol	28	
Ethyl γ-piperidino-butyrate	43	5	4000	250	2.0	4-Piperidino-1-butanol	16	40
						N-n-Butylpiperidine	35	
						N-Ethylpiperidine	24	
Ethyl piperidinovalerate	43	8	4000	250	2.0	5-Piperidino-1-pentanol	82	40
Ethyl piperidino-caproate	41	8	4000	240	1.0	6-Piperidino-1-hexanol	35	44
						1,6-Hexanediol	33	

Note: References 21–51 are listed on p. 27.

TABLE VIII

CARBALKOXY-SUBSTITUTED HETEROCYCLIC COMPOUNDS

	Experimental Conditions							
Ester	Weight of Ester g.	Weight of Catalyst g.	Pressure p.s.i.	Temperature °C.	Time hr.	Product	Yield %	Reference
Ethyl nicotinate	33	6	3500	250	7	Ethyl nipecotate	—	24
						Alkylpiperidines	—	
Ethyl N-ethyl-nipecotate	21	3	4000	250	2.2	N-Ethyl-β-pipecoline	99	24
5-Carbethoxy-2-pyrrolidone	38	4	4000	220	0.5	5-Hydroxymethyl-2-pyrrolidone	93	44
1,2-Dicarbethoxypyrrolidine	17	5	4000	250	0.5	1-Carbethoxy-2-hydroxymethylpyrrolidine	62	45
						1-Ethyl-2-hydroxymethylpyrrolidine	23	
1-Carbethoxy-2-hydroxymethyl-pyrrolidine	12	5	4000	200	2.0	1-Ethyl-2-hydroxymethylpyrrolidine	32	45
4-Carbethoxy-2-quinolone	16.3	4	4000	220	0.2	4-Hydroxymethyldihydro-2-quinolone	29	44
						4-Methyl-1,2,3,4-tetrahydroquinoline	24	
1-Ethyl-3-carbethoxy-2,4-dimethyl-pyrrolidine	22	5	—	190	1.0	1-Ethyl-3-hydroxymethyl-2,4-dimethyl-pyrrolidine	83	46
1-n-Amyl-4-carbethoxy-5-methyl-2,3-dihydro-2-pyrrolone	19	4	4000	230	0.7	1-n-Amyl-5-methyl-4-hydroxymethyl-2-pyrrolidone	60	44
1-n-Amyl-5-carbethoxy-6-methyl-2-piperidone	48	8	4000	250	0.3	1-n-Amyl-5-hydroxymethyl-6-methyl-2-piperidone	49	44
						1-n-Amyl-2,3-dimethylpiperidine	30	
1-Phenethyl-4-carbethoxy-5-methyl-2-pyrrolidone	41	4	4000	240	0.6	1-Phenethyl-4-hydroxymethyl-5-methyl-2-pyrrolidone	55	44
						1-Phenethyl-2,3-dimethylpyrrolidine	13	

Note: References 21–51 are listed on p. 27.

ZINC CHROMIUM OXIDE AND RANEY NICKEL AS CATALYSTS FOR ESTER HYDROGENATION

Although copper chromium oxide is the catalyst of greatest usefulness for the hydrogenation of esters, zinc chromium oxide, made in the same way as copper chromium oxide, is effective in some instances. This was probably the catalyst used in the earliest hydrogenation of esters to alcohols by Lazier.[19] Zinc chromium oxide is much less active for hydrogenation than copper chromium oxide so that a higher temperature (300°) is required even with a high ratio of catalyst to ester. However, zinc chromium oxide makes possible the hydrogenation of an unsaturated ester to an unsaturated alcohol. Ethyl oleate, for example, has been converted with this catalyst to a mixture of oleyl and octadecyl alcohols,[31] whereas copper chromium oxide has given only the saturated alcohol. It has not been feasible to separate the unsaturated from the saturated alcohol so that if oleyl alcohol is desired it is much more satisfactory to reduce the ethyl oleate with sodium rather than with hydrogen.

A properly prepared ("W-6") Raney nickel catalyst [47] is effective for the hydrogenation of α-amino and α-hydroxy esters even at room temperature. The results of such hydrogenations are summarized in Tables IX and X. A high ratio of catalyst to ester is required, but the reactions proceed rather rapidly at 50–100°, and the yields are excellent, particularly if allowance is made for the losses incidental to the separation of small amounts of an alcohol from a large amount of catalyst. Reaction may take place with explosive violence with "W-6" Raney nickel and an amino ester in an alcohol at temperatures above 100°, so that the temperature of reaction must be carefully controlled.

The low temperature at which α-amino esters and α-hydroxy esters are hydrogenated over Raney nickel in the presence of triethylamine to the corresponding amino alcohols or glycols may be advantageous in avoiding racemization of optically active esters and alcohols.[48] Even so, it is doubtful whether Raney nickel offers any advantage over copper chromium oxide as a catalyst for the hydrogenation of these esters, in view of the greater ease of preparation, stability in storage, and safety in use of copper chromium oxide.

TABLE IX

HYDROGENATION OF ESTERS OF AMINO ACIDS WITH RANEY NICKEL

	Experimental Conditions							
Ester	Weight of Ester g.	Weight of Catalyst g.	Pressure p.s.i.	Temperature °C.	Time hr.	Product	Yield %	Reference
Ethyl α-piperidino-acetate	10	12–W–3 *	3000	50	7	2-Piperidinoethanol	90	49
Ethyl α-piperidino-acetate	10	12–W–2	3000	50	7	2-Piperidinoethanol	90	49
Ethyl α-piperidino-acetate	10	15–W–6	5000	100	1.7	2-Piperidinoethanol	80	9
Diethyl oximino-malonate	10	15–W–6	5000	100	0.5	2-Amino-1,3-propane-diol	80	9
Ethyl N-phenyl-glycinate	10	15–W–5	5000	100	3	2-(N-Cyclohexylam-ino)ethanol	80	9
Ethyl N-phenyl-glycinate	10	15–W–6	5000	26	25	2-(N-Cyclohexylam-ino)ethanol	80	9
Ethyl hippurate	10	15–W–5	5000	100	4	2-(N-Hexahydro-benzoylamino)-ethanol	80	9
Ethyl alaninate	10	15–W–5	5000	100	2.5	2-Amino-1-propanol	80	9
Ethyl alaninate	5	12–W–3	3000	50	4	2-Amino-1-propanol	10	49
Ethyl α-piperidino-propionate	5	10–W–4	2600	50	7	2-Piperidino-1-propanol	42	49
Ethyl β-piperidino-propionate	10	15–W–6	5000	100	3	3-Piperidino-1-propanol	8	9
						Piperidine and ethyl propionate	72	
Ethyl β-piperidino-propionate	9	18–W–4	2600	50	7	3-Piperidino-1-propanol	30	49
Ethyl α-aminoiso-butyrate	10	15–W–5	5000	100	0.8	2-Amino-2-methyl-1-propanol	80	9
Ethyl α-methyl-α-piperidinopro-pionate	5	10–W–4	2600	50	7	2-Methyl-3-piperi-dinopropanol	24	49
Ethyl oximinoaceto-acetate	10	15–W–6	5000	100	0.2	2-Amino-1,3-butane-diol	80	9
Diethyl aminomethyl-enemalonate	10	15–W–6	5000	100	1	Diethyl methyl-malonate	80	9
Ethyl α-aminocap-roate	5	12–W–4	3000	50	7	2-Amino-1-hexanol	65	49
Methyl (+,−)-leu-cinate	9	—	2200	135	24	(+,−)-Leucinol hydrochloride	40	50
Methyl (+,−)-leu-cinate	10	—	2200	185	—	2,5-Diisobutylpiper-azine 2-Dimethylamino-4-methylpentane N,N-Dimethylleu-cinol N,N′-Dimethyl-2,5-diisobutylpiperazine	—	50

Note: References 21–51 are listed on p. 27.

* References 47 and 49 describe the preparation of the Raney nickel catalysts identified by "W" numbers.

TABLE IX—*Continued*

HYDROGENATION OF ESTERS OF AMINO ACIDS WITH RANEY NICKEL

Ester	Weight of Ester g.	Weight of Catalyst g.	Pressure p.s.i.	Temperature °C.	Time hr.	Product	Yield %	Reference
Ethyl (−)-leucinate	1	4	2200	70	9	(−)-Leucinol	—	50
Ethyl (+,−)-leucinate	10	18–W–2	2600	50	7	2-Amino-4-methyl-1-pentanol	55	49
Ethyl (+,−)-leucinate	2	—	2200	70	9	(+,−)-Leucinol	40	50
Ethyl (+,−)-leucinate	9	—	2200	135	22	(+,−)-Leucinol hydrochloride	44	50
Ethyl (+,−)-leucinate	10	—	2200	185	24	2-Dimethylamino-4-methylpentane	25	50
						N,N-Dimethylleucinol	49	
						N,N′-2,5-Diisobutyl-piperazine	35	
Ethyl (+,−)-leucinate	10	—	2200	185	4	2,5-Diisobutylpiper-azine hydrochloride	19	50
						N,N-Dimethylleucinol	64	
						N,N′-Dimethyl-2,5-diisobutyl-piperazine	18	
1-Amino-1-carbeth-oxycyclopentane	10	15–W–5	5000	100	1	1-Amino-1-hydroxy-methylcyclopentane	80	9
5-Carbethoxy-2-pyr-rolidone	10	15–W–4	5000	100	14	5-Hydroxymethyl-2-pyrrolidone	80	9
1-Amino-1-carbeth-oxycyclohexane	10	15–W–5	5000	100	0.8	1-Amino-1-hydroxy-methylcyclohexane	80	9
Ethyl picolinate	10	15–W–2	2600	50	5	2-Piperidylcarbinol	92	49
Methyl (+,−)-phenylglycinate	4	8	2200	185	9	1-Dimethylamino-cyclohexylethane	18	51
						N,N′-Dimethyl-2,5-di-cyclohexylpiperazine	56	
Ethyl (+)-phenyl-glycinate	5.5	31	2200	40	9	2-Amino-2-phenyl-ethanol	60	51
Ethyl phenylglycinate	6	12–W–4	2500	50	7	2-Amino-2-phenyl-ethanol	93	49
Ethyl phenylglycinate	5	7	2200	135	9	2-(Dimethylamino)-2-cyclohexylethanol	84	51
Methyl (+,−)-phenylalaninate	4	6	2200	185	9	1-(Dimethylamino)-1-hexahydrobenzyl-ethane	21	51
						N,N′-Dimethyl-2,5-di-hexahydrobenzyl-piperazine	52	
Ethyl β-phenyl-alaninate	10	15–W–5	5000	100	9	2-Amino-3-cyclohexyl-1-propanol	80	9
Ethyl β-phenyl-alaninate	7	12–W–4	3000	50	7	2-Amino-3-phenyl-1-propanol	52	49
Ethyl α-amino-α-phenylpropionate	10	15–W–5	5000	100	4	2-Amino-2-cyclo-hexyl-1-propanol	80	9
Ethyl tyrosinate	10	15–W–6	5000	100	6	2-Amino-3-(4-hy-droxycyclohexyl)-1-propanol	80	9

Note: References 21–51 are listed on p. 27.

TABLE X

HYDROGENATION OF ESTERS OF α- AND β-OXYGENATED ACIDS WITH RANEY NICKEL

	Experimental Conditions							
Ester	Weight of Ester g.	Weight of Catalyst g.	Pressure p.s.i.	Temperature °C.	Time hr.	Product	Yield %	Reference
Ethyl lactate	10	15-W-6 *	5000	100	1.5	1,2-Propanediol	80	9
Ethyl lactate	10	15-W-6	5000	25	13	1,2-Propanediol	80	9
Isopropyl lactate	10	15-W-6	5000	100	5.5	1,2-Propanediol	80	9
Diethyl oxomalonate	10	15-W-6	5000	100	5.5	Glycerol	50	9
Ethyl α-hydroxyiso-butyrate	10	15-W-6	5000	100	2	1,1-Dimethyl-1,2-ethanediol	80	9
Ethyl acetoacetate	10	15-W-6	5000	125	6	1,3-Butanediol	48	9
						Ethyl β-hydroxybutyrate	27	
Ethyl α,β-dioxobutyrate	10	15-W-6	5000	100	4	1,2,3-Butanetriol	80	9
Diethyl malate	10	15-W-6	5000	100	14	1,2,4-Butanetriol	50	9
Diethyl ethoxymethyl-enemalonate	10	15-W-6	5000	125	11	2-Methyl-1,3-propanediol	32	9
						Diethyl methyl-malonate	14	
Diethyl tartrate	10	15-W-6	5000	100	10	1,2,3,4-Butanetetrol	80	9
Diethyl acetonedi-carboxylate	10	15-W-6	5000	125	24	Ethyl β-hydroxyglutarate	36	9
						1,3,5-Pentanetriol	30	
Diethyl ethylmalonate	10	15-W-6	5000	125	24	2-Ethyl-1,3-propanediol	34	9
Ethyl α-tetrahydro-furoate	10	12-W-4	2500	50	7	Tetrahydrofuryl alcohol	55	49
Ethyl α-hydroxy-β,β-dimethylbutyrate	10	15-W-6	5000	100	15	3,3-Dimethyl-1,2-butanediol	80	9
Diethyl n-propyl-malonate	10	15-W-6	5000	125	23	2-(n-Propyl)-1,3-propanediol	11	9
Diethyl n-butyl-malonate	10	15-W-6	5000	125	24	2-(n-Butyl)-1,3-propanediol	7	9
Ethyl mandelate	10	15-W-6	5000	100	1.3	1-Cyclohexyl-1,2-ethanediol	53	9
						2-Cyclohexyl-1-ethanol	12	
Diethyl n-heptyl-malonate	10	15-W-6	5000	125	21	2-(n-Heptyl)-1,3-propanediol	4	9
Ethyl benzilate	10	15-W-6	5000	100	6	1,1-Dicyclohexyl-1,2-ethanediol	12	9
						Ethyl dicyclohexyl-acetate	60	

Note: References 21–51 are listed on p. 27.

* References 47 and 49 describe the preparation of the Raney nickel catalysts identified by "W" numbers.

REFERENCES TO TABLES I–X

[21] McClellan and Connor, *J. Am. Chem. Soc.*, **63**, 484 (1941).

[22] Adkins and Folkers, *J. Am. Chem. Soc.*, **53**, 1095 (1931).

[23] Bowden and Adkins, *J. Am. Chem. Soc.*, **56**, 689 (1934).

[24] Folkers and Adkins, *J. Am. Chem. Soc.*, **54**, 1145 (1932).

[25] Arnold and Dowdall, *J. Am. Chem. Soc.*, **70**, 2590 (1948).

[26] Adkins, Wojcik, and Covert, *J. Am. Chem. Soc.*, **55**, 1669 (1933).

[27] Cason, Brewer, and Pippen, *J. Org. Chem.*, **13**, 239 (1948).

[28] Lazier, U. S. pat. 2,109,844 [*C. A.*, **32**, 3420 (1938)].

[29] Dauben, *J. Am. Chem. Soc.*, **70**, 1376 (1948).

[30] Lazier, U. S. pat. 2,079,414 [*C. A.*, **31**, 4340 (1937)].

[31] Sauer and Adkins, *J. Am. Chem. Soc.*, **59**, 1 (1937).

[32] Connor and Adkins, *J. Am. Chem. Soc.*, **54**, 4678 (1932).

[33] Wojcik and Adkins, *J. Am. Chem. Soc.*, **55**, 4939 (1933); **56,** 2419 (1934).

[34] Lazier, U. S. pat. 2,094,611 [*C. A.*, **31**, 8544 (1937)].

[35] Clemence and Leffler, *J. Am. Chem. Soc.*, **70**, 2439 (1948).

[36] Bowden and Adkins, *J. Am. Chem. Soc.*, **62**, 2422 (1940).

[37] Zartman and Adkins, *J. Am. Chem. Soc.*, **55**, 4559 (1933).

[38] de Benneville and Connor, *J. Am. Chem. Soc.*, **62**, 283 (1940).

[39] de Benneville and Connor, *J. Am. Chem. Soc.*, **62**, 3067 (1940).

[40] Adkins, Kuick, Farlow, and Wojcik, *J. Am. Chem. Soc.*, **56**, 2425 (1934).

[41] Kerwin, Ullyot, Fuson, and Zirkle, *J. Am. Chem. Soc.*, **69**, 2961 (1947).

[42] Christman and Levene, *J. Biol. Chem.*, **125**, 709 (1938).

[43] Christman and Levene, *J. Biol. Chem.*, **124**, 453 (1938).

[44] Sauer and Adkins, *J. Am. Chem. Soc.*, **60**, 402 (1938).

[45] Signaigo and Adkins, *J. Am. Chem. Soc.*, **58**, 709 (1936).

[46] Rainey and Adkins, *J. Am. Chem. Soc.*, **61**, 1104 (1939).

[47] Adkins and Billica, *J. Am. Chem. Soc.*, **70**, 695 (1948).

[48] Adkins and Billica, *J. Am. Chem. Soc.*, **70**, 3118 (1948).

[49] Adkins and Pavlic, *J. Am. Chem. Soc.*, **69**, 3039 (1947).

[50] Ovakimian, Christman, Kuna, and Levene, *J. Biol. Chem.*, **134**, 151 (1940).

[51] Ovakimian, Kuna, and Levene, *J. Biol. Chem.*, **135**, 91 (1940).

CHAPTER 2

THE SYNTHESIS OF KETONES FROM ACID HALIDES AND ORGANOMETALLIC COMPOUNDS OF MAGNESIUM, ZINC, AND CADMIUM

David A. Shirley *

Tulane University of Louisiana

CONTENTS

* Present address: University of Tennessee.

INTRODUCTION

The synthesis of ketones from acid halides and organometallic compounds may be represented by the following equation:

$$RCOX + R'M \rightarrow RCOR' + MX$$

Freund first observed the formation of ketones from simple acid chlorides and dimethyl- and diethyl-zinc in 1861.[1] Organometallic compounds of sodium,[2,3] copper,[4] magnesium,[5] cadmium,[6] mercury,[7] aluminum,[5] tin,[5] and lead [5] have also been found to give this reaction. Only the organozinc, organocadmium, and organomagnesium reagents have been found to be generally useful for such syntheses, however.

The use of organozinc compounds in the synthesis of ketones was stimulated by the extensive work of Blaise [8] during the period 1900–1915. As a consequence the organozinc compounds, R_2Zn, and the organozinc halides, RZnX, were preferred for this purpose until 1936, when Gilman and Nelson [9] pointed out that organocadmium compounds are more satisfactory. Subsequently many investigators have employed organocadmium compounds for the synthesis of ketones. The literature on this reaction for the period 1936–1946 has been reviewed by Cason.[6] A shorter review by Vène is also available.[10]

MECHANISM

There is little information available on the mechanism of reaction of organometallic compounds with acid halides. The Grignard reagent has been considered [5] to react by addition to the carbonyl group followed by elimination of magnesium halide, or by a primary coordination of the Grignard reagent with the carbonyl oxygen followed by rearrangement of the coordination complex I and elimination of MgX_2. Support for

I

[1] Freund, *Ann.*, **118**, 3 (1861).

[2] André, *Compt. rend.*, **151**, 76 (1910).

[3] Bechi, *Ber.*, **12**, 463 (1879).

[4] Gilman and Straley, *Rec. trav. chim.*, **55**, 821 (1936).

[5] Gilman in Gilman, *Organic Chemistry*, Vol. I, 2nd ed., pp. 489–580, John Wiley & Sons, New York, 1943.

[6] Cason, *Chem. Revs.*, **40**, 15 (1947).

[7] Otto, *Ber.*, **3**, 197 (1870).

[8] Blaise, *Bull. soc. chim. France*, (4) **9**, I (1911).

[9] Gilman and Nelson, *Rec. trav. chim.*, **55**, 518 (1936).

[10] Vène, *Bull. soc. chim. France*, **1950**, D-163.

the idea of carbonyl addition has been given by the observation that acid fluorides are most reactive and acid iodides least reactive toward the Grignard reagent.[5, 11] Since this is just the reverse of the order of reactivity of C—X bonds in displacement reactions, it appeared unlikely that direct replacement of the halogen atom occurred.

In the reaction of organozinc and organomercury compounds with acid halides, it has been found that acid iodides are most reactive and acid fluorides least reactive.[5] This is in line with the reactivity of C—X bonds in displacement reactions and indicates that preliminary reaction of the organometallic compound at the carbonyl group may not be involved. Supporting this idea are the interesting results of Cason [12] in the reaction of α-ethyl-α-n-butylglutaric anhydride (II) with di-n-butyl-cadmium. The two keto acids III and IV were formed as expected, but the relative amounts of the two acids isolated were unexpected; 31.5% of the product consisted of the acid III, and 68.5% of the acid IV. If

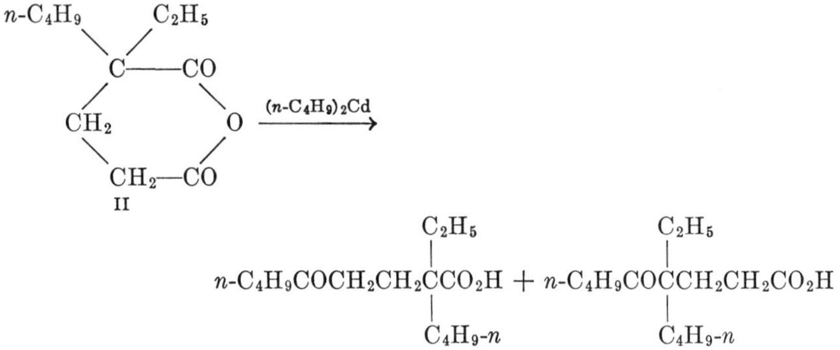

$$n\text{-}C_4H_9 \quad C_2H_5$$

$$
\begin{array}{c}
\text{C}\text{----}\text{CO} \\
\text{CH}_2 \qquad \text{O} \xrightarrow{\ (n\text{-}C_4H_9)_2Cd\ } \\
\text{CH}_2\text{----}\text{CO} \\
\text{II}
\end{array}
$$

$$
\begin{array}{cc}
C_2H_5 & C_2H_5 \\
| & | \\
n\text{-}C_4H_9COCH_2CH_2CCO_2H & + \quad n\text{-}C_4H_9COCCH_2CH_2CO_2H \\
| & | \\
C_4H_9\text{-}n & C_4H_9\text{-}n \\
\text{III} & \text{IV}
\end{array}
$$

it is assumed that the process occurred by the reaction of the organo-cadmium compound at the carbonyl group, then the anhydride carbonyl with lesser steric hindrance should be involved to the greater extent and give rise to a preponderance of acid III. The formation of the larger amount of acid IV indicates that the initial attack is not at the carbonyl group. Cason postulated an initial coordination of cadmium with the central oxygen atom followed by breaking of one of the carbon to oxygen single bonds, the Cd—O bond being formed preferentially at the unhindered carbonyl group.

PREPARATION OF THE ORGANOMETALLIC COMPOUND

Since the preparation of the Grignard reagent is such a well-known technique it will not be discussed here.

[11] Entemann and Johnson, J. Am. Chem. Soc., **55**, 2900 (1933).
[12] Cason, J. Org. Chem., **13**, 227 (1948).

The *organozinc compounds*, along with other organometallic compounds of lesser reactivity than the Grignard reagent, are best prepared by the action of metallic halides on the Grignard reagent.

$$RMgX + MX_2 \rightarrow RMX + MgX_2$$

$$2RMgX + MX_2 \rightarrow R_2M + 2MgX_2$$

As indicated in the equations the amount of metallic halide, MX_2, added to the Grignard reagent determines whether the organometallic compound RMX or the organometallic compound R_2M will be formed. Comparative studies have shown the essential equivalence of the R_2M and RMX compounds in their reactions.[9, 13] The smaller amount of metallic halide has therefore been used more frequently.

Before the advent of the Grignard reagent, organozinc compounds were prepared from metallic zinc and organic halides. Satisfactory yields were reported, and the reaction proceeded in a short time if a powdered mixture of zinc and copper was used.[14] It should be noted, however, that in more recent years only a few workers have used this direct preparation of organozinc compounds.[15, 16]

The use of zinc chloride for the preparation of organozinc compounds is attended with the difficulty of obtaining the anhydrous salt. Fusion of zinc chloride in moist air causes some conversion to the oxide, and its reconversion to the chloride is tedious. Satisfactory results in handling zinc chloride have been obtained by rapidly heating commercial c.p. anhydrous zinc chloride from a freshly opened bottle until it is liquid. Prolonged heating is avoided, and the fused mass is allowed to cool in a desiccator.[17] Weighed lumps of the solid salt are then ground rapidly in a mortar under anhydrous ether, in which the zinc chloride is soluble. The ethereal solution is used for reaction with the Grignard reagent.

Reaction of zinc chloride with the Grignard reagent is rapid and quantitative. Immediately after the rapid addition of zinc chloride to an ether solution of ethylmagnesium bromide at room temperature the Gilman test[5] for the Grignard reagent is negative.[18]

The formation of *organocadmium compounds* from cadmium chloride and the Grignard reagent is slower than the formation of the organozinc compounds. It is recommended[19] that cadmium chloride be added to the boiling ethereal solution of the Grignard reagent and that the resulting mixture be stirred and heated under reflux until a negative

[13] Michael, *Am. Chem. J.*, **25**, 423 (1901).
[14] Lachmann, *Am. Chem. J.*, **19**, 410 (1897).
[15] Ruzicka and Stoll, *Helv. Chim. Acta*, **10**, 693 (1927).
[16] Späth and Darling, *Ber.*, **63**, 739 (1930).
[17] Schmidt and Shirley, *J. Am. Chem. Soc.*, **71**, 3804 (1949).
[18] Shirley and Schmidt, unpublished observations.
[19] Cason, *J. Am. Chem. Soc.*, **68**, 2078 (1946).

Gilman test [5] showing complete conversion of the Grignard reagent is obtained. From twenty to fifty minutes is normally required for completion of the reaction, but considerably longer reaction periods are sometimes necessary. Organomagnesium bromides are reported to be superior to the corresponding organomagnesium iodides for the preparation of organocadmium compounds.[9]

Cadmium chloride is only slightly hygroscopic, and it requires only drying to constant weight at 110° and cooling in a desiccator before use. The dried salt may be stored in a desiccator. Cadmium chloride is not so soluble in ether as zinc chloride is, and the powdered salt is customarily added directly to the Grignard solution.[19] No advantage has been found in the use of cadmium bromide in place of the chloride for this reaction.[9]

Organolithium compounds may be employed in place of the Grignard reagent for the formation of organocadmium compounds, but they offer no particular advantage.[9]

REACTION OF GRIGNARD REAGENTS WITH ACID HALIDES

The use of the Grignard reagent for the preparation of ketones has been restricted rather severely because of the tendency of the Grignard reagents to undergo addition to the carbonyl group of the ketone produced to form tertiary alcohols.[20] In reactions of alkyl Grignard reagents with aliphatic acid chlorides, low yields (generally less than 30%) of the ketones have been obtained even when the Grignard reagent was added to excess acid chloride.[21, 22] Several investigators [20, 23-25] have used reaction temperatures in the range of −10 to −15°. Although no careful study has been made of the effect of temperature on the relative amounts of carbinol and ketone produced, it appears that a lower temperature suppresses the reaction of the Grignard reagent with ketones more than it does the reaction with acid halides.

The Grignard reagent has been used with moderate success in the preparation of aromatic,[20, 26-31] alicyclic,[24, 25, 32, 33] and sterically hindered

[20] Gilman, Fothergill, and Parker, *Rec. trav. chim.*, **48**, 751 (1929).
[21] Fordyce and Johnson, *J. Am. Chem. Soc.*, **55**, 3368 (1933).
[22] Davies and Adams, *J. Am. Chem. Soc.*, **50**, 1754 (1928).
[23] Clar, John, and Hawran, *Ber.*, **62**, 944 (1929).
[24] Darzens and Rost, *Compt. rend.*, **153**, 772 (1911).
[25] Meerwein, *Ann.*, **417**, 264, 270 (1918).
[26] Fuson and Hoch, *J. Am. Chem. Soc.*, **71**, 1585 (1949).
[27] Ross and Fuson, *J. Am. Chem. Soc.*, **59**, 1508 (1937).
[28] Lapkin and Lyubimova, *Zhur. Obshcheĭ Khim.*, **19**, 707 (1949) [*C. A.*, **44**, 1058 (1950)].
[29] Gilman and Mayhue, *Rec. trav. chim.*, **51**, 47 (1932).
[30] Clement, *Compt. rend.*, **202**, 425 (1936).
[31] Cole and Julian, *J. Am. Chem. Soc.*, **67**, 1372 (1945).
[32] Helferich and Malkomes, *Ber.*, **55**, 705 (1922).
[33] Rupe and Jäggi, *Ann.*, **428**, 164 (1922).

aliphatic ketones.[21, 34, 35, 36] Yields ranging from 30% to 70% have been reported in these syntheses, and it seems to make little difference whether the aromatic, alicyclic, or sterically hindered aliphatic group is in the Grignard reagent or the acid halide. An examination of the ketones produced from Grignard reagents listed in the table shows that in general the best yields (50–70%) have been obtained when both the Grignard reagent and the acid chlorides are of the types mentioned above. The explanation for this apparently resides in the steric inhibition of the reaction of a second molecule of the Grignard reagent with the previously formed ketone.

In ketone syntheses using the Grignard reagent, the addition of the Grignard reagent to the acid halide (inverse addition) and the use of excess acid halide are important in securing maximum yields. Addition of 0.3 mole of phenylmagnesium bromide to 0.5 mole of benzoyl chloride resulted in a yield of 45% of benzophenone and 33% of triphenyl-carbinol, while equimolar amounts of reagents under the same conditions gave a 29% yield of ketone and 38% of carbinol.[20] Addition of benzoyl chloride (0.17 mole) to phenylmagnesium bromide (0.5 mole) resulted in a 97% yield of triphenylcarbinol.[20]

Catalytic amounts of cuprous chloride exert a profound effect on the reaction of certain acid chlorides with Grignard reagents.[34] Di-t-butyl ketone is formed in 72% yield from equimolar quantities of t-butyl-magnesium chloride and trimethylacetyl chloride in the presence of cuprous chloride, whereas only 1–2% of the ketone is formed under corresponding conditions in its absence. It is postulated that the cuprous chloride initiates a free-radical chain reaction proceeding through magnesious halide ($\cdot$MgCl) as indicated in the accompanying equations.

$$RCOCl + \cdot CuCl \rightarrow \underset{\underset{O}{\|}}{RC}\cdot + CuCl_2$$

$$\underset{\underset{O}{\|}}{RC}\cdot + RMgCl \rightarrow \underset{\underset{O}{\|}}{RCR} + \cdot MgCl$$

$$\cdot MgCl + RCOCl \rightarrow \underset{\underset{O}{\|}}{RC}\cdot + MgCl_2$$

REACTION OF ORGANOZINC COMPOUNDS WITH ACID HALIDES

The organozinc compounds are definitely superior to Grignard reagents for the preparation of ketones from acid halides. This superiority

[34] Cook and Percival, *J. Am. Chem. Soc.*, **71**, 4141 (1949).

[35] Stehman, Cook, and Whitmore, *J. Am. Chem. Soc.*, **71**, 1509 (1949).

[36] Schmidlin, *Ber.*, **43**, 1140 (1910).

appears to depend largely on the low order of reactivity of organozinc compounds toward ketone carbonyl groups, with the result that formation of tertiary alcohols is not an important side reaction. The low reactivity of organozinc and organocadimum compounds toward carbonyl groups is illustrated by comparative experiments showing the times required for the development of a positive Gilman test [5] with Michler's ketone (V): the Grignard reagent gave an immediate test, but

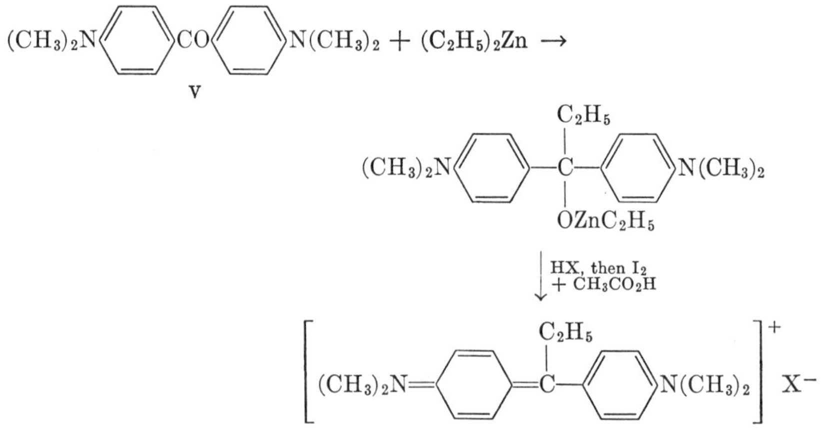

$$(CH_3)_2N\langle\rangle CO\langle\rangle N(CH_3)_2 + (C_2H_5)_2Zn \rightarrow$$

V

$$(CH_3)_2N\langle\rangle \overset{C_2H_5}{\underset{OZnC_2H_5}{\overset{|}{\underset{|}{C}}}}\langle\rangle N(CH_3)_2$$

HX, then I$_2$
+ CH$_3$CO$_2$H

$$\left[(CH_3)_2N{=}\langle\rangle{=}\overset{C_2H_5}{\underset{|}{C}}\langle\rangle N(CH_3)_2\right]^+ X^-$$

diethylzinc required 27.5 hours and diethylcadmium required 100 hours. With the organo-zinc and -cadmium compounds, addition of the organometallic compound to the acid halide is not necessary in order to minimize carbinol formation. The more convenient addition of acid halide to organometallic compound is usually employed.

The organozinc compounds, once very widely used for preparation of ketones, have been replaced to a considerable degree in more recent years by the organocadmium compounds. It has been stated that the organocadmium compounds are generally superior,[6] and this view is supported by several workers who have prepared certain ketones with both reagents. [9, 31, 37, 38] However, the position with respect to the usefulness of the organozinc compounds is not nearly so definite as one would like, for, while many workers have reported failures to obtain satisfactory yields of ketones from organozinc compounds, other workers have reported high yields of ketones. A series of eight ketones was prepared from octadecylzinc chloride and various long-chain acid chlorides in yield varying from 76% to 92%.[39] In another study, forty-two di-n-

[37] Suter and Weston, *J. Am. Chem. Soc.*, **61**, 234 (1939).
[38] Schuette, Mayloft, and Roth, *J. Am. Oil Chemists' Soc.*, **25**, 65 (1948).
[39] Jones, *J. Am. Chem. Soc.*, **69**, 2353 (1947).

alkyl ketones containing from fifteen to twenty-two carbon atoms were prepared in crude yields of 50–70% from various alkylzinc iodides and aliphatic acid chlorides.[39a]   The reaction of dimethylzinc and 1,2,2,3-tetramethyl-1-cyclopentanecarbonyl chloride gave the ketone in yields of 89%[40] and 93%.[25]   Other workers have reported obtaining ketones in yields of more than 75% using organozinc compounds.[15, 31, 41–44]

REACTION OF ORGANOCADMIUM COMPOUNDS WITH ACID HALIDES

The organocadmium compounds have been more widely used for the synthesis of ketones than the other organometallic compounds, and the syntheses with the organocadmium compounds have been studied more systematically.

For most purposes the use of 1.0 mole of alkyl or aryl bromide (for preparation of the organocadmium compound through the Grignard reagent) to 0.8 mole of acid halide is recommended.[19]   This results in nearly equivalent molar ratios of organocadmium compound and acid halide at the time of reaction, since the overall yield of organocadmium reagent is not consistently much greater than 80%.   An excess of organocadmium reagent will produce an improvement in the yield based on the acid halide.[6]   The reaction of dimethylcadmium with a steroid acid chloride at 5:1, 2:1, and 1:1 ratios of organometallic compound to acid chloride gave yields of ketone (based on acid chloride) of 95%, 91%, and 78%, respectively.   It is apparent that if the acid chloride is more difficult to obtain than the cadmium reagent an excess of the latter is advantageous; if both reagents are relatively valuable, approximately equivalent quantities represent optimum efficiency.   Excess cadmium reagent must be avoided, however, when the ketone formed is sufficiently reactive to yield a tertiary alcohol by interaction with the reagent.   The most striking example is the reaction between dimethylcadmium and the chloride of cyclobutanecarboxylic acid.   If this reaction is run in the ordinary way with excess dimethylcadmium the sole product is the tertiary carbinol, cyclobutyldimethylcarbinol; if, instead, 1.0 mole of the acid chloride is added to 0.7 mole of the well-stirred reagent at −70° and the reaction mixture is decomposed cold, the yield of methyl cyclobutyl ketone is 66%.[45]

[39a] Breusch and Baykut, *Ber.*, **86**, 684 (1953).
[40] Rupe and Kloppenburg, *Helv. Chim. Acta*, **2**, 368 (1919).
[41] Morgan, Drew, and Porter, *Ber.*, **58**, 337 (1925).
[42] Meerwein, *Ann.*, **405**, 161, 172 (1914).
[43] Perkin and Revay, *J. Chem. Soc.*, **65**, 240 (1894).
[44] Rupe and Schutz, *Helv. Chim. Acta*, **9**, 996 (1926).
[45] Pinson and Friess, *J. Am. Chem. Soc.*, **72**, 5333 (1950).

$$\begin{array}{c}\text{CH}_2\!\!-\!\!\text{CHCOCl} \\ | \qquad | \\ \text{CH}_2\!\!-\!\!\text{CH}_2\end{array} \xrightarrow{\text{(CH}_3)_2\text{Cd}} \begin{array}{c}\text{CH}_2\!\!-\!\!\text{CHCOCH}_3 \\ | \qquad | \\ \text{CH}_2\!\!-\!\!\text{CH}_2\end{array}$$

The use of the proper solvent in the reaction of acid chlorides with organocadmium compounds is important.[19] The preparation of the Grignard reagent and its reaction with cadmium chloride is carried out in ether, but usually the ether is advantageously replaced with benzene before the addition of the acid chloride.[19,46] Several advantages are found in the use of benzene in the latter stage of the reaction.[19] First, the precipitate which forms in the reaction mixture after addition of the acid chloride is less likely to become too thick for efficient stirring if benzene is used. Second, the side reaction between the organocadmium compound and the acid chloride or the ketone formed to yield a metallic enolate does not occur so rapidly in benzene as in ether.

$$\text{R}_2\text{Cd} + \text{R}'\text{CH}_2\text{COR}'' \rightarrow \text{RH} + [\text{R}'\text{CHCOR}'']^-[\text{RCd}]^+$$

Since this reaction consumes organocadmium compound its suppression is important if high yields are to be obtained. Third, the use of benzene allows a higher reflux temperature and accordingly the reactions require a shorter time in benzene. Last, it is noted that smaller quantities of ethyl esters are produced as by-products if the ether is largely replaced by benzene before the reaction with the acid chloride. The ethyl esters presumably arise from the cleavage of diethyl ether by the acid chloride.

$$\text{RCOCl} + \text{C}_2\text{H}_5\text{OC}_2\text{H}_5 \rightarrow \text{RCO}_2\text{C}_2\text{H}_5 + \text{C}_2\text{H}_5\text{Cl}$$

In a study of the reactions of chloroacetyl chloride and α-chloropropionyl chloride with different organocadmium compounds in ether, yields ranging from 13% to 26% were reported for five examples.[47] Using benzene as a solvent in three of the same reactions, yields of 33%, 43%, and 51% were obtained.[19] Di-n-butyl ether is a poor solvent for the reaction.[19]

The synthesis of propiophenone from (1) diethylcadmium and benzoyl chloride or (2) diphenylcadmium and propionyl chloride gives approximately the same yield, indicating little if any advantage in employing one set of reactants as compared with the other.[19]

(1) $(\text{C}_2\text{H}_5)_2\text{Cd} + \text{C}_6\text{H}_5\text{COCl} \rightarrow \text{C}_6\text{H}_5\text{COC}_2\text{H}_5$

(2) $(\text{C}_6\text{H}_5)_2\text{Cd} + \text{C}_2\text{H}_5\text{COCl} \rightarrow \text{C}_6\text{H}_5\text{COC}_2\text{H}_5$

The organocadmium compounds do not react with the nitro group in an aromatic nucleus. Advantage does not seem to have been taken of

[46] Cason and Prout, *J. Am. Chem. Soc.*, **66**, 47 (1944).
[47] Bunnett and Tarbell, *J. Am. Chem. Soc.*, **67**, 1944 (1945).

this in the synthesis of ketones from acid chlorides, but the synthesis of 2-acetyl-3-nitrobenzoic acid from 3-nitrophthalic anhydride has been accomplished.[48]

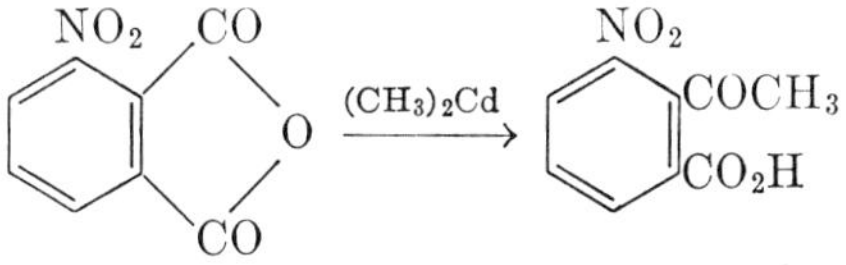

SCOPE AND LIMITATIONS

The most important application of the organometallic compounds to the synthesis of ketones has been in the preparation of keto esters from half ester acid chlorides. The success of the method depends upon the inertness of ester carbonyl groups toward organo-zinc and -cadmium compounds. With this reaction it is possible to build up a carbon chain by any reasonable number of carbon atoms and at the same time retain a reactive functional group (the ester group) at one end of the chain.

$$
R_2Cd + \underset{\underset{CO_2C_2H_5}{|}}{\overset{\overset{COCl}{|}}{(CH_2)_n}} \longrightarrow \underset{\underset{CO_2C_2H_5}{|}}{\overset{\overset{COR}{|}}{(CH_2)_n}} + RCdCl
$$

A difficulty which has limited the use of unsymmetrical ester acid chlorides is the apparent tendency of ester acid chlorides to undergo interchange of the two functional groups (VI $\rightleftarrows$ VII).

$$
\begin{array}{ccc}
\overset{CO_2C_2H_5}{\underset{|}{}} & & \overset{COCl}{\underset{|}{}} \\
(CH_2)_m & & (CH_2)_m \\
| & & | \\
CHR & \rightleftarrows & CHR \\
| & & | \\
(CH_2)_n & & (CH_2)_n \\
| & & | \\
COCl & & CO_2C_2H_5 \\
VI & & VII
\end{array}
$$

This equilibration leads to two different keto esters in subsequent reaction with the organocadmium compound. While it has been established that the reaction VI $\rightleftarrows$ VII takes place, it is also possible that a similar interchange takes place in the acid ester from which the acid chloride is formed, thus giving rise to the two acid chlorides VI and VII directly.[12] The extent to which interchange takes place in acid esters

[48] Wang, Isensee, Griffith, and Christensen, *J. Am. Chem. Soc.*, **69**, 1909 (1947).

in comparison with the ester acid chloride has not been determined. The reaction of the half ester acid chloride VIII with di-n-butylcadmium gives a mixture of the keto esters IX and X, in a total yield of 91%.[12]

$$
\begin{array}{ccc}
\text{CO}_2\text{CH}_3 & \text{CO}_2\text{CH}_3 & \text{COC}_4\text{H}_9\text{-}n \\
| & | & | \\
\text{C}_2\text{H}_5\text{—C—C}_4\text{H}_9\text{-}n & \text{C}_2\text{H}_5\text{—C—C}_4\text{H}_9\text{-}n & \text{C}_2\text{H}_5\text{—C—C}_4\text{H}_9\text{-}n \\
| \quad\xrightarrow{(n\text{-}C_4H_9)_2Cd} & | & | \\
(\text{CH}_2)_2 & (\text{CH}_2)_2 & (\text{CH}_2)_2 \\
| & | & | \\
\text{COCl} & \text{COC}_4\text{H}_9\text{-}n & \text{CO}_2\text{CH}_3 \\
\text{VIII} & \text{IX} & \text{X}
\end{array}
$$

The formation of α-diketones from oxalyl chloride and organocadmium compounds has not been achieved. The reaction of diethylcadmium and ethyl oxalyl chloride produces the hydroxy ester XI in 63% yield and

$$(\text{C}_2\text{H}_5)_2\text{C(OH)CO}_2\text{C}_2\text{H}_5$$
XI

does not furnish any of the expected α-keto ester. This result indicates that the keto ester first formed undergoes subsequent reaction at the ketone carbonyl group leading to the tertiary alcohol.[9] Such addition of an organocadmium reagent to a ketonic carbonyl occurs with particularly reactive carbonyl compounds or organocadmium reagents as pointed out earlier on p. 35.

Chloroacetyl chloride gives satisfactory yields of α-chloromethyl ketones with organocadmium reagents.[19]

In ketone syntheses in which it is necessary to use organometallic compounds containing a secondary alkyl group, the organozinc reagents seem to be definitely superior to the organocadmium compounds. Secondary and tertiary organocadmium compounds are thermally unstable in comparison with the primary types, and the tertiary compounds are less stable than the secondary.[9] Reaction of di-sec-amylcadmium and β-carbomethoxypropionyl chloride gives none of the expected keto ester by the use of the normal procedure, but a reaction temperature of $-5°$ to $-7°$ allows formation of the keto ester in 10–20% yield.[18, 46] When di-t-butylcadmium, prepared at $-70°$, is allowed to come to room temperature in the presence of acetyl chloride, a 17% yield of methyl t-butyl ketone is formed;[9] however, in view of the slowness with which organomagnesium compounds react with cadmium chloride to form organocadmium compounds,[19] there is some question whether the organometallic reactant in this synthesis was the organomagnesium or the organocadmium derivative. A 60% yield of n-propyl isopropyl ketone is reported from the reaction of diisopropylcadmium and n-butyryl chloride at $0°$. The reaction of diisopropylcadmium and 3-acetoxy-5-cholenic acid chloride at room temperature gives the corresponding ketone in 53% yield, but the moderately good yield obtained here is probably the result of the use of a very large excess of organo-metallic compound.[49]

Relatively few examples of the use of secondary organozinc compounds are found in the literature, but it appears (in contrast to the results with organocadmium compounds) that there is little difference in the yield of ketone when made from either a secondary or primary type. There is no record up to the present of an attempt to use a tertiary zinc compound. The ketone XII is formed in 50% yield from isopropylzinc

$$CH_3CHCOCH(CH_3)_2$$
$$|$$
$$CH_2OCOCH_3$$
XII

iodide and the corresponding acid chloride.[50] The reaction of 2-decylzinc chloride and 8-carbethoxyoctanoyl chloride gives ethyl 9-keto-10-methyl-octadecanoate (XIII) in 55% yield (see p. 43). These data confirm the

$$CH_3(CH_2)_8CH(CH_3)ZnCl + ClCO(CH_2)_7CO_2C_2H_5 \rightarrow$$

$$CH_3(CH_2)_8CH(CH_3)CO(CH_2)_7CO_2C_2H_5$$
XIII

greater utility of the secondary organozinc compounds as compared with the secondary organocadmium types.

The organozinc and organocadmium compounds have generally been regarded as superior to the Grignard reagent for the synthesis of ketones. It is therefore interesting that an occasional direct comparison of the Grignard reagent with one of the other organometallic compounds has shown the organomagnesium compound to be superior. In the reaction of dimethylzinc with 1-methyl-1-cyclopentanecarbonyl chloride a low yield of ketone was obtained in contrast with a 71% yield with methyl-magnesium iodide.[25] The use of mesitylmagnesium bromide allowed formation of the steroid ketone XIV in 40% yield; the use of dimesityl-cadmium gave an unstated but lower yield.[31] It will be noted that an

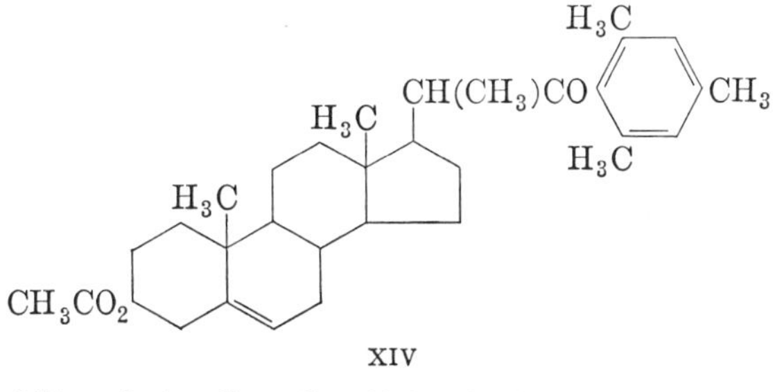

XIV

[49] Riegel and Kaye, *J. Am. Chem. Soc.*, **66**, 723 (1944).
[50] Blaise and Herman, *Ann. chim. phys.*, (8) **17**, 374, 385, 396 (1909).

acetoxy group, which is reactive toward most Grignard reagents, is present in the molecule. A 93% yield of the ketone XVI was obtained from the reaction under corresponding conditions of either dimethylzinc or methylmagnesium iodide with the acid halide XV.[25]

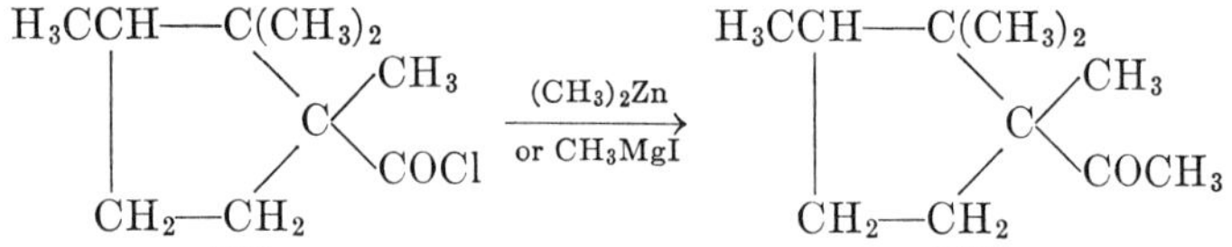

In addition to the work with steroids mentioned in earlier paragraphs,[30, 46] a series of ten steroid ketones has been prepared from steroid acid chlorides and diphenylcadmium.[51] A typical example is the formation in 64% yield of 3,12-dihydroxynorcholanyl phenyl ketone (XVII) from the corresponding acid chloride.

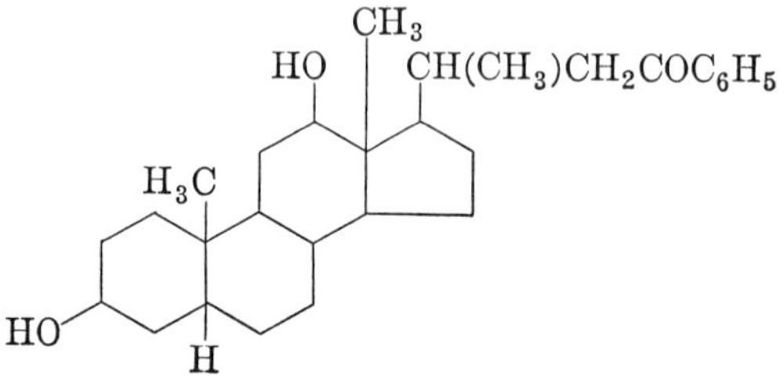

XVII

COMPARISON WITH OTHER METHODS OF SYNTHESIS OF KETONES

Reactions of organometallic compounds with other types of compounds than acid chlorides have been used for the preparation of ketones. Perhaps the best known of these is the reaction of the Grignard reagent with nitriles.[52] A direct comparison has been made in at least one instance between the preparation of a ketone from the action of a Grignard reagent on a nitrile and the preparation of the same ketone from the organocadmium compound and acid chloride.[53] 1-Phenyl-3-eicosanone was prepared using the Grignard reagent and organocadmium compound from phenethyl bromide. The yield of ketone was 49% from the nitrile and 66% from the acid chloride. It was pointed out that the use of the acid chloride represented a generally better method of operation, although good yields of ketones can be obtained from nitriles.

[51] Hoehn and Moffett, J. Am. Chem. Soc., 67, 742 (1945).
[52] Nef, Ann., 310, 323 (1900).
[53] Sherk, Augur, and Soffer, J. Am. Chem. Soc., 67, 2239 (1945).

For example, an 89% yield of ketone from the reaction of a substituted benzonitrile and α-naphthylmagnesium bromide is reported.[54] Hauser and Humphlett have shown that, in the reaction between a nitrile RCH_2CN and a Grignard reagent $R'MgX$, increased hindrance in R is favorable to the formation of the ketone RCH_2COR' while increased hindrance in R' is unfavorable, and that, further, the yield of ketone from nitriles increases in the order $C_6H_5CH_2CN$, CH_3CN, CH_3CH_2CN, so that the higher aliphatic nitriles give the best yields of ketones.[55]

Cyclic acid anhydrides have been used to prepare keto acids by reaction with organometallic compounds.[12, 48, 56, 57] A study of this reaction using organocadmium compounds and a variety of anhydrides indicated yields ranging from 30% to 75%;[57] however, the method does not appear to have achieved much use. The reaction of acetic anhydride with various Grignard reagents at $-70°$ gave excellent yields of methyl ketones.[58]

Amides will form ketones by reaction with the Grignard reagent.[59, 60, 61] A series of five alkyl 3,5-dimethoxyphenyl ketones has been prepared in 80–88% yield from the alkylmagnesium halides and 3,5-dimethoxy-benzamide.[37]

The common methods of synthesis of ketones which do not involve organometallic compounds may be divided into (1) syntheses from carboxylic acids, (2) Friedel-Crafts reactions, and (3) enolate condensations. The use of carboxylic acids and their salts for ketone syntheses suffers from the disadvantage that the reaction will produce in general only the symmetrical ketones in good yields. The Friedel-Crafts acylation reactions generally give good yields. However, their use is restricted by the orientation of the acyl group introduced and their application to the synthesis of aliphatic ketones presents difficulties. Enolate condensations give a wide variety of ketones; however, the overall yields are frequently not so good as those that can be obtained by other syntheses and the procedures frequently are more involved. Thus it appears that the reaction of acid halides with organo-zinc or -cadmium compounds is among the best methods of synthesis of ketones when the factors of yield, ease of manipulation in the laboratory, and applicability to the preparation of a wide variety of ketones are considered.

[54] Fieser and Seligmann, *J. Am. Chem. Soc.*, **58**, 2482 (1936).

[55] Hauser and Humphlett, *J. Org. Chem.*, **15**, 359 (1950).

[56] Fournier, *Bull. soc. chim. France*, (4) **7**, 836 (1910).

[57] deBenneville, *J. Org. Chem.*, **6**, 462 (1941).

[58] Newman and Smith, *J. Org. Chem.*, **13**, 592 (1948).

[59] Beis, *Compt. rend.*, **137**, 575 (1903).

[60] Ryan and Nolan, *Proc. Irish Acad.*, **30**, B, 1 (1912) [*C. A.*, **7**, 1712 (1913)].

[61] Levy and Jullien, *Bull. soc. chim. France*, (4) **45**, 941 (1929).

EXPERIMENTAL PROCEDURES

Grignard Reagents

10-Keto-12-methyltridecanoic Acid.[21] A solution of 24.9 g. (0.1 mole) of 9-carbethoxynonanoyl chloride in 50 ml. of ether is stirred during the dropwise addition of slightly less than the calculated quantity of iso-butylmagnesium bromide in ether solution. The mixture is allowed to stand for twelve hours and is then heated to reflux for one hour. Excess dilute acid is added, the ether layer is separated, and the ether is removed by distillation. The residue is hydrolyzed by boiling for four hours with excess alcoholic potassium hydroxide solution. The mixture is filtered to remove a small amount of alkali-insoluble material (probably the diketone, 2,15-dimethylhexadecane-4,13-dione), and the filtrate is added to excess dilute hydrochloric acid. The precipitated mixture of sebacic acid and keto acid is dissolved in aqueous alkali, and the keto acid is precipitated by careful fractional acidification of the solution, the sebacic acid remaining in solution. There is obtained 10.4–11.2 g. (43–47%) of the keto acid melting at 52–53°. Two recrystallizations from petroleum ether give a product melting at 54–55°.

1-Methyl-1-acetylcyclopentane.[25] A Grignard reagent is prepared from 34.1 g. (0.24 mole) of methyl iodide, 5.7 g. (0.235 gram atom) of magnesium, and 100 ml. of ether. The solution of the Grignard reagent is added slowly with vigorous stirring to a solution of 29.2 g. (0.20 mole) of 1-methyl-1-cyclopentanecarbonyl chloride in 50 ml. of ether at −15°. Excess ice water is added to the thick reaction mixture, and the ether layer is separated and washed with sodium bicarbonate solution. Acidification of the bicarbonate washes gives 8 g. of 1-methyl-1-cyclopentane-carboxylic acid from the unreacted acid chloride. The ether solution is dried and distilled. There is obtained 15 g. (60%) of 1-methyl-1-acetyl-cyclopentane boiling at 52–53°/13 mm.

In a second, similar experiment, Meerwein[25] obtained 37 g. (70%) of ketone from 61 g. of acid chloride.

Organozinc Compounds

Attention is called to the detailed general procedure for the preparation of di-*n*-alkyl ketones from alkyl iodides, zinc, and acid chlorides given by Breusch and Baykut.[39a]

12-Ketotriacontanoic Acid.[39] A mixture of 38 g. (0.27 mole) of freshly fused anhydrous zinc chloride and 100 ml. of ether is stirred under a reflux condenser while 0.27 mole of octadecylmagnesium bromide is added. After the initial reaction has subsided, the mixture is heated to boiling for two hours, during which time sufficient ether is distilled from the mixture to reduce its volume to about 300 ml. A solution of 54 g. (0.2 mole) of 11-carbethoxyundecanoyl chloride in 100 ml. of dry benzene is then added with stirring during fifteen minutes; the resulting mixture is stirred and heated to boiling for three hours, after which 500 ml. of 2 N hydrochloric acid is added. One liter of hot benzene is then added, and the benzene layer is separated and washed with one 400-ml. portion of hot dilute hydrochloric acid and two 400-ml. portions of hot water. The benzene solution is evaporated to 100 ml., a mixture of 30 ml. of 12 N sodium hydroxide and 50 ml. of ethanol is added, and the mixture is heated in an open beaker on a steam bath for two hours, during which time most of the solvent evaporates. The resulting solid is washed by suspension in two 500-ml. portions of warm benzene, dried, and then suspended in two 500-ml. portions of water. The solid is then suspended in 500 ml. of 2 N hydrochloric acid, and the mixture is digested on a steam bath for two hours. The resulting solid is recrystallized from benzene to give a 79% yield of 12-ketotriacontanoic acid melting at 102°.

Ethyl 9-Keto-10-methyloctadecanoate.[17]   The Grignard reagent is prepared from 280 g. (1.27 moles) of 2-bromodecane, 48 g. (2.0 gram atoms) of magnesium, and 600 ml. of ether; the yield as determined by acid titration of an aliquot is 80%. The Grignard solution is added to a solution of 136 g. (1.0 mole) of anhydrous zinc chloride in 350 ml. of ether at such a rate that gentle reflux is maintained. The mixture is then heated at reflux temperature for another one and one-half hours, during which time ether is distilled until the volume of the mixture is about 600 ml. A solution of 170 g. (0.72 mole) of 8-carbethoxyoctanoyl chloride in 400 ml. of dry benzene is added with stirring, and the mixture is heated under reflux for three hours. Excess dilute hydrochloric acid is added, the organic layer is separated and dried, and the solvent is removed by distillation. At this point the residue is heated to boiling with a mixture of ethanol and benzene plus a few drops of sulfuric acid. Heating is continued until all water is removed from the system as the ethanol-benzene-water azeotrope. In this way the ethyl hydrogen azelate present from unreacted acid chloride is converted to the diester and its subsequent separation by distillation from the keto ester, the main product, is facilitated. After removal of the excess benzene and ethanol, the reaction mixture is distilled through an efficient column to yield 78 g. of diethyl azelate and 133 g. of ethyl 9-keto-10-methyloctadecanoate boiling at 184–5°/0.5 mm., n_D^{25} 1.4470. The yield of keto ester is 55% based on the acid chloride, or 93% allowing for the diethyl azelate isolated.

Organocadmium Compounds

Methyl 4-Keto-7-methyloctanoate.[62] In this *Organic Syntheses* procedure the keto ester is prepared in 73–75% yield from 0.5 mole of diisoamylcadmium and 0.8 mole of β-carbomethoxypropionyl chloride. The procedure seems to embody most of the experimental details found satisfactory by Cason and co-workers in their extensive work on this type of reaction.

1-Chloro-2-hexanone.[19] A solution of di-*n*-butylcadmium in 175 ml. of benzene is prepared from 0.35 mole of *n*-butyl bromide, 0.35 g. atom of magnesium, and 0.188 mole of cadmium chloride. The organocadmium solution is cooled to 5° in an ice bath, and to it is added, with continued cooling over a period of forty seconds, a solution of 0.35 mole of chloroacetyl chloride in 70 ml. of benzene. After completion of the addition, the reaction mixture is stirred and held at a temperature of 15–20° for three hours and then at 20–25° for an additional one and one-half hours. Excess ice and dilute sulfuric acid are added, and the aqueous layer is separated and extracted with benzene. The benzene extracts and the benzene layer are combined and washed with water, 5% sodium bicarbonate solution, again with water, and then with saturated sodium chloride solution. After filtration and drying over anhydrous sodium sulfate, the benzene is removed by distillation and the residue fractionated through an 18-in. Podbielniak-type column. There is obtained 23.9 g. (51% yield based on butyl bromide) of 1-chloro-2-hexanone boiling at 71.0–72.5°/15 mm.

1-Phenyl-3-eicosanone.[53] An ether solution of phenethylmagnesium bromide is prepared from 42.7 g. (1.78 gram atoms) of magnesium and 325 g. (1.755 moles) of phenethyl bromide. To the stirred ice-cold Grignard solution, 171.5 g. (0.936 mole) of cadmium chloride is added during ten minutes. The mixture is allowed to warm to room temperature, and most of the solvent is then removed by distillation from a steam bath. Dry benzene (1.5 l.) is added, and the evaporation process is repeated again with stirring. Another 1.5-l. portion of benzene is added, and the mixture is stirred until the hard solid is evenly distributed. A solution of 400 g. (1.405 moles) of stearoyl chloride in 1 l. of dry benzene is added with stirring during two hours, and the mixture is heated under reflux for five hours. Excess ice and dilute hydrochloric acid are added to the cooled mixture. The benzene layer is extracted with aqueous sodium carbonate solution and the benzene removed by distillation. The residue is heated with ethanolic potassium hydroxide in order to saponify a small amount of ethyl stearate. After removal of

---

[62] Cason and Prout, *Org. Syntheses*, **28**, 75 (1948).

the ethanol, the residue is extracted with benzene. The benzene extracts are washed with water and saturated sodium chloride solution and dried over anhydrous magnesium sulfate. The benzene is removed by distillation, and the residue is distilled from a Claisen flask to give 342 g. (65.5%) of 1-phenyl-3-eicosanone boiling at 219°/1 mm. and melting at 56°. The melting point is unchanged by recrystallization from petroleum ether or ethanol.

α,α'-Diethyl-4-hydroxy-4'-acetylstilbene.[63] Cadmium chloride (0.3 g.) is added to 11 ml. of a 0.27 N ether solution of methylmagnesium bromide, and the resulting solution is stirred and heated under reflux until a negative Gilman test for the Grignard reagent is obtained (twenty minutes). Nearly all the ether is distilled, and 5 ml. of benzene is added. The acid chloride from 0.5 g. of α,α'-diethyl-4-acetoxy-4'-carboxystilbene, dissolved in 10 ml. of dry benzene, is added, and the mixture is stirred and heated under reflux for one hour. Excess cold dilute hydrochloric acid is added, and the mixture is extracted with two portions of ether. The ether layer is separated, the ether is allowed to evaporate, and the oily residue is heated under reflux for one hour with a mixture of 2 ml. of 45% aqueous potassium hydroxide solution and 4 ml. of methanol to hydrolyze the acetoxy group. Excess acid is added, and the mixture is extracted with ether. The ether is extracted with 5% aqueous sodium bicarbonate to remove unreacted acid (40 mg.). The ether is removed, and the solid residue is recrystallized several times from acetone-petroleum ether to give 273 mg. (63%) of the unsaturated hydroxy ketone, m.p. 142–146.5°.

TABLE OF KETONES PREPARED FROM ACID HALIDES AND ORGANO-METALLIC COMPOUNDS OF MAGNESIUM, ZINC, AND CADMIUM

An effort has been made to secure complete literature coverage up to mid-1950. A few later references are included.

The ketones prepared are listed according to molecular formula; the *Chemical Abstracts* method of arranging molecular formulas is used.

---

[63] Biggerstaff and Wilds, *J. Am. Chem. Soc.*, **71**, 2136 (1949).

KETONES PREPARED FROM ORGANO-MAGNESIUM, -CADMIUM, OR -ZINC COMPOUNDS AND ACID HALIDES

Formula	Ketone	Organometallic Compound	Acid Chloride	Yield %	Reference
C_3H_6O	Acetone	$(CH_3)_2Zn$	Acetyl	87	1, 64, 65
C_4H_8O	Methyl ethyl	$(C_2H_5)_2Zn$	Acetyl	80	1, 64, 65
		$(C_2H_5)_2Cd$	Acetyl	46	9
		C_2H_5CdBr	Acetyl	50	9
$C_5H_{10}O$	Methyl n-propyl	$(CH_3)_2Zn$	Butyryl	—	65
	Methyl isopropyl	$(CH_3)_2Zn$	Isobutyryl	60–70	64, 66, 67
	Diethyl	$(C_2H_5)_2Zn$	Propionyl	70	1, 66, 68
C_6H_6OS	3-Acetylthiophene	$(CH_3)_2Cd$	3-Thenoyl	81	69
$C_6H_{10}O$	Methyl cyclobutyl	$(CH_3)_2Zn$	Cyclobutanecarbonyl	78	70
		$(CH_3)_2Cd$	Cyclobutanecarbonyl	66	45
$C_6H_{10}O_3$	Ethyl acetoacetate	$BrMgCH_2CO_2C_2H_5$	Acetyl	26, 51	47, 19
$C_6H_{11}ClO$	1-Chloro-2-hexanone	$(n\text{-}C_4H_9)_2Cd$	Chloroacetyl	74	9
$C_6H_{12}O$	Methyl n-butyl	$(n\text{-}C_4H_9)_2Cd$	Acetyl	70	66
	Methyl isobutyl	CH_3ZnI	3-Methylbutanoyl	41–54	72
	Methyl t-butyl	$(CH_3)_3CMgCl$	Acetyl	17	9
		$(t\text{-}C_4H_9)_2Cd$	Acetyl	High	64, 73
		$(CH_3)_2Zn$	2,2-Dimethylpropanoyl	93 [a]	74
	Ethyl n-propyl	$(C_2H_5)_2Zn$	n-Butyryl	70	65, 66, 68
		C_2H_5ZnI	n-Butyryl	63	41
	Ethyl isopropyl	$(C_2H_5)_2Zn$	Isobutyryl	70	66
		C_2H_5ZnI	Isobutyryl	38	50
$C_6H_{12}O_2$	Ethyl ethoxymethyl	C_2H_5ZnI	Ethoxyacetyl	13, 23	75
$C_7H_8O_2$	Ethyl 2-furyl	$(C_2H_5)_2Cd$	2-Furoyl	61	9
$C_7H_{12}O$	1-Hepten-6-one	CH_3MgI	5-Hexenoyl	48	32
	1-Hepten-5-one	$(C_2H_5)_2Zn$	4-Pentenoyl	51	76
	Ethyl cyclobutyl	$(C_2H_5)_2Zn$	Cyclobutanecarbonyl	—	70
$C_7H_{12}O_3$	Ethyl 4-ketopentanoate	$(CH_3)_2Zn$	3-Carbethoxypropanoyl	50	77
$C_7H_{13}ClO$	1-Chloro-2-heptanone	$(n\text{-}C_5H_{11})_2Cd$	Chloroacetyl	24	47
	2-Chloro-3-heptanone	$(n\text{-}C_4H_9)_2Cd$	α-Chloropropionyl	43	19
$C_7H_{14}O$	Ethyl n-butyl	$(C_2H_5)_2Zn$	n-Pentanoyl	70	66, 78
	Ethyl isobutyl	$(C_2H_5)_2Zn$	3-Methylbutanoyl	—	74
		C_2H_5ZnI	3-Methylbutanoyl	70	66
	Ethyl t-butyl	$(C_2H_5)_2Zn$	2,2-Dimethylpropanoyl	—	79

Molecular Formula	Ketone	Organometallic Compound	Acyl Halide	Yield (%)	References
	3,3-Dimethyl-2-pentanone	(CH₃)₂Zn	2,2-Dimethylbutanoyl	—	79
		CH₃CH₂C(CH₃)₂MgCl	Acetyl	—	72
	Di-n-propyl	(n-C₃H₇)₂Zn	n-Butyryl	70	66
	n-Propyl isopropyl	(i-C₃H₇)₂Zn	Isobutyryl	70	66
		(CH₃)₂Cd	n-Butyryl	60	9
	Methyl n-amyl	CH₃MgBr	n-Pentanoyl	70	66
C₈H₅Cl₃O	2,4,6-Trichloroacetophenone	CH₃MgBr	2,4,6-Trichlorobenzoyl	68	27
C₈H₈O	Acetophenone	(CH₃)₂Zn	Benzoyl	—	65, 68, 80
		(CH₃)₂Cd	Benzoyl	85	81
		(C₆H₅)₂Cd	Acetyl	83	9
		C₆H₅CdCl	Acetyl	83	9
C₈H₉NO	Methyl α-picolyl	α-Picolylmagnesium bromide	Acetyl	10	82
C₈H₁₂O	1-(1-Cyclopentenyl)-2-propanone	CH₃ZnI	1-Cyclopentenylacetyl	58	83
	2,4-Octadien-6-one	(CH₃)₂Zn	2,4-Hexadienoyl	—	84
C₈H₁₄O	1-Methyl-1-acetylcyclopentane	CH₃MgI	1-Methyl-1-cyclopentanecarbonyl	71	25
		(CH₃)₂Zn	1-Methyl-1-cyclopentanecarbonyl	—	42
	Methyl cyclohexyl	CH₃MgI	Cyclohexanoyl	60	24
	4-Ethyl-4-hexen-2-one	CH₃ZnI	3-Ethyl-3-pentenoyl	68	83
	4-Ethyl-3-hexen-2-one	CH₃ZnI	3-Ethyl-2-pentenoyl	64	83
C₈H₁₄O₂	2,7-Octanedione	CH₃ZnI	Adipyl	50	85
C₈H₁₆O	Ethyl n-amyl	(C₂H₅)₂Zn	n-Hexanoyl	70	66, 78
	n-Propyl n-butyl	(n-C₃H₇)₂Zn	n-Pentanoyl	70	66
	Methyl n-hexyl	(CH₃)₂Zn	n-Heptanoyl	Excellent	86
	n-Propyl isobutyl	(n-C₃H₇)₂Zn	3-Methylbutanoyl	70	66
	Isopropyl isobutyl	(i-C₄H₉)₂Zn	Isobutyryl	—	87
	3-Methyl-3-ethyl-2-pentanone	(C₂H₅)₂C(CH₂)MgCl	Acetyl	18	72
	2-Methyl-5-heptanone	(C₂H₅)₂Zn	4-Methylpentanoyl	—	78
	3,3-Dimethyl-4-hexanone	(C₂H₅)₂Zn	2,2-Dimethylbutanoyl	—	79
C₈H₁₆O₂	Ethyl isobutoxymethyl	C₂H₅ZnI	Isobutoxyacetyl	50	88
	Ethoxyethyl n-butyl	n-C₄H₉ZnI	Ethoxyacetyl	21	75
C₈H₁₆O₃	Ethyl 6-ketoheptanoate	(CH₃)₂Cd	5-Carbethoxypentanoyl	76	46
C₉H₁₀O	Propiophenone	(C₂H₅)₂Zn	Benzoyl chloride	—	68, 80, 89
		C₂H₅ZnI	Benzoyl chloride	30	13
		(C₂H₅)₂Cd	Benzoyl chloride	50	9
		(C₆H₅)₂Cd	Benzoyl chloride	76–84	19
		(C₆H₅)₂Cd	Benzoyl chloride	26–34	37
		(C₆H₅)₂Cd	Propionyl	76–80	9, 19

Note: References 64–146 are listed on pp. 57–58.

ᵃ The product was impure.

KETONES PREPARED FROM ORGANO-MAGNESIUM, -CADMIUM, OR -ZINC COMPOUNDS AND ACID HALIDES—*Continued*

	Ketone	Organometallic Compound	Acid Chloride	Yield %	Reference
C9H10O (*Contd.*)	Methyl benzyl	(C6H5CH2)2Cd	Acetyl	18	9
		(CH3)2Zn	Phenylacetyl	—	90
		CH3ZnI	Phenylacetyl	72	41
	Methyl o-tolyl	o-CH3C6H4MgBr	Acetyl	30	28
		(CH3)2Zn	o-Toluyl	—	91
	Methyl m-tolyl	(CH3)2Zn	m-Toluyl	43	91
		CH3ZnI	m-Toluyl	83	92
		(CH3)2Cd	m-Toluyl	9	9
C9H10O2	p-Methoxyacetophenone	CH3ZnI	Anisoyl	25	92
		(CH3)2Cd	Anisoyl	84	9
C9H11NO	n-Propyl 3-pyridyl	(n-C3H7)2Cd	Nicotinyl	30	93
C9H14O	Cyclohexenylacetone b	CH3MgI	Cyclohexenylacetyl	40	24
	2-Cyclopentenyl-3-butanone b	CH3ZnI	α-Cyclopentenylpropionyl	Good	94
	1-(1-Cyclohexenyl)-2-propanone	CH3ZnI	1-Cyclohexenylacetyl	—	95
C9H16O	Cyclohexylacetone	CH3MgI	Cyclohexylacetyl	60	24
	3-Ethyl-4-methyl-4-hexen-2-one	CH3ZnI	3-Methyl-2-ethyl-3-pentenoyl	Good	96
	Ethyl cyclohexyl	(C2H5)2Zn	Cyclohexanecarbonyl	—	97
C9H16O3	Ethyl 6-ketoheptanoate	(C2H5)2Zn	5-Carbethoxypentanoyl	80-95	98, 99
		(CH3)2Cd	5-Carbethoxypentanoyl	59	100
	Methyl 4-ketoöctanoate	(n-C4H9)2Cd	3-Carbomethoxypropanoyl	45-80	19
	Ethyl 3,3-dimethyl-4-ketopentanoate	(CH3)2Zn	2,2-Dimethyl-3-carbethoxypropanoyl	—	77
	1-Acetoxy-2,2-dimethyl-3-pentanone	C2H5ZnI	2,2-Dimethyl-3-acetoxypropanoyl	78	50
	1-Acetoxy-2,4-dimethyl-3-pentanone	i-C3H7ZnI	1-Methyl-2-acetoxypropanoyl	50	50
C9H18O	Diisobutyl	(i-C4H9)2Zn	3-Methylbutanoyl	—	101
	Di-t-butyl	t-C4H9MgCl	2,2-Dimethylpropanoyl	72, 32	33, 102
	n-Propyl n-amyl	(n-C3H7)2Zn	n-Hexanoyl	70	66
	2-Methyl-6-octanone	(C2H5)2Zn	5-Methylhexanoyl	78	78
	3-Methyl-3-ethyl-2-hexanone	(CH3)2Cd	2-Methyl-2-ethylpentanoyl	47	103
	2,4,4-Trimethyl-3-hexanone	CH3CH2C(CH3)2MgCl	Isobutyryl	87	35
	3,3-Dimethyl-2-heptanone	n-C4H9C(CH3)2MgCl	Acetyl	9	72
C9H18O2	5-Methyl-1-ethoxy-2-hexanone	i-C6H11ZnI	Ethoxyacetyl	16	75
C10H12O	Ethyl benzyl	C2H5ZnI	Phenylacetyl	78	41
		(C2H5)2Zn	Phenylacetyl	—	90
	Ethyl o-tolyl	C2H5ZnI	o-Toluyl	≈8	92

Formula	Ketone	Organometallic compound	Acyl group	Yield	References
$C_{10}H_{12}O_2$	Ethyl p-tolyl	C_2H_5ZnI	p-Toluyl	45	92
	2-Phenyl-3-butanone	$(CH_3)_2Cd$	α-Phenylpropionyl	69	104
$C_{10}H_{12}O_3$	Ethyl phenoxymethyl	C_2H_5ZnI	Phenoxyacetyl	—	88
	2,2-Dimethoxyacetophenone	$(CH_3)_2Cd$	2,3-Dimethoxybenzoyl	71	105
	3,5-Dimethoxyacetophenone	$(CH_3)_3Cd$	3,5-Dimethoxybenzoyl	84	105
$C_{10}H_{16}O$	Methyl m-methyltetrahydrobenzyl [b]	CH_3MgI	m-Methyltetrahydrophenylacetyl	40	24
	Methyl o-methyltetrahydrobenzyl [b]	CH_3MgI	o-Methyltetrahydrophenylacetyl	40	24
	3-(1-Cyclopentenyl)-2-pentanone	CH_3ZnI	2-(1-Cyclopentenyl)butanoyl	60	96
	1-(1-Cyclohexenyl)-2-butanone	C_2H_5ZnI	1-Cyclohexenylacetyl	—	96
	1,1,2-Trimethyl-3-acetyl-2-cyclopentene	$(CH_3)_2Zn$	1,1,2-Trimethyl-2-cyclopentene-3-carbonyl	—	106
$C_{10}H_{18}O$	3-Methylcyclohexylacetone	CH_3MgI	3-Methylcyclohexylacetyl	60	24
	4-Methylcyclohexylacetone	CH_3MgI	4-Methylcyclohexylacetyl	60	24
	n-Propyl cyclohexyl	$n\text{-}C_3H_7MgBr$	Cyclohexanoyl	60	24
$C_{10}H_{18}O_2$	2,9-Decanedione	CH_3ZnI	Suberyl	—	85
	3,8-Decanedione	C_2H_5ZnI	Adipyl	72	85, 98
$C_{10}H_{18}O_3$	Ethyl 4-ketoöctanoate	$n\text{-}C_4H_9ZnI$	4-Carbethoxypropanoyl	74	98, 99
	Ethyl 6-ketoöctanoate	C_2H_5ZnI	5-Carbethoxypentanoyl	80–95	98, 99
	Methyl 4-keto-5-methyloctanoate	$(sec\text{-}C_5H_{11})_2Cd$	3-Carbomethoxypropanoyl	10, 22	19, 46
	Methyl 4-keto-6-methyloctanoate	$[CH_3CH_2CH(CH_3)CH_2]_2Cd$	3-Carbomethoxypropanoyl	60	46
	Methyl 4-keto-7-methyloctanoate	$(i\text{-}C_5H_{11})_2Cd$	3-Carbomethoxypropanoyl	41–44	19, 107
$C_{10}H_{20}O_2$	Ethyl 5-keto-4,4-dimethylhexanoate	$(CH_3)_2Zn$	4-Carbethoxy-4,4-dimethylbutanoyl	73–79	19, 46, 62
	2,2,5,5-Tetramethyl-3-hexanone	$t\text{-}C_4H_9MgCl$	3,3-Dimethylbutanoyl	20	77
$C_{11}H_{11}ClO_3$	Methyl β-(o-chlorophenyl)propionate	$(o\text{-}ClC_6H_4)_2Cd$	3-Carbomethoxypropanoyl	51, 87	108, 109
	Methyl β-(p-chlorophenyl)propionate	$(p\text{-}ClC_6H_4)_2Cd$	3-Carbomethoxypropanoyl	32	110
$C_{11}H_{12}O$	Phenyl 1-methyl-1-propenyl	C_6H_5ZnBr	2-Methyl-2-butenoyl	40	110
	1-Phenyl-1-penten-4-one	CH_3ZnI	4-Phenyl-3-butenoyl	9	111
	2-Acetylhydrindene	$(CH_3)_2Zn$	2-Hydrindenecarbonyl	30–45	112
	Phenyl 2-methyl-1-propenyl	C_6H_5ZnBr	3-Methyl-2-butenoyl	—	43
$C_{11}H_{12}O_3$	Ethyl benzoylacetate	$ClMgCH_2CO_2C_2H_5$	Benzoyl	90	111
		$BrMgCH_2CO_2C_2H_5$	Benzoyl [c]	19	71
	Methyl β-phenylpropionate	$(C_6H_5)_2Cd$	3-Carbomethoxypropanoyl	31	71
				51	110
$C_{11}H_{14}O$	Methyl mesityl	$2,4,6\text{-}(CH_3)_3C_6H_2MgBr$	Acetyl	10	28

Note. References 64–146 are listed on pp. 57–58.

[b] The location of the double bond in the acid chloride and the ketone was not given.

[c] The acid bromide was used in this experiment.

KETONES PREPARED FROM ORGANO-MAGNESIUM, -CADMIUM, OR -ZINC COMPOUNDS AND ACID HALIDES—*Continued*

	Ketone	Organometallic Compound	Acid Chloride	Yield %	Reference
$C_{11}H_{14}O_2$	1-Phenoxy-4-pentanone	$(CH_3)_2Cd$	4-Phenoxybutanoyl	78	113
	Ethyl 2-methoxy-3-methylphenyl	C_2H_5ZnI	2-Methoxy-3-methylbenzoyl	71	92
	Ethyl 2-methoxy-4-methylphenyl	C_2H_5ZnI	2-Methoxy-4-methylbenzoyl	69	92
	Ethyl 2-methoxy-5-methylphenyl	C_2H_5ZnI	2-Methoxy-5-methylbenzoyl	60	92
	Ethoxymethyl p-tolyl	$p\text{-}CH_3C_6H_4ZnBr$	Ethoxyacetyl	37	75, 88
$C_{11}H_{14}O_3$	Ethyl 3,5-dimethoxyphenyl	C_2H_5ZnI	3,5-Dimethoxybenzoyl	19	92
		$(C_2H_5)_2Zn$	3,5-Dimethoxybenzoyl	Low	37
$C_{11}H_{18}O$	3-(1-Cyclohexenyl)-2-pentanone	CH_3ZnI	2-(1-Cyclohexenyl)butanoyl	50–55	95, 96
$C_{11}H_{20}O$	1,2,2,3-Tetramethyl-1-acetylcyclopentane	$(CH_3)_2Zn$	1,2,2,3-Tetramethyl-1-cyclopentane-carbonyl	89, 93	25, 40
		CH_3MgI	1,2,2,3-Tetramethyl-1-cyclopentane-carbonyl	93	25
	1-Methyl-1-acetyl-3-isopropylcyclopentane	$(CH_3)_2Zn$	1-Methyl-3-isopropylcyclopentanecar-bonyl	88	42
$C_{11}H_{20}O_2$	2,10-Undecanedione	CH_3ZnI	Azelalyl	75–90	85, 98
	3,9-Undecanedione	C_2H_5ZnI	Pimelyl	83	85, 98
$C_{11}H_{20}O_3$	Ethyl 7-ketononanoate	C_2H_5ZnI	6-Carbethoxyhexanoyl	80–95	98, 99
	10-Ketoundecanoic acid d	CH_3ZnCl	9-Carbethoxynonanoyl	30 e	114
	Methyl 6-keto-8-methylnonanoate	$i\text{-}C_4H_9ZnI$	5-Carbomethoxypentanoyl	40	16
	6-Keto-9-methyldecanoic acid d	$(i\text{-}C_5H_{11})_2Cd$	5-Carbomethoxypentanoyl	45	115
$C_{12}H_{10}O$	Methyl α-naphthyl	$α\text{-}C_{10}H_7MgBr$	Acetyl	50	28
$C_{12}H_{12}O$	Methyl 3,4-dihydro-1-naphthyl	$(CH_3)_2Cd$	3,4-Dihydro-1-naphthoyl	—	116
$C_{12}H_{14}O$	Methyl 1,2,3,4-tetrahydro-1-naphthyl	$(CH_3)_2Cd$	1,2,3,4-Tetrahydro-1-naphthoyl	65	117
	2-Propionylhydrindene	$(C_2H_5)_2Zn$	2-Hydrindenecarbonyl	97	43
$C_{12}H_{14}O_2$	1,2-Dipropionylbenzene	$(C_2H_5)_2Zn$	Phthalyl	—	118
	Ethyl α-benzoylpropionate	$BrMgCH(CH_3)CO_2C_2H_5$	Benzoyl c	29	71
	Ethyl β-benzoylpropionate	$IMgCH_2CH_2CO_2C_2H_5$	Benzoyl c	15	71
$C_{12}H_{14}O_3$	Methyl β-(o-toluyl)propionate	$(o\text{-}CH_3C_6H_4)_2Cd$	3-Carbomethoxypropanoyl	58	110
	Methyl β-(m-toluyl)propionate	$(m\text{-}CH_3C_6H_4)_2Cd$	3-Carbomethoxypropanoyl	62	110
	Methyl β-(p-toluyl)propionate	$(p\text{-}CH_3C_6H_4)_2Cd$	3-Carbomethoxypropanoyl	56	110
	5-Benzoylpentanoic acid d	$(C_6H_5)_2Cd$	5-Carbethoxypentanoyl	64	119
$C_{12}H_{14}O_4$	Methyl β-(o-methoxybenzoyl)propionate	$(o\text{-}CH_3OC_6H_4)_2Cd$	3-Carbomethoxypropanoyl	43–50	110, 120
	Methyl β-(m-methoxybenzoyl)propionate	$(m\text{-}CH_3OC_6H_4)_2Cd$	3-Carbomethoxypropanoyl	27	110
	Methyl β-(p-methoxybenzoyl)propionate	$(p\text{-}CH_3OC_6H_4)_2Cd$	3-Carbomethoxypropanoyl	54	110

Formula	Ketone	Organometallic compound	Acyl group	Yield (%)	References
$C_{12}H_{20}O_3$	Methyl 1,2,2-trimethyl-1-acetyl-3-cyclopentanecarboxylate	$(CH_3)_2Cd$	1,2,2-Trimethyl-3-carbomethoxy-1-cyclopentanecarbonyl	60	33
$C_{12}H_{22}O$	1,2,2,3-Tetramethyl-1-propionylcyclopentane	$(C_2H_5)_2Cd$	1,2,2,3-Tetramethylcyclopentanecarbonyl	95	40
		C_2H_5ZnI	1,2,2,3-Tetramethylcyclopentanecarbonyl	53	40
$C_{12}H_{22}O_2$	3,10-Decanedione	C_2H_5ZnI	Suberyl	75–90	85, 98
$C_{12}H_{22}O_3$	Ethyl 9-ketodecanoate	$(CH_3)_2Cd$	8-Carbethoxyoctanoyl	64	100
		CH_3ZnI	8-Carbethoxyoctanoyl	—	15
	Ethyl 8-ketodecanoate	C_2H_5ZnI	7-Carbethoxyheptanoyl	80–95	98, 99
$C_{13}H_{10}O$	Benzophenone	$(C_6H_5)_2Cd$	Benzoyl	57	9
		C_6H_5MgBr	Benzoyl	29,[f] 45 [g]	20
		C_6H_5MgCl	Benzoyl	40, 55	28, 29
		C_6H_5MgI	Benzoyl	48	29
$C_{13}H_{16}O$	1-(1,2,3,4-Tetrahydro)naphthyl-2-propanone	$(CH_3)_2Cd$	1,2,3,4-Tetrahydro-1-naphthylacetyl	69	29
	2-Methyl-3-phenyl-2-hexen-4-one	C_2H_5ZnI	2-Phenyl-3-methyl-2-butenoyl	69	117
	3,3-Dimethyl-2-phenyl-1-penten-4-one	$(CH_3)_2Zn$	2,2-Dimethyl-3-phenyl-3-butenoyl	—	111
$C_{13}H_{16}O_3$	Phenyl α,α-dimethyl-β-acetoxyethyl	C_6H_5ZnBr	2-Methyl-2-acetoxymethylpropionyl	—	121
$C_{13}H_{18}O$	2,3,4,5,6-Pentamethylacetophenone	$(CH_3)_5C_6MgBr$	Acetyl	70	111
	2-(p-Tolyl)-5-hexanone	$(CH_3)_2Zn$	4-(p-Tolyl)-pentanoyl	38	30
$C_{13}H_{18}O_3$	n-Butyl 3,5-dimethoxyphenyl	$(n\text{-}C_4H_9)_2Cd$	3,5-Dimethoxybenzoyl	76	44
		$(n\text{-}C_4H_9)_2Zn$	3,5-Dimethoxybenzoyl	27	37
$C_{13}H_{20}O$	Cyclohexyl cyclohexenyl	$C_6H_{11}MgBr$	Cyclohexenecarbonyl	Low	37
$C_{13}H_{22}O_3$	Ethyl 10-ketoundecanoate	CH_3ZnI	9-Carbethoxynonanoyl	40	24
		$(CH_3)_2Cd$	9-Carbethoxynonanoyl	—	15
$C_{14}H_{12}O$	4-Methylbenzophenone	$p\text{-}CH_3C_6H_4MgBr$	Benzoyl	76	46
	2-Methylbenzophenone	$o\text{-}CH_3C_6H_4MgBr$	Benzoyl	55, 84	19
$C_{14}H_{16}O_3$	10-Keto-12-methyltridecanoic acid[d]	$i\text{-}C_4H_9MgBr$	9-Carbethoxynonanoyl	40	28
				50	28
$C_{14}H_{24}O$	Methyl methylbutyltetrahydrobenzyl[h]	CH_3MgI	Methylbutyltetrahydrophenylacetyl	43–47	21
				40	24

Note: References 64–146 are listed on pp. 57–58.

[d] The intermediate ester was hydrolyzed to the acid without isolation.

[e] This was the average yield of several runs; the highest yield was 43%.

[f] Equimolar quantities of acid chloride and organometallic compound were used.

[g] An 0.67 mole excess of acid chloride was used.

[h] The locations of the substituent alkyl groups and the double bond in the acid chloride and ketone are not known.

KETONES PREPARED FROM ORGANO-MAGNESIUM, -CADMIUM, OR -ZINC COMPOUNDS AND ACID HALIDES—*Continued*

	Ketone	Organometallic Compound	Acid Chloride	Yield %	Reference
$C_{14}H_{26}O_3$	Ethyl 9-ketododecanoate	$(n\text{-}C_3H_7)_2Cd$	8-Carbethoxyoctanoyl	95	122
	Ethyl 10-ketododecanoate	$(C_2H_5)_2Cd$	9-Carbethoxynonanoyl	88	122
$C_{14}H_{27}ClO$	1-Chloro-2-tetradecanone	$(n\text{-}C_{12}H_{25})_2Cd$	Chloroacetyl	18	47
$C_{15}H_{12}O$	Benzalacetophenone	$(C_6H_5)_2Cd$	Cinnamoyl	44	123
$C_{15}H_{14}O_3$	Methyl β-(1-naphthoyl)propionate	$(1\text{-}C_{10}H_7)_2Cd$	3-Carbomethoxypropanoyl	64	110
	Methyl β-(2-naphthoyl)propionate	$(2\text{-}C_{10}H_7)_2Cd$	3-Carbomethoxypropanoyl	34	110
$C_{15}H_{20}O_2$	4-(p-Hydroxyphenyl)hexahydropropiophe-none	$(C_2H_5)_2Cd$	p-Hydroxyphenylhexahydrobenzoyl	63	124
$C_{15}H_{30}O_3$	2,2-Dimethyl-1-phenyl-1-acetoxy-3-penta-none	C_2H_5ZnI	2,2-Dimethyl-3-phenyl-3-acetoxypro-panoyl	—	111
$C_{15}H_{29}ClO$	2-Chloro-3-pentadecanone	$(n\text{-}C_{12}H_{25})_2Cd$	α-Chloropropionyl	13	47
$C_{15}H_{30}O$	3-Pentadecanone	$n\text{-}C_{12}H_{25}ZnI$	Propionyl	*i*	39a
	4-Pentadecanone	$n\text{-}C_3H_7ZnI$	$n\text{-}C_{11}H_{23}COCl$	*i*	39a
	5-Pentadecanone	$n\text{-}C_4H_9ZnI$	$n\text{-}C_{10}H_{21}COCl$	*i*	39a
$C_{16}H_{10}OS$	Di-(3-thianaphthenyl)	3-Thianaphthenylmagnesium bromide	3-Thianaphthenecarbonyl	49	125
$C_{16}H_{16}O$	Phenyl mesityl	$2,4,6\text{-}(CH_3)_3C_6H_2MgBr$	Benzoyl	34	28
$C_{16}H_{22}O$	Phenyl 1,2,2,3-tetramethylcyclopentyl	C_6H_5MgBr	1,2,2,3-Tetramethyl-1-cyclopentane-carbonyl	55	33
$C_{16}H_{22}O_2$	4-(p-Hydroxyphenyl)hexahydro-n-butyro-phenone	$(n\text{-}C_3H_7)_2Cd$	p-Hydroxyphenylhexahydrobenzoyl	74	124
$C_{16}H_{30}O_3$	10-Ketohexadecanoic acid	$n\text{-}C_6H_{13}MgBr$	Sebacyl	28	21
	10-Keto-14-methylpentadecanoic acid	$i\text{-}C_6H_{13}MgBr$	Sebacyl	24	21
	Ethyl 13-ketotetradecanoate	CH_3ZnI	12-Carbethoxydecanoyl	76	15
	5-Ketohexadecanoic acid *d*	$(n\text{-}C_{11}H_{23})_2Cd$	4-Carbomethoxybutanoyl	79	126
	Methyl 4-ethyl-4-n-butyl-5-ketononanoate and methyl 2-ethyl-2-n-butyl-5-ketonon-anoate	$(n\text{-}C_4H_9)_2Cd$	4-Carbomethoxy-4-ethyl-4-n-butyl-butanoyl	91 (total)	12
$C_{16}H_{31}ClO$	1-Chloro-2-hexadecanone	$(n\text{-}C_{14}H_{29})_2Cd$	Chloroacetyl	15	47
$C_{16}H_{32}O$	3-Hexadecanone	C_2H_5ZnI	$n\text{-}C_{13}H_{27}COCl$	*i*	39a
	4-Hexadecanone	$n\text{-}C_{12}H_{25}ZnI$	Butyryl	*i*	39a
	5-Hexadecanone	$n\text{-}C_4H_9ZnI$	$n\text{-}C_{11}H_{23}COCl$	*i*	39a
$C_{17}H_{12}O$	Phenyl α-naphthyl	$\alpha\text{-}C_{10}H_7MgBr$	Benzoyl	69	28, 127
$C_{17}H_{17}BrO$	Phenyl 2,4,6-trimethyl-3-bromobenzyl	C_6H_5CdCl	2,4,6-Trimethyl-3-bromophenylacetyl	87	26
$C_{17}H_{18}O$	Benzyl 2,6-dimethyl-4-methoxyphenyl	$2,6\text{-}(CH_3)_2\text{-}4\text{-}CH_3OC_6H_2MgBr$	Phenylacetyl	29	26
$C_{17}H_{24}O$	Benzyl 1,2,2,3-tetramethylcyclopentyl	$C_6H_5CH_2MgCl$	1,2,2,3-Tetramethylcyclopentanecar-bonyl	35	33

Formula	Ketone	Organometallic reagent	Acyl component	Yield (%)	References
C$_{17}$H$_{32}$O$_3$	Methyl 9-ketohexadecanoate	n-C$_7$H$_{15}$MgBr	8-Carbomethoxyoctanoyl	—	22
	Methyl 4-ketohexadecanoate	(n-C$_{12}$H$_{25}$)$_2$Cd	3-Carbomethoxypropanoyl	34	128
	Ethyl 10-keto-13-methyltetradecanoate	(i-C$_5$H$_{11}$)$_2$Cd	9-Carbethoxynonanoyl	85	46
C$_{17}$H$_{34}$O	2-Heptadecanone	(CH$_3$)$_2$Cd	Hexadecanoyl	55	129
	3-Heptadecanone	n-C$_{14}$H$_{29}$ZnI	Propionyl	–	39a
	4-Heptadecanone	n-C$_3$H$_7$ZnI	n-C$_{13}$H$_{27}$COCl	–	39a
	5-Heptadecanone	n-C$_{12}$H$_{25}$ZnI	n-C$_4$H$_9$COCl	–	39a
	6-Heptadecanone	n-C$_5$H$_{11}$ZnI	n-C$_{11}$H$_{23}$COCl	–	39a
	7-Heptadecanone	n-C$_{10}$H$_{21}$ZnI	n-C$_6$H$_{13}$COCl	–	39a
	8-Heptadecanone	n-C$_7$H$_{15}$ZnI	n-C$_9$H$_{19}$COCl	–	39a
C$_{18}$H$_{20}$O	2,3,4,5,6-Pentamethylbenzophenone	(CH$_3$)$_5$C$_6$MgBr	Benzoyl	35	30
	Phenyl 2,3,4,6-tetramethylbenzyl	C$_6$H$_5$CdCl	2,3,4,6-Tetramethylphenylacetyl	47	26
	Phenyl 2,3,5,6-tetramethylbenzyl	C$_6$H$_5$CdCl	2,3,5,6-Tetramethylphenylacetyl	93	26
C$_{18}$H$_{26}$O	Phenethyl 1,2,2,3-tetramethylcyclopentyl	C$_6$H$_5$CH$_2$CH$_2$MgBr	1,2,2,3-Tetramethylcyclopentanecarbonyl	25	33
C$_{18}$H$_{26}$O$_2$	6-(4′-Acetylcyclohexyl)-4,4a,5,6,7,8-hexahydro-2(3H)-naphthalenone	(CH$_3$)$_2$Cd	6-(4′-chlorocarbonylcyclohexyl)-4,4a,5,6,7,8-hexahydro-2(3H)-naphthalenone	13	130
C$_{18}$H$_{34}$O$_3$	10-Ketooctadecanoic acid [d]	n-C$_8$H$_{17}$ZnCl	9-Carbethoxynonanoyl	40	131
	10-Ketooctadecanoic acid	n-C$_8$H$_{17}$MgBr	Sebacyl	12	21
	10-Keto-16-methylheptadecanoic acid	(CH$_3$)$_2$CH(CH$_2$)$_4$CH$_2$MgBr	Sebacyl	11	21
C$_{18}$H$_{35}$ClO	1-Chloro-2-octadecanone	(n-C$_{16}$H$_{33}$)$_2$Cd	Chloroacetyl	33	19
C$_{18}$H$_{36}$O	3-Octadecanone	(C$_2$H$_5$)$_2$Zn	n-C$_{15}$H$_{31}$COCl	Excellent	[132
	3-Octadecanone	C$_2$H$_5$ZnI	n-C$_{15}$H$_{31}$COCl	–	39a
	4-Octadecanone	n-C$_{14}$H$_{29}$ZnI	Butyryl	–	39a
	5-Octadecanone	n-C$_4$H$_9$ZnI	n-C$_{13}$H$_{27}$COCl	–	39a
	6-Octadecanone	n-C$_{12}$H$_{25}$ZnI	n-C$_5$H$_{11}$COCl	–	39a
	7-Octadecanone	n-C$_6$H$_{13}$ZnI	n-C$_{11}$H$_{23}$COCl	–	39a
	8-Octadecanone	n-C$_{10}$H$_{21}$ZnI	n-C$_7$H$_{15}$COCl	–	39a
	9-Octadecanone	n-C$_8$H$_{17}$ZnI	n-C$_9$H$_{19}$COCl	–	39a
C$_{19}$H$_{18}$O$_3$	4,4′-Dipropionylbenzophenone	(C$_2$H$_5$)$_2$Zn	Benzophenone-4,4′-dicarbonyl	45	133
C$_{19}$H$_{36}$O$_3$	Ethyl 9-ketoheptadecanoate	(n-C$_8$H$_{17}$)$_2$Cd	8-Carbethoxyoctanoyl	–	122
C$_{19}$H$_{38}$O	3-Nonadecanone	n-C$_{16}$H$_{33}$ZnI	Propionyl	–	39a
	4-Nonadecanone	n-C$_3$H$_7$ZnI	n-C$_{15}$H$_{31}$COCl	–	39a
	4-Nonadecanone	(n-C$_3$H$_7$)$_2$Zn	n-C$_{15}$H$_{31}$COCl	Excellent	132
	5-Nonadecanone	n-C$_{14}$H$_{29}$ZnI	n-C$_4$H$_9$COCl	–	39a
	6-Nonadecanone	n-C$_5$H$_{11}$ZnI	n-C$_{13}$H$_{27}$COCl	–	39a

Note: References 64–146 are listed on pp. 57–58.

[b] The yield in this experiment was not reported, but the experiment is one of a series for which 50-70% yields of crude products were reported.

KETONES PREPARED FROM ORGANO-MAGNESIUM, -CADMIUM, OR -ZINC COMPOUNDS AND ACID HALIDES—*Continued*

Ketone	Organometallic Compound	Acid Chloride	Yield %	Reference
$C_{19}H_{38}O$ (*Contd.*)				
7-Nonadecanone	n-$C_{12}H_{25}ZnI$	n-$C_6H_{13}COCl$	-	39a
8-Nonadecanone	n-$C_7H_{15}ZnI$	n-$C_{11}H_{21}COCl$	-	39a
9-Nonadecanone	n-$C_{10}H_{21}ZnI$	n-$C_8H_{17}COCl$	-	39a
$C_{20}H_{14}O_2$				
o-Dibenzoylbenzene	C_6H_5MgBr	Phthalyl	—	23
$C_{20}H_{22}O_2$				
3-(p-Hydroxyphenyl)-4-(p-acetylphenyl)-3-hexene ^{j}	$(CH_3)_2Cd$	α,α'-Diethyl-4'-acetoxy-4-stilbenecarboxylic acid	63	63
$C_{20}H_{24}O$				
Phenyl 2,4,6-triethylbenzyl	C_6H_5CdCl	2,4,6-Triethylphenylacetyl	33	26
α-Naphthyl 1,2,2,3-tetramethylcyclopentyl	α-$C_{10}H_7MgBr$	1,2,2,3-Tetramethylcyclopentanecarbonyl	—	33
$C_{20}H_{38}O_3$				
Ethyl 10-keto-14-ethylhexadecanoate	$[(C_2H_5)_2CHCH_2CH_2CH_2]_2Cd$	9-Carbethoxyoctanoyl	45	134
Ethyl 9-keto-16-methylheptadecanoate	$[(CH_3)_2CH(CH_2)_5CH_2]_2Cd$	8-Carbethoxyoctanoyl	55	135
Methyl 4-keto-8-methyloctadecanoate	$[CH_3(CH_2)_9CH(CH_3)CH_2CH_2CH_2]_2Cd$	3-Carbomethoxypropanoyl	38	136
Methyl 5-keto-9-methyloctadecanoate	$[CH_3(CH_2)_8CH(CH_3)CH_2CH_2CH_2]_2Cd$	4-Carbomethoxybutanoyl	40	135
$C_{20}H_{40}O$				
2-Eicosanone	n-$C_{18}H_{37}ZnI$	Acetyl	-	39a
3-Eicosanone	$(C_2H_5)_2Cd$	n-$C_{17}H_{35}COCl$	62	53
	$(C_2H_5)_2Zn$	n-$C_{17}H_{35}COCl$	—	137
	C_2H_5ZnI	n-$C_{17}H_{35}COCl$	-	39a
4-Eicosanone	n-$C_{16}H_{33}ZnI$	Butyryl	-	39a
5-Eicosanone	n-C_4H_9ZnI	n-$C_{15}H_{31}COCl$	-	39a
6-Eicosanone	n-$C_{14}H_{29}ZnI$	n-$C_5H_{11}COCl$	-	39a
7-Eicosanone	n-$C_6H_{13}ZnI$	n-$C_{13}H_{27}COCl$	-	39a
8-Eicosanone	n-$C_{12}H_{25}ZnI$	n-$C_7H_{15}COCl$	-	39a
9-Eicosanone	n-$C_8H_{17}ZnI$	n-$C_{11}H_{23}COCl$	-	39a
10-Eicosanone	n-$C_{10}H_{21}ZnI$	n-$C_9H_{19}COCl$	-	39a
$C_{21}H_{14}O$				
α,α-Dinaphthyl	α-$C_{10}H_7MgBr$	α-Naphthoyl	—	138
$C_{21}H_{20}O$				
Ethyl triphenylmethyl	C_2H_5MgI	Triphenylacetyl	37	36
$C_{21}H_{40}O_3$				
Methyl 5-keto-3,3-dimethyloctadecanoate	$(n$-$C_{13}H_{27})_2Cd$	4-Carbomethoxy-3,3-dimethylbutanoyl	88	139
Methyl 4-keto-2,3-dimethyloctadecanoate	$(n$-$C_{14}H_{29})_2Cd$	3-Carbomethoxy-2-methylbutanoyl	64	139
Ethyl 9-keto-10-methyloctadecanoate	$CH_3(CH_2)_7CH(CH_3)ZnCl$	8-Carbethoxyoctanoyl	55	17
Ethyl 10-keto-16-methyloctadecanoate	$[CH_3CH_2CH(CH_3)(CH_2)_4CH_2]_2Cd$	9-Carbethoxynonanoyl	77	46
Ethyl 9-keto-13-methyloctadecanoate	$[CH_3(CH_2)_4CH(CH_3)CH_2CH_2CH_2]_2Cd$	8-Carbethoxyoctanoyl	46	136
Ethyl 10-keto-14-methyloctadecanoate	$[CH_3(CH_2)_3CH(CH_3)CH_2CH_2CH_2]_2Cd$	9-Carbethoxynonanoyl	54	136
Ethyl 9-keto-12-methyloctadecanoate	$[CH_3(CH_2)_5CH(CH_3)CH_2CH_2]_2Cd$	8-Carbethoxyoctanoyl	43	136
Ethyl 9-keto-15-ethylheptadecanoate	$[(C_2H_5)_2CH(CH_2)_4CH_2]_2Cd$	8-Carbethoxyoctanoyl	49	134
Ethyl 7-keto-10-methyloctadecanoate	$[CH_3(CH_2)_7CH(CH_3)CH_2CH_2]_2Cd$	6-Carbethoxyhexanoyl	52–56	140

Formula	Ketone	Organometallic compound	Acyl component	Yield	Reference
	Ethyl 7-keto-11-methyloctadecanoate	$[CH_3(CH_2)_6CH(CH_3)CH_2CH_2CH_2]_2Cd$	6-Carbethoxyhexanoyl	49	135
	Ethyl 10-keto-17-methyloctadecanoate	$[(CH_3)_2CH(CH_2)_6CH_2]_2Cd$	9-Carbethoxynonanoyl	46	107
	Ethyl 10-keto-15-methyloctadecanoate	$[CH_3CH_2CH_2CH(CH_3)CH_2CH_2CH_2CH_2]_2Cd$	9-Carbethoxynonanoyl	65	141
$C_{21}H_{42}O$	7-Heneicosanone	$n\text{-}C_{14}H_{29}ZnI$	$n\text{-}C_6H_{13}COCl$	—	39a
	8-Heneicosanone	$n\text{-}C_7H_{15}ZnI$	$n\text{-}C_{13}H_{27}COCl$	—	39a
	9-Heneicosanone	$n\text{-}C_{12}H_{25}ZnI$	$n\text{-}C_8H_{17}COCl$	—	39a
	10-Heneicosanone	$n\text{-}C_9H_{19}ZnI$	$n\text{-}C_{11}H_{23}COCl$	—	39a
	11-Heneicosanone	$n\text{-}C_{10}H_{21}ZnI$	$n\text{-}C_{10}H_{21}COCl$	—	39a
$C_{22}H_{18}O_2$	1,2-Di-(o-toluyl)benzene	$o\text{-}CH_3C_6H_4MgBr$	Phthalyl	—	23
	1,4-Di-(o-toluyl)benzene	$o\text{-}CH_3C_6H_4MgBr$	Terephthalyl	—	23
$C_{22}H_{42}O_3$	10-Ketoeicosanoic acid d	$n\text{-}C_{12}H_{26}ZnCl$	9-Carbethoxynonanoyl	62	114
$C_{22}H_{44}O$	7-Docosanone	$n\text{-}C_6H_{13}ZnI$	$n\text{-}C_{15}H_{31}COCl$	—	39a
	8-Docosanone	$n\text{-}C_{14}H_{29}ZnI$	$n\text{-}C_7H_{15}COCl$	—	39a
	9-Docosanone	$n\text{-}C_8H_{17}ZnI$	$n\text{-}C_{13}H_{27}COCl$	—	39a
	10-Docosanone	$n\text{-}C_{12}H_{25}ZnI$	$n\text{-}C_9H_{19}COCl$	—	39a
	11-Docosanone	$n\text{-}C_{10}H_{21}ZnI$	$n\text{-}C_{11}H_{21}COCl$	—	39a
$C_{24}H_{21}O_2$	3-Ketoternorcholenyl methyl	$(CH_3)_2Zn$	3-Keto-4-bisnorcholenyl	—	31
$C_{24}H_{46}O_3$	10-Ketotetracosanoic acid d	$n\text{-}C_{14}H_{29}ZnCl$	9-Carbethoxynonanoyl	62	114
$C_{25}H_{24}O_3$	cis-2-Carbomethoxy-2-methyl-1-phenacyl-1,2,3,4-tetrahydrophenanthrene	$(C_6H_5)_2Cd$	cis-2-Carbomethoxy-2-methyl-1,2,3,4-tetrahydrophenanthrene-1-acetyl	68	142
$C_{25}H_{38}O_3$	3-Acetoxy-5-ternorcholenyl methyl	$(CH_3)_2Cd$	3-Acetoxybisnorcholenyl	75–95	31
		$(CH_3)_2Zn$	3-Acetoxybisnorcholenyl	75	31
$C_{26}H_{20}O$	Phenyl triphenylmethyl	C_6H_5MgBr	Triphenylacetyl	—	36
$C_{26}H_{40}O_3$	Ethyl 3-acetoxy-5-ternorcholenyl	$(C_2H_5)_2Cd$	3-Acetoxybisnorcholenyl	93	31
$C_{26}H_{40}O$	1-Phenyl-3-eicosanone	$(C_6H_5CH_2CH_2)_2Cd$	Octadecanoyl	66	53
$C_{26}H_{50}O_3$	Ethyl 9-keto-20-ethyldocosanoate	$[(C_2H_5)_2CH(CH_2)_8CH_2]_2Cd$	9-Carbethoxynonanoyl	74	122
	10-Ketohexacosanoic acid d	$(n\text{-}C_{16}H_{33})_2Cd$	9-Carbethoxynonanoyl	32	143
	Methyl 3-methyl-5-ketotetracosanoate	$(n\text{-}C_{19}H_{39})_2Cd$	4-Carbomethoxy-3-methylbutanoyl	80	129
	Ethyl 9-keto-18-n-propyleicosanoate	$[(n\text{-}C_3H_7)_2CH(CH_2)_7CH_2]_2Cd$	8-Carbethoxyoctanoyl	72	122
$C_{27}H_{44}O_2$	24-Ketocholesterol k	$(i\text{-}C_3H_7)_2Cd$	2-Acetoxy-5-cholenyl	53	49
$C_{27}H_{52}O_3$	Ethyl 7-ketopentacosanoate	$(n\text{-}C_{18}H_{37})_2Cd$	6-Carbethoxyhexanoyl	39	129
	Ethyl 10-keto-14-methyltetracosanoate	$[CH_3(CH_2)_9CH(CH_3)CH_2CH_2CH_2]_2Cd$	9-Carbethoxynonanoyl	78	141
$C_{28}H_{40}O_2$	Phenyl 3-hydroxyternorcholanyl	$(C_6H_5)_2Cd$	3-Hydroxyternorcholanyl	—	51
$C_{28}H_{54}O_3$	10-Ketoöctacosanoic acid d	$n\text{-}C_{18}H_{37}ZnCl$	9-Carbethoxynonanoyl	77	39

Note: References 64–146 are listed on pp. 57–58.

i The intermediate product was hydrolyzed to remove the acetoxy group.

k The intermediate product was hydrolyzed to remove the acetoxy group. The yield was based on 3-acetoxy-5-cholenic acid.

KETONES PREPARED FROM ORGANO-MAGNESIUM, -CADMIUM, OR -ZINC COMPOUNDS AND ACID HALIDES—*Continued*

	Ketone	Organometallic Compound	Acid Chloride	Yield %	Reference
C29H42O2	Phenyl 3-hydroxybisnorcholanyl	(C6H5)2Cd	3-Hydroxybisnorcholanyl	—	51
C29H42O3	Phenyl 3,12-dihydroxybisnorcholanyl	(C6H5)2Cd	3,12-Dihydroxybisnorcholanyl	—	51
C29H46O3	3-Methylbutyl 3-acetoxy-5-ternorcholenyl	(i-C5H11)2Cd	3-Acetoxybisnorcholanyl	91	31
C29H48O	Methyl 3-cholesteryl	(CH3)2Cd	Cholesteryl-3-carbonyl	82[l]	144
C29H56O3	11-Ketononacosanoic acid[d]	n-C18H37ZnCl	10-Carbethoxydecanoyl	92	39
C30H40O3	Phenyl 3-acetoxy-5-ternorcholenyl	C6H5ZnCl	3-Acetoxy-5-bisnorcholenyl	68	31
		(C6H5)2Cd	3-Acetoxy-5-bisnorcholenyl	73	31
C30H42O2	Phenyl 3-(β)-hydroxy-Δ^5-norcholanyl	(C6H5)2Cd	3-(β)-Hydroxy-Δ^5-norcholanyl	—	51
C30H42O3	Phenyl 3-hydroxy-12-ketonorcholanyl	(C6H5)2Cd	3-Hydroxy-12-ketonorcholanyl	—	51
C30H42O4	Phenyl 3,12-dihydroxy-7-ketonorcholanyl	(C6H5)2Cd	3,12-Dihydroxy-7-ketonorcholanyl	—	51
C30H44O	Phenyl norcholanyl	(C6H5)2Cd	Norcholanyl	—	51
C30H44O2	Phenyl 3-hydroxynorcholanyl	(C6H5)2Cd	3-Hydroxynorcholanyl	—	51
C30H44O3	Phenyl 3,12-dihydroxynorcholanyl	(C6H5)2Cd	3,12-Dihydroxynorcholanyl	64	51
C30H44O4	Phenyl 3,7,12-trihydroxynorcholanyl	(C6H5)2Cd	3,7,12-Trihydroxynorcholanyl	—	51
	Phenyl norcholyl	(C6H5)2Cd	Norcholyl	70-75	145
C30H58O3	12-Ketotriacontanoic acid[d]	n-C18H37ZnCl	11-Carbethoxyundecanoyl	79	39
C31H60O3	13-Ketohentriacontanoic acid[d]	n-C18H37ZnCl	12-Carbethoxydodecanoyl	89	39
C32H62O3	14-Ketodotriacontanoic acid[d]	n-C18H37ZnCl	13-Carbethoxytrideacanoyl	76	39
	10-Ketodotriacontanoic acid[d]	(n-C22H45)2Cd	9-Carbethoxynonanoyl	80	38
C33H46O3	Mesityl 3-acetoxy-5-ternorcholenyl	[2,4,6-(CH3)3C6H2]2Cd	3-Acetoxybisnorcholenyl	40	31
		2,4,6-(CH3)3C6H2MgBr	3-Acetoxy-5-bisnorcholenyl		31
C33H64O3	15-Ketotritriacontanoic acid[d]	n-C18H37ZnCl	14-Carbethoxytetradecanoyl	83	39
C34H66O3	18-Ketotetratriacontanoic acid[d]	(n-C16H33)2Cd	17-Carbethoxyheptadecanoyl	79	143
	16-Ketotetratriacontanoic acid[d]	n-C18H37ZnCl	15-Carbethoxypentadecanoyl	77	39
	Ethyl 10-ketodotriacontanoate	n-C22H45ZnCl	9-Carbethoxynonanoyl	35	146
C35H68O3	17-Ketopentatriacontanoic acid[d]	n-C18H37ZnCl	16-Carbethoxyhexadecanoyl	80	39
C38H74O2	1-Cyclohexoxy-11-ketodotriacontane	Di-(10-cyclohexoxydecyl)cadmium	Docosanoyl	12	143
C42H82O2	1-Cyclohexoxy-11-ketohexatriacontane	Di-(10-cyclohexoxydecyl)cadmium	Hexacosanoyl	15	143

Note: References 64–146 are listed on pp. 57–58.

[l] Under other experimental conditions the yield of ketone was only 40%. When the impure acid chloride was treated with methylmagnesium iodide the yield of ketone was very small.

[64] Pawlow, *Ann.*, **188**, 114, 139 (1877).
[65] Boutlerow, *Bull. soc. chim. France*, (2) **5**, 18 (1866).
[66] Michael, *J. Am. Chem. Soc.*, **41**, 412 (1919).
[67] Behal, *Ann. chim. phys.*, (6) **15**, 284 (1888).
[68] Popoff, *Ann.*, **161**, 285 (1872).
[69] Campaigne and LeSuer, *J. Am. Chem. Soc.*, **70**, 1557 (1950).
[70] Perkin and Sinclair, *J. Chem. Soc.*, **61**, 36 (1892).
[71] Meyer and Togel, *Ann.*, **347**, 76 (1906).
[72] Whitmore and Badertscher, *J. Am. Chem. Soc.*, **55**, 1564 (1933).
[73] Butlerow, *Ann.*, **174**, 126 (1874).
[74] Wagner, *J. prakt. Chem.*, (2) **44**, 261, 274 (1891).
[75] Blaise and Picard, *Ann. chim. phys.*, (8) **25**, 253 (1912).
[76] Helferich, *Ber.*, **52**, 1809 (1919).
[77] Blaise, *Bull. soc. chim. France*, (3) **21**, 647, 718 (1899).
[78] Ponzio and de Gaspari, *Gazz. chim. ital.*, **28** (II), 269 (1898).
[79] Wischnegradsky, *Ann.*, **178**, 104 (1875).
[80] Popoff, *Ber.*, **4**, 720 (1871).
[81] Dauben, Reid, Yankwich, and Calvin, *J. Am. Chem. Soc.*, **72**, 123 (1950).
[82] Gilman and Towle, *Rec. trav. chim.*, **69**, 432 (1950).
[83] Kon and Linstead, *J. Chem. Soc.*, **127**, 818 (1925).
[84] Doebner and Wolff, *Ber.*, **34**, 2222 (1901).
[85] Blaise and Kohler, *Bull. soc. chim. France*, (4) **5**, 681 (1909).
[86] Behal, *Bull. soc. chim. France*, (3) **6**, 133 (1891).
[87] Ponzio, *Gazz. chim. ital.*, **30** (II), 23 (1900).
[88] Blaise and Picard, *Compt. rend.*, **152**, 269 (1911).
[89] Kalle, *Ann.*, **119**, 166 (1861).
[90] Popoff, *Ber.*, **5**, 500 (1872).
[91] Klages, *Ber.*, **32**, 1560 (1899).
[92] Mauthner, *J. prakt. Chem.*, (2) **103**, 393 (1922).
[93] Frank and Weatherbee, *J. Am. Chem. Soc.*, **70**, 3482 (1950).
[94] Bardhan, *J. Chem. Soc.*, **133**, 2603 (1928).
[95] Birch, Kon, and Norris, *J. Chem. Soc.*, **123**, 1370 (1923).
[96] Kon and Narayanan, *J. Chem. Soc.*, **131**, 1536 (1927).
[97] Scharvin, *Ber.*, **30**, 2864 (1897).
[98] Blaise and Kohler, *Compt. rend.*, **148**, 490 (1909).
[99] Blaise and Kohler, *Bull. soc. chim. France*, (4) **7**, 215 (1910).
[100] McKennis and du Vigneaud, *J. Am. Chem. Soc.*, **68**, 832 (1946).
[101] Ponzio, *Gazz. chim. ital.*, **35** (II), 394 (1905).
[102] Greenwood, Whitmore, and Crooks, *J. Am. Chem. Soc.*, **60**, 2029 (1938).
[103] Lester and Proffitt, *J. Am. Chem. Soc.*, **71**, 1877 (1951).
[104] Campbell and Kenyon, *J. Chem. Soc.*, **1946**, 27.
[105] Woodruff, *J. Am. Chem. Soc.*, **64**, 2860 (1942).
[106] Blanc, *Compt. rend.*, **124**, 624 (1897).
[107] Cason, *J. Am. Chem. Soc.*, **64**, 1106 (1942).
[108] Whitmore and Heyd, *J. Am. Chem. Soc.*, **60**, 2030 (1938).
[109] Whitmore et al., *J. Am. Chem. Soc.*, **63**, 647 (1941).
[110] Dauben and Tilles, *J. Org. Chem.*, **15**, 785 (1950).
[111] Blaise and Herman, *Ann. chim. phys.*, (8) **23**, 522 (1911).
[112] Linstead and Williams, *J. Chem. Soc.*, **129**, 2744 (1926).
[113] Brown and Partridge, *J. Am. Chem. Soc.*, **67**, 1423 (1945).
[114] Schneider and Spielman, *J. Biol. Chem.*, **142**, 350 (1942).
[115] Wilson, *J. Am. Chem. Soc.*, **67**, 2162 (1945).
[116] Mukherji, *Science and Culture*, **13**, 39 (1947) [*C. A.*, **42**, 2957 (1948)].
[117] Newman and O'Leary, *J. Am. Chem. Soc.*, **68**, 259 (1946).
[118] Münchmeyer, *Ber.*, **19**, 1850 (1896).
[119] Kornblum and Iffland, *J. Am. Chem. Soc.*, **71**, 2142 (1949).

[120] Dauben and Tanabe, *J. Am. Chem. Soc.*, **71**, 2878 (1949).

[121] Courtot, *Bull. soc. chim. France*, (3) **35**, 359 (1906).

[122] Cason and Stanley, *J. Org. Chem.*, **14**, 137 (1949).

[123] Nightingale and Wadsworth, *J. Am. Chem. Soc.*, **67**, 418 (1945).

[124] Johnson and Offenhauer, *J. Am. Chem. Soc.*, **67**, 1049 (1945).

[125] Komppa and Weckman, *J. prakt. Chem.*, (2) **138**, 119 (1933).

[126] Dauben, *J. Am. Chem. Soc.*, **70**, 1378 (1948).

[127] Acree, *Ber.*, **37**, 628 (1904).

[128] Houston, *J. Am. Chem. Soc.*, **69**, 517 (1947).

[129] Cason, Wolfhagen, Tarpey, and Adams, *J. Org. Chem.*, **14**, 147 (1949).

[130] Wilds and Shunk, *J. Am. Chem. Soc.*, **72**, 2395 (1950).

[131] Spielman, *J. Biol. Chem.*, **106**, 93 (1934).

[132] Bertrand, *Bull. soc. chim. France*, (3) **15**, 765 (1896).

[133] Limpricht, *Ann.*, **309**, 111 (1899).

[134] Prout and Cason, *J. Org. Chem.*, **14**, 132 (1949).

[135] Cason and Winans, *J. Org. Chem.*, **15**, 139 (1950).

[136] Cason, Pippen, Taylor, and Winans, *J. Org. Chem.*, **15**, 136 (1950).

[137] Ponzio and de Gaspari, *Gazz. chim. ital.*, **29** (I), 471 (1899).

[138] Schmidlin and Massini, *Ber.*, **42**, 2388 (1909).

[139] Cason, Sumrell, and Mitchell, *J. Org. Chem.*, **15**, 850 (1950).

[140] Prout, Cason, and Ingersoll, *J. Am. Chem. Soc.*, **70**, 304 (1948).

[141] Cason, Adams, Bennett, and Register, *J. Am. Chem. Soc.*, **66**, 1764 (1944).

[142] Bachmann and Ramirez, *J. Am. Chem. Soc.*, **72**, 2526 (1950).

[143] Drake and Melamed, *J. Am. Chem. Soc.*, **70**, 364 (1948).

[144] Baker and Squire, *J. Am. Chem. Soc.*, **70**, 1487 (1948).

[145] Jacobsen, *J. Am. Chem. Soc.*, **66**, 662 (1944).

[146] Schuette, Roth, and Christenson, *Oil & Soap*, **22**, 108 (1945) [*C. A.*, **39**, 2418 (1945)|

CHAPTER 3

THE ACYLATION OF KETONES TO FORM β-DIKETONES OR β-KETO ALDEHYDES

Charles R. Hauser, Frederic W. Swamer,* and Joe T. Adams †

Duke University

CONTENTS

* Research associate, 1949–1950, supported by Office of Naval Research; present address: E. I. du Pont de Nemours and Co.

† Present address: Carbide and Carbon Chemicals Company.

INTRODUCTION

Under certain conditions, a ketone having an α-hydrogen atom may be acylated with an ester, an acid anhydride, or an acid chloride to form a β-diketone or, when the acylating agent is a formic ester, a β-keto aldehyde. The process consists in the replacement of an α-hydrogen atom of the ketone by an acyl group; it may be illustrated for methyl ketones. The reaction involves a carbon-carbon condensation; it is a

$$RCOX + HCH_2COR \rightarrow RCOCH_2COR + HX$$

$$(X = OR, OCOR, Cl)$$

convenient way to prepare many β-diketones and β-keto aldehydes, substances widely used in synthesis. The acylation of ketones may produce also the acyl derivative of the enolic form of the ketone, the O-acyl derivative, which may be rearranged thermally to give the β-diketone (see p. 107). In this review the formation of the O-acyl derivative is regarded as a side reaction.

The acylation of ketones with esters has generally been effected by means of a basic reagent such as sodium, sodium ethoxide, sodium amide, or sodium hydride. This type of reaction is called a Claisen condensation, another example of which is the acetoacetic ester reaction.[1] Special cases of the method include the rearrangement of esters of *o*-hydroxyacetophenones, the Kostanecki acylation of *o*-hydroxyacetophenones with anhydrides, and the acylation of ketones with acid chlorides. The acylation of ketones to form β-diketones may also be effected with acid anhydrides by means of the acidic reagent boron trifluoride.

In the present chapter the basic reagent and boron trifluoride methods of acylation of ketones are first considered separately. They are then compared with each other and with certain other ways of preparing β-diketones. Appropriate procedures are given, and the various acylations of ketones reported in the literature are tabulated.

It should be pointed out that, although β-diketones and β-keto aldehydes are commonly represented in the ketonic form, many of them exist mainly in the enolic form which is probably stabilized by a hydrogen bridge.

$$\underset{CH_3-C=CH-C-CH_3}{O-H\leftarrow O} \qquad \underset{H-C=CH-C-CH_3}{O-H\leftarrow O}$$

ACYLATION WITH BASIC REAGENTS

Mechanism

The acylation of ketones with esters by means of a basic reagent probably involves a three-step ionic mechanism similar to that of the acetoacetic ester reaction.[1] For example, the acetylation of acetone with ethyl acetate and sodium ethoxide or sodium amide involves first the removal of an α-hydrogen of the ketone as a proton to form acetone anion, which is a hybrid of the resonance structures $^-CH_2COCH_3$ and $CH_2=C(\bar{O})CH_3$. The second step may be formulated as the addition

$$CH_3COCH_3 + \overset{+\,-}{Na}OC_2H_5 \rightarrow \overset{+}{Na}(CH_2COCH_3)^- + C_2H_5OH \qquad (1)$$
$$(\text{or } \overset{+}{Na}\overset{-}{N}H_2) \qquad\qquad (\text{or } NH_3)$$

of the acetone anion to the carbonyl carbon of ethyl acetate, accompanied by the release of ethoxide ion to form acetylacetone. The third

---

[1] Hauser and Hudson, in Adams, *Organic Reactions*, Vol. I, Chapter 9, John Wiley & Sons, 1942.

$$CH_3\overset{\overset{\displaystyle O}{\|}}{\underset{\underset{\displaystyle OC_2H_5}{|}}{C}} + \overset{+}{Na}(CH_2COCH_3)^- \rightarrow$$

$$CH_3\overset{\overset{\displaystyle \overset{-}{O}\overset{+}{Na}}{|}}{\underset{\underset{\displaystyle OC_2H_5}{|}}{C}}CH_2COCH_3 \rightarrow CH_3COCH_2COCH_3 + \overset{+}{Na}\overset{-}{O}C_2H_5 \quad (2)$$

step consists in the removal of a methylenic hydrogen of the β-diketone as a proton to form acetylacetone anion, which is a resonance hybrid of structures $CH_3CO\overset{-}{C}HCOCH_3$ and $CH_3COCH{=}C(\overset{-}{O})CH_3$. This proton exchange may involve the base used as condensing agent, the ethoxide ion formed in the second step, or the ketone anion formed in the first step. With ethoxide ion, the equilibrium in the first step is probably on

$$CH_3COCH_2COCH_3 + \overset{+}{Na}\overset{-}{O}C_2H_5 \rightarrow \overset{+}{Na}(CH_3CO\overset{-}{C}HCOCH_3)^- + C_2H_5OH$$
$$\text{(or } Na\overset{+}{N}\overset{-}{H}_2\text{)} \qquad \qquad \text{(or NH}_3\text{)}$$
$$\text{[or } \overset{+}{Na}(CH_2COCH_3)^-\text{]} \qquad \text{(or CH}_3COCH_3\text{)}$$

$$(3)$$

the side of unchanged ketone, and the third step may be considered to be effected mainly by ethoxide ion. However, with amide ion an equivalent of ketone is converted essentially completely to its anion, and, unless excess amide ion is present, part of the ketone anion effects the third step, regenerating the corresponding amount of ketone.[2] These considerations are important in connection with the yields of β-diketones that may be obtained from ketones (see pp. 113–114).

There is ample evidence for the mechanism represented above. Ketone anions may be prepared by means of a sufficiently strong base, such as amide or triphenylmethide ion, and isolated in the form of their sodium salts. The anions of these salts may be acylated not only with esters but also, in certain cases, with acid chlorides (see p. 95); moreover, these ketone anions may be carbonated[3] or alkylated.[4] The condensation of the carbonyl group of esters with ketone anions, represented by equations 2 and 3, is formally analogous to the reactions of the carbonyl group with other types of basic anions, for example, hydroxyl ion, the mechanism

[2] Adams and Hauser, J. Am. Chem. Soc., 66, 1220 (1944).

[3] Levine and Hauser, J. Am. Chem. Soc., 66, 1768 (1944); Baumgarten, Levine, and Hauser, ibid., 66, 862 (1944).

[4] Bergstrom and Fernelius, Chem. Revs., 12, 108 (1933).

for which is generally represented in an analogous manner.[5] Bimolecular kinetics have been observed for the condensation of esters with ketone anions prepared by means of sodium triphenylmethide in ether solution.[5a] Since β-diketones are stronger acids than the ketones from which they are derived, their conversion to β-diketone anions would be expected. That this does occur when ketones are acylated with esters, even in the presence of ethoxide ion, is shown by the fact that an alkylated β-diketone may be obtained by addition of an alkyl halide to the reaction mixture.[6]

The three steps of the mechanism are reversible. In practice, the equilibrium of the over-all reaction is shifted in the direction of the condensation product by precipitation of the β-diketone as its sodium salt. When sodium ethoxide is used as the condensing agent, the equilibrium may be shifted still further in the same direction through removal by distillation of the alcohol formed during the reaction. The yields of certain β-diketones have been improved considerably by using these forcing conditions (see pp. 113, 116). The evolution of ammonia when sodium amide is used may not be particularly important, since amide ion appears to be a sufficiently strong base to convert most ketones essentially completely to their anions even in the presence of liquid ammonia.

With sodium hydride, the condensation is considered to be effected mainly by the hydride ion rather than by the ethoxide ion which is produced in the reaction mixture, since certain Claisen condensations may be brought about by sodium hydride but not by sodium ethoxide alone.[7] Sodium hydride is capable of converting ketones completely to their anions.[7]

$$CH_3COCH_3 + \overset{+}{N}a\overset{-}{H} \rightarrow \overset{+}{N}a(CH_2COCH_3)^- + H_2$$

With metallic sodium, the condensation appears to be effected partly by the metal which displaces atomic hydrogen from the ketone. How-

$$CH_3COCH_3 + Na \rightarrow \overset{+}{N}a(CH_2COCH_3)^- + \tfrac{1}{2}H_2$$

ever, a considerable part of the condensation might be caused by the ethoxide ion which is produced in the reaction mixture. The analogous

[5] Day and Ingold, Trans. Faraday Soc., 37, 689 (1941).
[5a] Hill, Burkus, Swamer, and Hauser, unpublished work.
[6] Sprague, Beckham, and Adkins, J. Am. Chem. Soc., 56, 2665 (1934).
[7] Swamer and Hauser, J. Am. Chem. Soc., 68, 2647 (1946).

acetoacetic ester condensation with sodium is considered to be brought about mainly by ethoxide ion.[8]

Structure of Reactants and Basicity of Condensing Agents

The influence of the structure of the ketone may be exhibited in the first step of the mechanism through the reactivity of the α-hydrogen, in the second step through the basic strength and size of the ketone anion, and in the third step through the acidic strength of the β-diketone. In general, the ease of acylation of ketones with a particular ester and base decreases as the complexity of the ketone increases. The decrease is marked in the series $CH_3CO > RCH_2CO > R_2CHCO$.

The structure of the ester influences the second step of the mechanism. In general, the ease of acylation of a particular ketone with a series of esters in the presence of a particular base is related directly to the relative rates of alkaline hydrolysis of the esters. Thus in acylations, as in alkaline hydrolysis,[9] oxalic and formic esters are especially reactive, ethyl acetate is more reactive than higher straight-chain aliphatic esters, and these in turn are more reactive than ethyl isobutyrate or ethyl trimethylacetate. Ethyl benzoate appears to be more reactive than ethyl anisate but less so than esters of the pyridinecarboxylic acids, particularly 2- and 4-pyridinecarboxylic acid. Methyl esters and especially phenyl esters are more reactive than the corresponding ethyl esters.

The strength of the base influences the first and third steps of the mechanism. In general, the effectiveness of the base increases with its basic strength. Thus, certain acylations that fail with ethoxide ion take place in the presence of the stronger bases, amide ion or triphenylmethide ion. Maximum effectiveness is reached with the latter bases which convert ketones completely to anions.

In the Claisen acylation of a ketone, at least an equivalent of the basic condensing agent is neutralized and the corresponding amount of a weaker base is formed. When it is impossible to form a weaker base, the condensation fails. This situation is encountered in the acylation of a ketone with sodium ethoxide as the condensing agent if the resulting β-diketone does not react with ethoxide ion to form an anion and ethyl alcohol. Thus the cyclization to the hexamethylcyclohexanetrione shown below cannot be brought about by ethoxide ion; but it can be effected by triphenylmethide ion [10] since a weaker base, ethoxide ion,

[8] Snell and McElvain, *J. Am. Chem. Soc.*, **53**, 2310 (1931).

[9] Hammett, *Physical Organic Chemistry*, pp. 211–212, McGraw-Hill Book Co., 1940.

[10] Hudson and Hauser, *J. Am. Chem. Soc.*, **61**, 3567 (1939).

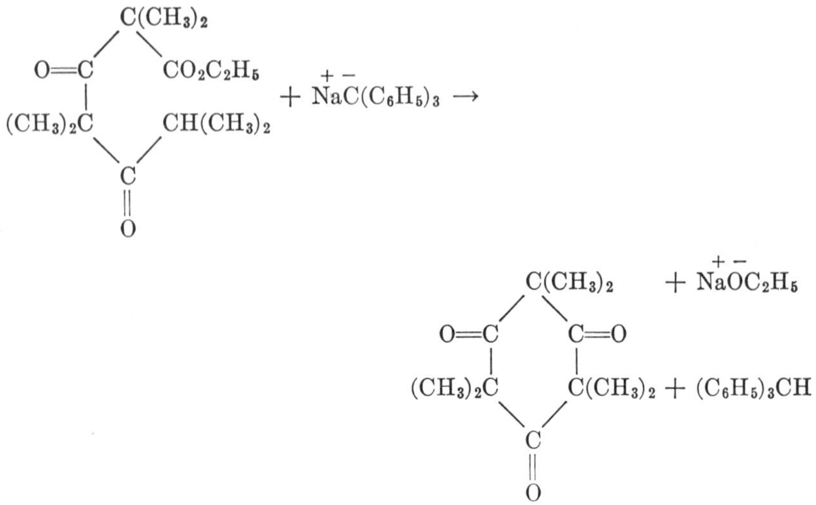

$$O=C \overset{C(CH_3)_2}{\underset{(CH_3)_2C \diagdown \diagup CH(CH_3)_2}{\diagup \diagdown CO_2C_2H_5}} + \overset{+ \; -}{NaC(C_6H_5)_3} \rightarrow$$

(with the ring carbonyl below: $\underset{O}{\overset{\|}{C}}$)

$$\overset{C(CH_3)_2}{O=C \diagup \diagdown C=O} \quad + \; \overset{+ \; -}{NaOC_2H_5}$$

$$(CH_3)_2C \diagdown \diagup C(CH_3)_2 + (C_6H_5)_3CH$$

(with ring carbonyl $\underset{O}{\overset{\|}{C}}$)

is formed. Although sodium ethoxide fails to effect the acylation of the methinyl group in the above cyclization, it apparently does effect the acylation of this same group in a cyclization [11] in which the product is capable of ionization.

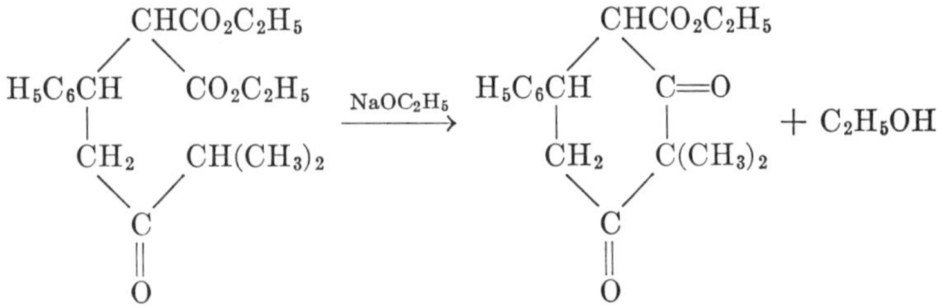

$$\overset{CHCO_2C_2H_5}{H_5C_6CH \diagup \diagdown CO_2C_2H_5} \xrightarrow{NaOC_2H_5} \overset{CHCO_2C_2H_5}{H_5C_6CH \diagup \diagdown C=O} + C_2H_5OH$$

(left ring: $CH_2 \diagdown \diagup CH(CH_3)_2$, carbonyl $\underset{O}{\overset{\|}{C}}$; right ring: $CH_2 \diagdown \diagup C(CH_3)_2$, carbonyl $\underset{O}{\overset{\|}{C}}$)

Phenyl esters may be more effective than the corresponding ethyl esters not only because they are more reactive but also because they produce the more weakly basic phenoxide ion in the second step (see p. 63). Acid chlorides are even more reactive, and they produce the still more weakly basic chloride ion. However, with few exceptions (Table XVIII), acid chlorides have usually not been so satisfactory as esters for the preparation of β-diketones since they also acylate the product formed in step 3 (see pp. 63, 95).

Side Reactions

The acylation of ketones with esters in the presence of a basic reagent may be accompanied by certain side reactions. The ketone may undergo

[11] Cox and McElvain, *J. Am. Chem. Soc.*, **56**, 2459 (1934).

self-condensation, involving the aldol reaction followed by elimination of water, to form an α,β-unsaturated ketone or a more complex condensation product. This side reaction occurs with certain methylene ketones if the acylating ester is relatively unreactive, especially when the reaction mixture is heated. Thus, although diethyl ketone can be acylated at low temperatures with ethyl propionate in the presence of sodium, the ketone undergoes self-condensation when the reaction mixture is warmed.[12] Similarly cyclohexanone and, especially, cyclo-

$$2(C_2H_5)_2C{=}O \rightarrow (C_2H_5)_2C{=}C(CH_3)COC_2H_5 + H_2O$$

pentanone undergo considerable self-condensation under the conditions usually employed for the benzoylation of ketones with ethyl or methyl benzoate by means of sodium amide.[13] In general, however, acylation of ketones may be effected without much self-condensation of the ketone.

If the ester used as acylating agent contains α-hydrogen atoms, it may condense with itself to form a β-keto ester. This side reaction occurs with ethyl acetate and its homologs when the ketone to be acylated is relatively unreactive. Thus, attempts to acetylate diisobutyl ketone with ethyl acetate by means of sodium amide or sodium triphenylmethide produced self-condensation of the ester even though the ketone was first converted to its sodium derivative.[14] In this reaction the base

$$2CH_3CO_2C_2H_5 \xrightarrow{\ Na^+[(CH_3)_2CHCHCOCH_2CH(CH_3)_2]^-\ }$$

$$CH_3COCH_2CO_2C_2H_5 + C_2H_5OH$$

responsible for the acetoacetic ester condensation is evidently the anion of the ketone. Some self-condensation of the ester has been observed during the acylation of methyl t-butyl ketone with ethyl acetate and sodium [6] and with ethyl n-valerate and sodium amide.[2] Attempts to acylate acetophenone or methyl nicotinyl ketone with ethyl laurate and sodium ethoxide have been reported to produce only self-condensation of the ester.[15] However, acylation of ketones with esters may usually be effected without much self-condensation of the ester.

Esters having α-hydrogen atoms may also undergo the aldol reaction with the carbonyl group of the ketones. The Stobbe condensation of succinic esters with ketones to form unsaturated acid esters is the most important example of this type of reaction.[16] Ketones seldom undergo

[12] Morgan, Drew, and Porter, *Ber.*, **58**, 333 (1925).
[13] Hauser, Ringler, Swamer, and Thompson, *J. Am. Chem. Soc.*, **69**, 2649 (1947).
[14] Levine, Conroy, Adams, and Hauser, *J. Am. Chem. Soc.*, **67**, 1510 (1945).
[15] Kuick and Adkins, *J. Am. Chem. Soc.*, **57**, 143 (1935).
[16] Johnson and Daub in Adams, *Organic Reactions*, Vol. VI, Chapter 1, John Wiley & Sons, 1951.

$$R_2C{=}O + \underset{\underset{CH_2CO_2C_2H_5}{|}}{CH_2CO_2C_2H_5} \xrightarrow[NaH]{NaOR\ or} \underset{\underset{CH_2CO_2Na}{|}}{R_2C{=}CCO_2C_2H_5} + C_2H_5OH$$

the aldol condensation with monocarboxylic esters or with dicarboxylic esters other than succinic ester.

With α,β-unsaturated esters or ketones the Michael condensation may occur. This type of condensation is observed with ethyl cinnamate and acetophenone in the presence of sodium ethoxide [17] or sodium amide.[18]

$$C_6H_5CH{=}CHCO_2C_2H_5 + CH_3COC_6H_5 \xrightarrow[or\ NaNH_2]{NaOC_2H_5} \underset{\underset{CH_2COC_6H_5}{|}}{C_6H_5CHCH_2CO_2C_2H_5}$$

This side reaction may be minimized by using phenyl cinnamate or cinnamoyl chloride instead of the ethyl cinnamate (see p. 75).

Instead of effecting the acylation of the ketone, the basic condensing agent may react with the carbonyl group of the ester. With sodium alkoxides this type of reaction may produce merely ester-alcohol exchange.[19] With sodium hydride, no reduction of the carbonyl group of the ester has been observed.[7,20] However, with sodium amide the ester is converted to the corresponding amide and, to the extent to which this occurs,[21] the acylation of the ketone is interrupted. The formation

$$\underset{\underset{OR'}{|}}{RC{=}O} + NaOR'' \rightleftarrows \underset{\underset{OR''}{|}}{RC{=}O} + NaOR'$$

$$\underset{\underset{OR'}{|}}{RC{=}O} + NaNH_2 \rightarrow \underset{\underset{NH_2}{|}}{RC{=}O} + NaOR'$$

of an amide may be avoided by converting the ketone to its sodium derivative with an equivalent of sodium amide and then adding the ester. This procedure has been recommended for the· acylation of camphor with formic esters.[22] In general the ketone is converted to its sodium derivative before adding the ester, but the use of two equivalents of sodium amide to one of the ketone is often advantageous even though some of the amide is formed (see p. 114).

Metallic sodium may react with the carbonyl group of esters to produce acyloins or α-diketones.[22a] In an attempt to acylate acetone with

[17] Stobbe and Volland, *Ber.*, **34**, 653 (1901).

[18] Hauser, Yost, and Ringler, *J. Org. Chem.*, **14**, 261 (1949).

[19] Freri, *Gazz. chim. ital.*, **68**, 612 (1938).

[20] Hansley and Carlisle, *Chem. Eng. News*, **23**, 1332 (1945).

[21] Hauser, Levine, and Kibler, *J. Am. Chem. Soc.*, **68**, 26 (1946).

[22] Rupe, Seiberth, and Kussmaul, *Helv. Chim. Acta*, **3**, 50 (1920).

[22a] McElvain in Adams, *Organic Reactions*, Vol. IV, Chapter 4, John Wiley & Sons, 1948.

ethyl hexahydrobenzoate by means of sodium, the acyloin was formed in 70% yield.[6] Sodium also may react with ketones to form pinacols.[5] Although little reduction occurs when a mixture of ester and ketone is treated with sodium, considerable reduction may occur if the attempt is made first to convert the ketone to its sodium derivative by means of sodium. Thus in an attempt to convert camphor to its sodium derivative with sodium, one-half of the camphor was reduced to borneol.[23]

In addition to the above side reactions the acylation of ketones to form β-diketones may be accompanied by the formation of the O-acyl derivative of the ketone. In general, however, little if any of the O-acyl derivative is formed when ketones are acylated with esters by means of a basic reagent; this type of derivative appears to be formed more often when the acylating agent is an acid chloride (see p. 95).

Scope and Limitations

Many ketones may be acylated with esters to form β-diketones or β-keto aldehydes, but there are definite limitations to the reaction. Under appropriate conditions the α-methyl group of ketones can be acylated with a variety of esters. The α-methylene group can usually be acylated satisfactorily with oxalic or formic esters, and sometimes with ethyl acetate, phenyl or methyl benzoate, and certain other esters. The α-methinyl group apparently has been acylated only rarely (see p. 66). With ketones of the type CH_3COCH_2R which have both α-methyl and α-methylene groups, the α-methyl group appears to be acylated preferentially by all esters except formic esters. With ketones of the type CH_3COCHR_2 which have both α-methyl and α-methinyl groups, apparently only the α-methyl group is acylated. Satisfactory results have been obtained with aromatic ketones containing hydroxy, methoxy, methyl, or halogen substituents and with aromatic esters containing methoxy or methyl substituents. The presence of the nitro group in either the ketone or the ester has led to complications. Actually, o-hydroxyacetophenones and certain related ketones appear to be acylated more readily than acetophenone itself. Intramolecular cyclizations, involving the acylation of either an α-methyl or an α-methylene group, can generally be effected when five- or six-membered rings are formed.

Sodium ethoxide generally brings about the acylation of methyl ketones with ethyl acetate, ethyl formate, ethyl oxalate, or pyridine-carboxylic esters, and of methylene ketones with ethyl formate or ethyl oxalate. This base failed to effect satisfactorily the acylation of even

[23] Ramart, *Bull. soc. chim. France*, [4] **39**, 1037 (1926).

methyl ketones with ethyl propionate or higher aliphatic esters or with ethyl benzoate under ordinary conditions. However, the benzoylation of acetophenone by means of sodium ethoxide is satisfactory under forcing conditions, and it is possible that certain acylations with higher aliphatic esters may be effected satisfactorily with sodium ethoxide under these conditions. Sodium generally causes not only those acylations which are brought about by sodium ethoxide but also some for which sodium ethoxide is unsatisfactory. In certain acylations, however, sodium produces more side reactions than does sodium ethoxide. Acylation of o-hydroxy- or o-methoxy-acetophenones with various esters has generally been effected with sodium. Sodium amide or sodium hydride is probably satisfactory for most of the acylations conducted with sodium ethoxide or sodium. In addition, sodium amide or sodium hydride can be used successfully for a number of condensations that have not been satisfactory with either sodium or sodium ethoxide; examples are the acylation of methyl ketones with the higher homologs of ethyl acetate and the acylation of methylene ketones with methyl or phenyl benzoate.

Acetylation with Ethyl Acetate (Table VIII). Many methyl alkyl and methyl aryl ketones have been acetylated satisfactorily with ethyl acetate by means of sodium, sodium ethoxide, sodium amide, or sodium hydride to form β-diketones containing a reactive methylene group. These reactions may be represented by the following general equation.

$$CH_3CO_2C_2H_5 + CH_3COR \xrightarrow[\text{NaNH}_2, \text{ or NaH}]{\text{Na, NaOC}_2H_5} CH_3COCH_2COR + C_2H_5OH$$

The acetylation has been successful with methyl alkyl ketones in which R is primary (as high as $C_{19}H_{39}$), secondary, or tertiary, and with methyl aryl ketones in which R is phenyl, biphenyl, naphthyl, 2-thenyl, and variously substituted aryl groups. Although only sodium has been employed in a number of these acetylations, sodium ethoxide, sodium hydride, or sodium amide would probably also be generally applicable. In certain reactions sodium ethoxide has been more satisfactory than sodium, while in others sodium amide or sodium hydride has been more satisfactory than either sodium or sodium ethoxide.

With methyl ethyl ketone in the presence of sodium amide [14] or sodium,[14] there is formed an appreciable amount of the methylene derivative $CH_3COCHCOCH_3$, although the main product is the methyl
$$\overset{|}{CH_3}$$
derivative in accordance with the above general equation. With methyl n-propyl or methyl n-amyl ketone in the presence of sodium amide only a little of the methylene derivative is formed,[14] and the yield of the

methyl derivative is somewhat better than with methyl ethyl ketone. In the presence of sodium ethoxide apparently only the methyl derivative is formed even with methyl ethyl ketone.[14] The structure of the acetylation product of methyl n-butyl ketone in the presence of sodium ethoxide was established by converting it to a known heterocyclic compound by reaction with hydrazine.[24] With methyl benzyl ketones in the presence of sodium both the methyl and methylene derivatives are formed.

The substituted methyl aryl ketones that have been acetylated satisfactorily include those having as substituents methyl, methoxyl, hydroxyl, or halogen. Examples of β-diketones prepared from ethyl acetate and methyl aryl ketones are listed below.

β-Diketone	Condensing Agent (Yield %)
$CH_3COCH_2COC_6H_4Br$-p	Na (62); NaNH$_2$ (50–80)

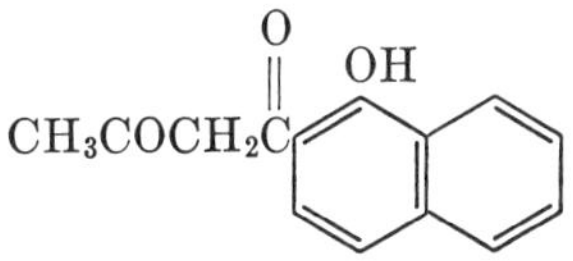	Na(85–90)

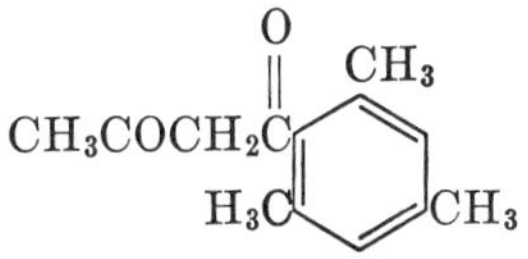	Na (69); NaOC$_2$H$_5$ (70)

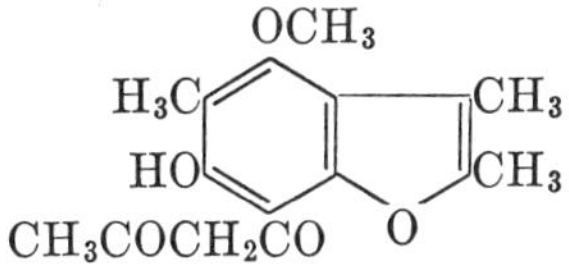	Na (57)

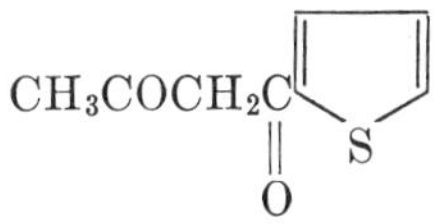	NaNH$_2$ (81); LiNH$_2$ (57)

Allylacetone and 2-methyl-2-hepten-6-one are acetylated satisfactorily by means of sodium, but this reagent was not suitable with methyl cinnamyl ketone.

$$CH_3CO_2C_2H_5 + CH_3COCH_2CH_2CH{=}CH_2 \xrightarrow{Na}$$

$$CH_3COCH_2COCH_2CH_2CH{=}CH_2 + C_2H_5OH$$

Diethyl ketone was acetylated by sodium in the cold to form 3-methyl-hexane-2,4-dione, but the yield was less than 30%; when the reaction

[24] Hurd and Kelso, *J. Am. Chem. Soc.*, **62**, 2184 (1940).

mixture was warmed, a different β-diketone, propionylacetone, was obtained. The formation of propionylacetone may be accounted for by assuming that the 3-methylhexane-2,4-dione first formed was cleaved to form some methyl ethyl ketone, which was then acetylated at the methyl group.[12] Similar results were obtained in the presence of sodium

$$CH_3CO_2C_2H_5 + (CH_3CH_2)_2CO \xrightarrow{Na} CH_3COCH(CH_3)COC_2H_5 + C_2H_5ONa$$

$$CH_3COCH(CH_3)COC_2H_5 \xrightarrow[C_2H_5OH]{NaOC_2H_5} CH_3COCH_2CH_3 + C_2H_5CO_2C_2H_5$$

$$CH_3CO_2C_2H_5 + CH_3COCH_2CH_3 \xrightarrow[NaOC_2H_5]{Na\ or}$$

$$CH_3COCH_2COC_2H_5 + C_2H_5OH$$

with ethyl n-propyl ketone, di-n-propyl ketone, ethyl phenyl ketone, and ethyl benzyl ketone. Ethyl benzyl ketone was acetylated preferentially at the benzyl group. In the presence of sodium, cyclohexanone and camphor gave only low yields on acetylation. The yields in the acetylation of 3-methylcyclohexanone and 3,3-dimethylcyclohexanone with sodium were better. Somewhat better yields were also obtained with certain of these ketones using sodium amide or sodium hydride.[25] Thus the acetylation of diethyl ketone with sodium amide at 0° gave a 45% yield of the corresponding acetyl derivative, and the acetylation of cyclohexanone with this base in boiling diethyl ether gave a 35% yield of acetylcyclohexanone; however, the acetylation of diisobutyl ketone failed (see p. 67). With sodium hydride, diethyl ketone has been acetylated in 60% yield and 1-tetralone in 84% yield.

$$CH_3CO_2C_2H_5 + (C_2H_5)_2CO \xrightarrow[\text{or NaH}]{NaNH_2 \text{ at } 0°} CH_3COCHCOC_2H_5 + C_2H_5OH$$

$$\underset{CH_3}{|}$$

(45–60%)

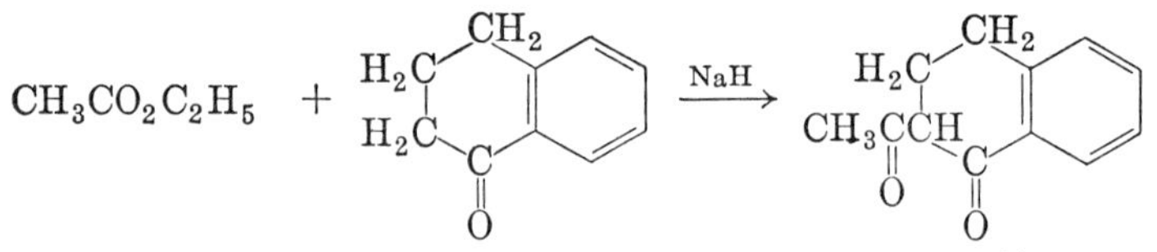

The synthesis of 2-ethyl-4-n-propylcyclopentane-1,3-dione from ethyl acetate and butyroin has been considered to involve, as the first step, the acetylation of the α-hydroxy ketone.[25a] Certain methyl ketones have

[25] Swamer and Hauser, J. Am. Chem. Soc., **72**, 1352 (1950).
[25a] Woodward and Blout, J. Am. Chem. Soc., **65**, 562 (1943).

$n\text{-}C_3H_7CHOHCOCH_2CH_2CH_3 + CH_3CO_2C_2H_5 \xrightarrow{NaOC_2H_5}$

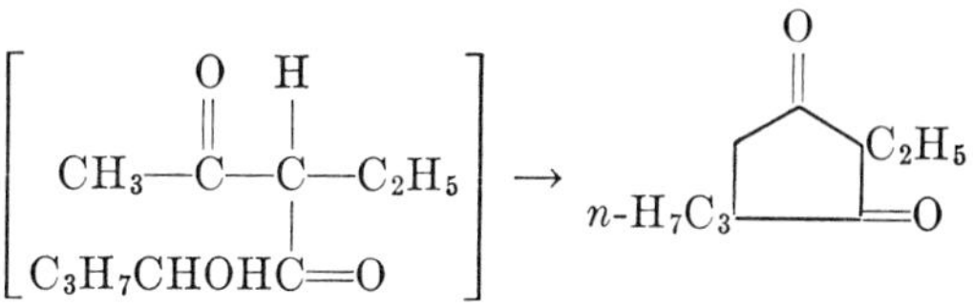

$$\left[\begin{array}{c} \overset{O}{\underset{}{\parallel}} \overset{H}{\underset{}{\mid}} \\ CH_3\text{---}C\text{---}C\text{---}C_2H_5 \\ \mid \\ C_3H_7CHOHC{=}O \end{array} \right] \rightarrow$$

been acylated with alkoxyl or halogen derivatives of ethyl acetate to form the corresponding alkoxyl or halogenated β-diketones. For example, acetone has been acylated with ethyl ethoxyacetate, and acetone and trifluoroacetone have been acetylated with ethyl trifluoroacetate in good yield.

$C_2H_5OCH_2CO_2C_2H_5 + CH_3COCH_3 \xrightarrow{Na}$

$$C_2H_5OCH_2COCH_2COCH_3 + C_2H_5OH$$
$$(40\%)$$

$CF_3CO_2C_2H_5 + CH_3COCF_3 \xrightarrow{NaOC_2H_5} CF_3COCH_2COCF_3 + C_2H_5OH$
$$(72\%)$$

Acylation with Higher Homologs of Ethyl Acetate and with Esters of Unsaturated Acids (Tables IX and X). Various methyl ketones are acylated satisfactorily with ethyl propionate and higher aliphatic ethyl or methyl esters by means of sodium amide or sodium hydride. The reaction may be represented by the general equation in which R is alkyl and R' is alkyl or aryl. The yields of β-diketones are generally satis-

$$RCO_2C_2H_5 + CH_3COR' \xrightarrow[\text{or NaH}]{NaNH_2} RCOCH_2COR' + C_2H_5OH$$

factory in acylations with straight-chain esters of as high molecular weight as ethyl laurate and methyl myristate. The yields are also good with ethyl isovalerate, but generally they have been only fair with ethyl or methyl esters such as ethyl isobutyrate, methyl diethylacetate, and ethyl pivalate which are branched at the α-carbon atom. However, the corresponding phenyl esters usually give satisfactory yields; two examples are represented below.

$(C_2H_5)_2CHCO_2C_6H_5 + CH_3COCH(C_2H_5)_2 \xrightarrow{NaNH_2}$

$$(C_2H_5)_2CHCOCH_2COCH(C_2H_5)_2 + C_6H_5OH$$
$$(62\%)$$

$(CH_3)_3CCO_2C_6H_5 + CH_3COC(CH_3)_3 \xrightarrow{NaNH_2}$

$$(CH_3)_3CCOCH_2COC(CH_3)_3 + C_6H_5OH$$
$$(64\%)$$

Like the acetylation, the acylation of methyl ethyl ketone with ethyl propionate and sodium amide or sodium hydride forms some of the methylene derivative of the ketone; however, a good yield of the methyl derivative is readily obtained.[2] Higher methyl alkyl ketones form almost exclusively the methyl derivative.[2]

Although sodium amide and sodium hydride generally produce good yields in the acylation of methyl ketones with higher esters, sodium ethoxide and sodium have usually not been satisfactory. Thus in the acylation of methyl n-propyl ketone with ethyl n-butyrate, the latter two basic reagents furnished only 11% and 23% yields, respectively. Attempted acylation of acetophenone with ethyl laurate by sodium ethoxide and of acetone with ethyl hexahydrobenzoate by sodium ethoxide or sodium failed. However, sodium gave satisfactory yields in the acylation of certain o-hydroxy- and o-methoxy-acetophenones with ethyl propionate or ethyl n-butyrate.

$$CH_3CH_2CO_2C_2H_5 + CH_3COC_6H_4OH\text{-}o \xrightarrow{Na}$$

$$CH_3CH_2COCH_2COC_6H_4OH\text{-}o + C_2H_5OH$$
$$(70\text{-}75\%)$$

$$CH_3CH_2CH_2CO_2C_2H_5 + CH_3C(\!\!\!<\!\!\!\overset{CH_3}{\underset{O\ OCH_3}{}}\!\!\!>\!\!\!)OCH_3 \xrightarrow{Na}$$

$$CH_3CH_2CH_2COCH_2C(\!\!\!<\!\!\!\overset{CH_3}{\underset{O\ OCH_3}{}}\!\!\!>\!\!\!)OCH_3 + C_2H_5OH$$
$$(49\%)$$

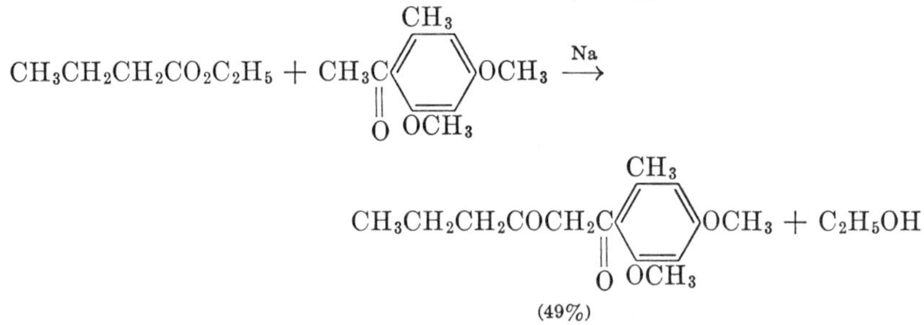

Acylation of methylene ketones, such as diethyl ketone and cyclohexanone, with ethyl propionate and ethyl n-butyrate gave only low to fair yields even with sodium amide or sodium hydride. The acylation of ω-methoxy- or ω-phenoxy-acetophenone with ethyl propionate failed. However, phenyl propionate acylates these ketones.

$$CH_3CH_2CO_2C_6H_5 + ROCH_2COC_6H_5 \xrightarrow{NaNH_2}$$

$$CH_3CH_2COCHCOC_6H_5 + C_6H_5OH$$
$$\underset{OR}{\big|}$$
$$\begin{pmatrix} R = CH_3,\ 25\% \\ R = C_6H_5,\ 50\% \end{pmatrix}$$

Several methyl ketones are acylated satisfactorily with ethyl phenylacetate and sodium amide or sodium.

$$C_6H_5CH_2CO_2C_2H_5 + CH_3COR \xrightarrow[\text{(R = CH}_3\text{, C}_2\text{H}_5\text{, C}_6\text{H}_5\text{)}]{\text{NaNH}_2 \text{ or Na}}$$

$$C_6H_5CH_2COCH_2COR + C_2H_5OH$$

Acetone is acylated with ethyl tetrahydrofuroate and sodium ethoxide, and several ketones have been acylated with methyl acetone glycerate by sodium.

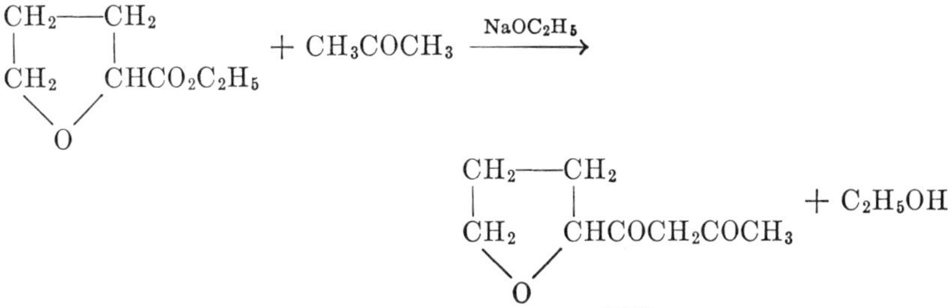

(60%)

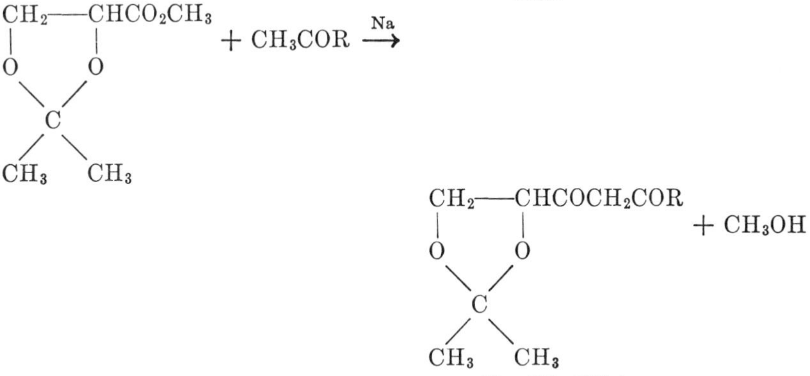

$$\left(\begin{array}{l}\text{R = CH}_3\text{, 46\%} \\ \text{R = C}_6\text{H}_5\text{, 58\%}\end{array}\right)$$

Methyl n-hexyl ketone is acylated satisfactorily with ethyl acrylate or ethyl crotonate in the presence of sodium ethoxide. Although ethyl cinnamate undergoes mainly the Michael reaction with acetone or acetophenone, phenyl cinnamate acylates these ketones fairly satisfactorily. Ethyl phenylpropiolate reacts with certain ketones in the

$$C_6H_5CH{=}CHCO_2C_6H_5 + CH_3COR \xrightarrow{\text{NaNH}_2}$$

$$C_6H_5CH{=}CHCOCH_2COR + C_6H_5OH$$
(R = CH$_3$, 30%)
(R = C$_6$H$_5$, 29%)

presence of sodium ethoxide to form pyrone derivatives. With acetone, for example, 2-methyl-6-phenyl-γ-pyrone is formed. Presumably the ketone is first acylated to form the corresponding β-diketone which then cyclizes.

$$C_6H_5C\equiv CCO_2C_2H_5 + CH_3COCH_3 \xrightarrow{\text{NaOC}_2\text{H}_5} C_6H_5C\equiv CCOCH_2COCH_3 \rightarrow$$

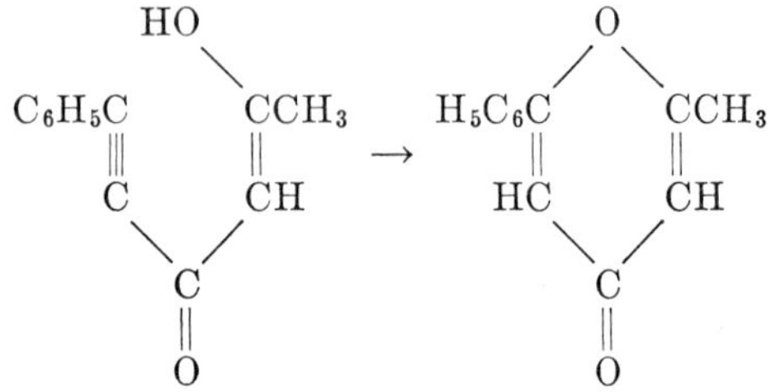

Acylation of ketones with dicarboxylic esters has not been very successful, except with oxalic esters which are considered below (p. 84). Diethyl malonate and diethyl succinate undergo aldol type reactions with ketones (see p. 67). Diethyl adipate and diethyl pimelate might be expected to undergo Dieckmann cyclizations rather than ketone acylations. However, dimethyl glutarate has been used for the acylation of cyclohexanone.

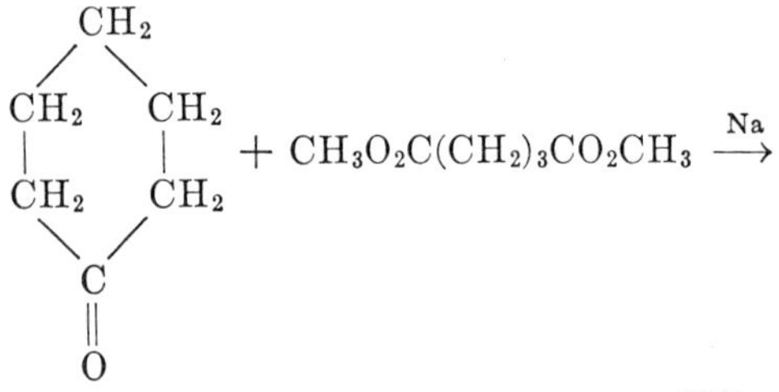

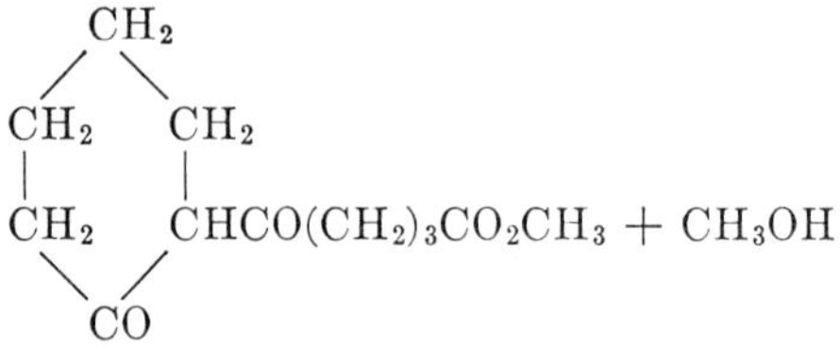

(26%)

Acylation with Esters of Aromatic Acids (Table XI). Acetone is benzoylated satisfactorily with ethyl benzoate by sodium amide and with methyl benzoate by sodium hydride, but sodium ethoxide or sodium has produced only low to fair yields. Sodium amide and sodium hydride are also satisfactory for the benzoylation of certain higher methyl alkyl ketones. Acetophenone is benzoylated satisfactorily in the presence of

$$C_6H_5CO_2R + CH_3CO\text{-alkyl} \xrightarrow[\text{or NaH}]{\text{NaNH}_2} C_6H_5COCH_2CO\text{-alkyl} + ROH$$

sodium ethoxide under forcing conditions,[26] and with sodium amide, lithium amide, and sodium. Even ethanolic potassium hydroxide has been reported to bring about this benzoylation in high yield. o-Hy-

$$C_6H_5CO_2C_2H_5 + CH_3COC_6H_5 \xrightarrow[\text{or NaOC}_2\text{H}_5]{\text{NaNH}_2, \text{ Na,}} C_6H_5COCH_2COC_6H_5 + C_2H_5OH$$

droxyacetophenone and various nuclear-substituted alkoxy aceto-phenones have been benzoylated satisfactorily; some examples are shown in the table. Nuclear-substituted benzoic esters have been used to

β-Diketone	Condensing Agent	Yield, %
$C_6H_5COCH_2COC_6H_4OH\text{-}o$	$NaOC_2H_5$	61–73
$C_6H_5COCH_2COC_6H_4OCH_3\text{-}p$	$NaNH_2$	88

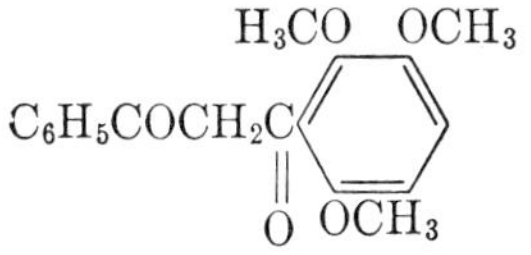

acylate acetophenones.

$$p\text{-}CH_3OC_6H_4CO_2C_2H_5 + CH_3COC_6H_5 \xrightarrow{\text{NaNH}_2}$$

$$p\text{-}CH_3OC_6H_4COCH_2COC_6H_5 + C_2H_5OH$$
$$(45\%)$$

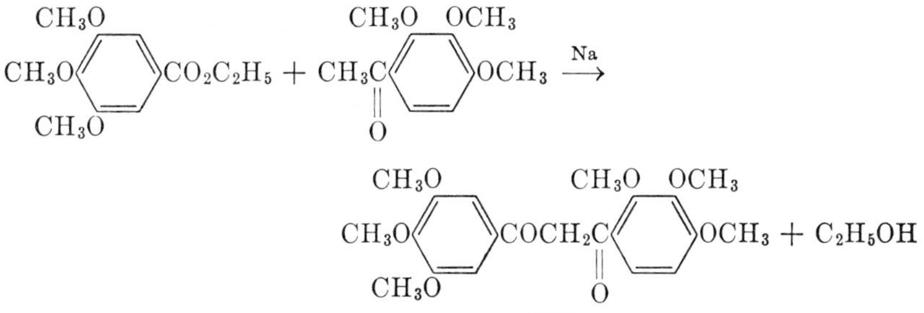

However, acylation of acetophenone with ethyl chlorobenzoates has given only fair yields, and attempted acylation with ethyl nitrobenzoates failed. Acylation of ketones with ethyl phthalate or ethyl terephthalate appears to have given low yields.

Several methylene ketones, including cyclohexanone, propiophenone, 1-hydrindone, and ω-phenoxyacetophenone, are benzoylated satis-factorily with phenyl benzoate with sodium amide as the condensing agent to furnish 2-benzoylcyclohexanone (69%), 1,1-dibenzoylethane

---

[26] Magnani and McElvain, *J. Am. Chem. Soc.*, **60**, 817 (1938).

(53%), 2-benzoylhydrindone (80%), and phenoxydibenzoylmethane (59%). Cyclohexanone has been benzoylated with methyl benzoate by

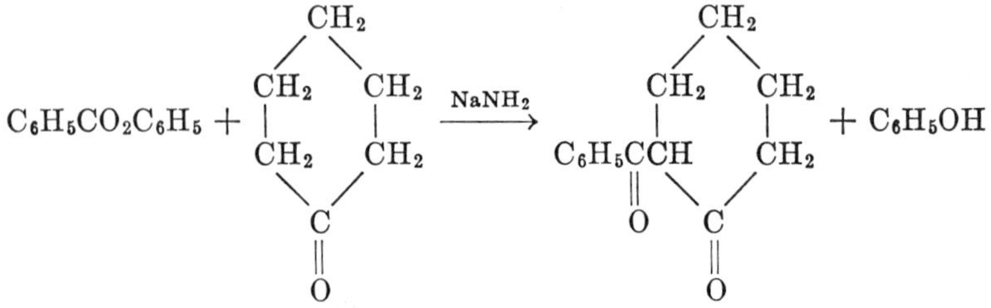

sodium amide or sodium hydride in fairly good yield, but benzoylation with ethyl benzoate gave poor yields. Attempts to benzoylate cyclopentanone with phenyl benzoate by sodium amide have yielded the benzoyl derivative of the self-condensation product of the ketone.[13]

Acylations with several heterocyclic aromatic esters are effected satisfactorily. Thus, acetone has been acylated with the three pyridinecarboxylic esters, ethyl picolinate, ethyl nicotinate, and ethyl isonicotinate, in the presence of sodium ethoxide. Ethyl nicotinate has also

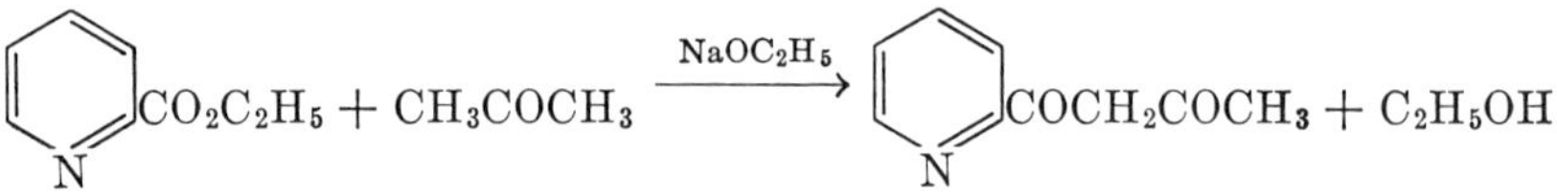

(74%)

been used successfully for the acylation of other methyl ketones including methyl isobutyl ketone, acetophenone, acetomesitylene, and methyl 3-pyridyl ketone. It seems likely that ethyl picolinate and ethyl iso-

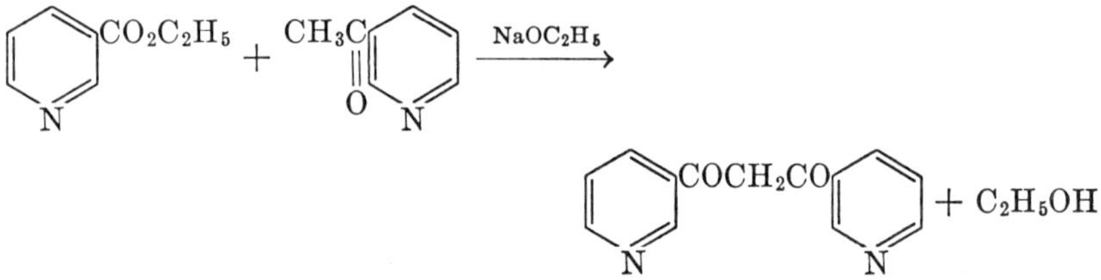

(51%)

nicotinate, which appear to be especially reactive,[27] may also prove useful for the acylation of other methyl ketones. Acylation of acetone with certain quinolinecarboxylic esters has been effected using sodium ethoxide, but no yields were reported. The acylation of 1-diethylaminopentan-4-one with ethyl 2-phenyl-7-chlorocinchoninate has been carried out with sodium amide.

[27] Koelsch, *J. Org. Chem.*, **10**, 34 (1945).

The acylation of acetone with ethyl furoate and of 2-acetylthiophene with 2-carbethoxythiophene is satisfactory.

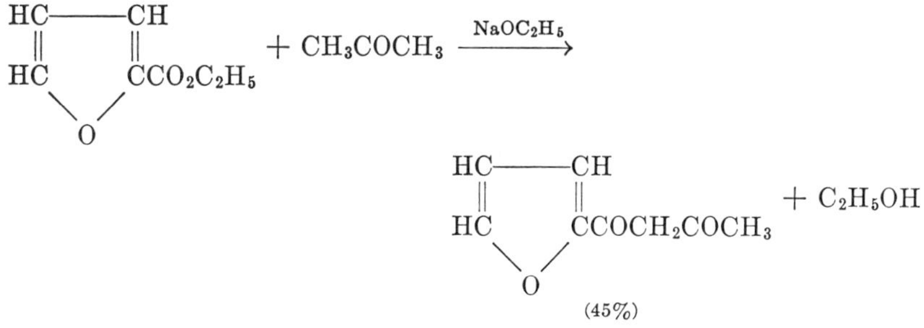

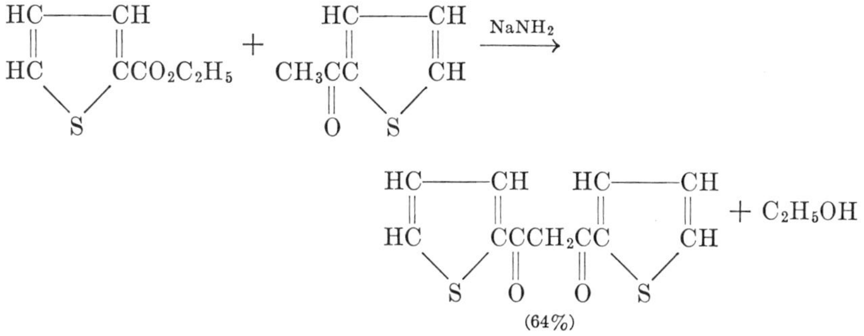

(45%)

(64%)

The acylation of acetone with 5-carbethoxy-3-methylisoxazole has been accomplished in excellent yield; other ketones also have been acylated with this ester.

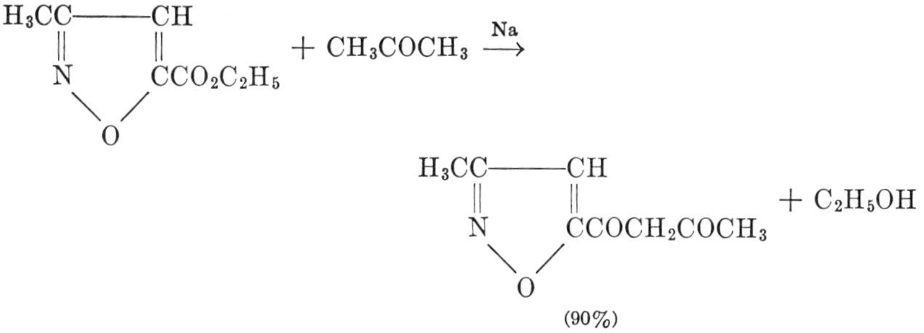

(90%)

Intramolecular Acylation: Cyclization (Tables XII and XIII). γ-, δ-, ϵ-, or ζ-Keto esters may undergo intramolecular acylation. The γ- and ϵ-keto esters, which may be represented by the general formulas I and II, respectively, form five-membered rings; δ- and ζ-keto esters, which may be represented by the general formulas III and IV, respectively, form six-membered rings. It should be noted that I and III form cyclic

1,3-diketones, whereas II and IV form the acyl derivatives of cyclic ketones, which may also be prepared by the acylation of the corresponding cyclic ketones (pp. 78, 102, 104, 109).

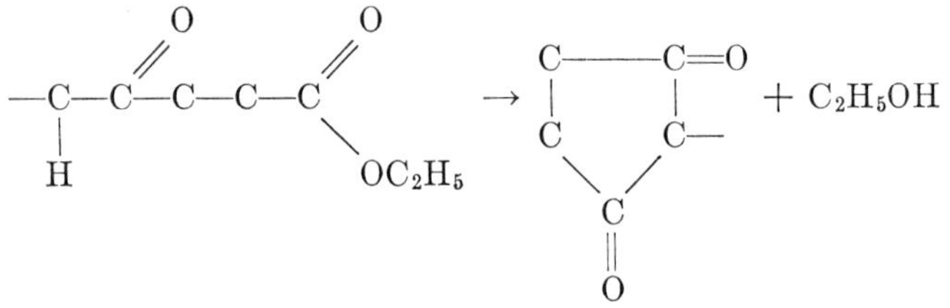

$$-\overset{\displaystyle H}{\underset{}{C}}-\overset{O}{\overset{\|}{C}}-C-C-\overset{O}{\overset{\|}{C}}\diagdown OC_2H_5 \quad \rightarrow \quad \begin{array}{c} C{-\!-\!-}C{=}O \\ |\qquad\ | \\ C\qquad C{-} \\ \diagdown\ \diagup \\ C \\ \| \\ O \end{array} \quad + C_2H_5OH$$

I

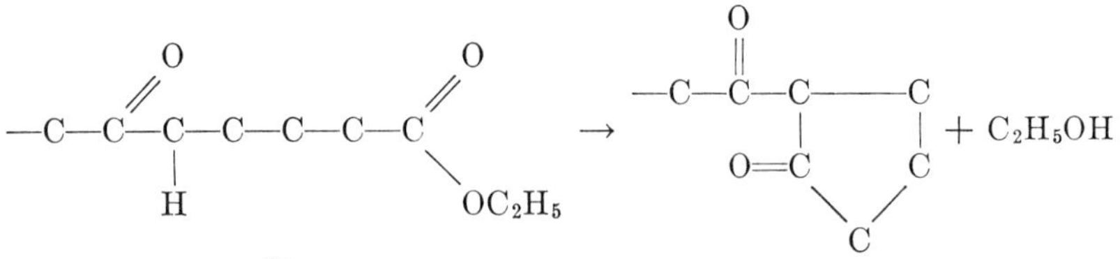

$$-\overset{\displaystyle H}{\underset{}{C}}-\overset{O}{\overset{\|}{C}}-C-C-C-\overset{O}{\overset{\|}{C}}\diagdown OC_2H_5 \quad \rightarrow \quad \begin{array}{c} \overset{O}{\overset{\|}{C}} \\ -C-C-C{-\!-\!-}C \\ |\qquad\ | \\ O{=}C\qquad C \\ \diagdown\ \diagup \\ C \end{array} \quad + C_2H_5OH$$

II

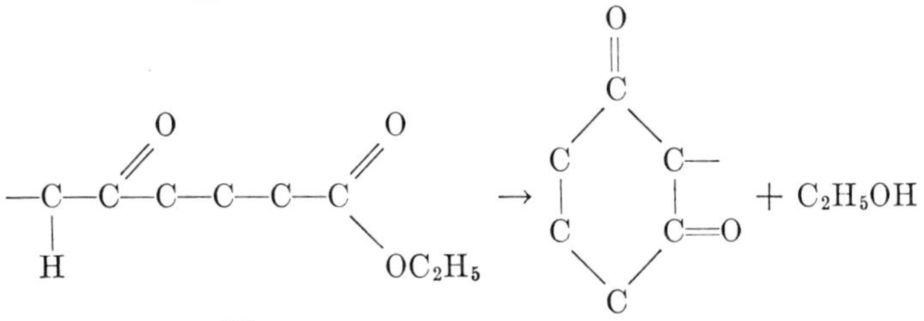

$$-\overset{\displaystyle H}{\underset{}{C}}-\overset{O}{\overset{\|}{C}}-C-C-C-\overset{O}{\overset{\|}{C}}\diagdown OC_2H_5 \quad \rightarrow \quad \begin{array}{c} \overset{O}{\overset{\|}{C}} \\ \diagup\ \diagdown \\ C\qquad C{-} \\ |\qquad\ | \\ C\qquad C{=}O \\ \diagdown\ \diagup \\ C \end{array} \quad + C_2H_5OH$$

III

$$-C-\overset{O}{\overset{\|}{C}}-\overset{\displaystyle H}{\underset{}{C}}-C-C-C-C-\overset{O}{\overset{\|}{C}}\diagdown OC_2H_5 \quad \rightarrow \quad \begin{array}{c} \overset{O}{\overset{\|}{C}}\qquad C \\ -C-C-C\quad\diagup\ \diagdown \\ |\qquad C \\ O{=}C\qquad | \\ \diagdown\quad C \\ \diagup \\ C \end{array} \quad + C_2H_5OH$$

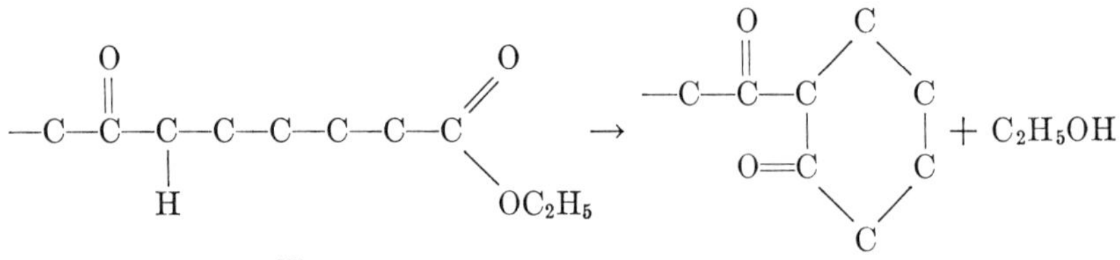

IV

In general, cyclization of these keto esters may be effected satisfactorily by sodium ethoxide, sodium methoxide, sodium amide, or sodium. One ester, $(CH_3)_2CHCOC(CH_3)_2COC(CH_3)_2CO_2C_2H_5$ (p. 66), has been cyclized with sodium triphenylmethide whereas sodium ethoxide failed. Although various keto esters of types I, II, III, and IV have been cyclized to produce β-diketones, the reaction has failed with others, for example ethyl levulinate and ethyl β-methyllevulinate. Some examples of successful cyclizations are given below.

Cyclization with Keto Esters of Type I.

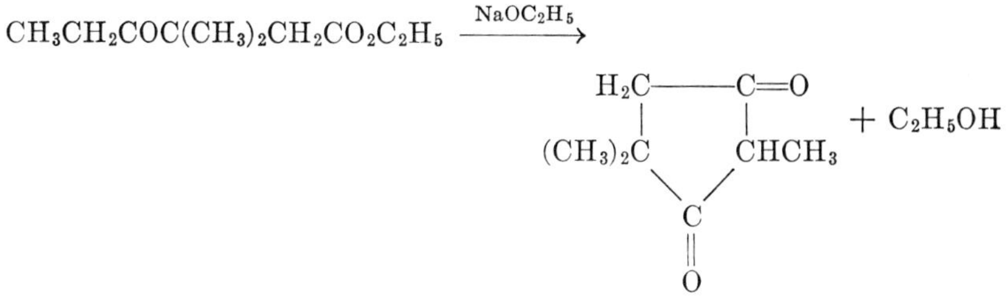

$$CH_3CH_2COC(CH_3)_2CH_2CO_2C_2H_5 \xrightarrow{NaOC_2H_5}$$

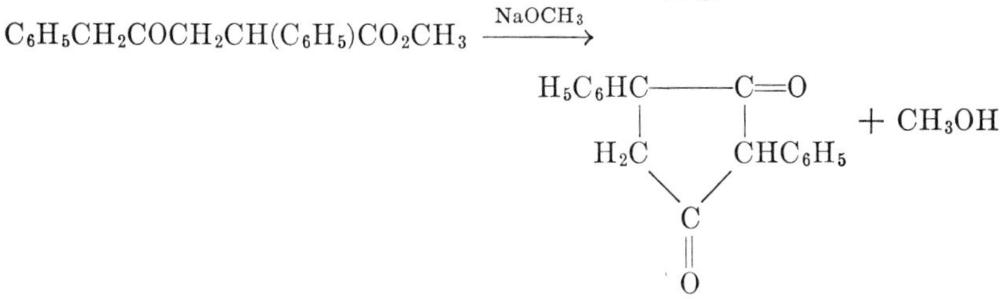

$$
\begin{array}{ccc}
H_2C\!\!-\!\!-\!\!-\!\!-\!\!C\!\!=\!\!O & \\
| \qquad\qquad | & \\
(CH_3)_2C \qquad CHCH_3 & + C_2H_5OH \\
\diagdown \quad\;\diagup & \\
C & \\
\| & \\
O & \\
(35\%) &
\end{array}
$$

$$C_6H_5CH_2COCH_2CH(C_6H_5)CO_2CH_3 \xrightarrow{NaOCH_3}$$

$$
\begin{array}{ccc}
H_5C_6HC\!\!-\!\!-\!\!-\!\!-\!\!C\!\!=\!\!O & \\
| \qquad\qquad | & \\
H_2C \qquad CHC_6H_5 & + CH_3OH \\
\diagdown \quad\;\diagup & \\
C & \\
\| & \\
O & \\
(75\%) &
\end{array}
$$

Cyclizations with Keto Esters of Type II.

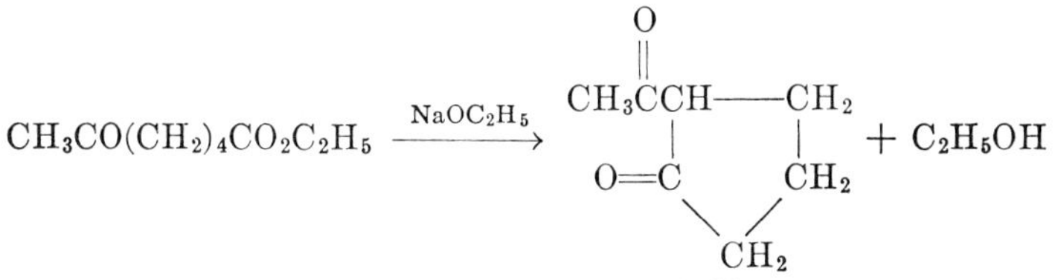

$$CH_3CO(CH_2)_4CO_2C_2H_5 \xrightarrow{NaOC_2H_5}$$

$$
\begin{array}{ccc}
O & \\
\| & \\
CH_3CCH\!\!-\!\!-\!\!-\!\!CH_2 & \\
| \qquad\qquad | & + C_2H_5OH \\
O\!\!=\!\!C \qquad CH_2 & \\
\diagdown \quad\;\diagup & \\
CH_2 & \\
(90\%) &
\end{array}
$$

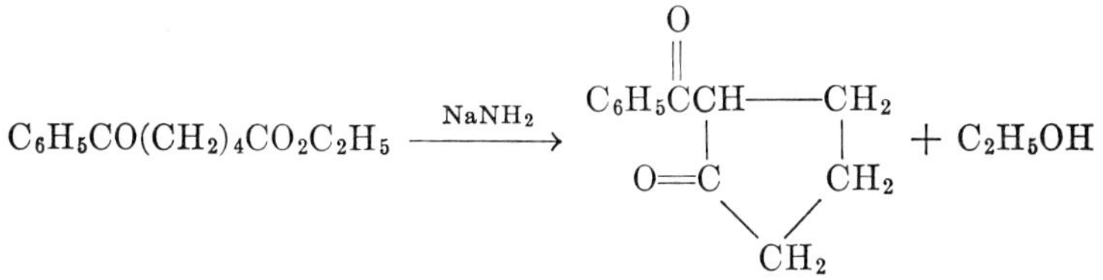

$$C_6H_5CO(CH_2)_4CO_2C_2H_5 \xrightarrow{NaNH_2}$$

$$
\begin{array}{ccc}
O & \\
\| & \\
C_6H_5CCH\!\!-\!\!-\!\!-\!\!CH_2 & \\
| \qquad\qquad | & + C_2H_5OH \\
O\!\!=\!\!C \qquad CH_2 & \\
\diagdown \quad\;\diagup & \\
CH_2 & \\
(90\%) &
\end{array}
$$

Cyclizations with Keto Esters of Type III.

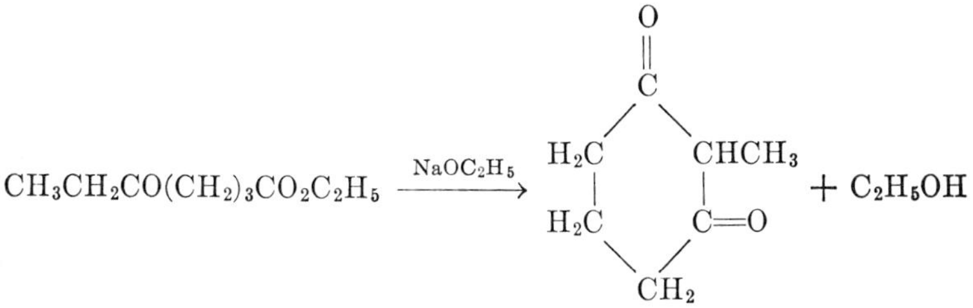

$$CH_3CH_2CO(CH_2)_3CO_2C_2H_5 \xrightarrow{NaOC_2H_5}$$

$$
\begin{array}{ccc}
O & \\
\| & \\
C & \\
\diagup \quad\;\diagdown & \\
H_2C \qquad CHCH_3 & + C_2H_5OH \\
| \qquad\qquad | & \\
H_2C \qquad C\!\!=\!\!O & \\
\diagdown \quad\;\diagup & \\
CH_2 & \\
(Quant.) &
\end{array}
$$

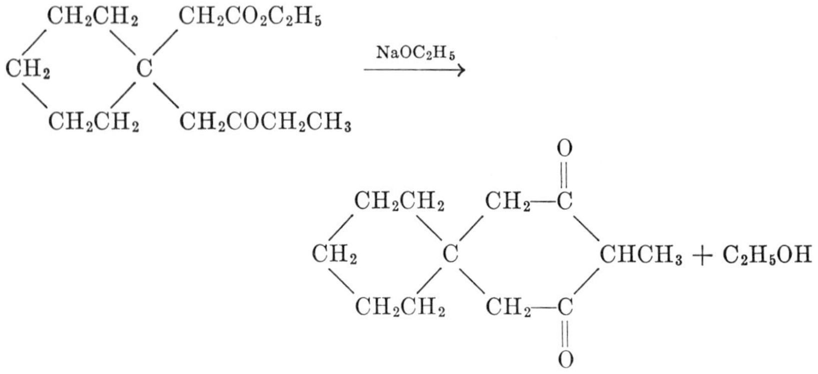

$$
\begin{array}{c}
\text{CH}_2\text{CH}_2 \quad \text{CH}_2\text{CO}_2\text{C}_2\text{H}_5 \\
\text{CH}_2 \qquad \text{C} \\
\text{CH}_2\text{CH}_2 \quad \text{CH}_2\text{COCH}_2\text{CH}_3
\end{array}
\xrightarrow{\text{NaOC}_2\text{H}_5}
$$

$$
\begin{array}{c}
\qquad\qquad\qquad \text{O} \\
\qquad\qquad\qquad \| \\
\text{CH}_2\text{CH}_2 \quad \text{CH}_2{-}\text{C} \\
\text{CH}_2 \qquad \text{C} \qquad\qquad \text{CHCH}_3 + \text{C}_2\text{H}_5\text{OH} \\
\text{CH}_2\text{CH}_2 \quad \text{CH}_2{-}\text{C} \\
\qquad\qquad\qquad \| \\
\qquad\qquad\qquad \text{O}
\end{array}
$$

(Quant.)

Cyclizations with Keto Esters of Type IV.

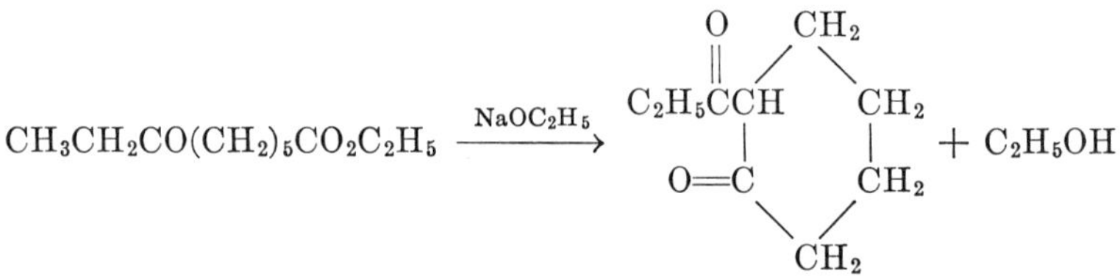

$$
\text{CH}_3\text{CH}_2\text{CO(CH}_2)_5\text{CO}_2\text{C}_2\text{H}_5
\xrightarrow{\text{NaOC}_2\text{H}_5}
\begin{array}{c}
\text{O} \quad \text{CH}_2 \\
\| \quad\ \diagup\ \diagdown \\
\text{C}_2\text{H}_5\text{CCH} \quad \text{CH}_2 \\
| \qquad\quad | \\
\text{O}{=}\text{C} \qquad \text{CH}_2 \\
\diagdown\quad\diagup \\
\text{CH}_2
\end{array}
+ \text{C}_2\text{H}_5\text{OH}
$$

(83%)

$$
\begin{array}{c}
\text{O} \quad \text{CH}_3 \\
\| \qquad | \\
\text{CH}_3\text{OC} \quad \text{CH}_2 \\
\text{C}_6\text{H}_5\text{COCH}_2 \quad \text{C} \quad \text{CH}_2 \\
| \qquad | \qquad | \\
\text{CH}_2 \quad \text{CH} \quad \text{CH}_2 \\
\text{CH}_2 \quad \text{CH}_2
\end{array}
\xrightarrow{\text{NaOCH}_3}
$$

$$
\begin{array}{c}
\text{O} \quad \text{CH}_3 \\
\| \qquad | \\
\text{O} \quad \text{C} \quad \text{CH}_2 \\
\| \qquad\quad \\
\text{C}_6\text{H}_5\text{CCH} \quad \text{C} \quad \text{CH}_2 \\
| \qquad | \qquad | \\
\text{CH}_2 \quad \text{CH} \quad \text{CH}_2 \\
\text{CH}_2 \quad \text{CH}_2
\end{array}
+ \text{CH}_3\text{OH}
$$

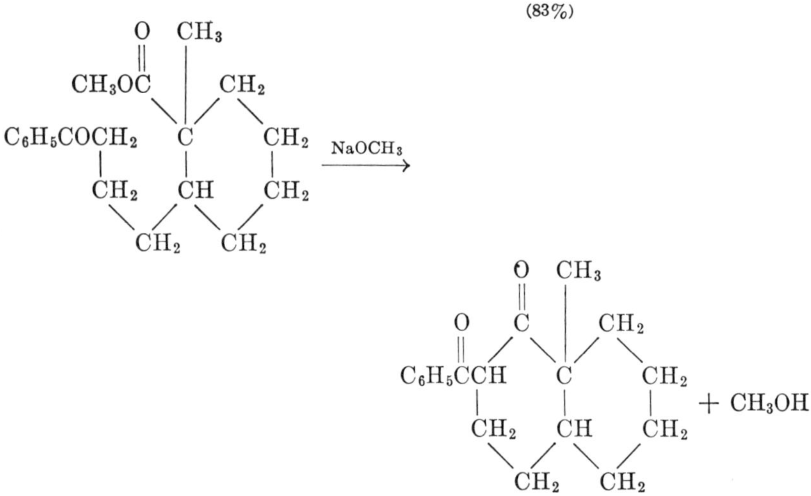

(60%)

The Michael condensation between α,β-unsaturated carbonyl compounds and active hydrogen compounds often leads to the formation of δ-keto esters (Type III) and, when sufficient sodium ethoxide or other strong base is present, these δ-keto esters may undergo intramolecular cyclization to form dihydroresorcinol derivatives (V and Va). A number of such Michael condensations accompanied by Claisen cyclizations are listed in Table XIII in which over-all yields are given. They may be illustrated by the following equations.

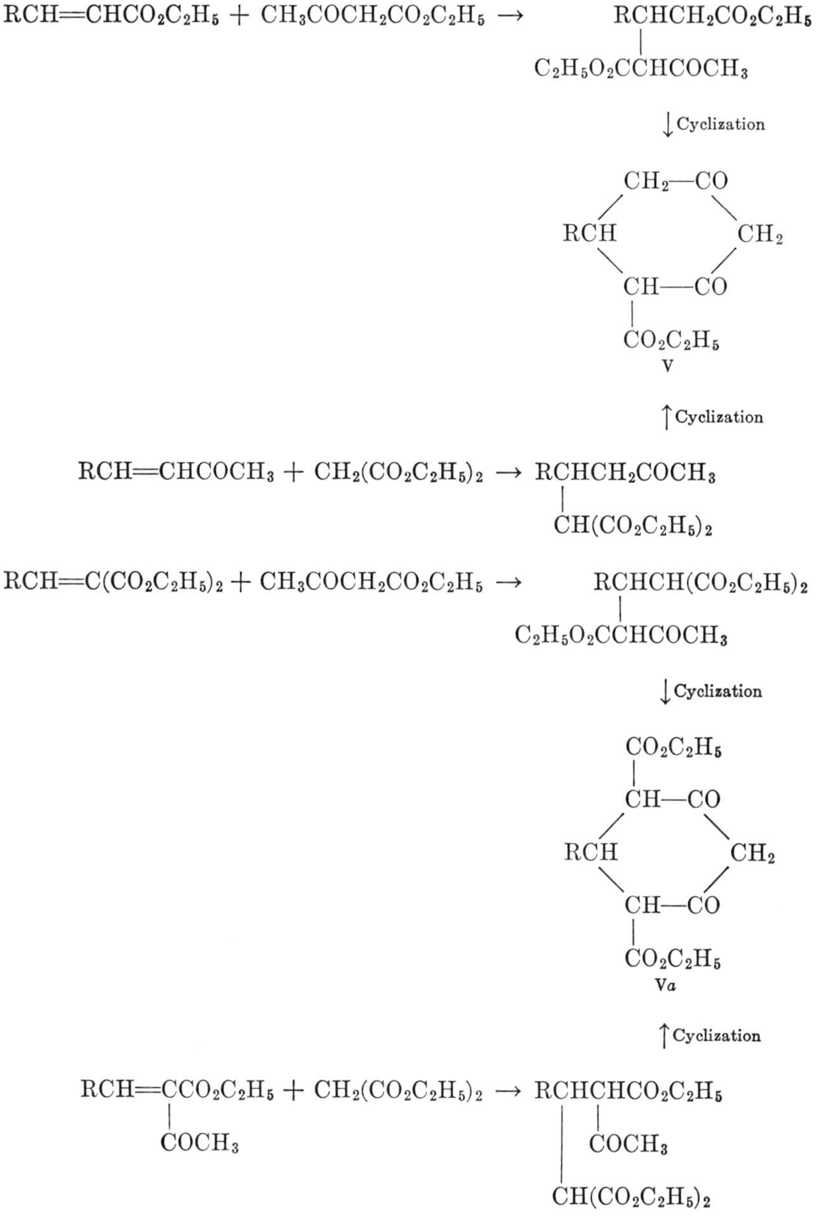

$$RCH{=}CHCO_2C_2H_5 + CH_3COCH_2CO_2C_2H_5 \rightarrow \underset{\underset{\displaystyle C_2H_5O_2CCHCOCH_3}{|}}{RCHCH_2CO_2C_2H_5}$$

$\downarrow$ Cyclization

$$\begin{array}{ccc} & CH_2{-}CO & \\ \diagup & & \diagdown \\ RCH & & CH_2 \\ \diagdown & & \diagup \\ & \underset{\displaystyle \underset{CO_2C_2H_5}{|}}{CH{-}CO} & \end{array}$$
V

$\uparrow$ Cyclization

$$RCH{=}CHCOCH_3 + CH_2(CO_2C_2H_5)_2 \rightarrow \underset{\underset{\displaystyle CH(CO_2C_2H_5)_2}{|}}{RCHCH_2COCH_3}$$

$$RCH{=}C(CO_2C_2H_5)_2 + CH_3COCH_2CO_2C_2H_5 \rightarrow \underset{\underset{\displaystyle C_2H_5O_2CCHCOCH_3}{|}}{RCHCH(CO_2C_2H_5)_2}$$

$\downarrow$ Cyclization

$$\begin{array}{ccc} & \overset{\displaystyle \overset{CO_2C_2H_5}{|}}{CH{-}CO} & \\ \diagup & & \diagdown \\ RCH & & CH_2 \\ \diagdown & & \diagup \\ & \underset{\displaystyle \underset{CO_2C_2H_5}{|}}{CH{-}CO} & \end{array}$$
Va

$\uparrow$ Cyclization

$$\underset{\underset{\displaystyle COCH_3}{|}}{RCH{=}CCO_2C_2H_5} + CH_2(CO_2C_2H_5)_2 \rightarrow \underset{\underset{\displaystyle CH(CO_2C_2H_5)_2}{|}}{\overset{}{\underset{\underset{\displaystyle COCH_3}{|}}{RCHCHCO_2C_2H_5}}}$$

Acylation with Esters of Oxalic Acid (Table XIV). The acylation of ketones with oxalic esters, which is generally effected with sodium ethoxide or sodium, may involve one molecule of the ester and one of the ketone, two molecules of the ester and one of the ketone, or one molecule of the ester and two of the ketone. The first reaction, monoacylation, has been successful with a variety of ketones; the second, diacylation, has been carried out with acetone and cyclopentanone; the third has been done with acetone, acetophenone, and a few other ketones. All three reactions may be illustrated with acetone. In addition, cyclization

$$\begin{array}{c} CO_2C_2H_5 \\ | \\ CO_2C_2H_5 \end{array} + CH_3COCH_3 \xrightarrow{NaOC_2H_5} \begin{array}{c} COCH_2COCH_3 \\ | \\ CO_2C_2H_5 \end{array} + C_2H_5OH$$
$$(70\text{--}90\%)$$

$$\begin{array}{c} 2CO_2C_2H_5 \\ | \\ CO_2C_2H_5 \end{array} + CH_3COCH_3 \xrightarrow{NaOC_2H_5} \begin{array}{c} COCH_2COCH_2CO \\ | \qquad\qquad | \\ CO_2C_2H_5 \quad CO_2C_2H_5 \end{array} + 2C_2H_5OH$$
$$(85\%)$$

$$\begin{array}{c} CO_2C_2H_5 \\ | \\ CO_2C_2H_5 \end{array} + 2CH_3COCH_3 \xrightarrow{NaOC_2H_5} \begin{array}{c} COCH_2COCH_3 \\ | \\ COCH_2COCH_3 \end{array} + 2C_2H_5OH$$

of the monoacylation product may occur to form a 1,2,4-cyclopentane-trione. This type of cyclic product is formed with dibenzyl or diethyl ketone.

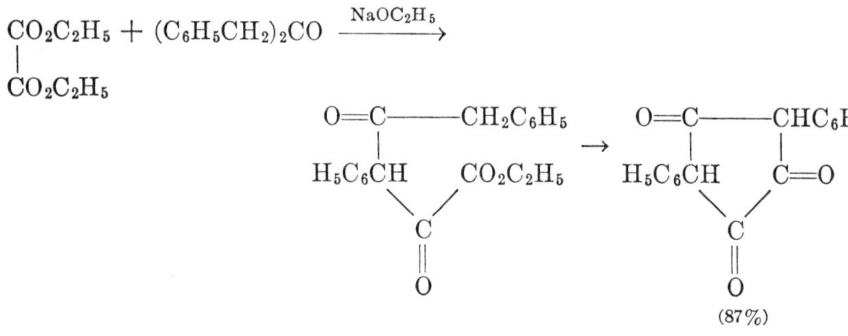

$$\begin{array}{c} CO_2C_2H_5 \\ | \\ CO_2C_2H_5 \end{array} + (C_6H_5CH_2)_2CO \xrightarrow{NaOC_2H_5}$$

$$\begin{array}{ccc} O{=}C\text{------}CH_2C_6H_5 & & O{=}C\text{------}CHC_6H_5 \\ | & & | \qquad\qquad | \\ H_5C_6CH \quad CO_2C_2H_5 & \rightarrow & H_5C_6CH \qquad C{=}O \\ \diagdown\;\diagup & & \diagdown\;\diagup \\ C & & C \\ \| & & \| \\ O & & O \\ & & (87\%) \end{array}$$

With methyl ethyl, methyl n-propyl, or methyl benzyl ketone, cyclization involves one molecule of the ketone to two of the ester. The products are glyoxalates of 1,2,4-cyclopentanetriones. They may result either by the acylation of a cyclopentanetrione, formed as indicated above, or by the cyclization of the diacylation product of the ketone, e.g.,

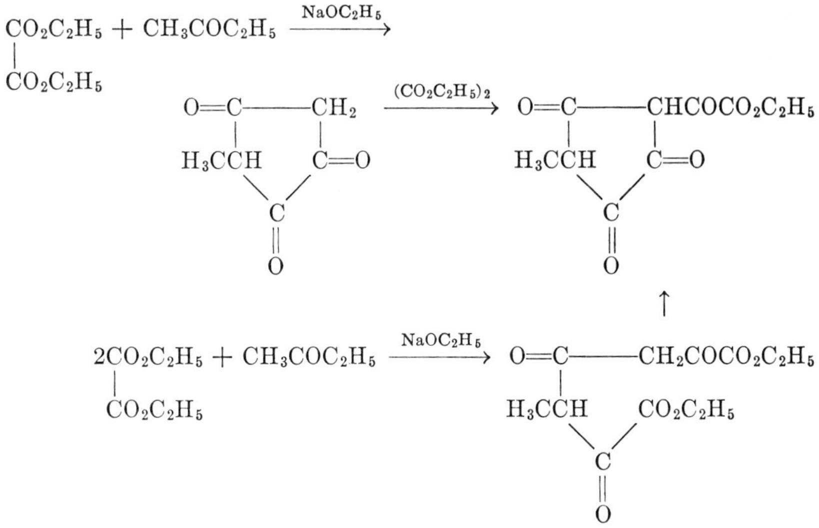

$$\begin{array}{l} CO_2C_2H_5 \\ | \\ CO_2C_2H_5 \end{array} + CH_3COC_2H_5 \xrightarrow{NaOC_2H_5}$$

O=C——CH$_2$ $\xrightarrow{(CO_2C_2H_5)_2}$ O=C——CHCOCO$_2$C$_2$H$_5$

H$_3$CCH   C=O   H$_3$CCH   C=O

 \\C\\ //

C
‖
O

C
‖
O

↑

$$2\begin{array}{l} CO_2C_2H_5 \\ | \\ CO_2C_2H_5 \end{array} + CH_3COC_2H_5 \xrightarrow{NaOC_2H_5}$$ O=C——CH$_2$COCO$_2$C$_2$H$_5$

H$_3$CCH   CO$_2$C$_2$H$_5$

C
‖
O

The monoacylation of ketones with ethyl oxalate has been studied rather extensively. The reaction has been successful with various methyl alkyl and methyl aryl ketones. As usual, methyl ethyl ketone forms the methyl derivative; this has been established by reaction of the product with cyanoacetamide to form a cyclic compound of known structure.[28] The reaction has been successful also with certain α,β-unsaturated ketones, including mesityl oxide and benzalacetone, and with phenyl propenyl and mesityl propenyl ketones which are vinylogs of acetophenone and acetomesitylene, respectively.

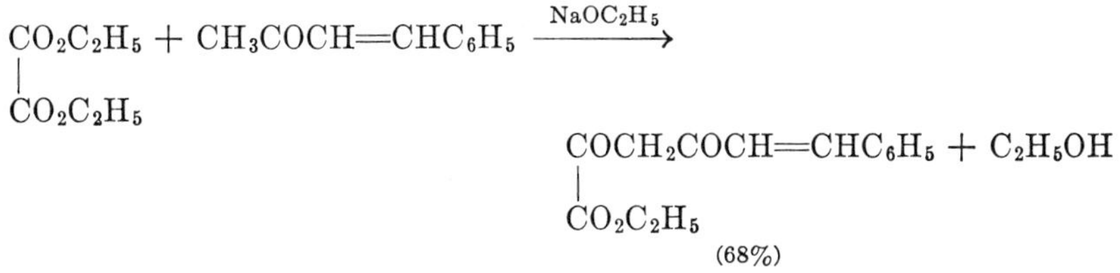

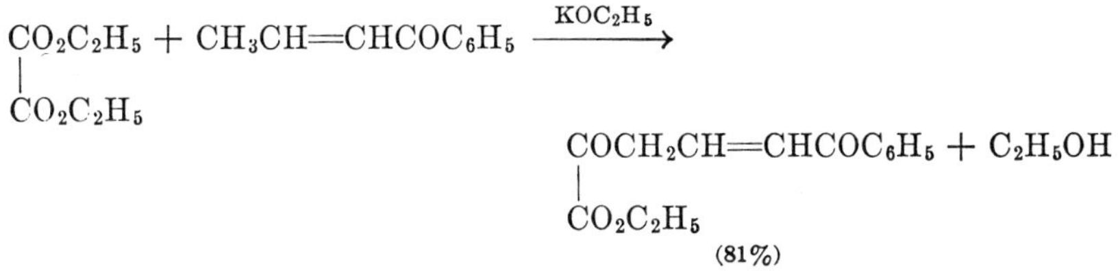

$$\begin{array}{l} CO_2C_2H_5 \\ | \\ CO_2C_2H_5 \end{array} + CH_3COCH{=}CHC_6H_5 \xrightarrow{NaOC_2H_5}$$

$$\begin{array}{l} COCH_2COCH{=}CHC_6H_5 \\ | \\ CO_2C_2H_5 \end{array} + C_2H_5OH$$
(68%)

$$\begin{array}{l} CO_2C_2H_5 \\ | \\ CO_2C_2H_5 \end{array} + CH_3CH{=}CHCOC_6H_5 \xrightarrow{KOC_2H_5}$$

$$\begin{array}{l} COCH_2CH{=}CHCOC_6H_5 \\ | \\ CO_2C_2H_5 \end{array} + C_2H_5OH$$
(81%)

[28] Tracy and Elderfield, *J. Org. Chem.*, **6**, 70 (1941).

Monoacylation of a variety of cyclic methylene ketones has been accomplished. Typical are the reactions with cyclopentanone, cyclohexanone, camphor, 1-hydrindone, and 1-tetralone. Several polyhydrophenanthrene or steroid-type ketones have been acylated, usually in excellent yield.

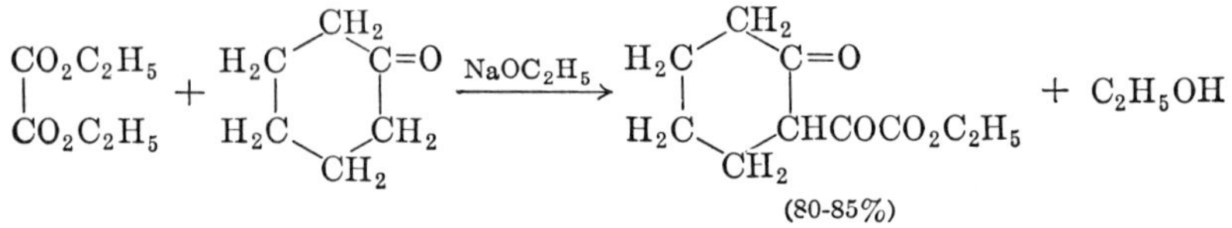

(80-85%)

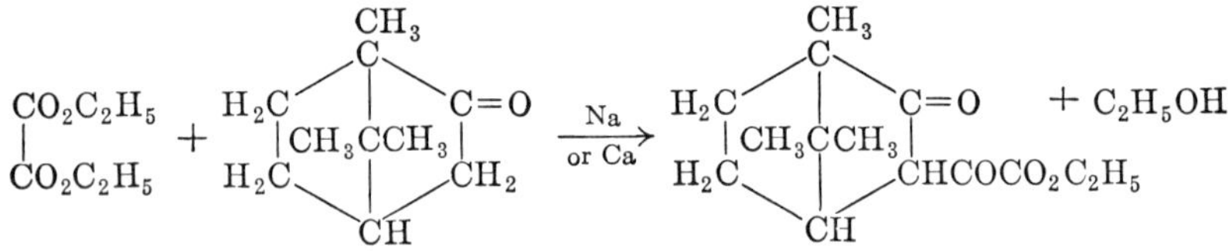

(50-63%)

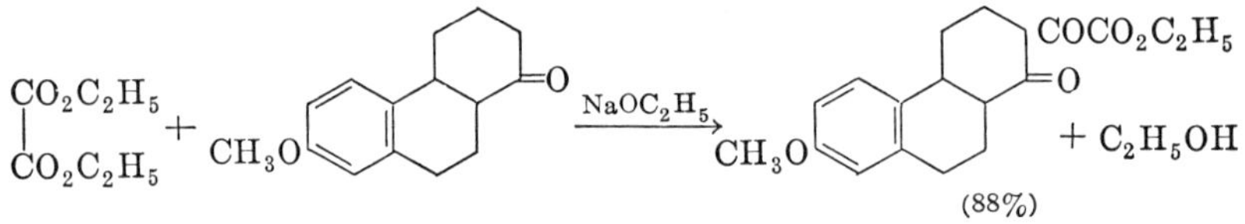

(88%)

The monoacylation of certain pyrrole methyl and pyrrole methylene ketones has also been satisfactory.

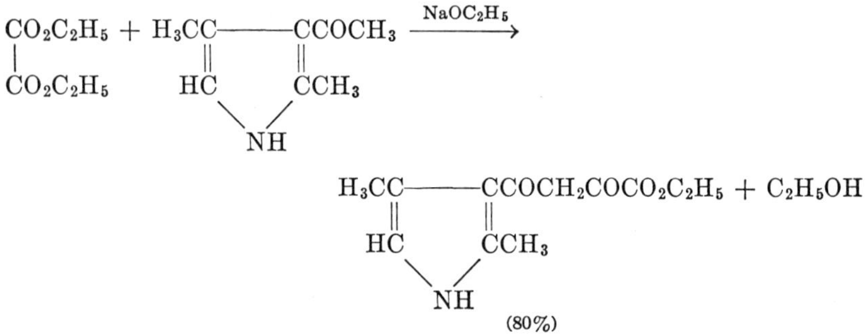

(80%)

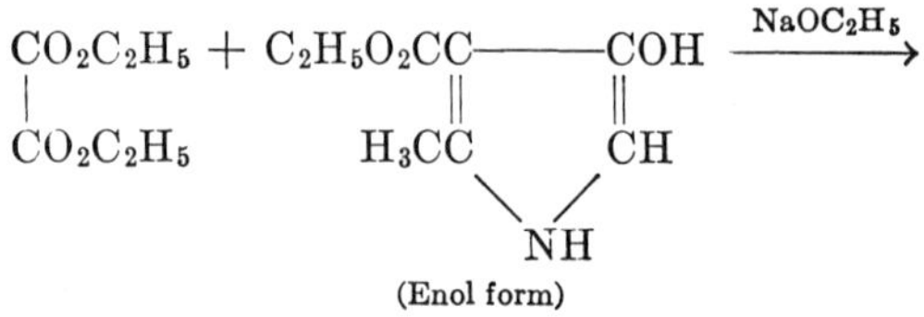

(Enol form)

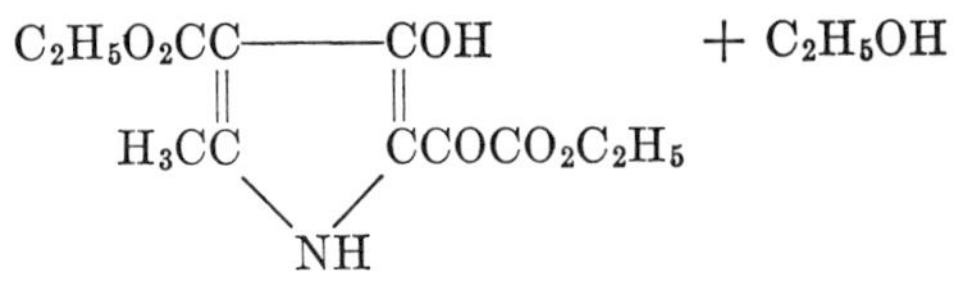

$$C_2H_5O_2CC\text{————}COH \qquad + C_2H_5OH$$

with structure showing H_3CC and $CCOCO_2C_2H_5$ double bonds joined through NH

NH

(Quant.)

$$\begin{array}{c} CO_2C_2H_5 \\ | \\ CO_2C_2H_5 \end{array} + \xrightarrow{\text{NaOC}_2\text{H}_5}$$

$$COCO_2C_2H_5 \qquad + C_2H_5OH$$

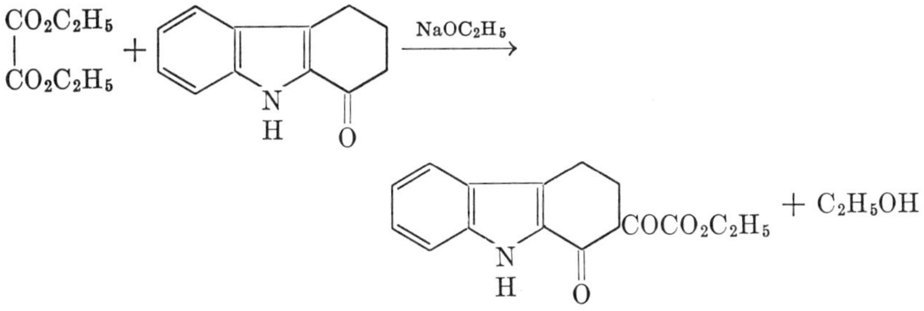

(75%)

The oxalyl derivatives obtained by monoacylation of ketones are at the same time β-diketones and α-keto esters. Since α-keto esters often lose carbon monoxide on heating, these oxalyl derivatives can be used advantageously to prepare certain β-keto esters—a reaction used successfully in the synthesis of equilenin.[29] In the same way certain

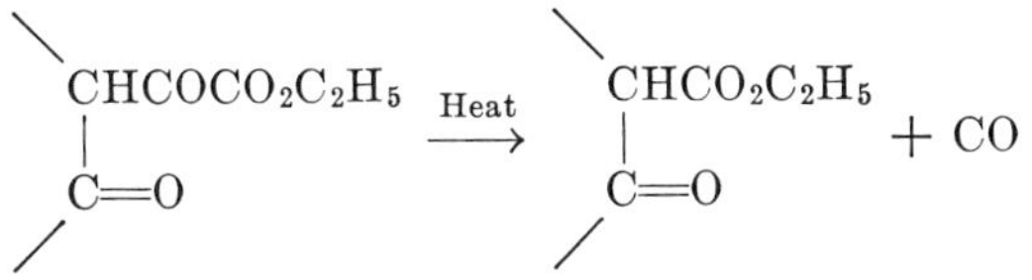

$$\begin{array}{c} \diagdown \\ CHCOCO_2C_2H_5 \\ | \\ C{=}O \\ \diagup \end{array} \xrightarrow{\text{Heat}} \begin{array}{c} \diagdown \\ CHCO_2C_2H_5 \\ | \\ C{=}O \\ \diagup \end{array} + CO$$

α,β-unsaturated keto esters might be obtained [30] from the oxalyl derivatives of the appropriate α,β-unsaturated ketones (see p. 85). However, an attempt to prepare ethyl propionylacetate in this manner from the oxalyl derivative of methyl ethyl ketone failed.[31]

Acylation with Esters of Formic Acid (Table XV). Various methyl and methylene ketones are acylated satisfactorily with formic esters and sodium, sodium ethoxide, sodium methoxide, or sodium amide. The products are β-keto aldehydes, which often are named as hydroxymethylene ketones because they exist chiefly in the enolic modification. The free β-keto aldehyde or hydroxymethylene ketone from acetone has not been isolated. Acidification of an aqueous solution of its sodium salt is accompanied by self-condensation to form 1,3,5-triacetylben-

[29] Bachmann, Cole, and Wilds, *J. Am. Chem. Soc.*, **62**, 824 (1940).
[30] Fuson, Christ, and Whitman, *J. Am. Chem. Soc.*, **58**, 2450 (1936).
[31] Bloom and Hauser, unpublished results.

zene,[32,33,34] while acidification in methanol solutions leads to the formation of the β-keto acetal, $CH_3COCH_2CH(OCH_3)_2$.[34a] In contrast to other esters, formic esters react with methyl ethyl ketone preferentially at the methylene group. The ratio of the products from reaction at the

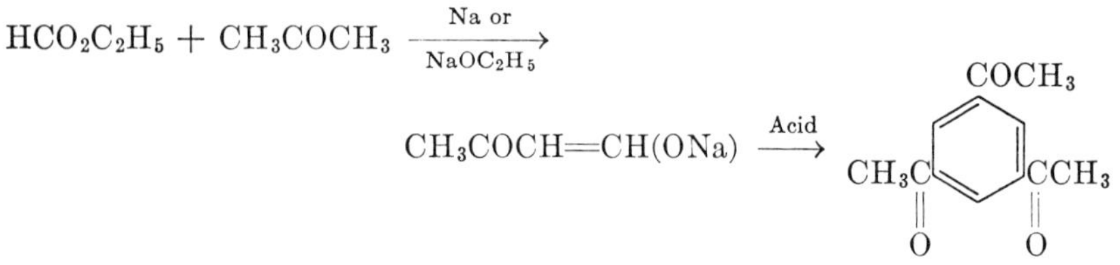

$$HCO_2C_2H_5 + CH_3COCH_3 \xrightarrow[\text{NaOC}_2\text{H}_5]{\text{Na or}}$$

$$CH_3COCH{=}CH(ONa) \xrightarrow{\text{Acid}}$$

methylene and methyl groups is 3 or 4 to 1.[34a] The structure of the main product has been established by its reaction with cyanoacetamide [35,36] or hydrazine [37] to form known heterocyclic derivatives. Unlike methyl formyl derivatives, such methylene formyl derivatives do not trimerize readily.[33,36] Although certain other methyl-methylene

$$HCO_2C_2H_5 + CH_3COCH_2CH_3 \rightarrow$$

$$\underset{\underset{CH_3}{|}}{CH_3COC}{=}CHONa \xrightarrow{\text{Acid}} \underset{\underset{CH_3}{|}}{CH_3COCHCHO}$$

ketones may be formylated preferentially at the α-methylene group, methyl n-propyl ketone reacts mainly at the methyl group,[34a] and methyl isobutyl ketone largely or exclusively at the methyl group. The structure of the principal product from methyl isobutyl ketone was established by its reaction with cyanoacetamide.[38]

$$HCO_2C_2H_5 + CH_3COCH_2CH(CH_3)_2 \xrightarrow{\text{Na}} Na[HCOCHCOCH_2CH(CH_3)_2]^{-}$$

Diethyl ketone and a variety of cyclic methylene ketones including cyclopentanone and higher homologs, 1-hydrindone, camphor, and certain polyhydrophenanthrene or steroidal ketones have been formylated successfully.

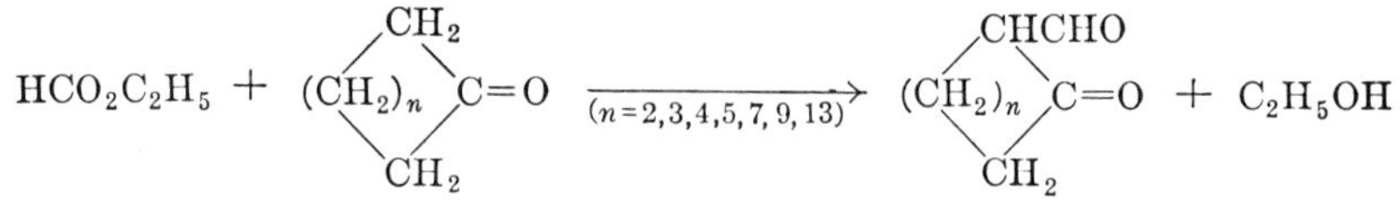

[32] Claisen and Stylos, *Ber.*, **21**, 1144 (1888).

[33] Kaushal, Sovani, and Deshapande, *J. Indian Chem. Soc.*, **19**, 107 (1942).

[34] Frank and Varland, *Org. Syntheses*, **27**, 91 (1947).

[34a] Royals and Brannock, *J. Am. Chem. Soc.*, **75**, 2050 (1953).

[35] Tracy and Elderfield, *J. Org. Chem.*, **6**, 63 (1941).

[36] Joshi, Kaushal, and Deshapande, *J. Indian Chem. Soc.*, **18**, 479 (1941).

[37] Diels and Ilberg, *Ber.*, **49**, 158 (1916).

[38] Mariella, *J. Am. Chem. Soc.*, **69**, 2670 (1947).

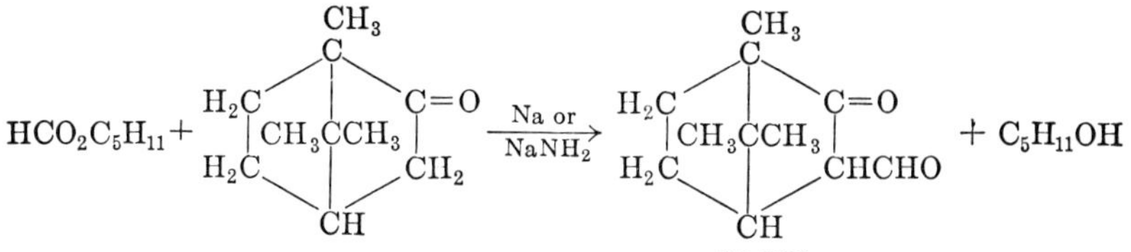

$$HCO_2C_5H_{11} + \quad \text{(structure)} \quad \xrightarrow[\text{NaNH}_2]{\text{Na or}} \quad \text{(structure)} \quad + C_5H_{11}OH$$

(60-70%)

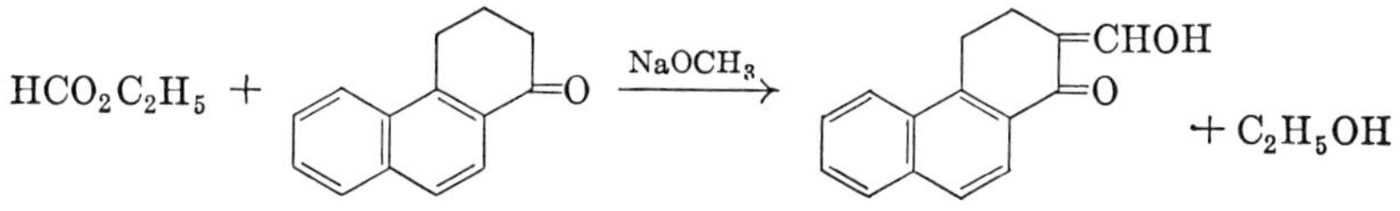

$$HCO_2C_2H_5 + \quad \text{(structure)} \quad \xrightarrow{\text{NaOCH}_3} \quad \text{(structure)} \quad + C_2H_5OH$$

(94%)

$$HCO_2C_2H_5 + \quad \text{(structure)} \quad \xrightarrow[\text{(Pyridine)}]{\text{NaOC}_2H_5} \quad \text{(structure)} \quad + C_2H_5OH$$

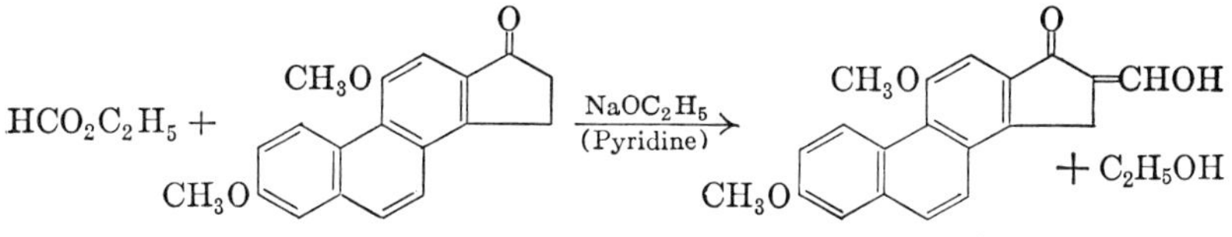

(97%)

In the last reaction cited, an excellent yield was obtained using sodium ethoxide in pyridine, whereas the acylation with ethyl formate or isoamyl formate failed in the presence of sodium ethoxide in ether, or sodium in benzene or dioxane. With potassium t-butoxide, an aldol reaction occurred between the formylation product and the original ketone.[39]

2-Hydroxyphenyl benzyl ketone and ethyl formate in the presence of sodium produce isoflavone. Presumably the reaction involves first the acylation of the ketone with the formic ester, followed by cyclization. Various derivatives of isoflavones, for example, 7-methoxyisoflavone and 2-hydroxyhexahydroösajin dimethyl ether, have been prepared in a similar manner.

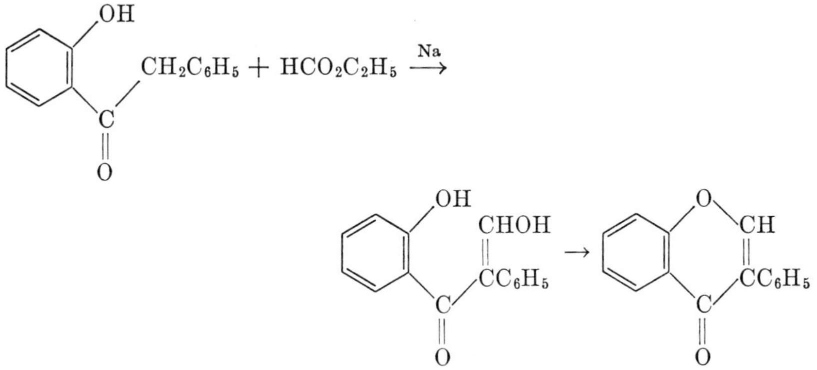

Isoflavone (40%)

[39] Robinson and Rydon, *J. Chem. Soc.*, **1939**, 1394.

Special Types of Acylation

Rearrangement of Esters of o-Hydroxyacetophenones (Table XVI).
Aroyl derivatives of o-hydroxy-acetophenones and -acetonaphthones on treatment with various basic reagents including potassium carbonate or hydroxide, sodium ethoxide, sodium amide, or metallic sodium undergo a rearrangement involving the acylation of the ketone portion of the molecule by the ester portion. Some examples are shown in the accompanying equations. It is to be noted that the reaction occurs with the

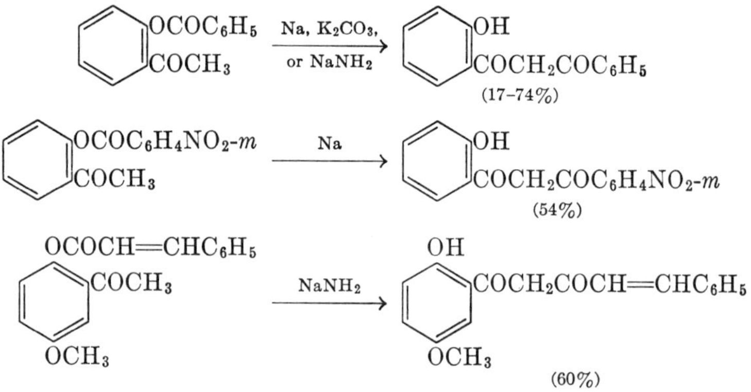

m-nitrobenzoyl and cinnamoyl esters, although ethyl m-nitrobenzoate and ethyl cinnamate failed to acylate acetophenone satisfactorily (see pp. 68, 75, 77).

Some of the o-hydroxy β-diketones obtained by rearrangement cyclize to form chromones; generally, cyclization requires treatment with acid (see pp. 94–95). However, esters of o-hydroxyacetoarones have been converted to flavones merely by heating in glycerol. This conversion is considered to involve rearrangement to a β-diketone followed by cyclization.[39a] Diflavones have also been prepared in this manner.[39b]

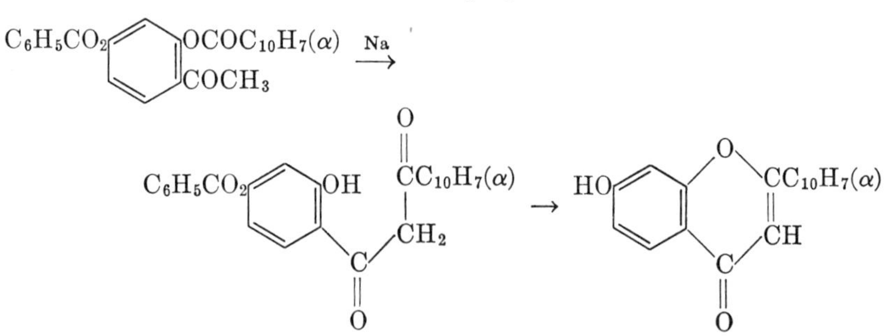

[39a] Wheeler and co-workers, *J. Chem. Soc.*, **1950**, 1252.
[39b] Lynch, O'Toole, and Wheeler, *J. Chem. Soc.*, **1952**, 2063.

Evidently the rearrangement occurs intramolecularly, at least with potassium carbonate, since not only do *p*-benzoyloxyacetophenone and *o*-hydroxy-*p*-benzoyloxyacetophenone fail to exhibit the rearrangement, but *o*-anisoyloxy-*p*-benzoyloxyacetophenone yields only the anisoyl derivative.[40] The mechanism of the reaction is probably analogous to

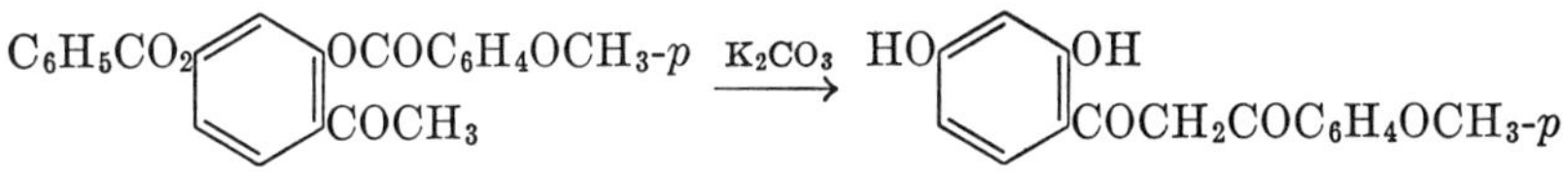
C6H5CO2
OCOC6H4OCH3-p
COCH3
K2CO3
HO
OH
COCH2COC6H4OCH3-p

that of the ordinary intermolecular acylation of ketones (see p. 62). This would involve ionization of the hydrogen α to the ketonic carbonyl group followed by addition of the resulting anion to the carbonyl group of the ester, accompanied by displacement of the phenolate anion.[40a]

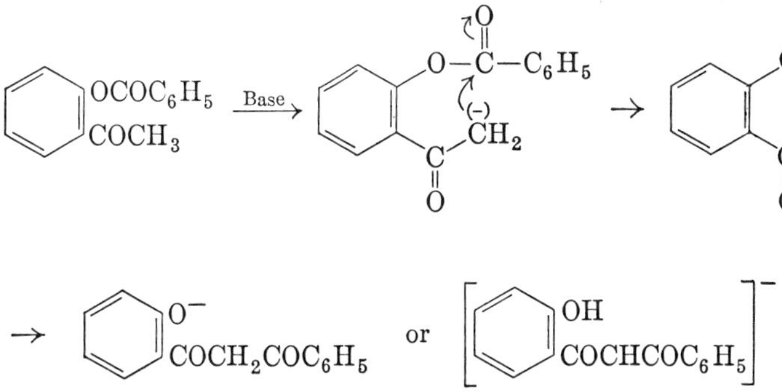
OCOC6H5
COCH3
Base
O
O—C—C6H5
(-)
CH2
C
O
C—C6H5
CH2
O—
COCH2COC6H5
or
OH
COCHCOC6H5

Although various *o*-aroyloxyacetophenones undergo the rearrangement, the reaction failed with 2,4-diacetoxyacetophenone in the presence of potassium carbonate. However, the stronger basic reagent sodium causes rearrangement of the acetyl group in 1-acetoxy-2-acetylnaphthalene, while sodium ethoxide effects the rearrangement of 2-palmitoyloxy-1-acetylnaphthalene.

Kostanecki Acylation of *o*-Hydroxy Ketones with Anhydrides To Furnish Chromones (Table XVII). *o*-Hydroxy ketones of type VI (with or without substituents in the benzene ring) when heated with acid anhydrides in the presence of the sodium or potassium salts of the corresponding acids form chromones, flavones, or isoflavones. The most probable course of this transformation, called the Kostanecki reaction, is that shown below: acylation of the phenolic hydroxyl group to form the ester VII, rearrangement to the diketone VIII, and cyclization of the diketone. The Kostanecki reaction has been conducted successfully

[40] Baker, *J. Chem. Soc.*, **1933**, 1381.

[40a] Gowan and Wheeler, *J. Chem. Soc.*, **1950**, 1925.

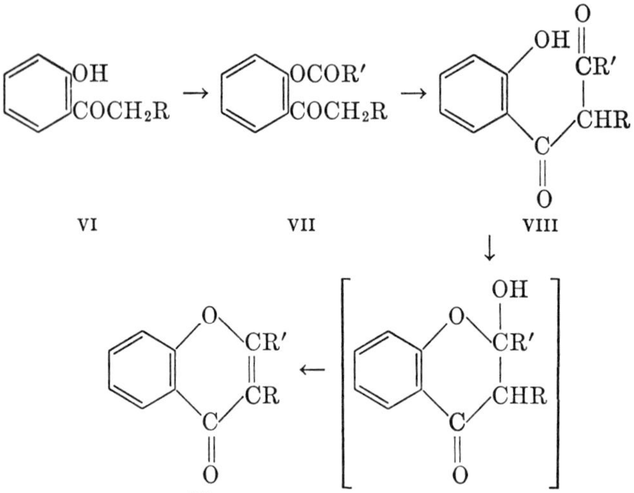

VI   VII   VIII

IX

with esters of the general structure VII. The rearrangement of an ester like VII to a β-diketone like VIII is an acylation of the ketonic portion of the molecule by the ester portion and is analogous to the rearrangements in the presence of potassium carbonate, sodium ethoxide, sodium, or sodium amide which were described in the preceding section.

When the o-hydroxy ketone is an acetophenone derivative (VI, R = H), the β-diketone VIII is probably acylated by the anhydride before cyclization. This would furnish a triketone, X, which could undergo cyclization to yield the acyl derivative of a chromone, XI. These acyl derivatives may be isolated; but, since the reaction mixture is generally treated with alkali, the acyl group is usually removed by hydrolysis. When phenolic groups in addition to the one in the *ortho*

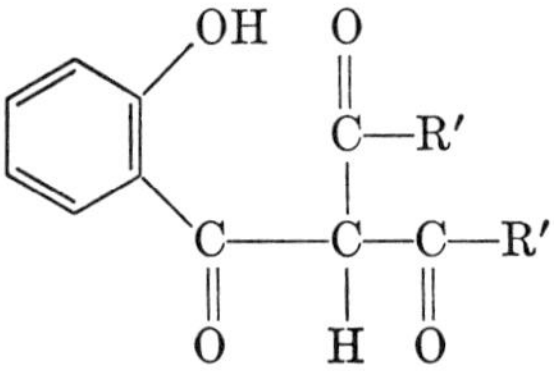

X 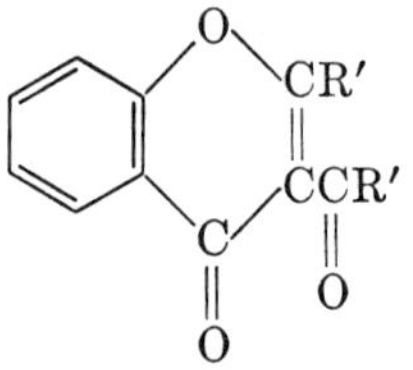   XI

position are present in the molecule, they also are probably acylated during the reaction, but, in working up the reaction mixture, the free phenolic groups are generally regenerated.

The Kostanecki reaction has been used to prepare various chromones, flavones, and isoflavones. The reaction has been successful with o-hydroxy ketones VI in which R is hydrogen, n-alkyl (up to $C_{16}H_{33}$), isopropyl (but apparently not other iso-alkyl groups),[41] phenyl or substituted phenyl, benzyl, alkoxy, acyloxy, or halogen, and with anhydrides in which R′ is n-alkyl or isopropyl, chloromethyl, phenyl or substituted phenyl, phenethyl, or styryl. In most of the o-hydroxy ketones, the benzene ring is substituted with alkyl, hydroxy, alkoxy, acyloxy, or halogen or is fused with other rings which may be either carbocyclic or heterocyclic.

With anhydrides having at least two α-hydrogen atoms, the Kostanecki reaction is often accompanied by the formation of coumarins. These compounds evidently arise from an aldol reaction involving the α-hydrogen of the ester portion of VII and the carbonyl group of the ketone portion. Phenylacetic anhydride, in which the α-hydrogen atoms are especially reactive, leads almost exclusively to coumarins. With

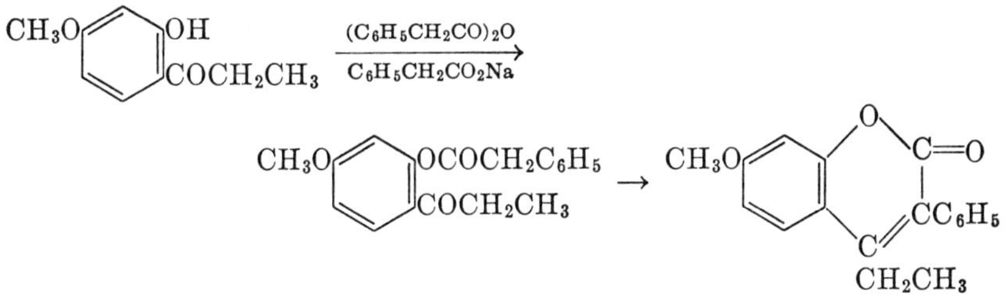

$$CH_3O\!\!\bigcirc\!\!\begin{smallmatrix}OH\\COCH_2CH_3\end{smallmatrix} \quad \xrightarrow[C_6H_5CH_2CO_2Na]{(C_6H_5CH_2CO)_2O} \quad$$

$$CH_3O\!\!\bigcirc\!\!\begin{smallmatrix}OCOCH_2C_6H_5\\COCH_2CH_3\end{smallmatrix} \quad \rightarrow \quad CH_3O\!\!\bigcirc\!\!\begin{smallmatrix}O\\\diagdown C=O\\ \diagup CC_6H_5\\C\\CH_2CH_3\end{smallmatrix}$$

(a coumarin)

acetic or propionic anhydride the chromone is usually formed in good yield, but in a few reactions the coumarin is the main product.

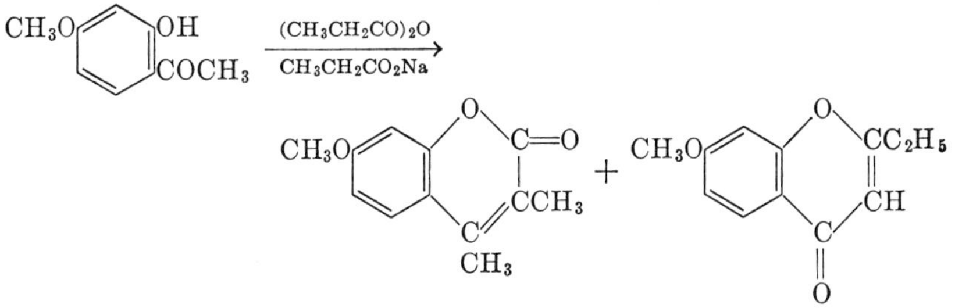

$$CH_3O\!\!\bigcirc\!\!\begin{smallmatrix}OH\\COCH_3\end{smallmatrix} \quad \xrightarrow[CH_3CH_2CO_2Na]{(CH_3CH_2CO)_2O} \quad$$

$$CH_3O\!\!\bigcirc\!\!\begin{smallmatrix}O\\\diagdown C=O\\ \diagup CCH_3\\C\\CH_3\end{smallmatrix} \quad + \quad CH_3O\!\!\bigcirc\!\!\begin{smallmatrix}O\\\diagdown CC_2H_5\\ \diagup CH\\C\\O\end{smallmatrix}$$

(a coumarin)   (a chromone)

o-Hydroxypropiophenones have a greater tendency to form chromones than do o-hydroxyacetophenones;[42] but o-hydroxyisobutyrophenones, which are difficult to acylate, furnish only coumarins.[43]

Although the sodium salt of the carboxylic acid corresponding to the anhydride has generally been used as the catalyst, triethylamine has

[41] Chudgar and Shah, J. Indian Chem. Soc., 21, 175 (1944).
[42] Chakravarti and Majumdar, J. Indian Chem. Soc., 16, 151 (1939).
[43] Ali, Desai, and Shroff, Proc. Indian Acad. Sci., 13A, 184 (1941) [C. A., 36, 91 (1942)].

been employed instead of the sodium salt. In certain cases, the tertiary amine has produced the better yield.

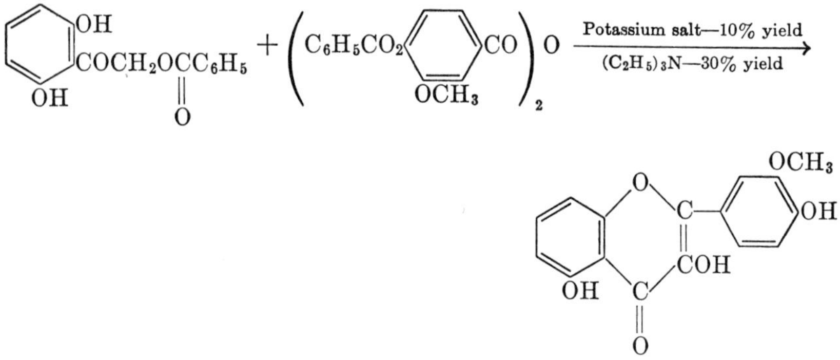

$$\text{(benzene ring with OH, COCH}_2\text{OCC}_6\text{H}_5\text{, OH)} + \left(C_6H_5CO_2\text{—}\underset{OCH_3}{\underset{|}{\bigcirc}}\text{—CO}\right)_2 O \xrightarrow[\text{(C}_2\text{H}_5)_3\text{N—30\% yield}]{\text{Potassium salt—10\% yield}}$$

[structure: chromone with OCH$_3$, OH, COH, OH groups]

It is sometimes convenient to use the acid chloride instead of the anhydride; the anhydride may be formed and serve as the acylating agent in such reactions.

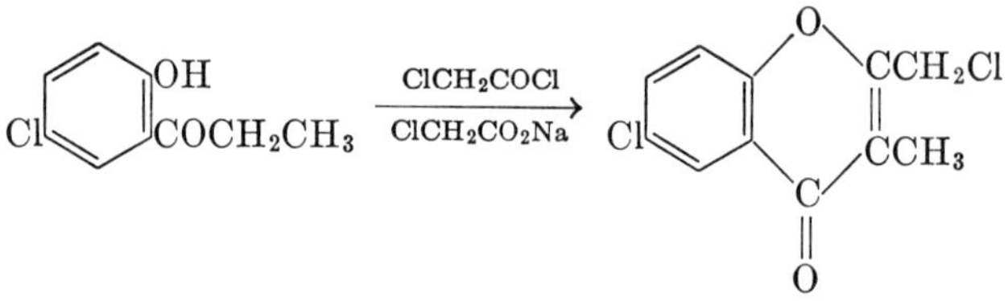

$$\text{Cl—}\bigcirc\text{—OH, COCH}_2\text{CH}_3 \xrightarrow[\text{ClCH}_2\text{CO}_2\text{Na}]{\text{ClCH}_2\text{COCl}} \text{Cl—}\bigcirc\text{(ring with O, CCH}_2\text{Cl, CCH}_3, \text{C=O)}$$

When the appropriate groups are present, diflavones may be formed, although usually a mixture of the mono- and di-flavone results.

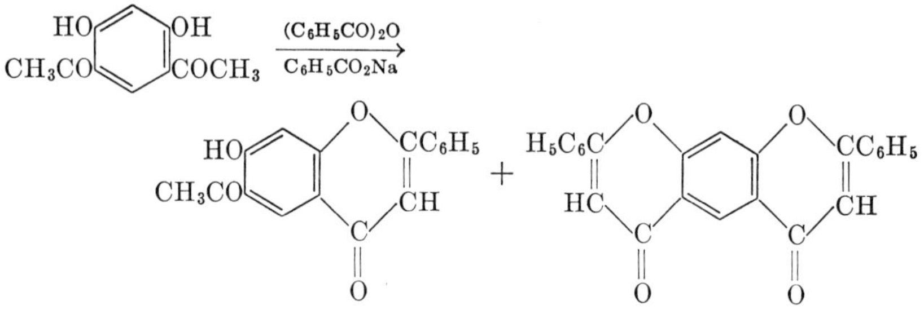

$$\underset{CH_3CO}{\overset{HO}{\bigcirc}}\text{OH, COCH}_3 \xrightarrow[\text{C}_6\text{H}_5\text{CO}_2\text{Na}]{(C_6H_5CO)_2O}$$

[structures: $\underset{CH_3CO}{\overset{HO}{\bigcirc}}$ with O, CC$_6$H$_5$, CH, C=O] + [H$_5$C$_6$C, HC, ring with O, CC$_6$H$_5$, CH, C=O, C=O]

It should be pointed out that o-hydroxy (or o-alkoxy) ketones can also be converted to chromones, flavones, or isoflavones by first acylating the ketones with esters by means of sodium or sodium ethoxide, then cyclizing with an acidic reagent;[44] this method avoids the formation of coumarins. The acylation with ethyl acetate, higher aliphatic esters,

[44] Link, "The Anthocyanins and Flavones," in Gilman, *Organic Chemistry*, Vol. II, p. 1335, John Wiley & Sons, 1943.

and aromatic esters has been discussed on pp. 70, 73, and 76, respectively. Acylation of o-hydroxyphenyl benzyl ketone with formic esters is accompanied by cyclization to form isoflavones directly (see p. 89). The rearrangement of esters of o-hydroxyacetophenones also forms β-diketones which may be cyclized to chromones, flavones, or isoflavones; these rearrangements are discussed on pp. 90–91. The cyclization of β-diketones containing an o-hydroxyphenyl group to form chromones may be represented by the following general equation.

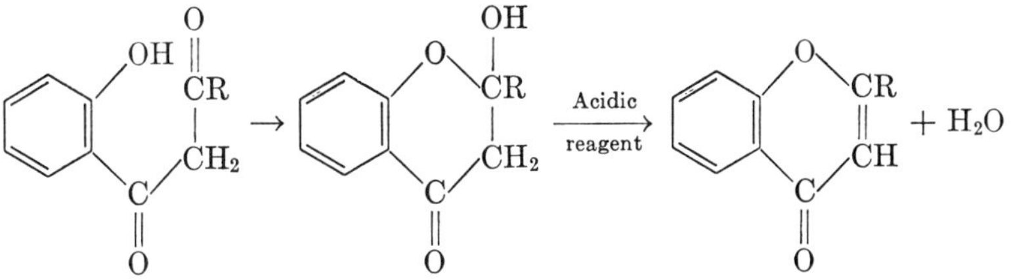

Acylation with Acid Chlorides or Other Acid Derivatives (Table XVIII). Acid chlorides have usually not been very satisfactory for the preparation of β-diketones, since the corresponding triketone or the O-acyl derivative of the diketone is often produced. Thus, molecular equivalents of cinnamoyl chloride and the sodium derivative of acetophenone produce mainly dicinnamoylacetophenone (XII). Benzoyl chloride and the sodium derivative of cyclohexanone yield the O-benzoyl derivative of 2-benzoylcyclohexanone (XIII). Moreover, acid chlorides or acid anhydrides often produce O-acylation, especially with α-substituted ketones. Thus, α,α-diphenylacetophenone reacts with benzoyl chloride even in the presence of pyridine to form the enol benzoate XIV. This type of reaction appears to be general with hindered ketones which exist in the enol form, that is, as vinyl alcohols.[45] How-

$(C_6H_5CH{=}CHCO)_2CHCOC_6H_5$

XII

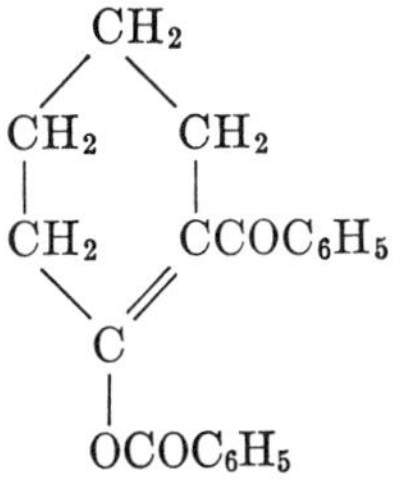

XIII

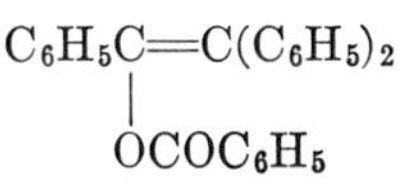

$$C_6H_5C{=}C(C_6H_5)_2$$
$$OCOC_6H_5$$

XIV

ever, the sodium derivative of ethyl isobutyrylisobutyrate, prepared by means of sodium triphenylmethide, can be acylated with acetyl or isobutyryl chloride in accordance with the following equation.

[45] Fuson and co-workers, *J. Am. Chem. Soc.*, **68**, 389 (1946).

$$RCOCl + Na^+[C(CH_3)_2COC(CH_3)_2CO_2C_2H_5]^- \rightarrow$$

$$RCOC(CH_3)_2COC(CH_3)_2CO_2C_2H_5 + NaCl$$

The reaction of acid chlorides with the magnesium derivatives of hindered ketones, prepared by means of ethylmagnesium bromide,* can sometimes be arrested at the β-diketone stage. Thus, in the presence of one half molecular equivalent of acetyl or benzoyl chloride, the magnesium derivative of acetomesitylene is converted mainly to the corresponding β-diketone. Even in the presence of excess acetyl chloride, the magnesium derivative of methyl methyl-*t*-butylneopentyl-carbinyl ketone is converted only to the β-diketone. However, in other cases diacylation or O-acylation often occurs. The conversion of acetomesitylene to its magnesium derivative and the condensation of the latter with an acid chloride might involve the following cyclic mechanisms.

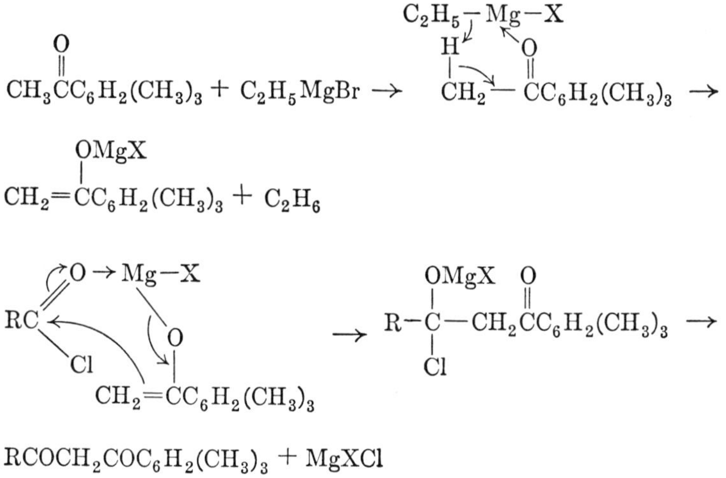

$$CH_3\overset{\overset{\displaystyle O}{\|}}{C}C_6H_2(CH_3)_3 + C_2H_5MgBr \rightarrow \quad CH_2 - \overset{\overset{\displaystyle O}{\|}}{C}C_6H_2(CH_3)_3 \rightarrow$$

$$CH_2{=}\overset{\overset{\displaystyle OMgX}{|}}{C}C_6H_2(CH_3)_3 + C_2H_6$$

$$RC\overset{\diagdown}{\underset{\diagdown{Cl}}{\overset{\nearrow{O} \to Mg-X}{}}} \quad \rightarrow \quad R-\overset{\overset{\displaystyle OMgX}{|}}{\underset{\displaystyle Cl}{C}}-CH_2\overset{\overset{\displaystyle O}{\|}}{C}C_6H_2(CH_3)_3 \rightarrow$$

$$CH_2{=}CC_6H_2(CH_3)_3$$

$$RCOCH_2COC_6H_2(CH_3)_3 + MgXCl$$

Acylation of *o*-hydroxyacetophenones with acid anhydrides has been discussed in the previous section. The acylation of acetophenone with N,N-diphenylacetamide to form benzoylacetone has been effected in 25% yield.[46]

$$CH_3CON(C_6H_5)_2 + CH_3COC_6H_5 \overset{Na}{\longrightarrow} CH_3COCH_2COC_6H_5 + (C_6H_5)_2NH$$

* When the carbonyl group of ketones is sufficiently hindered, the Grignard reagent reacts with the α-hydrogen instead of the carbonyl group to form the bromomagnesium derivative (or enolate) of the ketone.

[46] Chelintsev and Osetrova, *Compt. rend. acad. sci. U.S.S.R.*, **4**, 419 (1936) [*C. A.*, **31**, 3467 (1937)].

Some Related Reactions

Several important types of reactions are closely related to the acylation of ketones by the basic reagent method.   These include the carbethoxylation of ketones with diethyl carbonate to form β-keto esters,[25, 47] the acylation of esters to form β-keto esters (acetoacetic ester reaction),[1, 25] the carbethoxylation of esters to form malonic esters,[25, 48] the carbethoxylation or acylation of nitriles to form β-cyano esters or β-keto nitriles,[49] and the acylation or carbethoxylation of quinaldine, lepidine, and α-picoline.[50]   Examples of these types of reactions are represented by the following equations.

$$C_2H_5OCO_2C_2H_5 + CH_3COR \xrightarrow[\text{or NaNH}_2]{\text{NaOC}_2H_5} RCOCH_2CO_2C_2H_5 + C_2H_5OH$$

$$RCH_2CO_2C_2H_5 + RCH_2CO_2C_2H_5 \xrightarrow{\text{NaOC}_2H_5}$$
$$RCH_2COCHRCO_2C_2H_5 + C_2H_5OH$$

$$C_2H_5OCO_2C_2H_5 + RCH_2CO_2C_2H_5 \xrightarrow[\text{or NaNH}_2]{\text{NaOC}_2H_5} RCH(CO_2C_2H_5)_2 + C_2H_5OH$$

$$C_2H_5OCO_2C_2H_5 + RCH_2CN \xrightarrow[\text{or NaNH}_2]{\text{NaOC}_2H_5} RCH(CN)CO_2C_2H_5 + C_2H_5OH$$

$$RCO_2C_2H_5 + RCH_2CN \xrightarrow[\text{or NaNH}_2]{\text{NaOC}_2H_5} RCH(CN)COR + C_2H_5OH$$

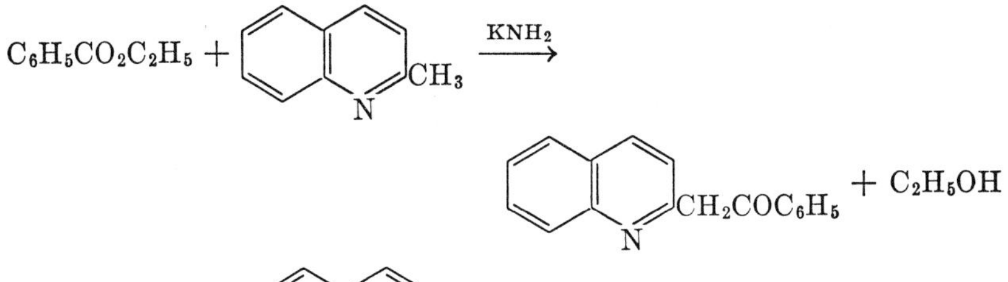

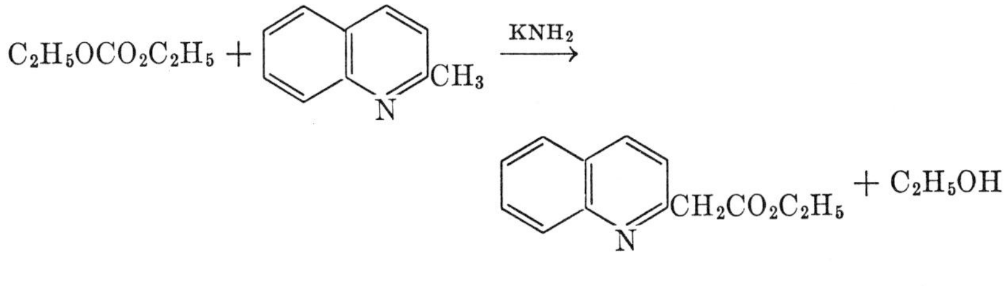

[47] Wallingford, Homeyer, and Jones, *J. Am. Chem. Soc.*, **63**, 2252 (1941); Levine and Hauser, *ibid.*, **66**, 1768 (1944).

[48] Wallingford, Homeyer, and Jones, *J. Am. Chem. Soc.*, **63**, 2056 (1941); Walker, Levine, Kibler, and Hauser, *ibid.*, **68**, 672 (1946).

[49] Wallingford, Jones, and Homeyer, *J. Am. Chem. Soc.*, **64**, 576 (1942); Levine and Hauser, *ibid.*, **68**, 760 (1946).

[50] Bergstrom and Moffat, *J. Am. Chem. Soc.*, **59**, 1494 (1937); Weiss and Hauser, *ibid.*, **71**, 2023 (1949).

ACYLATION WITH BORON TRIFLUORIDE

In the boron fluoride catalyzed acylation of ketones a mixture of an acid anhydride and a ketone is saturated with boron trifluoride, followed by treatment with aqueous sodium acetate. The over-all reaction may be illustrated with acetic anhydride and acetone.

$$(CH_3CO)_2O + CH_3COCH_3 \xrightarrow[\substack{\text{followed by} \\ CH_3CO_2Na}]{BF_3} CH_3COCH_2COCH_3 + CH_3CO_2H$$

The quantity of boron trifluoride absorbed on saturation generally amounts to about 100 mole per cent (based on the total moles of ketone and anhydride). Catalytic amounts of the reagent fail to effect the condensation satisfactorily.[50a] This is in line with the observation that the β-diketone is evidently produced in the reaction mixture as the boron difluoride complex XVIII, p. 100. Certain of these complexes have been isolated.[50a]

There is evidence [50a] that the β-diketone may arise not only by the direct C-acylation of the ketone [51] as represented in equation 4 but also, indirectly, by the O-acylation of the ketone followed by the C-acylation of the resulting ketone enol ester as represented in equations 5 and 6, respectively. Actually certain ketone enol esters have been isolated from reaction mixtures and converted, by further treatments with the anhydride and boron trifluoride, to the enol ester of the β-diketone and, finally, to the boron difluoride complex as shown in equation 6.[50a] The acetyl fluoride represented as a by-product in 6 has been isolated;[50a] and, in an analogous reaction of the enol benzoate of dibenzoylmethane with boron trifluoride, benzoyl fluoride was isolated along with the boron difluoride complex.[51a] The O-acylation of the ketone is presumably brought about by the acid formed as a by-product in equation 4; such O-acylations are known to be effected by sulfuric acid and other acids.[52] However, such acids by themselves, and even boron trichloride and aluminum chloride, have been found incapable of effecting the acylation of ketones to form β-diketones.[52a]

$$(CH_3CO)_2O + CH_3COCH_3 \xrightarrow{2BF_3} \overset{\overset{\displaystyle BF_2}{\diagup \; \diagdown}}{\underset{\displaystyle CH_3C-CH=CCH_3}{O \qquad O}} + [CH_3CO_2H_2]^+[BF_4]^-$$

$$(4)$$

[50a] Frostick, Man, Sanderson, Walker, Manyik, and Hauser, unpublished results.
[51] Hauser and Adams, *J. Am. Chem. Soc.*, **66**, 345 (1944).
[51a] Hauser, Frostick, and Man, *J. Am. Chem. Soc.*, **74**, 3231 (1952).
[52] Young, Frostick, Sanderson, and Hauser, *J. Am. Chem. Soc.*, **72**, 3635 (1950).
[52a] Walker, Sanderson, and Hauser, *J. Am. Chem. Soc.*, **75**, 4109 (1953).

$$(CH_3CO)_2O + CH_3COCH_3 \xrightarrow{H^+} \overset{\displaystyle OCOCH_3}{\underset{\displaystyle |}{CH_2}}\!\!=\!\!C\!-\!CH_3 + CH_3CO_2H \qquad (5)$$

$$(CH_3CO)_2O + \overset{\displaystyle OCOCH_3}{\underset{\displaystyle |}{CH_2}}\!\!=\!\!C\!-\!CH_3 \xrightarrow{BF_3}$$

$$\underset{\displaystyle CH_3C\!-\!CH=\!C\!-\!CH_3}{\overset{\displaystyle O \qquad\quad OCOCH_3}{\overset{\displaystyle \|\qquad\quad |}{}}} \xrightarrow{BF_3} \quad CH_3CCH\!=\!\!CCH_3 + CH_3COF \qquad (6)$$

Thus, during the initial period of the reaction before much acid is present, the β-diketone may be produced solely by the direct C-acylation of the ketone (equation 4), but, as by-product acid is produced, the β-diketone may also be formed by the indirect course (equations 5 and 6). During the latter stages, the indirect course may even become predominant. The direct course would presumably be favored by rapid saturation of the reaction mixture with boron trifluoride, and the indirect course, by slow saturation with the reagent. Apparently because the acid formed as by-product in equation 4 catalyzes not only the O-acylation of the ketone but also its self-condensation (aldol reaction), the best yields of a number of β-diketones have been obtained by adding the boron trifluoride as rapidly as possible.[52b]

Mechanism

The direct C-acylation of the ketone (equation 4) probably involves the conversion, by the boron trifluoride, of both the anhydride and the ketone to reactive intermediates which condense.[51] The anhydride is presumably converted to a carbonium ion such as XV or XVI, and the ketone is apparently converted to an enol type of complex which, by analogy with an ordinary enol, would have structure XVII. Evidence that ketones are converted by boron trifluoride to enol-type complexes is the observation that, after saturation with this reagent, p-bromo-acetophenone rapidly added bromine to form p-bromophenacyl bromide whereas this ketone failed to add bromine in the absence of the fluoride under similar conditions.[50a] The condensation of carbonium ion XV with enol complex XVII to form the boron difluoride complex of the β-diketone XVIII is indicated below.

[52b] Manyik, Frostick, Sanderson, and Hauser, *J. Am. Chem. Soc.*, **75**, 5030 (1953).

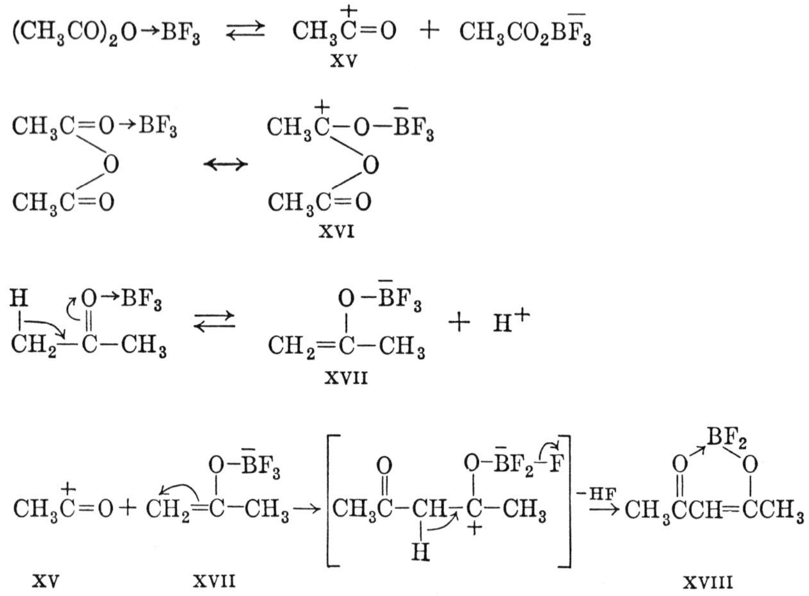

$$(CH_3CO)_2O \rightarrow BF_3 \rightleftarrows CH_3\overset{+}{C}=O + CH_3CO_2\overset{-}{BF_3}$$

XV

$$\begin{array}{c} CH_3C=O \rightarrow BF_3 \\ \diagdown \\ O \\ \diagup \\ CH_3C=O \end{array} \quad \longleftrightarrow \quad \begin{array}{c} CH_3\overset{+}{C}-O-\overset{-}{BF_3} \\ \diagdown \\ O \\ \diagup \\ CH_3C=O \end{array}$$

XVI

$$\begin{array}{c} H \quad O \rightarrow BF_3 \\ | \quad \| \\ CH_2-C-CH_3 \end{array} \rightleftarrows \begin{array}{c} O-\overset{-}{BF_3} \\ | \\ CH_2=C-CH_3 \end{array} + H^+$$

XVII

$$CH_3\overset{+}{C}=O + \begin{array}{c} O-\overset{-}{BF_3} \\ | \\ CH_2=C-CH_3 \end{array} \rightarrow \left[\begin{array}{c} O \quad O-\overset{-}{BF_2}-F \\ \| \quad | \\ CH_3C-CH_2-\overset{+}{C}-CH_3 \\ | \\ H \end{array} \right] \overset{-HF}{\rightarrow} \begin{array}{c} BF_2 \\ O \quad O \\ \| \quad | \\ CH_3CCH=CCH_3 \end{array}$$

XV   XVII   XVIII

The O-acylation of the ketone (equation 5) presumably involves the proton-catalyzed enolization of the ketone accompanied by the acylation of the resulting enol.[52]

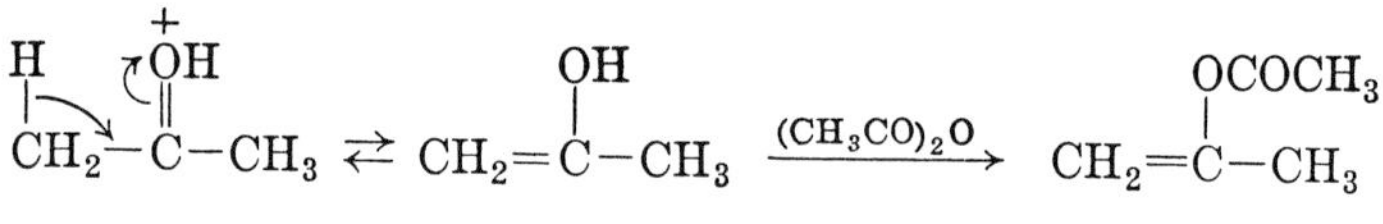

$$\begin{array}{c} H \quad \overset{+}{O}H \\ | \quad \| \\ CH_2-C-CH_3 \end{array} \rightleftarrows \begin{array}{c} OH \\ | \\ CH_2=C-CH_3 \end{array} \overset{(CH_3CO)_2O}{\longrightarrow} \begin{array}{c} OCOCH_3 \\ | \\ CH_2=C-CH_3 \end{array}$$

The C-acylation of the ketone enol ester (equation 6) probably involves the condensation of carbonium ion XV or XVI (from the anhydride) with the ketone enol ester to form the enol ester of the β-diketone which, in the presence of boron trifluoride, eliminates the acid fluoride and forms the boron difluoride complex of the β-diketone XVIII.[51a] This mechanism for the formation of the enol ester of the β-diketone XIX is analogous to that often represented for the common Friedel-Crafts type of acylation.

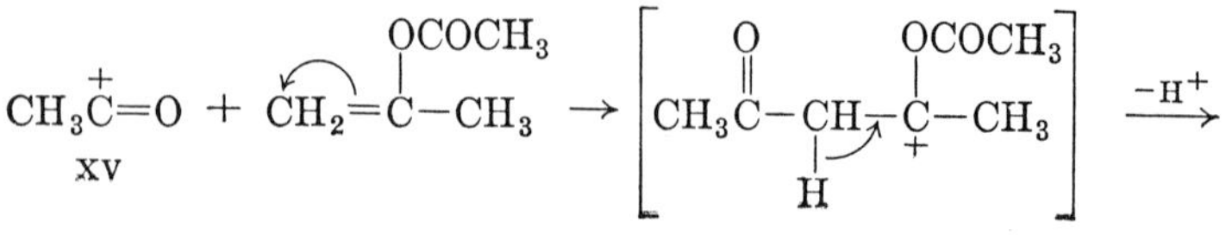

$$CH_3\overset{+}{C}=O + \begin{array}{c} OCOCH_3 \\ | \\ CH_2=C-CH_3 \end{array} \rightarrow \left[\begin{array}{c} O \quad OCOCH_3 \\ \| \quad | \\ CH_3C-CH_2-\overset{+}{C}-CH_3 \\ | \\ H \end{array} \right] \overset{-H^+}{\longrightarrow}$$

XV

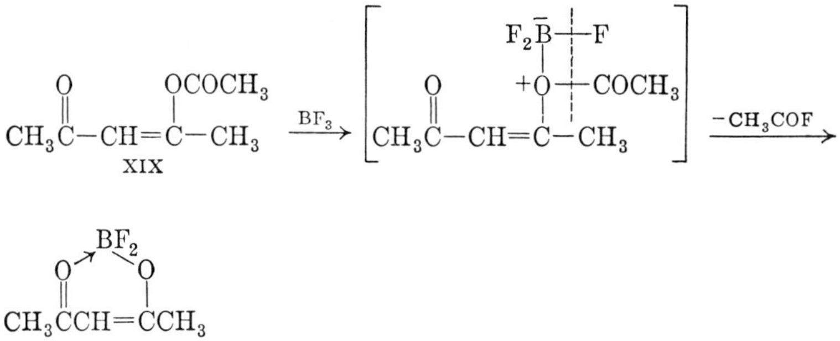

$$CH_3\overset{\overset{O}{\|}}{C}-CH=\overset{\overset{OCOCH_3}{|}}{C}-CH_3 \quad \xrightarrow{BF_3} \quad \left[CH_3\overset{\overset{O}{\|}}{C}-CH=\overset{\overset{+O-COCH_3}{|}}{C}-CH_3 \right] \quad \xrightarrow{-CH_3COF}$$

XIX

(with $F_2\overline{B}-F$ above)

$$CH_3\overset{\overset{O}{\|}}{C}CH=\overset{\overset{O}{|}}{C}CH_3$$

(with BF_2 bridging the two O's)

XVIII

Side Reactions

The acylation of ketones with anhydrides by boron trifluoride may be accompanied by the self-condensation of the anhydride or the ketone. Self-condensation of acetic anhydride involves the formation of an intermediate which, on hydrolysis and decarboxylation, yields acetylacetone.[53] This side reaction appears to take place to some extent in

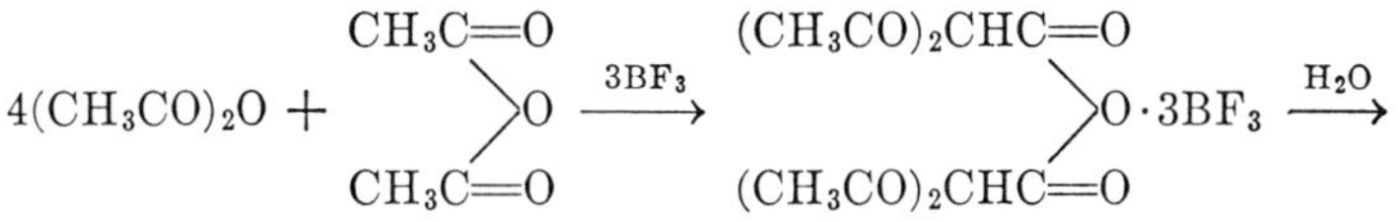

$$4(CH_3CO)_2O + \begin{matrix} CH_3C{=}O \\ {>}O \\ CH_3C{=}O \end{matrix} \xrightarrow{3BF_3} \begin{matrix} (CH_3CO)_2CHC{=}O \\ {>}O \cdot 3BF_3 \\ (CH_3CO)_2CHC{=}O \end{matrix} \xrightarrow{H_2O}$$

$$2(CH_3CO)_2CHCO_2H \xrightarrow{-CO_2} 2CH_3COCH_2COCH_3$$

acetylation of a variety of ketones. In the acetylation of acetone the self-condensation of the acetic anhydride should cause no difficulty,[54] but in the acetylations of other ketones the acetylacetone from the anhydride may be a troublesome by-product.

Self-condensation of propionic anhydride similarly produces 4-methylheptane-3,5-dione,[53] but the main product is diethyl ketone resulting from the hydrolysis and decarboxylation of an intermediate of type XX.[53] Higher aliphatic anhydrides self-condense to produce almost exclusively the monoketone.[55]

$$(RCH_2COCHRCO)_2O \cdot 3BF_3$$
XX

Self-condensation of the ketones involves aldol-type reactions accompanied by the elimination of water to form α,β-unsaturated ketones or further condensation products. Such reactions appear to account for

[53] Meerwein and Vossen, *J. prakt. Chem.*, (2) **141**, 149 (1934).
[54] Adams and Hauser, *J. Am. Chem. Soc.*, **67**, 284 (1945).
[55] Man and Hauser, *J. Am. Chem. Soc.*, **72**, 3294 (1950).

the formation of high-boiling mixtures which have been obtained especially when the procedure of slow saturation with boron trifluoride has been employed. With desoxybenzoin and acetic anhydride the self-condensation of the ketone occurred exclusively.[53]

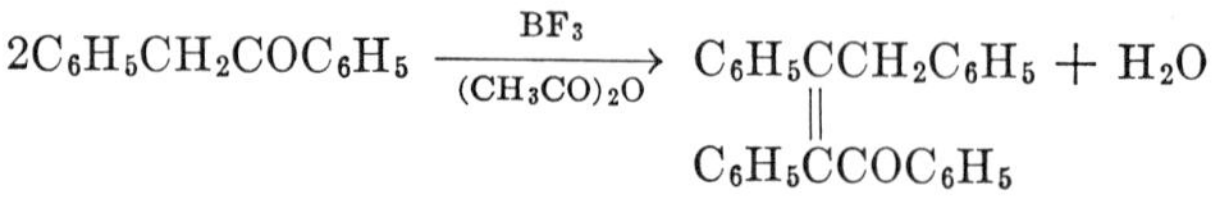

$$2C_6H_5CH_2COC_6H_5 \xrightarrow[\text{(CH}_3\text{CO)}_2\text{O}]{\text{BF}_3} \begin{array}{c} C_6H_5CCH_2C_6H_5 \\ \| \\ C_6H_5CCOC_6H_5 \end{array} + H_2O$$

Scope and Limitations (Tables XIX and XX)

Various ketones having α-hydrogen atoms have been acetylated with acetic anhydride by means of boron trifluoride. Methyl ketones such as acetone, acetophenone, and o-, m-, and p-nitroacetophenone give good yields of the corresponding methyl derivatives. Similarly methylene

$$(CH_3CO)_2O + CH_3COC_6H_4NO_2 \xrightarrow{\text{BF}_3}$$

$$CH_3COCH_2COC_6H_4NO_2 + CH_3CO_2H$$
$$(64\text{–}68\%)$$

ketones such as diethyl ketone, cyclopentanone, cyclohexanone, and tetralone give good yields of the corresponding methylene derivatives. Acetophenone, cyclopentanone, and cyclohexanone give better yields when the boron trifluoride is added rapidly to the anhydride-ketone mixture than when the reagent is added slowly.[52b]

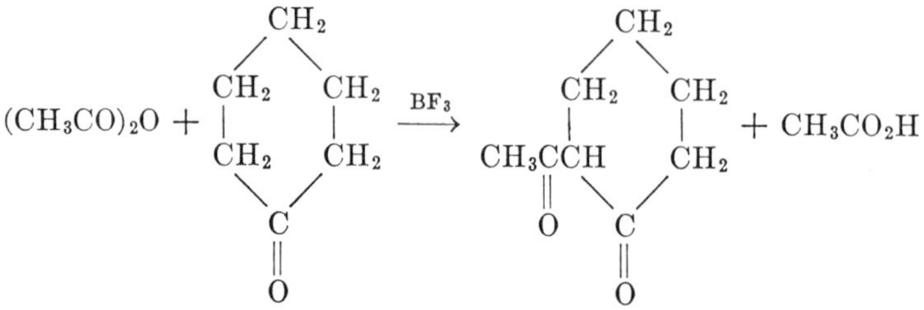

(73%)

Methyl methylene ketones of the type CH_3COCH_2R may form both the methyl and methylene derivatives. The proportions of the isomers appear to be dependent on the nature of R and on the rate of saturation of the reaction mixture with boron trifluoride.[50a, 51] When the saturation is carried out slowly, methyl ethyl ketone gives exclusively the methylene derivative, but methyl n-propyl and higher methyl alkyl ketones form also the methyl derivative. The proportion of the methyl derivative increases as branching at the β-carbon of the ketone is increased.[51] Thus, the ratio of the methylene to methyl derivative is about 90 to 10 for methyl n-propyl and higher methyl n-alkyl ketones, but it is 45 to 55 for methyl isobutyl ketone. When three methyl groups are attached to the β-carbon, as in methyl neopentyl ketone, the methyl derivative is formed exclusively.[50a] In general, the proportion of the methyl derivative may be increased by increasing the rate of saturation with boron trifluoride, whereas that of the methylene derivative may be increased by adding this reagent slowly in the presence of acid.[50a]

In contrast to basic reagents, boron trifluoride is useful for preparing the methylene derivatives of a number of methyl methylene ketones. The method is often satisfactory even when some of the methyl derivative also is formed, since this derivative may usually be extracted readily from the methylene derivative by means of cold dilute alkali. Moreover certain methyl n-alkyl ketones that form some of the methyl derivative on acetylation with boron trifluoride alone give exclusively the methylene derivative when the acetylation is carried out in the presence of a catalytic amount of p-toluenesulfonic acid.[50a] Thus the methylene derivative is obtained exclusively and in good yield from methyl n-amyl and methyl n-hexyl ketone under these conditions. Similarly the

$$(CH_3CO)_2O + CH_3COCH_2C_4H_9\text{-}n \xrightarrow[H^+]{BF_3}$$

$$CH_3COCH(C_4H_9\text{-}n)COCH_3 + CH_3CO_2H$$
$$(66\text{--}74\%)$$

methylene derivative may be obtained in good yield from phenylacetone and p-nitrophenylacetone.

$$(CH_3CO)_2O + CH_3COCH_2C_6H_5 \xrightarrow[H^+]{BF_3}$$

$$CH_3COCH(C_6H_5)COCH_3 + CH_3CO_2H$$
$$(50\text{--}60\%)$$

The acetylation of methyl methinyl ketones such as methyl isopropyl ketone forms both the methyl and methinyl derivatives, but neither of these derivatives has been obtained in satisfactory yield.

A number of ketones have been acylated with propionic anhydride and with certain higher aliphatic anhydrides up to and including caproic and 2-ethylhexanoic anhydride. In general, the yields have been comparable with the corresponding reactions using acetic anhydride. Examples of successful acylations with higher aliphatic anhydrides are represented by the following equations.

$[CH_3(CH_2)_2CO]_2O + CH_3COC_6H_5 \xrightarrow{BF_3}$

$$CH_3(CH_2)_2COCH_2COC_6H_5 + C_3H_7CO_2H$$
$$(63\%)$$

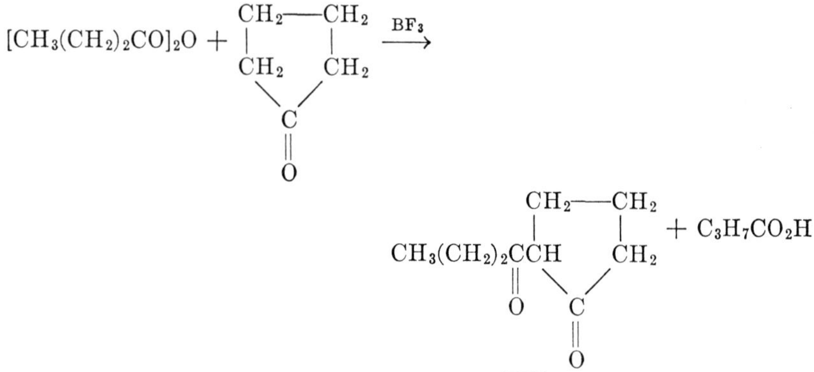

$[CH_3(CH_2)_2CO]_2O +$
$$\begin{array}{c} CH_2\!-\!\!-\!CH_2 \\ | \qquad | \\ CH_2 \qquad CH_2 \\ \diagdown \quad \diagup \\ C \\ \| \\ O \end{array} \xrightarrow{BF_3}$$

$$\begin{array}{c} CH_2\!-\!\!-\!CH_2 \\ | \qquad | \\ CH_3(CH_2)_2CCH \quad CH_2 \\ \| \quad \diagdown \diagup \\ O \quad C \\ \| \\ O \end{array} + C_3H_7CO_2H$$
$$(54\%)$$

$[CH_3(CH_2)_4CO]_2O + CH_3COCH_2CH_3 \xrightarrow{BF_3}$

$$CH_3COCHCO(CH_2)_4CH_3 + C_5H_{11}CO_2H$$
$$\underset{CH_3}{|}$$
$$(64\%)$$

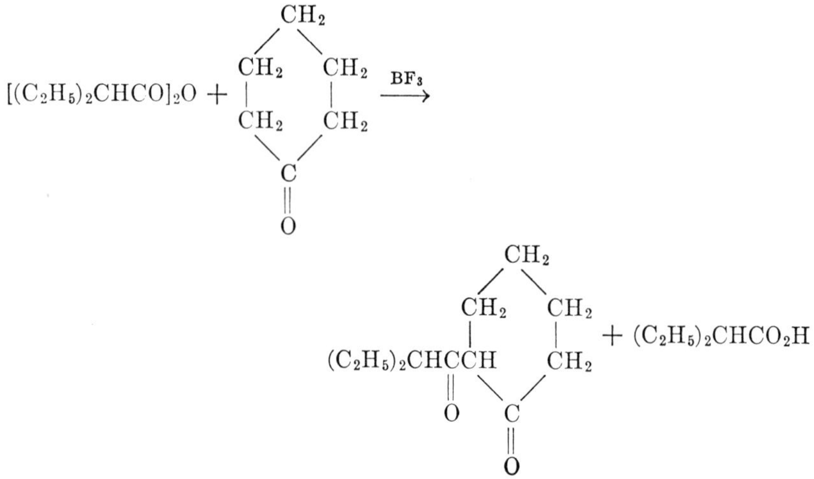

$[(C_2H_5)_2CHCO]_2O +$
$$\begin{array}{c} CH_2 \\ \diagup \quad \diagdown \\ CH_2 \quad CH_2 \\ | \qquad | \\ CH_2 \quad CH_2 \\ \diagdown \quad \diagup \\ C \\ \| \\ O \end{array} \xrightarrow{BF_3}$$

$$\begin{array}{c} CH_2 \\ \diagup \quad \diagdown \\ CH_2 \quad CH_2 \\ | \qquad | \\ (C_2H_5)_2CHCCH \quad CH_2 \\ \| \quad \diagdown \diagup \\ O \quad C \\ \| \\ O \end{array} + (C_2H_5)_2CHCO_2H$$
$$(68\%)$$

Attempts to acylate acetophenone with benzoic, phthalic, or succinic anhydride and with benzoyl chloride [54] by boron trifluoride failed. Moreover, this reagent failed to effect the acylation of methyl ethyl ketone with ethyl oxalate.[54]

As might be expected, boron trifluoride brings about the Friedel-Crafts acetylation of certain aromatic compounds with acetic anhydride to form acetophenone derivatives which may be acetylated further in the reaction mixture to produce β-diketones (Table XX). Thus, in the presence of a sufficient excess of acetic anhydride, such compounds as toluene, anisole, and mesitylene have been "acetoacetylated" to form β-diketones in satisfactory yields. The process may be illustrated with mesitylene. However, only very poor yields of β-diketones were obtained

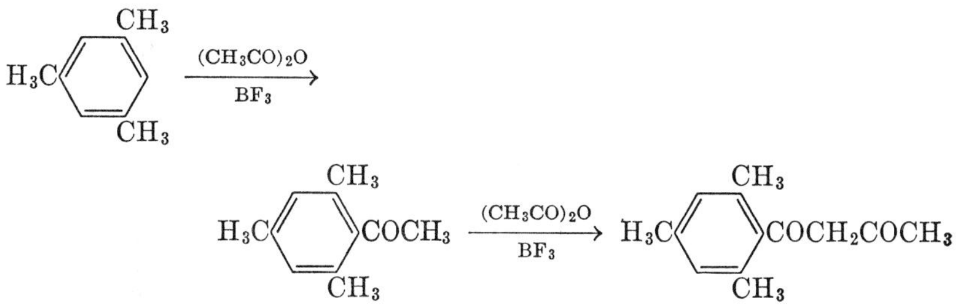

$$\text{mesitylene} \xrightarrow[\text{BF}_3]{(\text{CH}_3\text{CO})_2\text{O}} \text{2,4,6-trimethylacetophenone} \xrightarrow[\text{BF}_3]{(\text{CH}_3\text{CO})_2\text{O}} \text{ArCOCH}_2\text{COCH}_3$$

from benzene or chlorobenzene under similar conditions. The analogous process with propionic anhydride failed even with toluene.[52a]

Related Reactions

The self-condensation of aliphatic anhydrides in the presence of boron trifluoride, considered under Side Reactions (p. 101), appears to be closely related to the acylation of ketones by this reagent. Also, the acylation of enol esters with anhydrides by boron trifluoride,[52] a reaction which probably occurs to some extent whenever ketones are acylated with anhydrides (see p. 99), is somewhat related to the "direct" acylation of ketones by means of this reagent. The self-condensation of enol esters is similar.[52]

Apparently esters or nitriles having α-hydrogen atoms have not been acylated by means of boron trifluoride. Attempts to acylate aliphatic aldehydes with aliphatic anhydrides by means of this reagent resulted in the addition of the anhydride to the carbonyl group.[56] For example, with propionaldehyde and acetic anhydride, propylidene diacetate was obtained.

$$\text{CH}_3\text{CH}_2\text{CHO} + (\text{CH}_3\text{CO})_2\text{O} \xrightarrow{\text{BF}_3} \text{CH}_3\text{CH}_2\text{CH}(\text{OCOCH}_3)_2$$

Friedel-Crafts acylations of aromatic compounds, especially the Fries modification,[57] are somewhat related to the acylation of ketones by boron

[56] Man, Sanderson, and Hauser, *J. Am. Chem. Soc.*, **72**, 847 (1950).
[57] Blatt, *Chem. Revs.*, **27**, 413 (1940).

trifluoride. Indeed, certain Friedel-Crafts acylations catalyzed by this reagent are accompanied by the acylation of the resulting ketone to form a β-diketone (see p. 105).

COMPARISON OF METHODS OF ACYLATION

It can be seen from the section on Scope and Limitations that the basic reagents have had a much wider application than the boron trifluoride method for the acylation of ketones. Only the basic reagents have been found applicable to acylations involving the replacement of the α-hydrogen of the ketone by the oxalyl, formyl, or aromatic acyl groups.

The replacement of an α-hydrogen of a ketone by an aliphatic acyl group may be accomplished by either basic reagents or boron trifluoride. A ketone such as acetone, acetophenone, or cyclohexanone can form only one β-diketone, and the choice of reagent would generally be determined by the yields reported or by the relative availability of the appropriate ester or anhydride. In general, boron trifluoride would be chosen for the acylation of methylene ketones such as cyclohexanone with aliphatic anhydrides and for the acylation of o-, m-, and p-nitroacetophenone.[58] However, a methyl methylene ketone may be acylated at either the methyl or methylene group. Basic reagents form mainly the methyl derivative, whereas boron trifluoride generally forms mainly the methylene derivative. Thus a basic reagent would be chosen for the preparation of the methyl derivative of methyl ethyl or higher methyl alkyl ketones, whereas boron trifluoride would be chosen for the synthesis of the methylene derivative of methyl n-alkyl or methyl benzyl ketones. A general scheme for acetylations may be represented as follows.

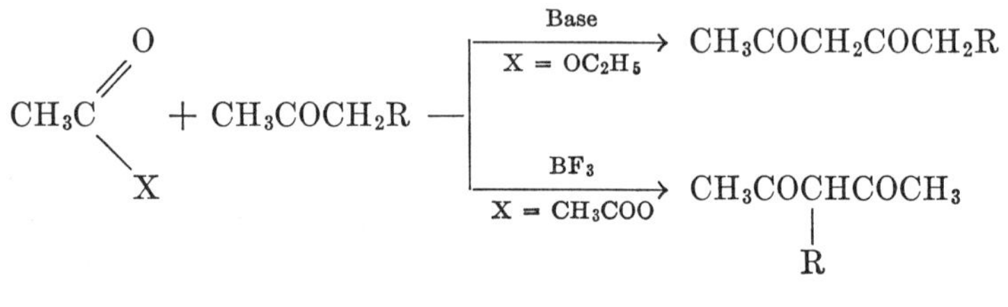

$$CH_3C\overset{O}{\underset{X}{\diagup}} + CH_3COCH_2R \longrightarrow
\begin{cases}
\xrightarrow[X\,=\,OC_2H_5]{\text{Base}} CH_3COCH_2COCH_2R \\
\\
\xrightarrow[X\,=\,CH_3COO]{BF_3} CH_3COCHCOCH_3 \underset{R}{\overset{|}{}}
\end{cases}$$

The preceding paragraphs compared the use of basic reagents and of boron trifluoride for the direct acylation of ketones. In the succeeding five sections the direct acylation of ketones will be compared with other methods for the synthesis of β-diketones, β-keto aldehydes, and α,γ-diketo esters.

[58] Walker and Hauser, J. Am. Chem. Soc., 68, 2742 (1946).

Synthesis of β-Diketones of the Type RCOCH₂COR′

For the synthesis of a β-diketone such as XXI one would ordinarily use the direct acylations described in this chapter: a methyl ketone $RCOCH_3$ or $R'COCH_3$ would be acylated, and the new carbon-carbon bond would be formed at a or b. The reactants are generally available, and the

$$\overset{a}{} \quad \overset{b}{}$$
$$RCO\text{-}\!\!\mid\!\!\text{-}CH_2\text{-}\!\!\mid\!\!\text{-}COR'$$
$$\text{XXI}$$

procedures are convenient. However, other methods have been employed, and they may sometimes be preferred.

Another direct way would be to effect a carbon-carbon condensation at position c or d. Syntheses of this type have been accomplished by re-

$$\overset{c}{} \qquad\qquad \overset{d}{}$$
$$R\text{-}\!\!\mid\!\!\text{-}CO\text{---}CH_2\text{---}CO\text{-}\!\!\mid\!\!\text{-}R'$$

action of a Grignard reagent with either a β-keto acid chloride [24] or a β-keto nitrile [59, 60] (followed by hydrolysis), and by the Friedel-Crafts reaction of benzene with either acetoacetyl chloride or diketene.[61] However, none of these methods appears to have been so satisfactory as the acylation of ketones.

$$CH_3COCH_2COCl + RMgX \longrightarrow CH_3COCH_2COR$$

$$C_6H_5COCH_2CN + RMgX \longrightarrow C_6H_5COCH_2COR$$

$$CH_3COCH_2COCl + C_6H_6 \xrightarrow{AlCl_3} CH_3COCH_2COC_6H_5$$

$$(CH_2CO)_2 + C_6H_6 \xrightarrow{AlCl_3} CH_3COCH_2COC_6H_5$$

Several indirect methods have been employed. One involves the O-acylation of a ketone to form an enol ester which is converted to a β-diketone by thermal rearrangement.[52] This process has been employed for the commercial preparation of acetylacetone.[52] Enol esters may also

$$\overset{OCOCH_3}{}$$
$$CH_2{=}C{=}O + CH_3COCH_3 \xrightarrow{H^+} CH_3\overset{\mid}{C}{=}CH_2 \xrightarrow{500°} CH_3COCH_2COCH_3$$

be acylated with themselves (self-condensation) or with anhydrides by

[59] Rehberg and Henze, *J. Am. Chem. Soc.*, **63**, 2785 (1941).
[60] Mavrodin, *Bull. soc. chim. Romania*, **15**, 99 (1933) [*C. A.*, **28**, 3396 (1934)].
[61] Hurd and Kelso, *J. Am. Chem. Soc.*, **62**, 1548 (1940).

means of boron trifluoride to form β-diketones.[52] Actually the latter process probably accompanies the "direct" acylation of ketones by the boron trifluoride method (see pp. 98–99).

Another indirect method is the acylation of acetoacetic ester, hydrolysis of the ester group, and decarboxylation of the resulting acid.[62]

$$\overset{+}{Na}[CH_3COCHCO_2C_2H_5]^- \xrightarrow{RCOCl}$$

$$CH_3COCHCO_2C_2H_5 \xrightarrow[-CO_2]{HOH} CH_3COCH_2COR$$
$$\overset{|}{R\overset{|}{C}O}$$

This method does not appear to be particularly satisfactory since C-acylation is usually accompanied by O-acylation, and hydrolysis of the ester group is generally accompanied by cleavage of the acetyl or the other acyl group. However, the method has been successful in the synthesis of the natural pigment, curcumin.[63] A recent development of this method consists in heating equimolecular quantities of an alkyl acetoacetate and an aliphatic anhydride in the presence of a catalytic amount of magnesium or magnesium compound.[64] Good yields of acetylacetone and other aliphatic β-diketones have been reported.[64] The reaction may be represented by the following equations.

$$CH_3COCH_2CO_2CH_3 + (CH_3CO)_2O \xrightarrow[140°]{Mg}$$

$$CH_3COCHCO_2CH_3 + CH_3CO_2H \rightarrow$$
$$\overset{|}{CH_3CO}$$

$$CH_3COCH_2COCH_3 + CH_3CO_2CH_3 + CO_2$$

Certain symmetrical β-diketones have been prepared in fair yield by the acylation of vinyl acetate with acid chlorides using aluminum chloride as catalyst.[64a]

$$2RCOCl + CH_2{=}CHOCOCH_3 \xrightarrow{AlCl_3} (RCO)_2C{=}CHOCOCH_3 \xrightarrow{HCl}$$
$$(RCO)_2CHCHO \xrightarrow{Heat} (RCO)_2CH_2 + CO$$

An indirect method that has been used especially for the preparation of dibenzoylmethane or substituted dibenzoylmethanes [65] involves an

[62] Fischer and Bulow, *Ber.*, **18**, 2131 (1885); Bouveault, *Compt. rend.*, **131**, 45 (1900); Bouveault and Bongert, *ibid.*, **132**, 701 (1901); Bongert, *ibid.*, **133**, 821 (1901).

[63] Lampe, *Ber.*, **51**, 1347 (1918).

[64] Reeder and Lescisin, U. S. pat. 2,369,250 [*C. A.*, **40**, 901 (1946)].

[64a] Sieglitz and Horn, *Ber.*, **84**, 607 (1951).

[65] Pond, Maxwell, and Norman, *J. Am. Chem. Soc.*, **21**, 955 (1899); Kohler and Barnes, *ibid.*, **55**, 690 (1933).

aldol condensation between an aromatic aldehyde and an acetophenone, followed by bromination, treatment with alkali, and hydrolysis. Al-

$$C_6H_5CHO + CH_3COC_6H_5 \xrightarrow{NaOH} C_6H_5CH{=}CHCOC_6H_5 \xrightarrow{Br_2}$$

$$C_6H_5CHBrCHBrCOC_6H_5 \xrightarrow[\text{then HCl}]{NaOCH_3} C_6H_5COCH_2COC_6H_5$$

though the over-all yield of dibenzoylmethane is satisfactory,[66] the writers prefer the direct acylation of acetophenone with ethyl benzoate since the reaction can be carried out in much less time. However, the indirect method is applicable to the preparation of nitro-substituted dibenzoylmethanes,[67] which have not thus far been made satisfactorily by the acylation of ketones.

Other indirect ways for preparing β-diketones include the hydration of acetylenic methyl ketones [68] or certain diacetylenic compounds [69] and the self-condensation of anhydrides (see p. 101) or acetyl chloride.[70a]

Synthesis of β-Diketones of the Type RCOCH(R′)COR″

β-Diketones of this type where R′ is an alkyl group are usually prepared by the alkylation of unsubstituted β-diketones such as acetylacetone.[6, 71] However, the acylation of methylene ketones may be

$$RX + \overset{+}{Na}[CH_3COCHCOCH_3]^- \rightarrow CH_3COCHRCOCH_3 + NaX$$

preferred for the synthesis of certain of these β-diketones. The boron trifluoride method of acylation with aliphatic anhydrides is applicable not only to the acylation of methylene ketones such as diethyl ketone but also to methyl ethyl ketone, higher aliphatic methyl n-alkyl ketones, and methyl benzyl ketone, which are acylated preferentially at the α-methylene group. The acylation of methyl benzyl ketone forms $RCOCH(C_6H_5)COCH_3$, which cannot be prepared from the unsubstituted β-diketone. Moreover, the acylation of cyclic methylene ketones such as cyclohexanone forms β-diketones such as acetylcyclohexanone (see p. 102) or benzoylcyclohexanone (see p. 78) for which the simple alkylation procedure is not applicable. Acylcyclohexanones may be prepared by the cyclization of esters of ϵ-acylcaproic acids (ζ-keto esters, p. 82), but the acylation of cyclohexanone usually is to be preferred.

[66] Allen, Abell, and Normington, *Org. Syntheses, Coll. Vol.* **1**, 1941, p. 205.

[67] Barnes and Snead, *J. Am. Chem. Soc.*, **67**, 138 (1945).

[68] Moureu and Delange, *Compt. rend.*, **131**, 710 (1900).

[69] Dupont, *Compt. rend.*, **148**, 1522 (1909).

[70] (a) Combes, *Ann. chim. phys.*, [6] **12**, 207 (1887); (b) Gustavson, *J. prakt. Chem.*, **37**, 108 (1888).

[71] Adkins, Kutz, and Coffman, *J. Am. Chem. Soc.*, **52**, 3212 (1930).

Certain ϵ-acylcaproic acids can be prepared conveniently by the alkaline cleavage of acylcyclohexanones in which the ring carbonyl group reacts preferentially,[72] for example:

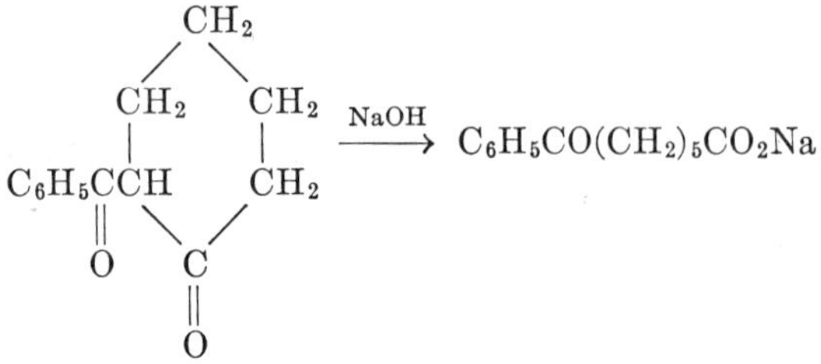

$$
\begin{array}{c}
\quad\quad CH_2 \\
\quad\diagup\quad\diagdown \\
CH_2\quad\quad CH_2 \\
|\quad\quad\quad| \\
C_6H_5CCH\quad\quad CH_2 \\
\|\quad\diagdown\quad\diagup \\
O\quad\quad C \\
\quad\quad\| \\
\quad\quad O
\end{array}
\xrightarrow{\text{NaOH}}
C_6H_5CO(CH_2)_5CO_2Na
$$

Although the benzoylation of the sodium derivative of p-methoxypropiophenone with ethyl benzoate apparently failed to yield the expected β-diketone,[73] benzoylation of the sodium derivative of propiophenone with phenyl benzoate has been shown to yield methyldibenzoylmethane.[13]

Synthesis of β-Diketones of the Type RCOC(R′)(R″)COR‴

β-Diketones of this type in which R″ is an alkyl group have been prepared by the alkylation of monosubstituted β-diketones such as monosubstituted acetylacetones.[71] Certain β-diketones of this type may be

$$RX + \overset{+}{Na}[CH_3COCR'COCH_3]^- \rightarrow CH_3COCRR'COCH_3 + NaX$$

prepared by the acylation of the methinyl group of ketones by the boron trifluoride method, but the yields have been low (see p. 103).

Synthesis of α,γ-Diketo Esters

These compounds are usually prepared by the acylation of ketones with oxalic esters (p. 84).

Synthesis of β-Keto Aldehydes

These compounds are generally prepared by the acylation of ketones with formic esters (p. 87). They might also be prepared by the acylation of aldehydes; this method has been successful with diphenylacetaldehyde.[74]

$$C_6H_5COCl + (C_6H_5)_2CHCHO \xrightarrow{(C_6H_5)_3CNa} C_6H_5COC(C_6H_5)_2CHO + NaCl$$

[72] Hauser, Swamer, and Ringler, *J. Am. Chem. Soc.*, **70**, 4023 (1948).
[73] Bickel, *J. Am. Chem. Soc.*, **67**, 2045 (1945).
[74] Schlenck, Hilleman, and Rodloff, *Ann.*, **487**, 135 (1931).

EXPERIMENTAL PROCEDURES

Condensation by Basic Reagents

Choice of Basic Reagent. Sodium ethoxide, sodium methoxide, metallic sodium, sodium amide, and sodium hydride have been employed most widely (see Tables VIII–XV). When the yield of β-diketone is satisfactory, sodium ethoxide or sodium methoxide * usually would be chosen, since they are less hazardous to use than metallic sodium [6] or sodium hydride [20] and they are less likely to produce side-reaction products than metallic sodium [6] or sodium amide.[2] Moreover, because half of the sodium alkoxide used is regenerated in the second step of the condensation (equation 2, p. 63), only one mole of this reagent may be required for each mole of ketone, whereas two moles of metallic sodium,[6, 71] sodium amide,[2] or sodium hydride [20] appear to be required under the conditions generally employed.† This may be illustrated by the following balanced equations with sodium ethoxide and sodium amide.

$$CH_3CO_2C_2H_5 + CH_3COR + NaOC_2H_5 \rightarrow$$

$$Na[CH_3COCHCOR]^- + 2C_2H_5OH$$

$$CH_3CO_2C_2H_5 + CH_3COR + 2NaNH_2 \rightarrow$$

$$Na[CH_3COCHCOR]^- + 2NH_3 + NaOC_2H_5$$

However, the yield of β-diketone is often much better with metallic sodium, sodium amide, lithium amide, or sodium hydride than with the sodium alkoxides. In such cases the writers generally have preferred sodium amide or sodium hydride, since the yield is usually better and the reaction can be carried out more conveniently. Sodium amide may be chosen even when the yield is equally good with sodium ethoxide because the reaction can be effected in less time.[2] Sodium hydride may sometimes be preferred, although it is somewhat hazardous to handle.[20]

For the preparation of the sodium and potassium derivatives of ketones, sodium and potassium amides or triphenylmethides are particularly suitable. The metallic derivatives of ketones may be acylated not only with ethyl or methyl esters but also with phenyl esters, acid chlorides, and other acylating agents.

* The sodium alkoxide employed usually corresponds to the alkoxyl group of the ester but this is not necessary.

† Of course the sodium alkoxide produced in the reaction mixture when metallic sodium, sodium amide, or sodium hydride is used should be capable of condensing another mole of ketone and ester in reactions in which sodium alkoxide is *an effective condensing agent*.

In special cases, certain other basic reagents may be chosen. Thus, with sufficiently hindered ketones, ethylmagnesium bromide may be preferred; with o-hydroxyacetophenones or related ketones in the Kostanecki reaction, tertiary amines or the sodium or potassium salts of carboxylic acids appear especially suitable.

Choice of Ester and Ketone. Since the alkoxy portion of the ester is eliminated in the formation of the β-diketone, various esters of a particular acid may be used. The ethyl ester has usually been employed, but, if equally available, the more reactive methyl ester may be preferable. When even the methyl ester fails to produce satisfactory yields, the still more reactive phenyl ester is recommended. However, the phenol formed as a by-product with phenyl esters is sometimes difficult to remove from the β-diketone.

A number of β-diketones can be prepared from two different ester-ketone combinations. For example, propionylacetone may be synthesized either from ethyl propionate and acetone or from ethyl acetate and methyl ethyl ketone in the presence of sodium amide. The choice would

$$\begin{array}{c} \text{C}_2\text{H}_5\text{CO}_2\text{C}_2\text{H}_5 + \text{CH}_3\text{COCH}_3 \xrightarrow{(60\%)} \\ \qquad\qquad\qquad\qquad\qquad\qquad \xrightarrow{\text{NaNH}_2} \text{C}_2\text{H}_5\text{COCH}_2\text{COCH}_3 \\ \text{CH}_3\text{CO}_2\text{C}_2\text{H}_5 + \text{CH}_3\text{COC}_2\text{H}_5 \xrightarrow[(40\%)]{} \qquad + \text{C}_2\text{H}_5\text{OH} \end{array}$$

be determined by the yield of β-diketone and by the availability of the esters and ketones.

Selection of Experimental Conditions. In general, the ester, the ketone, and the basic condensing agent are allowed to react, often in the presence of an inert solvent. After an appropriate period, the mixture is cooled and acidified. The β-diketone may be isolated by the usual technique of distillation or filtration, but often it is isolated as its copper derivative [74a] from which the β-diketone may be regenerated readily. The ketone and the ester should be pure and dry. The apparatus should be clean and dry and protected from atmospheric moisture. A suitable apparatus consists of a three-necked round-bottomed flask, a reflux condenser, and a sealed stirrer.

In most of the reactions with sodium alkoxide, either the ester has been stirred with the alkoxide and the ketone then added, or a mixture of the ester and the ketone has been added to the reagent. Sometimes the reaction has been carried out under nitrogen. The sodium alkoxide should be of good quality. In general, alcohol-free sodium alkoxide

---

[74a] These copper derivatives are probably chelate structures consisting of two molecules of β-diketone to one copper atom; Claisen, *Ber.*, **22**, 1009 (1889). The copper chelates of β-diketones of the type RCOCH₂COR′ are usually blue (purple when R or R′ is t-butyl), whereas those of β-diketones of the type RCOCHR′COR″ usually are gray.[2,12]

should be employed. However, acylations with oxalic or formic esters often can be carried out satisfactorily in the presence of alcohol.

Generally one mole of sodium alkoxide is employed to one of ketone and at least one of ester. In acetylations, a considerable excess of ethyl acetate is frequently used as a solvent.[6] Forcing conditions, involving the removal by distillation of the alcohol formed during the reaction, may be selected if the yield is low under ordinary conditions (see pp. 64, 116). However, forcing conditions are feasible only when the alcohol boils sufficiently lower than the ester and the ketone employed. The use of sodium alkoxides often permits the β-diketones to be isolated satisfactorily without making the copper derivative.[6]

In the reactions with sodium, the metal has generally been added in the form of powder, wire, or small pieces to a cooled mixture of the ester and ketone. A nitrogen atmosphere is desirable. When relatively large amounts of sodium are used, the reaction may get out of control if the sodium is added too rapidly. The best yields are obtained using two gram atoms of sodium to one of ketone and at least one of ester;[6, 71] excess ester is often employed. One of the writers (F. W. S.) has found that the acylation of certain ketones with higher-molecular-weight esters may sometimes be facilitated by the addition of a small amount of alcohol (which apparently merely cleans the surface of the sodium). Because side reactions may occur in the presence of sodium, isolation of the β-diketone as the copper derivative may be advantageous.[6]

In most of the early experiments with sodium amide, either a mixture[75] of ketone and ester was added to the sodium amide (suspended in ether or another inert solvent) or dry powdered sodium amide was added to a mixture of ketone and ester. The writers prefer to add the ketone to an ether suspension of sodium amide (contained in the flask in which it is prepared) and then to add the ester.[2] In this way the ketone is first converted to its sodium derivative which is the reactive intermediate in the condensation. In order to minimize the self-condensation of the ketone, the ester should be added to the sodium derivative of the ketone within a few minutes after its preparation.[14] The proportions of reactants, especially those of sodium amide and ketone, are important. The use of two molecular equivalents of sodium amide to one of ketone (and at least one of ester) often has given yields of β-diketones twice as large as those obtained using equivalent amounts of sodium amide and ketone.[2] With the latter proportions, the maximum yield based on the ketone appears to be 50%,* since half of the ketone is regenerated

---

[75] Fischer and Orth, *Die Chemie des Pyrrols*, Band I, Akademische Verlagsgesellschaft, 1934. (a) pp. 402ff.; (b) p. 311.

* In certain reactions, yields greater than 50% may be obtained if the ethoxide ion formed during the reaction also effects some of the condensation.[2]

(see p. 63). The influence of excess ester on the yields is much less pronounced.[2]

In acylations with sodium amide two sets of proportions of reactants are recommended, depending on whether the yield is to be based on the ketone or on the ester. When the yield is to be based on the ketone, the use of two equivalents of sodium amide to one of ketone and at least one of ester, designated method A, is recommended; when the yield is to be based on the ester, the use of two equivalents each of sodium amide and ketone to one of ester, designated method B, is recommended.[14] In method A, two equivalents of ester have generally been employed, but, when the ester as well as the ketone is expensive, the use of only one equivalent (or slightly more) of the ester may be advantageous.[2, 14] The use of equivalent amounts of all three reactants does not appear to be advantageous, although these proportions may be employed.[2] Because side reactions may occur with sodium amide, the β-diketone usually has been isolated as its copper derivative.[2] However, when method B is employed, it sometimes suffices to purify liquid β-diketones by fractional distillation.   Benzoylcyclohexanone and certain related β-diketones, which form copper derivatives only with difficulty, may be isolated satisfactorily (even when method A is employed) by pouring the reaction mixture into water and isolating the β-diketone from the aqueous solution of its sodium salt (see p. 123).   However, this procedure is not satisfactory with many β-diketones, such as n-butyrylisovalerylmethane, dibenzoylmethane, and lauroylacetone, apparently because their sodium salts are partly soluble in ether.[76]

When sodium hydride is employed as the condensing agent, it is usually suspended in the ester, and the ketone is added slowly to the stirred reaction mixture in an atmosphere of nitrogen. Since sodium hydride may take fire on contact with moist air, precautions should be observed in handling the reagent. The use of two molecular equivalents of sodium hydride to one of ketone and at least one of ester (method A) is recommended when the yield is to be based on the ketone, whereas the use of two equivalents each of sodium hydride and ketone to one of ester (method B) is recommended when the yield is to be based on the ester.[25] In method A, two or more equivalents of ester usually are employed; 60–80% of the excess ester ordinarily can be recovered. However, when the ester and the ketone are expensive, it may be advantageous to use only one equivalent of the ester.[25] Excess ester may serve as the solvent, or inert solvents such as ether, benzene, or xylene may be employed. Since hydrogen is evolved during the acylation, the progress of

---

[76] Swamer and Hauser, unpublished results.

the reaction can be followed conveniently by passing the gas through a gas meter. The reaction may be initiated by the addition of a few drops of absolute ethanol or methanol which activates the sodium hydride. The use of sodium hydride often permits the isolation of the β-diketone without making the copper derivative.

Procedures Using Sodium Ethoxide

The preparation of ethanol-free sodium ethoxide is described in *Organic Syntheses* [77] and *Organic Reactions.*[1] Adaptations of these methods are described in connection with the following procedures.

Acylation of Methyl Ketones with Ethyl Acetate, Ethyl Furoate, or Ethyl Tetrahydrofuroate. The acylation of acetone with ethyl acetate to form acetylacetone in 38–45% yield is described in *Organic Syntheses.*[77] Various acylations (Table I) have been effected by the following general procedure.[6]

The sodium ethoxide (prepared from equimolecular amounts of powdered sodium and ethanol in ether or xylene),[1] the ester, and the solvent (diisopropyl ether or toluene) are stirred for fifteen to twenty minutes and then cooled in an ice bath. The ketone is added slowly over a period of one-half to one hour. The ice bath is removed frequently at first to make sure that condensation, as evidenced by the evolution of heat or the disappearance of sodium ethoxide, has begun. After all the ketone has been added, the reaction mixture is stirred for two to three hours in the ice bath and then allowed to stand at room temperature for twelve to sixteen hours. The mixture is then cooled in an ice bath, and an equal volume (or more, if the solid does not dissolve) of ice water is added. The aqueous and organic layers are separated and washed two or three times with ether and water, respectively. The combined aqueous layers are acidified with 65 ml. of glacial acetic acid per mole of sodium ethoxide used in the condensation.* If the diketone is a solid, it is filtered from the acid solution and recrystallized. If it is a liquid, it is extracted with ether, and the water layer is extracted three or four times with ether. The combined ether extracts are washed with water and two or three portions of saturated sodium bicarbonate solution. After drying over calcium chloride and removing the ether, the products are fractionated.

[77] Adkins and Rainey, *Org. Syntheses,* **20,** 7 (1940).

* The condensation also may be carried out [6] under reflux by adding the ketone during fifteen to thirty minutes to the ester-sodium ethoxide-solvent mixture without cooling. The reaction mixture is then heated under reflux on a steam bath for two to five hours and worked up after cooling.

Yields, moles of reactants, and boiling points of products are given in Table I.

TABLE I

ACYLATION OF KETONES WITH ETHYL ESTERS IN THE PRESENCE OF SODIUM ETHOXIDE [6]

Ester (moles)	Ketone (moles)	Moles of NaOC$_2$H$_5$	Product	Yield %	Boiling Point
Acetate (3)	Methyl isopropyl (1)	1	Isobutyrylacetone	40	161–164
Acetate (8)	Methyl isobutyl (4)	4	Isovalerylacetone	60	71–76/18
Acetate (4)	Acetophenone (2)	2	Benzoylacetone	65–70	134–136/16
Acetate (1.5)	Acetomesitylene (0.5)	0.5	Mesitoylacetone	70	143–146/8
Acetate (7)	p-Phenylacetophenone (0.5)	0.5	p-Phenylbenzoylacetone	50	156–157 (m.p.)
Furoate (2)	Acetone (2)	2	Furoylacetone	40–45	107–110/10
Furoate (1)	Acetophenone (1)	1	Furoylbenzoylmethane	55	160–165/3 (m.p. 68)
Tetrahydrofuroate (0.4)	Acetone (0.4)	0.4	Tetrahydrofuroylacetone	60	95–97/8

Dibenzoylmethane (Acylation of Acetophenone with Ethyl Benzoate under Forcing Conditions). The preparation of dibenzoylmethane in 62–71% yield from acetophenone and ethyl benzoate is described in *Organic Syntheses*.[78] The procedure should be applicable to other acylations when the boiling points of the ester and ketone are sufficiently higher than that of the alcohol distilled during the reaction.

Acylation of Methyl Ketones with Ethyl Nicotinate.[15] One-half mole of powdered sodium and 0.5 mole of absolute ethanol are allowed to react in ether for several hours with stirring in a 1-l. three-necked flask fitted with a dropping funnel, a reflux condenser, and a stirrer.[77] The ether is removed by distillation, and 100–150 ml. of xylene and 0.5 mole of ethyl nicotinate are added to the sodium ethoxide. One and two-tenths moles of the ketone is added slowly at such a rate that the temperature of the reaction mixture remains between 45° and 60°. The mixture is stirred without heating for one hour after the addition of the ketone; then the flask is heated on a steam bath with stirring for one to four hours. The reflux condenser is replaced by a fractionating column, and 30 to 40 ml. of ethanol and xylene is distilled. [This last step is omitted in the preparation of nicotinylacetylmethane (see Table II) because an excess of acetone (2 moles) is used.] The reaction mixture is cooled with ice, and enough water (150–200 ml.) is added to dissolve the salt of the diketone. The mixture is extracted twice with 60-ml. portions of ether and acidified with glacial acetic acid. A saturated solution of sodium carbonate is added until the mixture is basic to litmus. The diketone is taken up with ether, and the aqueous portion is extracted once with ether. The combined extracts are dried over anhydrous sodium sulfate and distilled

[78] Magnani and McElvain, *Org. Syntheses*, **20**, 32 (1940).

under reduced pressure in an ordinary Claisen distilling flask. (Nicotinylbenzoylmethane and dinicotinylmethane are not soluble in ether; consequently they are filtered from the aqueous solution and purified by crystallization from 95% ethanol.)

The procedure for dissolving the sodium salt of the diketone in water is modified in the preparation of nicotinylbenzoylmethane. One-half of the sodium salt of this diketone is partially dissolved by the addition of 200 ml. of water. The mixture is acidified with glacial acetic acid and stirred for twenty minutes. Sodium carbonate solution is then added until the mixture is basic to litmus, after which the solid is separated by filtration and recrystallized from 95% ethanol.

Yields, boiling points, and melting points of the products are given in Table II.

TABLE II

Acylation of Ketones with Ethyl Nicotinate in the Presence of Sodium Ethoxide [15]

Ketone	Product	Yield %	Boiling Point	Melting Point
Acetone	Nicotinylacetylmethane	63	134–135/6	83.5
Methyl n-butyl	Nicotinyl-n-valerylmethane	46	165–168/8	
Methyl isobutyl	Nicotinylisovalerylmethane	70	134–135/3	44
Methyl t-butyl	Nicotinyltrimethylacetylmethane	42	135–136/5	44.5
Methyl n-amyl	Nicotinyl-n-caproylmethane	47	150–152/2	29.5
Acetophenone	Nicotinylbenzoylmethane	70	198–200/3	121.5
Acetomesitylene	Nicotinylmesitoylmethane	60	186–190/1	47.8
Methyl 3-pyridyl	Dinicotinylmethane	51		198

4-Carbethoxy-5,5-dimethylcyclohexane-1,3-dione (Intramolecular Cyclization Accompanying a Michael Condensation).[79] The cyclization of ethyl α-carbethoxy-β,β-dimethyl-γ-acetylbutyrate, obtained from mesityl oxide and ethyl malonate, to form 4-carbethoxy-5,5-dimethylcyclohexane-1,3-dione in 65% yield is described in *Organic Syntheses*. The crude product is converted to 5,5-dimethylcyclohexane-1,3-dione.

Mono- and Di-acylation of Ketones with Ethyl Oxalate. Acylation of acetone with ethyl oxalate to form ethyl acetopyruvate [80] or diethoxalylacetone (not isolated) [81] and of cyclohexanone with ethyl oxalate to form ethyl cyclohexanone-2-glyoxalate [82] is described in *Organic Syntheses*. The acylation of methyl ethyl ketone with ethyl oxalate to form ethyl propionylpyruvate [83] is described below.*

---

[79] Shriner and Todd, *Org. Syntheses, Coll. Vol.* **2**, 200 (1943).
[80] Marvel and Dreger, *Org. Syntheses, Coll. Vol.* **1**, 238 (1941).
[81] Riegel and Zwilgmeyer, *Org. Syntheses, Coll. Vol.* **2**, 126 (1943).
[82] Snyder, Brooks, and Shapiro, *Org. Syntheses, Coll. Vol.* **2**, 531 (1943).
[83] Diels, Sielisch, and Muller, *Ber.*, **39**, 1328 (1906).
* The procedure was checked by M. S. Bloom in this laboratory.

In a 500-ml. round-bottomed flask fitted with a reflux condenser, a mercury-sealed stirrer, and a dropping funnel is placed 280 ml. of absolute ethanol, and 12.5 g. (0.54 mole) of sodium is added gradually. After cooling the sodium ethoxide solution with an ice bath, a mixture of 73 g. (0.5 mole) of ethyl oxalate and 36 g. (0.5 mole) of methyl ethyl ketone is added in thirty-five minutes. Stirring is continued for one hour, and the reaction mixture is left overnight, during which time a considerable amount of the sodium salt of the condensation product precipitates. Most of the ethanol is distilled, and the residue is treated with 150 ml. of water and 100 g. of cracked ice. A mixture of ice and 20 ml. of concentrated sulfuric acid is added with stirring, and the resulting clear solution is extracted four times with 60-ml. portions of benzene. The benzene solution is dried over Drierite, and, after removing the benzene, the residue is distilled in vacuum. Ethyl propionylpyruvate, b.p. 87–90°/2 mm., is obtained in a yield of 45 g. (52%).

Ethyl 2-Methylcyclopentane-1,3,4-trione-5-glyoxalate (Acylation of Methyl Ethyl Ketone with Ethyl Oxalate Accompanied by Cyclization).[84] To an ice-cold solution of sodium ethoxide prepared from 23 g. (1 mole) of sodium and 315 ml. of absolute ethanol there is added with good stirring and cooling a cold solution of 36 g. (0.5 mole) of methyl ethyl ketone and 160 g. (1.1 moles) of ethyl oxalate. The addition takes about fifteen minutes, and the color of the reaction mixture changes from light yellow to orange red. The mixture is allowed to come to room temperature with stirring. It is then heated under reflux for half an hour, cooled, and decomposed with 55 ml. of 1:1 sulfuric acid. The sodium sulfate is filtered and washed with ethanol; the filtrate and washings are concentrated under reduced pressure (water pump) to about 100 ml. and cooled in an ice bath. The solid which precipitates is filtered, washed with several small quantities of ice water, and allowed to dry in air. The light-brown powder so obtained is dissolved in ethyl acetate, treated with decolorizing carbon (Norite), filtered, and the filtrate concentrated. The yield of yellow needles of ethyl 2-methylcyclopentane-1,3,4-trione-5-glyoxalate, m.p. 160–163°, is 40–43 g. (35–38%).

Procedures Using Sodium Methoxide

The preparation of methanol-free sodium methoxide is described in *Organic Reactions*.[1] The reagent also can be prepared * by dissolving the appropriate amount of sodium in absolute methanol and evaporating the solution to dryness at 100° under reduced pressure (water pump). The solid residue is then heated at 200° for one-half hour at the water

[84] Orchin and Butz, *J. Am. Chem. Soc.*, **65**, 2298 (1943).
  * Private communication from Dr. W. S. Johnson, University of Wisconsin.

pump and finally for one-half hour at about 1 mm. The flask (still under reduced pressure) is then cooled, and the residue powdered by striking the flask against the palm of the hand. Dry nitrogen or air then is admitted to the flask

Commercial (Mathieson) * sodium methoxide appears to be satisfactory for certain acylations.

Acylation of Cyclic Methylene Ketones with Ethyl Formate. *A. 2-Hydroxymethylene-5-methoxy-1-hydrindone.*[85] A solution of sodium methoxide prepared from 0.74 g. (0.032 mole) of sodium and 10 ml. of methanol is evaporated to dryness at 200°, finally under reduced pressure. The colorless cake of sodium methoxide is powdered (see above), a solution of 2.38 g. (0.032 mole) of ethyl formate in 16 ml. of dry benzene is added, and the system is evacuated and filled with nitrogen. To the cooled mixture is added with swirling a solution of 2.60 g. (0.016 mole) of 5-methoxy-1-hydrindone in 20 ml. of dry benzene. A precipitate that is tinged pink gradually forms. After keeping the reaction mixture slightly below room temperature for four to five hours, it is hydrolyzed with cold water, and a few milliliters of ether is added to minimize emulsion formation. The organic layer is washed once with water and once with dilute sodium hydroxide. The aqueous portions are combined, washed with ether, and acidified with ice and hydrochloric acid. Almost pure 2-hydroxymethylene-5-methoxy-1-hydrindone precipitates; yield 2.98 g. (98%), m.p. 136.5–138°. On recrystallization from benzene the pure product is obtained as almost colorless plates, m.p. 138–138.5° (dec.), which give an intense purple color with ferric chloride.

This procedure has been successful also with certain other cyclic methylene ketones including one which has served as the starting material in a recent synthesis of equilenin.[86]

B. 2-Hydroxymethylene-1-keto-1,2,3,4-tetrahydrophenanthrene.[87] A 1-l. round-bottomed flask is charged with 13.5 g. (0.25 mole) of commercial (Mathieson) powdered sodium methoxide to which is added a solution of 18.52 g. (0.25 mole) of ethyl formate (dried over Drierite and distilled) in 250 ml. of dry benzene. The flask is stoppered, and the mixture cooled in an ice bath. A solution of 19.6 g. (0.1 mole) of 1-keto-1,2,3,4-tetrahydrophenanthrene (m.p. 95–96°) in 250 ml. of dry benzene is then added, and the stoppered flask is shaken vigorously to effect thorough mixing of reagents. The mixture is allowed to stand at room temperature with occasional swirling for five to seven hours during which period it gradually turns to a heavy pinkish yellow pasty sus-

---

* Mathieson Alkali Works, Niagara Falls, N. Y.

[85] Johnson, Anderson, and Shelberg, *J. Am. Chem. Soc.*, **66**, 220 (1944).

[86] Johnson, Petersen, and Gutsche, *J. Am. Chem. Soc.*, **69**, 2942 (1947).

[87] This procedure was furnished through the courtesy of Professor W. S. Johnson and Dr. R. W. Sharpe of the University of Wisconsin.

pension. (Standing for 36 hours did not affect the yield adversely.) Water is added, followed by a few milliliters of ether to minimize emulsion formation. The organic layer is separated and washed with water, followed by 10% sodium hydroxide solution. All the aqueous solutions are combined, washed once with ether, and acidified by pouring with stirring into a mixture of ice and 250 ml. of concentrated hydrochloric acid. The yellow hydroxymethylene ketone which precipitates is separated by suction filtration, washed thoroughly with water, and dried to constant weight in a vacuum desiccator at room temperature; yield, 21.8 g. (97%), m.p. 83.5–84.5° (cor.). Recrystallization from dilute ethanol does not raise the melting point appreciably. The product gives an intense purple-brown color with aqueous ferric chloride.

Procedures Using Sodium

The acylation of o-hydroxyacetophenone with ethyl propionate and sodium to form o-hydroxybenzoylpropionylmethane is described in *Organic Syntheses*.[88] The crude product was converted to 2-ethylchromone. The acylation of a variety of methyl ketones with ethyl acetate and sodium has been described in detail.[6] The quantities of reagents, yields, and boiling points of the products are given in Table III.

TABLE III

ACYLATION OF METHYL KETONES WITH ETHYL ACETATE IN THE PRESENCE
OF SODIUM [6]

Ketone (moles)	Moles of Ethyl Acetate	Gram Atoms of Sodium	Product	Yield %	Boiling Point
Acetone (2)	12	4	Acetylacetone	58	133–136
Methyl ethyl (2)	12	4	Propionylacetone	35	154–157
Methyl n-propyl (2)	12	4	Butyrylacetone	45	87–90/38
Methyl isopropyl (0.5)	3 *	1	Isobutyrylacetone	54	160–162.5
Methyl n-butyl (2)	12	4	n-Valerylacetone	56–62	79–81/17
Methyl sec-butyl (2)	12	4	5-Methylheptane-2,4-dione	47	96–100/45
Methyl isobutyl (2)	12	4	Isovalerylacetone	64	74–77/17
Methyl cyclohexyl (0.25)	2.5 *	0.5	Hexahydrobenzoylacetone	50	101–105/7
Acetophenone (2)	12	4	Benzoylacetone	65	59–60 (m.p.)

* Diisopropyl ether or toluene was used as the solvent.

3-Hydroxymethylenecamphor.* In a 2-l. three-necked flask fitted with a reflux condenser, a mechanical stirrer, and a dropping funnel, 31 g.

[88] Mozingo, *Org. Syntheses*, **21**, 42 (1941).

* This procedure was furnished through the courtesy of Professor Mary L. Sherrill and Miss Betty W. Alden of Mount Holyoke College. Their work was done under a contract recommended by the Committee on Medical Research between the Office of Scientific Research and Development and Mount Holyoke College.

(1.35 gram atoms) of powdered sodium is covered with 150 ml. of anhydrous ether. A solution of 200 g. (1.31 moles) of $(+,-)$-camphor or $(+)$-camphor dissolved in 600 ml. of anhydrous ether is added at a rate which keeps the ether refluxing gently. If the addition is too rapid, it is necessary to cool the reaction flask in an ice bath. As soon as refluxing ceases, 175 ml. (153 g., 1.31 moles) of isoamyl formate is added through the dropping funnel sufficiently rapidly to maintain refluxing. The mixture is stirred during the addition, which requires two to two and a half hours. A yellowish white solid is gradually formed in the yellow-orange solution. After all the sodium has reacted and the reaction appears to be complete, the mixture is stirred for an additional hour and left overnight.

The pasty solid and solution are then stirred into 1 l. of ice and water, the ether layer is separated, and the water layer is extracted three times with 50-ml. portions of ether.* The dissolved ether is removed by passing a current of air through the solution of the sodium salt of hydroxymethylenecamphor for three or four hours.† Approximately 350 ml. of 30% acetic acid is added with stirring until the solution is acid. A creamy white powder precipitates, which becomes somewhat crystalline on standing. This crude product, collected on a suction filter and dried, melts at 78–80°. It is steam distilled, and the hydroxymethylenecamphor forms white plates in the distillate. The racemic 3-hydroxymethylenecamphor, m.p. 80–81° (cor.), is obtained in 70–80 g. yield (30–35% based on the camphor used). The $(+)$-hydroxymethylenecamphor, m.p. 81–82° (cor.), is obtained in 75–80 g. yield (32–35%). A mixture of the two forms melts at 80–81° (cor.). The $(+)$-form on standing in the air for some days or rapidly in vacuum over sulfuric acid becomes yellow and forms a surface layer of gummy material. The racemic form undergoes the same changes somewhat more slowly.

Procedures Using Sodium Amide

Anhydrous powdered sodium amide may be prepared from gaseous ammonia and molten sodium in large batches,[89] or it can be obtained commercially.‡ The authors prefer to make sodium amide from liquid ammonia and sodium as it is needed for a reaction. Details of this

---

* It is advisable to extract with sufficient ether to remove any unreacted camphor or borneol.

† The complete removal of dissolved ether from the solution of the sodium salt of the hydroxymethylenecamphor prior to acidification is important if the best quality of crude product is to be obtained. In one preparation the air was passed through pyrogallol before it was passed through the solution, but the quality of the product was not noticeably improved.

[89] Bergstrom, *Org. Syntheses*, **20**, 86 (1940); *Inorg. Syntheses*, **I**, 74 (1939).

‡ Certain samples of commercial sodium amide have been found dangerous to handle.

method of preparation are given below in the general procedure for the use of sodium amide in acylating ketones.

Acylation of Various Ketones with Various Esters. The acylation of acetophenone with ethyl acetate to form benzoylacetone is described in the laboratory manual of Cumming, Hopper, and Wheeler.[90] Various acylations are effected by the following general procedure [2, 13, 14] using the proportions of reactants designated in methods A and B (p. 114).

In a 500-ml. three-necked round-bottomed flask having ground-glass joints and equipped with a mercury-sealed stirrer, a removable glass plug, and a reflux condenser with a soda-lime tube, is placed 300 ml. of commercial anhydrous liquid ammonia. A minimum amount of sodium is added to the stirred solution to produce a permanent blue color. A few crystals of ferric nitrate (to catalyze the conversion of sodium to sodium amide) are added, followed by 0.6 mole (13.8 g.) of clean sodium metal cut in small pieces. When the sodium has been converted completely to sodium amide (as indicated by the change from a blue solution to a gray suspension), the ammonia is evaporated by means of a steam bath, sufficient anhydrous ether being added through a dropping funnel so that the volume of the liquid remains at approximately 300 ml. After practically all the ammonia has evaporated (indicated by the refluxing of the ether) the suspension of sodium amide is stirred and heated under reflux for a few minutes and then cooled to room temperature. The procedure thus far may be carried out in one hour.

To the stirred ether suspension of the sodium amide (approximately 0.6 mole) is added during five to ten minutes a solution of the ketone (0.3 mole in method A; 0.6 mole in method B) in 50 ml. of absolute ether. After about five minutes a solution of the ester (0.6 mole in method A; 0.3 mole in method B) in 50 ml. of absolute ether is added, and the stirring continued for two hours while the mixture is heated under reflux on the steam bath. A gelatinous precipitate of the sodium salt of the β-diketone is usually formed.

Generally [2, 14] the reaction mixture is poured into a mixture of 300 g. of crushed ice and a slight excess (over the sodium amide used) of hydrochloric acid. After shaking the mixture, the ether phase is separated, washed with sodium bicarbonate solution followed by water, and the solvent distilled. To the residue dissolved in an equal volume of methanol is added a hot filtered solution of 40 g. of copper acetate in 350 ml. of water, and the mixture is allowed to stand until it has cooled to room temperature. The copper salt of the β-diketone is collected on a Büchner funnel, sucked dry in air, washed with 100 ml. of ligroin (b.p. 30–60°), and again sucked dry. The copper salt is shaken with 500 ml. of 10%

[90] Cumming, Hopper, and Wheeler, *Systematic Organic Chemistry*, 3rd ed., pp. 96–98, Van Nostrand Co., 1937.

sulfuric acid and 200 ml. of ether until the salt is completely decomposed. The aqueous acid layer is again extracted with ether. The combined ether extracts are washed with sodium bicarbonate solution and dried over sodium sulfate. The solvent is distilled, and the residue is crystallized or fractionated under reduced pressure.

When method B is employed, certain liquid β-diketones may be isolated satisfactorily merely by drying the washed ether solution obtained as described above, distilling the solvent, and fractionating the residue. This procedure is satisfactory for the preparation of n-butyryl-isovalerylmethane from ethyl n-butyrate and methyl isobutyl ketone. However, dibenzoylmethane is not obtained pure by direct recrystallization of the product without first preparing the copper derivative.[76]

In the benzoylation of cyclohexanone, 1-tetralone, or 1-hydrindone with phenyl benzoate by method A or B,[13] the reaction mixture is poured carefully onto 200 g. of crushed ice and water, and the resulting mixture is shaken in a separatory funnel until all the solid has dissolved; in the experiments with tetralone and hydrindone, more ice water (600 and 1300 ml., respectively) is added to effect solution. The cold aqueous phase containing the β-diketone, phenol, and some benzoic acid (as sodium salts), after washing with a little ether is acidified with ice-cold 10% hydrochloric acid, and the resulting mixture is extracted with ether. The combined ether extracts are washed with 5% sodium bicarbonate solution, then with water, dried over Drierite, and the solvent distilled, leaving a residue of β-diketone and phenol. In the preparation of benzoylcyclohexanone, the residue is placed in a small von Braun flask (having a short column) heated on a water bath and most of the phenol is removed by distillation at about 5 mm. pressure; the crude β-diketone remaining in the flask is recrystallized from dilute ethanol. With benzoylhydrindone, the residue is recrystallized from methanol, the phenol remaining in solution. With benzoyltetralone, the residue is ground with warm water in a mortar until most of the phenol is dissolved, and the crude β-diketone is filtered and recrystallized from ligroin (60–90°). The reaction mixture from the benzoylation of cyclohexanone with methyl benzoate is worked up in a similar manner except that the residue obtained on distilling the solvent from the dried ether solution is recrystallized from dilute ethanol.

In the benzoylation of propiophenone with phenyl benzoate by method A or B the reaction mixture is poured into ice and acid and extracted with ether. After washing the ether solution with cold 10% sodium hydroxide until free from phenol and then with water, the solvent is distilled and the residue recrystallized from ethanol.[13]

The yields and boiling points or melting points of β-diketones obtained by these procedures using methods A and B are given in Table IV.

TABLE IV

ACYLATION OF KETONES WITH ESTERS IN THE PRESENCE OF SODIUM AMIDE [2,13,14]

Ethyl Ester	Ketone	Method	Product	Yield %	Boiling Point
Acetate	Acetone	A	Acetylacetone	54	139–141/758
Acetate	Methyl n-propyl	A	n-Butyrylacetone	47	67.5–70/20
Acetate	Methyl isobutyl	A	Isovalerylacetone	59	76–77/19
Acetate	Methyl t-butyl	A	Pivaloylacetone	43	70–71/20
Acetate	Methyl n-amyl	A	Caproylacetone	61	103.5–105.5/20
Acetate	Diethyl	A	3-Methylhexane-2,4-dione	45 *	181–183/760
Acetate	Cyclohexanone	A	2-Acetylcyclohexanone	35	110–115/20
Propionate	Acetone	A	Propionylacetone	60	155–158/760
Propionate	Methyl ethyl	A	Dipropionylmethane	57	78–80/30
Propionate	Methyl n-propyl	A	Propionyl-n-butyrylmethane	70	84–86/20
Propionate	Acetophenone	A	Propionylacetophenone	55	124–127/5
n-Butyrate	Methyl ethyl	A	Propionyl-n-butyrylmethane	60 †	84–86/20
n-Butyrate	Methyl n-propyl	A	Di-n-butyrylmethane	76	101–102/20
n-Butyrate	Methyl isopropyl	A	n-Butyrylisobutyrylmethane	59	89–90.5/20
n-Butyrate	Methyl isobutyl	A	n-Butyrylisovalerylmethane	80 ‡	109–110/20
n-Butyrate	Acetophenone	A	n-Butyrylacetophenone	42	166–171/20
Isobutyrate	Acetone	A	Isobutyrylacetone	42	66–67/20
Isobutyrate	Acetone	B	Isobutyrylacetone	30	65–67/20
n-Valerate	Acetophenone	A	n-Valerylacetophenone	40	183–186/30
Isovalerate	Methyl isobutyl	A	Diisovalerylmethane	76	115–116/20

Ester	Ketone	Method	Product	Yield %	B.p./M.p.
Isovalerate	Methyl isobutyl	B	Diisovalerylmethane	75	115–116/20
n-Caproate	Methyl n-amyl	A	Di-n-caproylmethane	68	162–164/20
n-Caproate	Methyl n-amyl	B	Di-n-caproylmethane	60	162–164/20
Laurate	Acetone	A	Lauroylacetone	76	31.5–32 (m.p.)
Laurate	Acetone	B	Lauroylacetone	75	31.5–32 (m.p.)
Hexahydrobenzoate	Acetone	A	Hexahydrobenzoylacetone	62	130/20
Formate	Methyl t-butyl	A	Pivaloylacetaldehyde	50	43.5–45/13
Phenylacetate	Methyl ethyl	A	Phenylacetylpropionylmethane	54	160/20
Benzoate	Methyl ethyl	A	Propionylacetophenone	42	124.5–127/5
Benzoate	Methyl n-propyl	A	n-Butyrylacetophenone	38	166–171/20
Benzoate	Acetophenone	A	Dibenzoylmethane	70	77–78 (m.p.)
Anisate	Acetophenone	B	4-Methoxydibenzoylmethane	45	132 (m.p.)
Phenyl benzoate	Propiophenone	A	Methyldibenzoylmethane	53	83–84 (m.p.)
Phenyl benzoate	Cyclohexanone	A	2-Benzoylcyclohexanone	69	88–89 (m.p.)
Phenyl benzoate	Cyclohexanone	B	2-Benzoylcyclohexanone	62	88–89 (m.p.)
Phenyl benzoate	1-Hydrindone	A	2-Benzoyl-1-hydrindone	80	100–101 (m.p.)
Phenyl benzoate	1-Tetralone	A	2-Benzoyl-1-tetralone	46	75–77 (m.p.)

* This reaction was carried out at 0° for two hours.

† The yield reported is that of the copper derivative.

‡ Commercial lithium amide (Metalloy Corporation, Minneapolis, Minn.), which became available after this chapter was submitted, has been found to effect the acylation of methyl isobutyl ketone with ethyl n-butyrate in slightly lower yields than sodium amide. The ketone was added to a stirred ether suspension of lithium amide and the mixture refluxed for fifteen minutes. The ester was then added and refluxing was continued for two to three hours. The β-diketone was isolated as described for sodium amide.

Procedures Using Sodium Hydride

Sodium hydride may be prepared by the hydrogenation of fused metallic sodium.[20] Commercial (du Pont) * sodium hydride has been used in the acylations described below.

Acylation of Various Ketones with Various Esters.[25] The general procedure described below employs the proportions of reactants designated for methods A and B (see p. 114). The apparatus consists of a 1-l. three-necked round-bottomed flask fitted with a thermometer, a dropping funnel, a mercury-sealed stirrer, and a reflux condenser to which is attached a tube leading through a solid carbon dioxide-acetone trap to a wet-test gas meter.

The apparatus is thoroughly purged with dry nitrogen. In the reaction flask is placed 9.6 g. (0.4 mole) of commercial sodium hydride. *This reagent should be weighed and transferred rapidly to the flask; if the humidity is high, this operation should be carried out under dry nitrogen* (p. 111). The ester (0.4 mole in method A; 0.2 mole in method B) is added through the dropping funnel, the stirrer is started, and a catalytic amount (0.5 ml.) of absolute ethanol or methanol is added. After a few minutes (when some hydrogen has been evolved), the ketone (0.2 mole in method A; 0.4 mole in method B) in 50 ml. of dry ether is added during thirty to sixty minutes so that the reaction proceeds at a convenient rate. In acylations of acetone, the temperature of the reaction mixture is kept at 30–40° by occasional cooling in a solid carbon dioxide-xylene bath. *The reaction should definitely begin (as evidenced by the evolution of hydrogen) before much acetone is added; otherwise it may become too vigorous.* In acylations of higher ketones, the temperature of the reaction mixture is kept at 40–50° by gentle warming on an oil bath. After all the ketone has been added, the mixture is stirred at 40–50° until at least 80% of the theoretical amount of hydrogen has been evolved, sufficient dry ether being added to keep the mixture fluid and easily stirred. This generally requires about three hours in acylations of acetone and four to ten hours in acylations of higher ketones. The reaction mixture is cooled to room temperature or below, and sufficient dry ether is added to bring the total volume to about 400 ml. Unreacted sodium hydride is destroyed by adding 20–30 ml. of absolute ethanol and stirring the mixture until no more hydrogen is evolved. The mixture is cooled to about 10° and, while stirring and passing in a rapid stream of nitrogen, a mixture of 300 g. of ice and a slight excess of hydrochloric acid is added

* Electrochemicals Department, E. I. du Pont de Nemours and Co., Niagara Falls, N. Y. Sodium hydride is now produced by Metal Hydrides, Inc., Beverly, Mass.

TABLE V

ACYLATION OF KETONES WITH ESTERS IN THE PRESENCE OF SODIUM HYDRIDE

Ester	Ketone	Method	Product	Yield %	Boiling Point
Ethyl isobutyrate	Acetone	B	Isobutyrylacetone	41	63–64/19
Ethyl caproate	Acetone	A	Caproylacetone	80	101–103/19
Ethyl caproate	Acetone	B	Caproylacetone	65	101–103/19
Ethyl laurate	Acetone	B	Lauroylacetone	83	148–150/3
Methyl benzoate	Acetone	B	Benzoylacetone	66	60–61° (m.p.)
Ethyl propionate	Methyl ethyl	A	Dipropionylmethane	51 *	78–80/30
Ethyl acetate	Diethyl	A	3-Methylhexane-2,4-dione	60	181–184/760
Methyl benzoate	Methyl n-propyl	A	Benzoyl-n-butyrylmethane	31 *	168–171/20
Ethyl propionate	Methyl isobutyl	A	Propionylisovalerylmethane	75	91–93/19
Ethyl propionate	Methyl isobutyl	A †	Propionylisovalerylmethane	68	91–93/19
Ethyl isovalerate	Methyl isobutyl	A	Diisovalerylmethane	45 *	113–115/20
Ethyl acetate	Pinacolone	A	Pivaloylacetone	32 *	70–71/20
Ethyl n-valerate	Pinacolone	A	n-Valerylpivaloylmethane	22	114–118/20
Methyl benzoate	Acetophenone	A	Dibenzoylmethane	79 *	77–78° (m.p.)
Ethyl propionate	Cyclohexanone	A	α-Propionylcyclohexanone	29	124–125/20
Methyl benzoate	Cyclohexanone	A	α-Benzoylcyclohexanone	41	87–88° (m.p.)

* The product was isolated by the copper derivative procedure.
† In this experiment, 0.2 mole each of ketone and ester and 0.4 mole of sodium hydride were used.

all at once. After the solid has dissolved, the ether phase is separated and the aqueous phase is extracted with an additional 100 ml. of ether. The combined ether extracts are washed with sodium bicarbonate solution, then with water, and dried over Drierite. The solvent is distilled and the residue is either fractionated through a 25-cm. Vigreux column or treated with copper acetate as described in the procedure with sodium amide (p. 122). If the β-diketone is isolated by direct fractionation, a fraction of fairly wide boiling point (15–20°) is collected and redistilled; in this manner essentially pure β-diketone boiling over a narrow range (1–3°) is usually obtained. In general, the copper derivative procedure is recommended for the purification of solid β-diketones since they are often contaminated with high boiling residues.

Yields and boiling or melting points of β-diketones obtained by methods A and B are given in Table V.

Kostanecki Reaction

6-Methyl-2,3-diphenylchromone.* A mixture of 24 g. of 2-hydroxy-5-methyl-α-phenylacetophenone, 48 g. of benzoic anhydride, and 24 g. of sodium benzoate is heated in an oil bath at 180° for three hours. The mixture is cooled, refluxed for five minutes with 100 ml. of 10% sodium hydroxide solution and cooled again. The 6-methyl-2,3-diphenylchromone is collected on a filter and washed first with sodium hydroxide solution and then with water. After recrystallization from ethanol, 23 g. (70%) of light tan crystals melting at 170.5–172° is obtained.

7-Hydroxyflavone.[91]† A mixture of 5 g. of 2,4-dihydroxyacetophenone (resacetophenone), 30 g. of benzoic anhydride, and 6 g. of sodium benzoate is heated in an oil bath at 185–190° for four hours with occasional stirring. After cooling, the reaction mixture is pulverized and dissolved in 160 ml. of boiling ethanol. A solution of 18 g. of potassium hydroxide in 200 ml. of water is added, and the resulting mixture is heated under reflux for thirty minutes. The ethanol is then distilled, the residue is dissolved in water, and the solution is filtered. The product is precipitated from the alkaline solution by saturation with carbon dioxide. There is obtained 4.5 g. of crude product which, after two recrystallizations from a mixture of three parts of acetic acid and one part of water, gives 4.0 g. (50%) of light yellow crystals of 7-hydroxyflavone, m.p. 236–239°.

---

* This procedure was furnished through the courtesy of Professor R. L. Shriner.

[91] Robinson and Venkataraman, *J. Chem. Soc.*, **1926**, 2344.

† This procedure was checked by one of the authors (J. T. A.).

Acylation with Boron Trifluoride

Selection of Experimental Conditions. The general procedure involves the saturation of a stirred mixture of ketone and anhydride with boron trifluoride at approximately 0°. The saturation with this reagent and transfer of the reaction product should be carried out in a well-ventilated hood. The β-diketone is liberated from the coordination complex by heating the reaction mixture under reflux with an aqueous solution of two moles of sodium acetate per mole of anhydride. In many reactions the free β-diketone has been steam distilled from the sodium acetate solution.[51] However, steam distillation appears unnecessary in most cases.[52b] After the complex is decomposed, the free β-diketone can usually be extracted with ether or ligroin. The organic extract is washed thoroughly with sodium bicarbonate solution to remove acids, and, after drying, the solvent is removed. The product is purified by distillation or recrystallization.

In general the acylations have been carried out in dry apparatus and with purified reagents. However, the addition of small amounts of water to the reactants does not appear to decrease the yield.[52b] Solvents such as ethylene dichloride or excess anhydride have sometimes been employed to dissolve solid ketones or to increase the rate of saturation by boron trifluoride. Ethyl ether is not recommended as a solvent.

The rate of saturation by boron trifluoride appears to influence the yield of β-diketone, the amount of high-boiling material, and, with a methyl methylene ketone, the relative proportion of the isomeric methyl acyl derivative.[50a] Rapid saturation (within a few minutes) by the reagent gave better yields of β-diketone than slow saturation (during a few hours) with ketones such as cyclohexanone, cyclopentanone, and acetophenone. Even better yields have been obtained with these ketones by rapidly adding mixtures of the anhydride and ketone to boron fluoride complexes with acetic acid or ethyl acetate.[52b] Moreover, rapid mixing of the reactants has produced less high-boiling residue. With methyl n-amyl ketone, which is acylated mainly at the methylene group, rapid saturation also produced a higher total yield of β-diketones. However, the increase in yield was largely an increase in the amount of the methyl derivative.[50a] In such cases, the rapid saturation procedure appears to have little advantage over the older procedure of slow saturation. The relatively small amount of methyl derivative formed has been removed satisfactorily from the methylene derivative by alkali extraction.[51] This method of separation depends on the greater solubility of the methyl isomer in dilute aqueous sodium hydroxide and on a difference in color of the ferric chloride complex. Thus a mixture of methyl and methylene isomers containing even a relatively small proportion of the methyl derivative generally gives the dominant cherry-red enol test of the methyl isomer. Extraction with dilute sodium hydroxide solution removes this isomer preferentially; extraction is continued until the purple enol test (or negative test) * of the methylene isomer is obtained. In this manner, fairly pure methylene-acyl derivatives of various methyl methylene ketones have been obtained.

In certain cases where the slow saturation procedure has produced mainly the methylene isomer from the acetylation of methyl methylene ketones, the methylene isomer may be obtained exclusively by the addition of a catalytic amount of p-toluenesulfonic acid (10 mole per cent of the total moles of anhydride and ketone) to the anhydride-ketone mixture prior to the slow saturation with boron trifluoride.[50a]

Acetylacetone. The acetylation of acetone with acetic anhydride to form acetylacetone in 80–85% yield is described in *Organic Syntheses*.[92]

2-Acetylcyclohexanone. *Acylations of Cyclohexanone, Cyclopentanone, and Acetophenone* (Table VI).[52b] Procedure A. A mixture of the anhydride (0.6 mole) and the ketone (0.3 mole) is placed in a three-necked flask fitted with an efficient, sealed stirrer, a gas inlet tube reaching to within 1–2 cm. of the surface of the liquid, and (in the third neck) a calcium chloride outlet tube and a thermometer immersed in the liquid. The flask is immersed in a solid carbon dioxide-acetone bath, the mixture is stirred vigorously, and commercial boron fluoride (bubbled first through 95% sulfuric acid) is passed in as fast as possible (ten to twenty minutes) until the mixture, kept at 0–10° (for the methylene ketones) or at 5–15° (for acetophenone), is saturated (copious evolution of white fumes). The solid carbon dioxide-acetone bath is then replaced by an ice bath and the reagent passed in at a slower rate for fifteen minutes to insure maximum absorption. Stirring is continued for a total time of four hours, during which time the ice bath is allowed to come slowly to room temperature. The reaction mixture is poured into a solution of sodium acetate (two moles per mole of anhydride), refluxed for thirty minutes to one hour (until the boron fluoride complexes are hydrolyzed), chilled, and extracted with ether or ligroin (b.p. 30–60°).† If the product is soluble in the hydrolysis mixture, the solution is partly neutralized with solid sodium bicarbonate before extraction. The extracts are washed free of acid with saturated sodium bicarbonate solution and dried over Drierite. The β-diketones are isolated by distillation.

---

* The methylene derivative of methyl isobutyl ketone produces no color.

[92] Denoon, *Org. Syntheses*, **20**, 6 (1940).

† Ligroin is usually advantageous, especially in acetylations, because it removes very little acetic acid from the aqueous phase, whereas ether removes a considerable amount of the acid and its subsequent removal requires numerous washings with sodium bicarbonate solution.

In experiments in which the reaction mixtures become difficult to stir because of the formation of solid boron fluoride complexes, ethylene dichloride is used as solvent. After the reaction mixture is treated with the sodium acetate solution, the ethylene dichloride is removed by distillation until the vapor temperature rises above 90°. The residue is then refluxed and worked up as described above.

Procedure B. Acetic acid (0.8 mole) or ethyl acetate * (0.6 mole) is placed in a three-necked flask fitted with an efficient, sealed stirrer, a gas inlet tube, and an outlet tube loosely closed with a cotton plug. The flask is immersed in an ice bath, and, with vigorous stirring, boron fluoride passed in as rapidly as it is absorbed. Addition is continued

TABLE VI

ACYLATIONS OF CYCLOHEXANONE, CYCLOPENTANONE, AND ACETOPHENONE IN THE PRESENCE OF BORON FLUORIDE BY PROCEDURES A AND B[52b]

Anhydride	Ketone	β-Diketone	Boiling Point ° mm.	Yield % A	B
Acetic	Cyclohexanone	2-Acetylcyclohexanone	95–98/10	75	86 [a]
Propionic	Cyclohexanone	2-Propionylcyclohexanone	123–125/20	63	79 [a]
n-Butyric	Cyclohexanone	2-n-Butyrylcyclohexanone	133–135/20	74	83 [a]
Caproic	Cyclohexanone	2-Caproylcyclohexanone	140–145/9.5		68 [b]
2-Ethylbutyric	Cyclohexanone	2-(2-Ethylbutyryl)cyclo-hexanone	143–146/20.5	68	
2-Ethylhexanoic	Cyclohexanone	2-(2-Ethylhexanoyl)cyclo-hexanone	135–138/5	56	
Acetic	Cyclopentanone	2-Acetylcyclopentanone	72–75/8	59	76 [a]
n-Butyric	Cyclopentanone	2-n-Butyrylcyclopentanone	99–101/10	54	88 [b]
Acetic	Acetophenone	1-Phenylbutane-1,3-dione	142–145/19	83	70 [a]
Propionic	Acetophenone	1-Phenylpentane-1,3-dione	153–154/16	54	67 [a]
n-Butyric	Acetophenone	1-Phenylhexane-1,3-dione	165–166/14	63	81 [c]

[a] Acetic acid was used.
[b] Ethyl acetate was used.
[c] Butyric acid was used.

(at a reduced rate as saturation is approached) until the contents of the flask become a powdery solid.† At this point, the acid has absorbed 75–85 mole per cent of the reagent,‡ and the ester, 100 mole per cent.

* For acylations with anhydrides higher than acetic anhydride, ethyl acetate or the carboxylic acid corresponding to the higher anhydride may be preferred to acetic acid, which appears to produce small amounts of the acetyl derivative through anhydride-acetic acid exchange.

† Ethylene dichloride (75–100 ml.) may be used to keep the solid complex from caking, which occurs when the stirring is not sufficiently rapid.

‡ The solid appears to consist of a mixture of mono- and di-acetic acid-boron fluoride complexes. The monoacetic acid complex may be prepared conveniently on a relatively large scale and used as required, 0.6 mole being employed with 0.2 mole of ketone and 0.4 mole of anhydride. Since the diacid complex, which is a liquid [Meerwein and Pannwitz, J. prakt. Chem., 141, 123 (1934)], is soluble in ethylene chloride, the solid monoacetic acid complex is obtained by saturating an ethylene chloride solution of acetic acid with boron fluoride, filtering, and washing the precipitate with the solvent. It is hygroscopic and should be protected from moisture.

A dropping funnel is then substituted for the gas inlet tube, and a mixture of the ketone (0.2 mole) and anhydride (0.4 mole) is added with vigorous stirring during two to four minutes while cooling with an ice bath. After stirring for thirty minutes the ice bath is removed. The reaction mixture is allowed to stand four hours and is then worked up as described in the rapid saturation procedure. Ethyl acetate is removed as described for ethylene chloride in Procedure A.

Table VI gives the yields and physical constants of various β-diketones that have been prepared by Procedure A and/or B.

m-Nitrobenzoylacetone.[58] The apparatus in this procedure is the same as that described above for the acetylation of cyclohexanone. m-Nitroacetophenone (0.1 mole) is dissolved in 70 ml. (about 0.7 mole) of acetic anhydride, and the stirred reaction mixture is saturated slowly at 0° with boron trifluoride over a period of two to three hours. An ice-salt bath provides sufficient cooling. After saturation is complete, boron trifluoride is passed in for an additional fifteen to twenty minutes. The reaction mixture is then added to 700 ml. of 13% sodium acetate solution, and the resulting mixture is heated under reflux for twenty minutes. The mixture is chilled in an ice bath, and the precipitated diketone is removed by filtration. The crude m-nitrobenzoylacetone is washed thoroughly with water, crushed in a mortar, and dissolved in cold 2% sodium hydroxide solution. The alkaline solution is shaken with ether and separated. The ether phase is extracted with additional cold 2% sodium hydroxide solution until it no longer gives a positive ferric chloride test. The combined alkaline extracts are filtered and acidified with 10% sulfuric acid. The precipitated m-nitrobenzoylacetone is collected and recrystallized from 95% ethanol; m.p. 113.5–114.5°, m.p. of copper derivative 277–278°. The pure product weighs 13.3 g. (64%).

In a similar manner, p-nitrobenzoylacetone (m.p. 112.0–112.8°) and o-nitrobenzoylacetone (m.p. 54–55°) may be prepared in yields of 66% and 68%, respectively.

3-n-Butylpentane-2,4-dione.[50a] The apparatus is the same as that in the preparations described above. A mixture of 0.4 mole of acetic anhydride, 0.2 mole of methyl n-amyl ketone, and 0.06 mole of p-toluenesulfonic acid monohydrate is stirred five minutes and then saturated slowly with stirring at 0–10° (ice bath) with boron trifluoride over a period of two to three hours. The addition of the reagent is continued for fifteen minutes after saturation. After stirring four hours longer (warming to room temperature), the mixture is worked up as described above for 2-acetylcyclohexanone. The yield of 3-n-butylpentane-2,4-dione, b.p. 104–106°/20 mm., is 66–74%.

In a similar manner, 3-n-amylpentane-2,4-dione (b.p. 112–113°/15 mm.) can be prepared from acetic anhydride and methyl n-hexyl ketone in 63% yield.

Application of this procedure to the acylation of methyl n-amyl ketone with n-butyric anhydride gives a mixture of the methyl and methylene derivatives from which the latter derivative, 3-n-butyl-heptane-2,4-dione (b.p. 127–129°/20 mm.), can be isolated in 49% yield. The ether solution of the mixture of the two isomeric β-diketones is extracted with small (about 50-ml.) portions of ice-cold 1% sodium hydroxide solution * until an alkaline extract (after acidification) just gives a purple enol test with 5% ferric chloride solution. The ether solution is then washed with water, dried, and the solvent removed. Fractionation of the residue yields the methylene derivative.

Table VII gives the yields and physical constants of various methylene derivatives from methylene acylation of methyl alkyl ketones. With the

TABLE VII

METHYLENE ACYLATION OF ALIPHATIC METHYL METHYLENE KETONES IN THE PRESENCE OF BORON TRIFLUORIDE

Anhydride	Ketone	β-Diketone	Boiling Point	Yield %
Acetic	Methyl ethyl	3-Methylpentane-2,4-dione	77–79/30	32
Propionic	Methyl ethyl	3-Methylhexane-2,4-dione	88–91/30	31
n-Butyric	Methyl ethyl	3-Methylheptane-2,4-dione	93–96/30	44
n-Caproic	Methyl ethyl	3-Methylnonane-2,4-dione	120–123/30	64
Acetic	Methyl n-amyl	3-n-Butylpentane-2,4-dione	104–106/20	74–77 *
Propionic	Methyl n-amyl	3-n-Butylhexane-2,4-dione	117–118/20	47
n-Butyric	Methyl n-amyl	3-n-Butylheptane-2,4-dione	127–129/20	49 *
Isobutyric	Methyl n-amyl	3-n-Butyl-5-methylhexane-2,4-dione	125–128/20	29
Acetic	Methyl isoamyl	3-Isobutylpentane-2,4-dione	92–93/20	46
Acetic	Methyl n-hexyl	3-n-Amylpentane-2,4-dione	112–113/15	63

* This yield was obtained by adding 10 mole per cent of p-toluenesulfonic acid to the anhydride-ketone mixture prior to slow saturation with boron trifluoride.

exception of those starred, the yields were obtained by slow saturation of the anhydride-ketone mixture with boron trifluoride, decomposition of the reaction mixture by steam distillation,[51, 54] and removal of the methyl derivative by dilute alkali.† At least in some of these acylations, the yields could probably be improved by the procedure described above employing p-toluenesulfonic acid.

3-Phenylpentane-2,4-dione.[92a] A mixture of 0.4 mole of phenyl-acetone (purified through its bisulfite addition product), 0.8 mole of

* The methyl derivative may be recovered from these alkaline extracts by acidification.

† This alkali extraction may usually be omitted in acylation of methyl ethyl ketone, which forms almost exclusively the methylene derivative.

[92a] Hauser and Manyik, J. Org. Chem., 18, 588 (1953).

acetic anhydride, and 0.12 mole of p-toluenesulfonic acid monohydrate is stirred for five minutes and then saturated at 0–10° with boron trifluoride during three to four hours. Toward the end of this time, the reaction mixture becomes quite viscous, and, unless stirring and cooling are very efficient, the rate of addition of the reagent must be decreased to keep the temperature below 10°. After saturation, the flow of boron trifluoride is continued for 15 minutes, and then the reaction mixture is allowed to come to room temperature over a three-hour period. The reaction mixture is worked up as in the preparation of 2-acetylcyclo-hexanone. There is obtained 54.5 g. of material, b.p. 116–118°/20 mm., m.p. 55–59°. Recrystallization from ligroin (b.p. 60–90°) gives, on cooling the solution in solid carbon dioxide-acetone, 44.6 g. (63%) of 3-phenylpentane-2,4-dione, m.p. 58.5–59.5°.

3-Phenylpentane-2,4-dione has been obtained in 41% yield [54] by carrying out the reaction in the absence of p-toluenesulfonic acid, and 3-(p-nitrophenyl)pentane-2,4-dione (m.p. 116–117°) has similarly been prepared in 49% yield from acetic anhydride and p-nitrophenylace-tone.[50a]

TABULAR SURVEY OF THE ACYLATION OF KETONES

Tables VIII through XX list examples of acylation of ketones which have been reported prior to January, 1949. Certain results reported later than this date are also included. Doubtless some examples have been overlooked, particularly in the Michael-Claisen (Table XIII) and Kostanecki (Table XVII) types of acylations, on which an exhaustive literature survey was not carried out.

TABLE VIII

ACYLATIONS WITH ACETIC ESTERS

Ester	Ketone	Condensing Agent	Product	Yield % Low	Reference
Ethyl acetate	Acetone	$NaOC_2H_5$, ethanol	Acetylacetone		93
		$NaOC_2H_5$	Acetylacetone	38–45	6, 77, 93
		Na	Acetylacetone	50–60	6, 71, 93
		$NaNH_2$	Acetylacetone	54	2, 94
		$LiNH_2$	Acetylacetone	50	95
		NaH	Acetylacetone	85	96, 97
	Methyl ethyl	$NaOC_2H_5$	Propionylacetone	60	93, 98, 99
		Na	Propionylacetone	35–47	71, 99, 100, 101
		$NaNH_2$	Propionylacetone	40	14
		$NaNH_2$	3-Methylpentane-2,4-dione	9 *	
	3-Methoxyimino-2-butanone	Na	5-Methoxyiminohexane-2,4-dione	19–20 *	102
	Methyl n-propyl	Na	n-Butyrylacetone	45	6, 93, 103–106
		$NaNH_2$	n-Butyrylacetone	47	14
		$NaNH_2$	3-Ethylpentane-2,4-dione	2 *	
	Methyl isopropyl	$NaOC_2H_5$	Isobutyrylacetone	40	6
	5-Diethylaminopentan-2-one	$NaOC_2H_5$	7-Diethylaminoheptane-2,4-dione	34	107
	Methyl isopropyl	Na	Isobutyrylacetone	54	6, 100, 101, 103
	Diethyl	Na { warm	Propionylacetone	16 *	12, 93, 108
		cold	3-Methylhexane-2,4-dione	29 *	14
		$NaNH_2$	3-Methylhexane-2,4-dione	45	25
		NaH	3-Methylhexane-2,4-dione	60	6, 24, 106, 109
	Methyl n-butyl	Na	n-Valerylacetone	56–62	6
	Methyl isobutyl	$NaOC_2H_5$	Isovalerylacetone	56–60	6, 101, 103, 106
		Na	Isovalerylacetone	64	14
		$NaNH_2$	Isovalerylacetone	59	6, 106
	Methyl sec-butyl	Na	sec-Valerylacetone	47	6, 110
	Methyl t-butyl	$NaOC_2H_5$	Pivaloylacetone	15–25	6, 98, 106, 110, 111
		Na	Pivaloylacetone	25–30	25
		NaH	Pivaloylacetone	32	2
		$NaNH_2$	Pivaloylacetone	43	12
	Ethyl n-propyl	Na	Propionylacetone	—	
		$NaNH_2$	Butyrylacetone	—	
	Methyl n-amyl	Na	n-Hexanoylacetone	61	109
		$NaNH_2$	3-n-Butylpentane-2,4-dione	0.4 *	14

Ketone	Base	Product	Yield %	References
Di-n-propyl	Na {warm	n-Butyrylacetone	20*	12
	cold}	3-Ethylheptane-2,4-dione	20*	
Methyl n-hexyl	Na	n-Heptanoylacetone	69	93, 98, 103, 112
5-Methyl-2-heptanone	NaOC₂H₅	7-Methylnonane-2,4-dione	33	24
6-Methyl-2-heptanone	Na	8-Methylnonane-2,4-dione	—	113
Methyl n-heptyl	Na	n-Octanoylacetone	Good	114
Methyl n-octyl	Na	n-Nonanoylacetone	48*	115
Methyl n-nonyl	Na	n-Decanoylacetone	69*	98, 109
Diisobutyl	NaNH₂	Acylation failed		14
Methyl n-decyl	Na	n-Undecanoylacetone	70*	115
Methyl n-undecyl	Na	n-Dodecanoylacetone	50*	115, 116
Methyl n-dodecyl	Na	n-Tridecanoylacetone	54*	115
Methyl n-tridecyl	Na	n-Tetradecanoylacetone	52*	115
Methyl n-tetradecyl	Na	n-Pentadecanoylacetone	35*	115
Methyl n-pentadecyl	Na	n-Hexadecanoylacetone	34*	115
Methyl n-hexadecyl	Na	n-Heptadecanoylacetone	27*	115
Methyl n-heptadecyl	Na	n-Octadecanoylacetone	55*	115
Methyl n-octadecyl	Na	n-Nonadecanoylacetone	32*	115
Methyl n-nonadecyl	Na	n-Eicosanoylacetone	28*	115
Allylacetone	Na	1-Octene-5,7-dione	Good	114
Mesityl oxide	NaOC₂H₅ or Na	2-Methyl-2-heptene-4,6-dione	—	93
2-Methyl-2-hepten-6-one	Na	2-Methyl-2-nonene-6,8-dione	47	117
Cyclohexanone	Na	2-Acetylcyclohexanone	12–15	118, 119
	NaNH₂	2-Acetylcyclohexanone	35	14
Methyl cyclohexyl	Na	Hexahydrobenzoylacetone	50	6, 106
3-Methylcyclohexanone	Na	3-Methyl-6-acetylcyclohexanone	25–30	116, 120, 121
3,3-Dimethylcyclohexanone	Na	3,3-Dimethyl-6-acetylcyclohexanone	48	114, 119
Camphor	Na	3-Acetylcamphor	Low	122
2-Acetylthiophene	NaNH₂	2-Thenoylacetylmethane	81	123
	LiNH₂	2-Thenoylacetylmethane	57	123
Acetophenone	NaOC₂H₅	Benzoylacetone	65–70	6, 71, 90, 93, 124, 125
	Na	Benzoylacetone	65–74	6, 71, 106, 126
	NaNH₂	Benzoylacetone	75–77	90, 94, 123, 127
4-Methylacetophenone	Na	4-Methylbenzoylacetone	49	128
Acetomesitylene	NaOC₂H₅	2,4,6-Trimethylbenzoylacetone	70	6
	C₂H₅MgBr	2,4,6-Trimethylbenzoylacetone	26	129
4-Bromoacetophenone	Na	4-Bromobenzoylacetone	69	130
	Na	4-Bromobenzoylacetone	62	131, 132

Note: References 93–572 are listed on pp. 187–196.
* The product was isolated as the copper derivative.

TABLE VIII—Continued

ACYLATIONS WITH ACETIC ESTERS

Ester	Ketone	Condensing Agent	Product	Yield %	Reference
Ethyl acetate—Continued	4-Bromoacetophenone—Continued	$NaNH_2$	4-Bromobenzoylacetone	50–80	133
	2-Hydroxyacetophenone	Na	2-Hydroxybenzoylacetone	65	134, 135
	2-Hydroxy-3-methylacetophenone	Na	2-Hydroxy-3-methylbenzoylacetone	85–90	134
	2-Hydroxy-4-methylacetophenone	Na	2-Hydroxy-4-methylbenzoylacetone	60	134
	2-Hydroxy-5-methylacetophenone	Na	2-Hydroxy-5-methylbenzoylacetone	60	136
	2-Hydroxy-3,5-dimethylacetophenone	Na	2-Hydroxy-3,5-dimethylbenzoylacetone	60	136
	2-Hydroxy-4,6-dimethylacetophenone	Na	2-Hydroxy-4,6-dimethylbenzoylacetone	75–80	137
	2-Hydroxy-4-methoxy-3-methylacetophenone	Na	2-Hydroxy-4-methoxy-3-methylbenzoylacetone	—	134
	2-Hydroxy-3,4-dimethoxyacetophenone	Na	2-Hydroxy-3,4-dimethoxybenzoylacetone	—	138
	2-Hydroxy-5-chloroacetophenone	Na	2-Hydroxy-5-chlorobenzoylacetone	Good	135
	2-Hydroxy-4-methyl-5-chloroacetophenone	Na	2-Hydroxy-4-methyl-5-chlorobenzoylacetone	—	136
	2-Hydroxy-4,6-dimethyl-5-chloroacetophenone	Na	2-Hydroxy-4,6-dimethyl-5-chlorobenzoylacetone	55	136
	3-Methoxyacetophenone	$NaOC_2H_5$	3-Methoxybenzoylacetone	—	139
	4-Methoxyacetophenone	$NaOC_2H_5$	4-Methoxybenzoylacetone	—	140
	2-Ethoxyacetophenone	$NaOC_2H_5$	2-Ethoxybenzoylacetone	—	140
	2-Methoxy-5-methylacetophenone	Na	2-Methoxy-5-methylbenzoylacetone	—	140
	2-Methoxy-4-methylacetophenone	Na	2-Methoxy-4-methylbenzoylacetone	—	141
	2,4-Dimethoxyacetophenone	Na	2,4-Dimethoxybenzoylacetone	68	142
	3,4-Dimethoxyacetophenone	Na	3,4-Dimethoxybenzoylacetone	—	143
	2,4-Dimethoxy-6-methylacetophenone	Na	2,4-Dimethoxy-6-methylbenzoylacetone	62–68	140
	2,3,4-Trimethoxyacetophenone	Na	2,3,4-Trimethoxybenzoylacetone	—	144a, 145
	2,4-Diethoxyacetophenone	Na	2,4-Diethoxybenzoylacetone	—	146
	2,5-Diethoxyacetophenone	Na	2,5-Diethoxybenzoylacetone	—	140, 147
	2,4-Diethoxypropiophenone	Na	1-(2,4-Diethoxyphenyl)-2-methylbutane-1,3-dione	—	140, 148
	4,6-Diacetylresorcinol dimethyl ether	Na	CH_3O—[ring with OCH_3]—$COCH_2COCH_3$, $COCH_2COCH_3$	—	149
					150
	Propiophenone	Na, cold	Propionylacetone	4	12
			1-Phenyl-2-methylbutane-1,3-dione	18	
		Na, warm	Propionylacetone	—	
			Propionylbenzoylmethane	—	

Ketone / Ester	Ketone	Reagent	Product	Yield (%)	References
Methyl benzyl		Na {cold	{ 3-Phenylpentane-2,4-dione	13	12
			1-Phenylpentane-2,4-dione	8	
		Na {warm	{ 3-Phenylpentane-2,4-dione	10	
			1-Phenylpentane-2,4-dione	30	
Ethyl benzyl		Na {cold	3-Phenylhexane-2,4-dione	23	12
		Na {warm	{ 1,5-Diphenylpentane-2,4-dione	—	
			3-Phenylpentane-2,4-dione	—	
Methyl cinnamyl		Na	Acylation failed		151
Phenyl benzyl		Na	Acylation failed		12
p-Acetylbiphenyl		$NaOC_2H_5$	1-(p-Xenyl)butane-1,3-dione	50	6
4-Hydroxy-3-acetylbiphenyl		Na	H_5C_6–C₆H₃(OH)–$COCH_2COCH_3$ (structure)	—	152
1-Tetralone		NaH	2-Acetyl-1-tetralone	84	96, 97
1-Acetylnaphthalene		Na	1-Naphthoylacetone	—	133
2-Acetylnaphthalene		$NaNH_2$	2-Naphthoylacetone	Low	133
2-Acetylnaphthalene		Na	2-Naphthoylacetone	42–57	133
1-Hydroxy-2-acetylnaphthalene		Na	1-Hydroxy-2-naphthoylacetone	85–90	134
2-Hydroxy-1-acetylnaphthalene		Na	2-Hydroxy-1-naphthoylacetone	—	134
2-Methoxy-1-acetylnaphthalene		Na	2-Methoxy-1-naphthoylacetone	41	130, 153
2-Hydroxy-3-acetyl-9,10-dihydrophenanthrene		Na	1-(2-Hydroxy-9,10-dihydro-phenanthryl)butane-1,3-dione	77	154
6-Hydroxy-4-methoxy-7-acetyl-2,3,5-trimethyl-benzofuran		Na	1-(6-Hydroxy-4-methoxy-2,3,5-trimethyl-7-benzofuryl)butane-1,3-dione	57 (crude)	155
Tropinone		Na or $NaOC_2H_6$	Acetyltropinone	—	156
Ethyl ethoxyacetate	Acetone	Na	Ethoxyacetylacetone	40 †	157
Ethyl trifluoroacetate	Acetone	$NaOC_2H_5$	Trifluoroacetylacetone	70	158
Ethyl trifluoroacetate	Trifluoroacetone	$NaOC_2H_5$	1,1,1,5,5,5-Hexafluoropentane-2,4-dione	72	158
Ethyl methoxyacetate	Acetone	Na	1-Methoxypentane-2,4-dione	31	159
Ethyl methoxyacetate	Methyl ethyl	—	1-Methoxyhexane-2,4-dione	—	160
Ethyl phenoxyacetate	Acetophenone	$NaOC_2H_5$	ω-Phenoxyacetylacetophenone	—	161
Ethyl diethoxyacetate	Acetone	Na	1,1-Diethoxypentane-2,4-dione	—	162
Ethyl dichloroacetate	Acetone	Na	1,1-Dichloropentane-2,4-dione	30–34 *	102
Ethyl dichloroacetate	Acetophenone	$NaOCH_3$	1-Phenyl-4,4-dichlorobutane-1,3-dione	—	163

Note: References 93–572 are listed on pp. 187–196.
* The product was isolated as the copper derivative.
† The product was isolated as the sodium derivative.

TABLE IX

ACYLATIONS WITH HIGHER ESTERS

Ester	Ketone	Condensing Agent	Product	Yield %	Reference
Ethyl propionate	Acetone	Na	Propionylacetone	15	100
		NaNH₂	Propionylacetone	60	14
	Methyl ethyl	Na	Dipropionylmethane	18*	101, 164
		NaNH₂	3-Methylhexane-2,4-dione	13	2, 75a
			Dipropionylmethane	57	
		NaH	3-Methylhexane-2,4-dione	9	25
			Dipropionylmethane	51	
		LiNH₂	3-Methylhexane-2,4-dione	11	95
			Dipropionylmethane	51	
	Methyl n-propyl	Na	Propionyl-n-butyrylmethane	9	100
		NaNH₂	3-Ethylhexane-2,4-dione	3	2
			Propionyl-n-butyrylmethane	70	
	Methyl isobutyl	NaH	Propionylisovalerylmethane	75	25
	Diethyl	NaNH₂	4-Methylheptane-3,5-dione	28	14
		Na	4-Methylheptane-3,5-dione	13*	12
	Cyclohexanone	NaNH₂	2-Propionylcyclohexanone	4	14
		NaH	2-Propionylcyclohexanone	29	25
	2-Acetylthiophene	NaNH₂	2-Thenoylpropionylmethane	53	123
		LiNH₂	2-Thenoylpropionylmethane	49	123
	Acetophenone	NaOC₂H₅	Benzoylpropionylmethane	—	114, 125
		NaNH₂	Benzoylpropionylmethane	55	14
		Na	Benzoylpropionylmethane	70–75	140, 165
	2-Hydroxyacetophenone	Na	2-Hydroxybenzoylpropionylmethane	57	88, 166
	2-Hydroxy-5-methylacetophenone	Na	2-Hydroxy-5-methylbenzoylpropionylmethane	—	40
	2-Ethoxyacetophenone	Na	2-Ethoxybenzoylpropionylmethane	52	140
	2-Hydroxy-4-methoxyacetophenone	Na	2-Hydroxy-4-methoxybenzoylpropionylmethane	—	166
	2-Hydroxy-5-chloroacetophenone	Na	2-Hydroxy-5-chlorobenzoylpropionylmethane	58†	42
	2,4-Dimethoxyacetophenone	Na	2,4-Dimethoxybenzoylpropionylmethane	—	166
	2,4-Diethoxyacetophenone	Na	2,4-Diethoxybenzoylpropionylmethane	—	140, 167
	2,5-Diethoxyacetophenone	Na	2,5-Diethoxybenzoylpropionylmethane	—	140, 167
	2,4-Dimethoxy-6-methylacetophenone	Na	2,4-Dimethoxy-6-methylbenzoylpropionylmethane	52	144b, 145
	2-Hydroxy-3,5-dimethylacetophenone	Na	6,8-Dimethyl-2-ethylchromone	—	137

Ester	Ketone	Condensing agent	Product	Yield (%)	Reference
Phenyl propionate	ω-Methoxyacetophenone	NaNH₂	Acylation failed		168
	ω-Methoxyacetophenone	NaNH₂	1-Phenyl-2-methoxypentane-1,3-dione	25	168
	ω-Phenoxyacetophenone	NaNH₂	1-Phenyl-2-phenoxypentane-1,3-dione	50*	168
Ethyl propionate	1-Hydroxy-2-acetylnaphthalene	Na	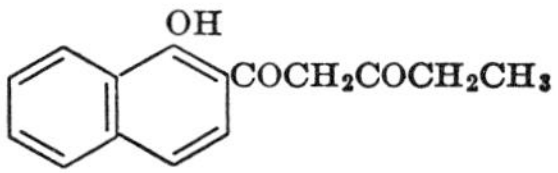 naphthalene–OH, –$COCH_2COCH_2CH_3$	48	166
	1-Methoxy-2-acetylnaphthalene	Na	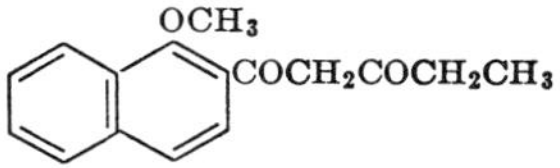 naphthalene–OCH_3, –$COCH_2COCH_2CH_3$	54†	166
	1-Methoxy-2-propionylnaphthalene	NaNH₂	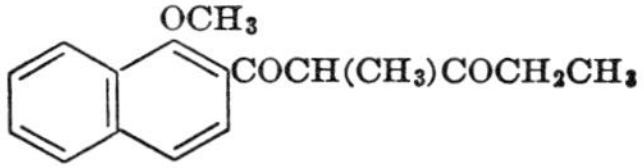 naphthalene–OCH_3, –$COCH(CH_3)COCH_2CH_3$	16	166
Ethyl β,β-diethoxy-α-chloropropionate	3-Methyl-5-acetylisoxazole	Na	Acylation failed		169
Methyl acetoneglycerate	Acetophenone	NaOC₂H₅	Acylation failed		170
	Acetone	Na	5,6-Dioxyisopropylidenehexane-2,4-dione	46	171
	Methyl t-butyl	Na	2,2-Dimethyl-6,7-dioxyisopropylideneheptane-3,5-dione	15	171
	Mesityl oxide	Na	2-Methyl-7,8-dioxyisopropylidene-2-octene-4,6-dione	14	171
	Cyclohexanone	Na	α,β-Dioxyisopropylidenepropionylcyclohexanone	35	171
	Acetophenone	Na	1-Phenyl-4,5-dioxyisopropylidenepentane-1,3-dione	58	171
Ethyl n-butyrate	Acetone	Na	n-Butyrylacetone	—	93
n-Butyl n-butyrate	Acetone	Na	n-Butyrylacetone	25	103
Ethyl n-butyrate	Methyl ethyl	NaNH₂	Propionyl-n-butyrylmethane	60*	100
n-Butyl n-butyrate	Methyl ethyl	Na	Propionyl-n-butyrylmethane	14*	2
Ethyl n-butyrate	Methyl n-propyl	NaOC₂H₅	Propionyl-n-butyrylmethane	11*	101
Methyl n-propyl	Methyl n-propyl	Na	Di-n-butyrylmethane	22*	2
		LiNH₂	Di-n-butyrylmethane	76	2, 172
		KNH₂	Di-n-butyrylmethane	41	95
		NaNH₂	Di-n-butyrylmethane	76	2, 75, 173

Note: References 93–572 are listed on pp. 187–196.

* The product was isolated as the copper derivative.

† The product was isolated as the sodium derivative.

TABLE IX—*Continued*

ACYLATIONS WITH HIGHER ESTERS

Ester	Ketone	Condensing Agent	Product	Yield %	Reference
n-Butyl n-butyrate	Methyl n-propyl	Na	Di-n-butyrylmethane	10 *	172
Ethyl n-butyrate	Methyl n-propyl	NaNH₂	Di-n-butyrylmethane	25–28 *	75, 173
	Methyl isopropyl	NaNH₂	n-Butyrylisobutyrylmethane	59	14
	Diethyl	NaNH₂	4-Methyloctane-3,5-dione	42	14
	Methyl isobutyl	NaNH₂	n-Butyrylisovalerylmethane	80	2
	Cyclohexanone	NaNH₂	2-n-Butyrylcyclohexanone	6–12	14
	2-Acetylthiophene	NaNH₂	2-Thenoyl-n-butyrylmethane	41	123
		LiNH₂	2-Thenoyl-n-butyrylmethane	37	123
	Acetophenone	NaOC₂H₅	1-Phenylhexane-1,3-dione	—	125
		Na	1-Phenylhexane-1,3-dione	2	165
		NaNH₂	1-Phenylhexane-1,3-dione	42	14
	2-Hydroxy-4-methoxyacetophenone	Na	1-(2-Hydroxy-4-methoxyphenyl)hexane-1,3-dione	42	166
	2,4-Dimethoxyacetophenone	Na	1-(2,4-Dimethoxyphenyl)hexane-1,3-dione	33	166
	2,4-Diethoxyacetophenone	Na	1-(2,4-Diethoxyphenyl)hexane-1,3-dione	—	167
	2,4-Dimethoxy-6-methylacetophenone	Na	1-(2,4-Dimethoxy-6-methylphenyl)hexane-1,3-dione	49	144b, 145
	Benzalacetone	NaNH₂	Acylation failed		14
Ethyl isobutyrate	Acetone	Na	Isobutyrylacetone	6	100
		NaNH₂	Isobutyrylacetone	42	2, 14
		NaH	Isobutyrylacetone	41	25
	Methyl isopropyl	Na	Diisobutyrylmethane	28	174, 175
	Methyl n-amyl	NaNH₂	2-Methyldecane-3,5-dione	16–22	176
Phenyl isobutyrate	Methyl n-amyl	NaNH₂	2-Methyldecane-3,5-dione	50	176
		NaH	2-Methyldecane-3,5-dione	21	176
Ethyl isobutyrate	2-Acetylthiophene	NaNH₂	2-Thenoylisobutyrylmethane	49	123
		LiNH₂	2-Thenoylisobutyrylmethane	30	123
	Acetophenone	(C₆H₅)₃CNa	1-Phenyl-4-methylpentane-1,3-dione	41	177
		NaOC₂H₅	1-Phenyl-4-methylpentane-1,3-dione	—	125
Ethyl n-valerate	Methyl n-butyl	NaNH₂	Acylation failed		6
		NaOC₂H₅	Di-n-valerylmethane	—	178
	Methyl t-butyl	NaNH₂	Acylation failed		6
		NaNH₂	n-Valerylpivaloylmethane	52	2
		NaH	n-Valerylpivaloylmethane	22	25

Ester	Ketone	Base	Product	Yield %	References
	Acetophenone	NaOC₂H₅	1-Phenylheptane-1,3-dione	—	125
		NaNH₂	1-Phenylheptane-1,3-dione	40	14
Ethyl isovalerate	Methyl isobutyl	NaNH₂	Diisovalerylmethane	76	2, 14
		NaH	Diisovalerylmethane	45	25
		LiNH₂	Diisovalerylmethane	75	95
	Acetophenone	Na	1-Phenyl-5-methylhexane-1,3-dione	—	165
Ethyl pivalate	Methyl n-butyl	NaOC₂H₅	Acylation failed		6
	Methyl t-butyl	NaOC₂H₅	Acylation failed		6
Phenyl pivalate	Methyl t-butyl	NaNH₂	Dipivaloylmethane	28	2
		NaNH₂	Dipivaloylmethane	64	176
Ethyl n-caproate	Acetone	NaH	Caproylacetone	65–80	25, 179
	Methyl n-amyl	NaNH₂	Di-n-caproylmethane	68	2, 14
		LiNH₂	Di-n-caproylmethane	65	95
	2-Acetylthiophene	NaNH₂	2-Thenoyl-n-caproylmethane	69	123
		LiNH₂	2-Thenoyl-n-caproylmethane	42	123
Methyl 2-ethylbutanoate	Methyl n-amyl	NaNH₂	3-Ethylundecane-4,6-dione	23	176
		NaH	3-Ethylundecane-4,6-dione	20	176
Phenyl 2-ethylbutanoate	Methyl n-amyl	NaNH₂	3-Ethylundecane-4,6-dione	51	176
		NaH	3-Ethylundecane-4,6-dione	41	176
	3-Ethyl-2-pentanone	NaNH₂	3,7-Diethylnonane-4,6-dione	62	176
Methyl 2-ethylhexanoate	Methyl n-amyl	NaNH₂	Acylation failed		176
Phenyl 2-ethylhexanoate	Methyl n-amyl	NaH	5-Ethyltridecane-6,8-dione	43	176
		NaNH₂	5-Ethyltridecane-6,8-dione	10	176
	Acetophenone	NaNH₂	1-Phenyl-4-ethyloctane-1,3-dione	43	176
Methyl n-decanoate	Acetone	NaH	Tridecane-2,4-dione	92	96, 97
Methyl laurate	Acetone	NaNH₂	Lauroylacetone	70	96, 97
Ethyl laurate	Acetone	NaOC₂H₅	Lauroylacetone	83	25
		NaOC₂H₅	Lauroylacetone	76	14
Methyl myristate	Acetophenone	NaH	Acylation failed		143
	Methyl nicotinyl	NaOC₂H₅	Acylation failed		143
	Acetone	NaH	2,4-Heptadecanedione	84	96, 97
Ethyl phenylacetate	Acetone	NaOC₂H₅	Acylation failed		6
		Na	1-Phenylpentane-2,4-dione	50 *	62, 180
	Methyl ethyl	Na	1-Phenylhexane-2,4-dione	34 *	12
		NaNH₂	1-Phenylhexane-2,4-dione	54	14

Note: References 93–572 are listed on pp. 187–196.
* The product was isolated as the copper derivative.

TABLE IX—*Continued*

ACYLATIONS WITH HIGHER ESTERS

Ester	Ketone	Condensing Agent	Product	Yield %	Reference
Ethyl phenylacetate— *Continued*	Methyl t-butyl	Na	1-Phenyl-5,5-dimethylhexane-2,4-dione	—	181
	Acetophenone	NaNH₂	1,4-Diphenylbutane-1,3-dione	30	182, 183
		Na	1,4-Diphenylbutane-1,3-dione	50	124, 140, 184
	4-Methoxyacetophenone	Na	1-(4-Methoxyphenyl)-4-phenylbutane-1,3-dione	—	140
	2,4-Dimethoxyacetophenone	Na	1-(2,4-Dimethoxyphenyl)-4-phenylbutane-1,3-dione	—	185
	2,4-Diethoxyacetophenone	Na	1-(2,4-Diethoxyphenyl)-4-phenylbutane-1,3-dione	—	140
Methyl phenylacetate	4,6-Diacetylresorcinol dimethyl ether	Na	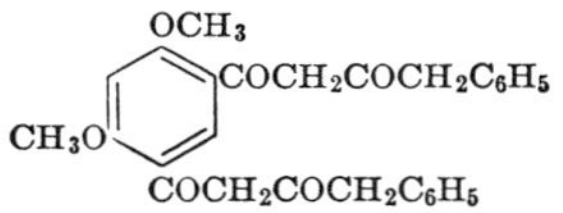 $COCH_2COC_6H_5$ / OCH_3 ring / CH_3O / $COCH_2COC_6H_5$	—	150
Ethyl 2,4,6-trimethylphenylacetate	Acetone	NaNH₂	1-(2,4,6-Trimethylphenyl)pentane-2,4-dione	43	186
Ethyl β-phenylpropionate	Acetone	NaOC₂H₅	Acylation failed		6
	Acetone	Na	1-Phenylhexane-3,5-dione	28	180, 187
Ethyl tetrahydrofuroate	Acetone	NaOC₂H₅	Tetrahydrofuroylacetone	60	6
Ethyl N-ethylnipecotate	Acetone	NaOC₂H₅	Acylation failed		15
	Acetophenone	NaOC₂H₅	Acylation failed		15
Ethyl hexahydrobenzoate	Acetone	NaOC₂H₅	Acylation failed		6
	Acetone	Na	Acylation failed		6
	Acetone	NaNH₂	Hexahydrobenzoylacetone	62	14

Ester	Ketone	Base	Product	Yield	Ref.
Ethyl 1,2,2,3-tetramethylcyclopentane-1-carboxylate	Acetophenone	$NaNH_2$	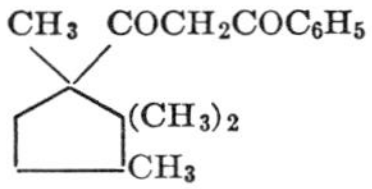 CH_3 $COCH_2COC_6H_5$ (cyclopentane ring with two CH_3 groups)	Low	188
Dimethyl succinate	Cyclohexanone	$NaOCH_3$	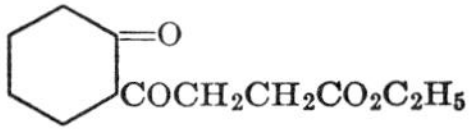 (cyclohexanone) $COCH_2CH_2CO_2C_2H_5$	Low	189
Di-t-butyl succinate	Acetophenone	NaH	1,8-Diphenyloctane-1,3,6,8-tetraone	19–34	190
Dimethyl succinate	1-Keto-1,2,3,4-tetrahydrophenanthrene	NaH	Methyl β-(1-keto-1,2,3,4-tetrahydro-2-phenanthroyl)-propionate	7	190
Diethyl succinate	1-Keto-1,2,3,4-tetrahydrophenanthrene	NaH	Ethyl β-(1-keto-1,2,3,4-tetrahydro-2-phenanthroyl)-propionate	3	190
Dimethyl glutarate	Cyclohexanone	Na	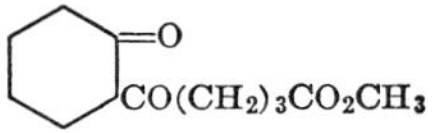 (cyclohexanone) $CO(CH_2)_3CO_2CH_3$	26	189
Diethyl glutarate	1-Tetralone	$NaOC_2H_5$	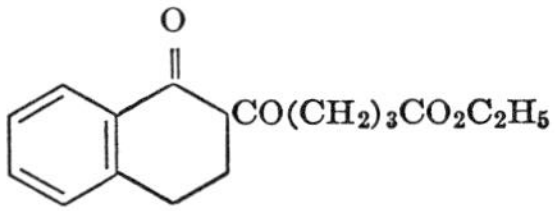 (tetralone) $CO(CH_2)_3CO_2C_2H_5$	—	191

Note: References 93–572 are listed on pp. 187–196.

TABLE X

Acylations with Unsaturated Esters

Ester	Ketone	Condensing Agent	Product	Yield %	Reference
Ethyl acrylate	Methyl n-hexyl	NaOC$_2$H$_5$	1-Hendecene-3,5-dione	54	24
Ethyl crotonate	Methyl n-hexyl	NaOC$_2$H$_5$	2-Dodecene-4,6-dione	53	24
Ethyl cinnamate	Acetone	Na	Cinnamoylacetone	9	151
		NaNH$_2$	Cinnamoylacetone	6	14
Phenyl cinnamate	Acetone	NaNH$_2$	Cinnamoylacetone	30	18
Methyl cinnamate	Methyl ethyl	Na	Cinnamoylpropionylmethane	—	151
Ethyl cinnamate	Methyl isopropyl	Na	Cinnamoylisobutyrylmethane	—	151
	Acetophenone	Na	Cinnamoylbenzoylmethane	7	151
Phenyl cinnamate	Acetophenone	NaNH$_2$	Cinnamoylbenzoylmethane	29	18
Ethyl cinnamate	2-Hydroxy-4-methoxyacetophenone	Na	Acylation failed		135
	1-Hydroxy-2-acetylnaphthalene	Na	Acylation failed		135
	Camphor	Ca	α-Cinnamoylcamphor	—	192
		Na	α-Cinnamoylcamphor	—	192
Ethyl phenyl-propiolate	Acetone	NaOC$_2$H$_5$	2-Phenyl-6-methyl-4-pyrone	48–50	193
	Acetophenone	NaOC$_2$H$_5$	2,6-Diphenyl-4-pyrone	—	193, 194
	α-Hydrindone	NaOC$_2$H$_5$	6-Phenyl-2,3-indeno-4-pyrone	—	195
	Phenyl benzyl	NaOC$_2$H$_5$	4,5,6-Triphenyl-2-pyrone	—	196

Note· References 93–572 are listed on pp. 187–196.

TABLE XI

ACYLATIONS WITH AROMATIC ESTERS

A. Carbocyclic Esters

Ester	Ketone	Condensing Agent	Product	Yield %	Reference
Methyl benzoate	Acetone	NaH	Benzoylacetone	66	25
Ethyl benzoate	Acetone	NaOC$_2$H$_5$	Benzoylacetone	Low	197
	Acetone	Na	Benzoylacetone	18–22	198
		NaNH$_2$	Benzoylacetone	63	94
	Methyl ethyl	NaNH$_2$	Benzoylpropionylmethane	42	14, 199
Methyl benzoate	Methyl n-propyl	NaH	Benzoyl-n-butyrylmethane	61	25
Ethyl benzoate	Methyl n-propyl	NaNH$_2$	Benzoyl-n-butyrylmethane	38	14
Ethyl benzoate	Isoamylacetone	NaNH$_2$	1-Phenyl-6-methylheptane-1,3-dione	—	113
Methyl benzoate	Cyclopentanone	NaH	2-Benzoyl-5-cyclopentylidenecyclopentanone	21	13
	Cyclohexanone	NaNH$_2$	2-Benzoylcyclohexanone	40	7
	Cyclohexanone	NaNH$_2$	2-Benzoylcyclohexanone	47	13
Ethyl benzoate	Cyclohexanone	NaNH$_2$	2-Benzoylcyclohexanone	7 *	14, 200
Phenyl benzoate	Cyclohexanone	NaNH$_2$	2-Benzoylcyclohexanone	69	13
Ethyl benzoate	1-Hydrindone	Na	2-Benzoyl-1-hydrindone	10	201
Phenyl benzoate	1-Hydrindone	NaNH$_2$	2-Benzoyl-1-hydrindone	80	13
	1-Tetralone	NaNH$_2$	2-Benzoyl-1-tetralone	46	13
Ethyl benzoate	2-Acetylthiophene	LiNH$_2$	Benzoyl-2-thenoylmethane	45	123
	Acetophenone	KOH	Dibenzoylmethane	75	202
	Acetophenone	NaOC$_2$H$_5$	Dibenzoylmethane	62–71	78, 197
	Acetophenone	Na	Dibenzoylmethane	80–90	126, 198
	Acetophenone	NaNH$_2$	Dibenzoylmethane	70–73	14, 94, 203
	Acetophenone	LiNH$_2$	Dibenzoylmethane	71	95
	2-Hydroxyacetophenone	NaOC$_2$H$_5$	2-Hydroxydibenzoylmethane	61–73	204
	4-Methoxyacetophenone	NaNH$_2$	4-Methoxydibenzoylmethane	88	205
	2-Ethoxyacetophenone	Na	2-Ethoxydibenzoylmethane	—	140, 206
	4-Isopropoxyacetophenone	Na	4-Isopropoxydibenzoylmethane	Fair	205

Note: References 93–572 are listed on pp. 187–196.

* The product was isolated as the copper derivative.

TABLE XI—*Continued*

ACYLATIONS WITH AROMATIC ESTERS

A. Carbocyclic Esters—Continued

Ester	Ketone	Condensing Agent	Product	Yield %	Reference
Ethyl benzoate—*Continued*	2,4-Dimethoxyacetophenone	NaNH₂	2,4-Dimethoxydibenzoylmethane	—	140, 207
	3,4-Dimethoxyacetophenone	Na	3,4-Dimethoxydibenzoylmethane	Poor	205
	2,5-Diethoxyacetophenone	Na	2,5-Diethoxydibenzoylmethane	—	140, 148
Methyl benzoate	6-Methyl-2,4-dimethoxyacetophenone	Na	6-Methyl-2,4-dimethoxydibenzoylmethane	—	208
Ethyl benzoate	4-Methyl-2,6-dimethoxyacetophenone	Na	4-Methyl-2,6-dimethoxydibenzoylmethane	—	209
	2,4,6-Trimethoxyacetophenone	Na	2,4,6-Trimethoxydibenzoylmethane	33	210, 211
Methyl benzoate	2,4,5-Trimethoxyacetophenone	Na	2,4,5-Trimethoxydibenzoylmethane	—	212, 213
Ethyl benzoate	2,3,4,6-Tetramethoxyacetophenone	Na	2,3,4,6-Tetramethoxydibenzoylmethane	65	214, 215
	2,3,4,5,6-Pentamethoxyacetophenone	Na	2,3,4,5,6-Pentamethoxydibenzoylmethane	8	216
	α-Methoxyacetophenone	NaNH₂	Acylation failed	—	168
Phenyl benzoate	α-Methoxyacetophenone	NaNH₂	2-Methoxy-1,3-diphenylpropane-1,3-dione	26	168
	α-Phenoxyacetophenone	NaNH₂	2-Phenoxy-1,3-diphenylpropane-1,3-dione	59	168
Ethyl benzoate	Propiophenone	NaNH₂	Acylation failed	—	217, 218
Phenyl benzoate	Propiophenone	NaNH₂	1,1-Dibenzoylethane	53	13
Ethyl benzoate	4-Methoxypropiophenone	NaNH₂	1-Phenyl-2-methyl-3-anisylpropane-1,3-dione	33	205, 219
	2-Naphthyl methyl	Na	2-Naphthoylbenzoylmethane	(crude)	133
	Benzalacetone	Na	Acylation failed	—	151
	1,2,2,3-Tetramethyl-1-acetylcyclopentane	NaNH₂	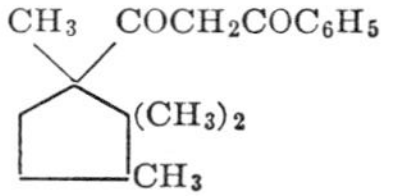 CH₃ COCH₂COC₆H₅ / (CH₃)₂ / CH₃	Good	188
Camphor		NaOC₂H₅	α-Benzoylcamphor	—	220
		Na	α-Benzoylcamphor	16 (crude)	192, 220
Phenyl benzoate		NaNH₂	α-Benzoylcamphor	Trace	192
Camphor		NaNH₂	α-Benzoylcamphor	11	13

Ester	Ketone	Reagent	Product	Poor	References
Ethyl benzoate	2-Acetylcamphane	$NaNH_2$	(camphane structure: C bearing CH_3, H_2C, CH_3CH_3, H_2C, CH_2, CH — side chain $CHCOCH_2COC_6H_5$)		221
Phenyl anisate	Cyclohexanone	$NaNH_2$	2-Anisoylcyclohexanone	48	72
Ethyl anisate	Acetophenone	$NaNH_2$	4-Methoxydibenzoylmethane	45	14, 205
		Na	4-Methoxydibenzoylmethane		140
	4-Methoxyacetophenone	Na	4,4'-Dimethoxydibenzoylmethane		140
	2-Ethoxyacetophenone	Na	2-Ethoxy-4'-methoxydibenzoylmethane		140
	3,4-Dimethoxyacetophenone	$NaNH_2$	3,4,4'-Trimethoxydibenzoylmethane		205
Methyl anisate	4-Methyl-2,6-dimethoxyacetophenone	Na	4-Methyl-2,6,4'-trimethoxydibenzoylmethane		222
Ethyl anisate	2,4,6-Trimethoxyacetophenone	Na	2,4,6,4'-Tetramethoxydibenzoylmethane		223
	2,4,5-Trimethoxyacetophenone	Na	2,4,5,4'-Tetramethoxydibenzoylmethane		224
	2,3,4,6-Tetramethoxyacetophenone	Na	2,3,4,6,4'-Pentamethoxydibenzoylmethane		215
Methyl anisate	2,3,4,6-Tetramethoxyacetophenone	Na	2,3,4,6,4'-Pentamethoxydibenzoylmethane	51	225
Ethyl anisate	4,6-Diacetylresorcinol dimethyl ether	Na	(resorcinol dimethyl ether ring, OCH_3/CH_3O, bearing $COCH_2COC_6H_4OCH_3$-p and $COCH_2COC_6H_4OCH_3$-p)		150
Methyl o-methoxybenzoate	Propiophenone	$NaNH_2$	Acylation failed	40	205
Ethyl o-methoxybenzoate	Acetone	Na	2-Methoxybenzoylacetone	51 *	143, 226
Methyl o-methoxybenzoate	Acetophenone	$NaNH_2$	2-Methoxydibenzoylmethane		205
Ethyl o-methoxybenzoate	2-Ethoxyacetophenone	Na	2-Methoxy-2'-ethoxydibenzoylmethane		227
Methyl o-methoxybenzoate	3-Ethoxyacetophenone	Na	2-Methoxy-3'-ethoxydibenzoylmethane		228
	4-Methyl-2,6-dimethoxyacetophenone	Na	4-Methyl-2,6,2'-trimethoxydibenzoylmethane		222
	2,4-Dimethoxyacetophenone		2,4,2'-Trimethoxydibenzoylmethane	42	213
Ethyl m-methoxybenzoate	Acetophenone	$NaNH_2$	3-Methoxydibenzoylmethane	28 *	205

Note: References 93–572 are listed on pp. 187–196.
* The product was isolated as the copper derivative.

TABLE XI—*Continued*

ACYLATIONS WITH AROMATIC ESTERS

A. Carbocyclic Esters—Continued

Ester	Ketone	Condensing Agent	Product	Yield %	Reference
Ethyl m-methyoxybenzoate— *Continued*	4-Methoxyacetophenone	NaNH₂	3,4′-Dimethoxydibenzoylmethane	26*	205
	3,4-Dimethoxyacetophenone	Na	3,4,3′-Trimethoxydibenzoylmethane	21*	205
Methyl m-methoxybenzoate	6-Methyl-2,4-dimethoxyacetophenone	Na	6-Methyl-2,4,3′-trimethoxydibenzoylmethane	—	208
	4-Methyl-2,6-dimethoxyacetophenone	Na	4-Methyl-2,6,3′-trimethoxydibenzoylmethane	—	222
Ethyl p-ethoxybenzoate	Acetophenone	Na	4-Ethoxydibenzoylmethane	—	205
Ethyl o-ethoxybenzoate	Acetophenone	Na	2-Ethoxydibenzoylmethane	—	206
	p-Ethoxyacetophenone	Na	2,4′-Diethoxydibenzoylmethane	—	229
Ethyl m-ethoxybenzoate	2,4,6-Trimethoxyacetophenone	Na	3-Ethoxy-2′,4′,6′-trimethoxydibenzoylmethane	—	230
Ethyl p-isopropoxybenzoate	Acetophenone	Na	4-Isopropoxydibenzoylmethane	Low	205
Ethyl p-nitrobenzoate	Acetone	NaNH₂	p-Nitrobenzoylacetone	10	231
Ethyl veratrate	Acetophenone	Na	3,4-Dimethoxydibenzoylmethane	26*	205, 232
	4-Methoxyacetophenone	NaNH₂	3,4,4′-Trimethoxydibenzoylmethane	—	205
	3,5-Dimethoxyacetophenone	Na	3,5,3′,4′-Tetramethoxydibenzoylmethane	Low	233
Methyl veratrate	4-Methyl-2,6-dimethoxyacetophenone	Na	4-Methyl-2,6,3′,4′-tetramethoxydibenzoylmethane	—	222
	6-Methyl-2,4-dimethoxyacetophenone	Na	6-Methyl-2,4,3′,4′-tetramethoxydibenzoylmethane	—	208
Ethyl veratrate	2,4,6-Trimethoxyacetophenone	Na	2,4,6,3′,4′-Pentamethoxydibenzoylmethane	14	234
	2,3,4-Trimethoxyacetophenone	Na	2,3,4,3′,4′-Pentamethoxydibenzoylmethane	75	235
Methyl 3,5-dimethoxybenzoate	Acetophenone	Na	3,5-Dimethoxydibenzoylmethane	Good	236
Ethyl 2,4-dimethoxybenzoate	Acetophenone	Na	2,4-Dimethoxydibenzoylmethane	26	237
Methyl 2,3,5-trimethoxybenzoate	Acetophenone	Na	2,3,5-Trimethoxydibenzoylmethane	21*	238
Ethyl 3,4,5-trimethoxybenzoate	Acetophenone	NaNH₂	3,4,5-Trimethoxydibenzoylmethane	—	205
Methyl 3,4,5-trimethoxybenzoate	2-Methoxyacetophenone	Na	2′,3,4,5-Tetramethoxydibenzoylmethane	68	213
Ethyl 3,4,5-trimethoxybenzoate	2,3,4-Trimethoxyacetophenone	Na	2,3,4,3′,4′,5′-Hexamethoxydibenzoylmethane	—	235
	2,4,6-Trimethoxyacetophenone	Na	2,4,6,3′,4′,5′-Hexamethoxydibenzoylmethane	—	239
Methyl 2,4,6-trimethoxybenzoate	5,6-Dimethoxy-1-hydrindone	Na	Acylation failed	—	201
Ethyl 3,4-methylenedioxybenzoate	Acetophenone	Na	3,4-Methylenedioxydibenzoylmethane	—	205
	2,4,6-Trimethoxyacetophenone	Na	2,4,6-Trimethoxy-3′,4′-methylenedioxydibenzoyl- methane	—	234
Methyl p-benzoyloxybenzoate	2,4,6-Trimethoxyacetophenone	Na	2,4,6-Trimethoxy-4′-benzoyloxydibenzoylmethane	18	240
Methyl 2-methoxy-3-naphthoate	Acetophenone	Na	1-Phenyl-3-(2-methoxy-3-naphthyl)propane-1,3-dione	—	241

Ester	Ketone	Condensing agent	Product	Yield (%)	References
	2-Methoxyacetophenone	Na	1-(2-Methoxyphenyl)-3-(2-methoxy-3-naphthyl)-propane-1,3-dione	—	241
	2-Acetylnaphthalene	Na	1-(2-Naphthyl)-3-(2-methoxy-3-naphthyl)propane-1,3-dione	—	241
	2-Methoxy-1-acetylnaphthalene	Na	1-(2-Methoxy-1-naphthyl)-3-(2-methoxy-3-naphthyl)propane-1,3-dione	—	241
Methyl 1-methoxy-2-naphthoate	1-Methoxy-2-acetylnaphthalene	Na	Di-(1-methoxy-2-naphthoyl)methane	—	241
Ethyl m-chlorobenzoate	Acetophenone	Na	3-Chlorodibenzoylmethane	30 *	205
Ethyl p-chlorobenzoate	Acetophenone	Na	4-Chlorodibenzoylmethane	36 *	205
Ethyl m-nitrobenzoate	Acetophenone	Na	Acylation failed		205
Ethyl p-nitrobenzoate	Acetophenone	NaNH$_2$	Acylation failed		14
	Acetophenone	Na	4-Nitrodibenzoylmethane	Very poor	205
Diethyl phthalate	Acetone	NaOC$_2$H$_5$	2-Acetyl-1,3-diketohydrindene	—	242
	Methyl ethyl	NaOC$_2$H$_5$	2-Propionyl-1,3-diketohydrindene	—	242
	Acetophenone	NaOC$_2$H$_5$	2-Benzoyl-1,3-diketohydrindene	—	242
	Camphor	Na	α-Phthaloylcamphor		192, 198, 220
Diethyl terephthalate	Acetone	NaNH$_2$	$1,4\text{-}C_6H_4(COCH_2COCH_3)_2$	20	243
	Acetophenone	NaNH$_2$	4-Carbethoxydibenzoylmethane	—	244

B. Heterocyclic Esters

Ester	Ketone	Condensing agent	Product	Yield (%)	References
Ethyl furoate	Acetone	NaOC$_2$H$_5$	Furoylacetone	40-45	6, 106
	Acetophenone	NaOC$_2$H$_5$	Benzoylfuroylmethane	—	6, 245
2-Carbethoxythiophene	2-Acetylthiophene	NaNH$_2$	Di-2-thenoylmethane	64	123
5-Carbethoxy-3-methylisoxazole	Acetone	Na	1-(3-Methyl-5-isoxazolyl)butane-1,3-dione	90	169
	Methyl ethyl	Na	1-(3-Methyl-5-isoxazolyl)pentane-1,3-dione	—	169
	Acetophenone	Na	1-(3-Methyl-5-isoxazolyl)-3-phenylpropane-1,3-dione	—	169
	5-Acetyl-3-methylisoxazole	Na	1,3-Bis(3-methyl-5-isoxazolyl)propane-1,3-dione	—	246
	3-Acetyl-5-methylisoxazole	Na	1-(3-Methyl-5-isoxazolyl)-3-(5-methyl-3-isoxazolyl)propane-1,3-dione	—	246
3-Carbethoxy-5-methylisoxazole	5-Acetyl-3-methylisoxazole	Na	1-(3-Methyl-5-isoxazolyl)-3-(5-methyl-3-isoxazolyl)propane-1,3-dione	—	246

Note: References 93–572 are listed on pp. 187–196.
* The product was isolated as the copper derivative.

TABLE XI—*Continued*

ACYLATIONS WITH AROMATIC ESTERS

B. Heterocyclic Esters—Continued

Ester	Ketone	Condensing Agent	Product	Yield %	Reference
3-Carbethoxy-5-methylisoxazole—Continued	3-Acetyl-5-methylisoxazole	Na	1,3-Bis-(5-methyl-3-isoxazolyl)propane-1,3-dione	—	246
3-Carbethoxy-5-styrylisoxazole	Acetone	Na	1-(5-Styryl-3-isoxazolyl)butane-1,3-dione	—	247
Ethyl picolinate	Acetone	NaOC$_2$H$_5$	1-(2-Pyridyl)butane-1,3-dione	70–74	248
Ethyl nicotinate	Acetone	NaOC$_2$H$_5$	1-(3-Pyridyl)butane-1,3-dione	63	15, 249
	Acetone	Na	1-(3-Pyridyl)butane-1,3-dione	45	250
	Methyl n-butyl	NaOC$_2$H$_5$	1-(3-Pyridyl)heptane-1,3-dione	46	15
	Methyl isobutyl	NaOC$_2$H$_5$	1-(3-Pyridyl)-5-methylhexane-1,3-dione	70	15
	Methyl t-butyl	NaOC$_2$H$_5$	1-(3-Pyridyl)-4,4-dimethylpentane-1,3-dione	42	15
	Methyl n-amyl	NaOC$_2$H$_5$	1-(3-Pyridyl)octane-1,3-dione	47	15
	Acetophenone	NaOC$_2$H$_5$	1-(3-Pyridyl)-3-phenylpropane-1,3-dione	70	15
	Acetomesitylene	NaOC$_2$H$_5$	1-(3-Pyridyl)-3-(2,4,6-trimethylphenyl)propane-1,3-dione	60	15
	Methyl 3-pyridyl	NaOC$_2$H$_5$	Di-(3-pyridyl)propane-1,3-dione	51	15
	Methyl tridecyl	NaOC$_2$H$_5$	Acylation failed		15
	p-Phenylacetophenone	NaOC$_2$H$_5$	Acylation failed		15
Ethyl isonicotinate	Acetone	NaOC$_2$H$_5$	1-(4-Pyridyl)butane-1,3-dione	50–55	251
	Acetophenone	NaOC$_2$H$_5$	1-(4-Pyridyl)-3-phenylpropane-1,3-dione	—	251
Ethyl cinchoninate	Acetone	NaOC$_2$H$_5$	1-(4-Quinolyl)butane-1,3-dione	—	252
Ethyl quininate	Acetone	NaOC$_2$H$_5$	1-(6-Methoxy-4-quinolyl)butane-1,3-dione	—	253
Ethyl 2-phenyl-7-chlorocinchoninate	1-Diethylamino-4-pentanone	NaNH$_2$	1-(7-Chloro-2-phenyl-4-quinolyl)-5-diethylamino-hexane-1,3-dione	15	254

Note: References 93–572 are listed on pp. 187–196.

TABLE XII

INTRAMOLECULAR CYCLIZATIONS

Keto Ester	Condensing Agent	Product	Yield %	Reference
Ethyl levulinate	NaOC₂H₅	Cyclization failed		255
Ethyl β-methyllevulinate	NaOC₂H₅	Cyclization failed		255
Ethyl β,β-dimethyllevulinate	NaOC₂H₅	5,5-Dimethylcyclopentane-1,3-dione	20–25	256
Ethyl β,β,δ-trimethyllevulinate	NaOC₂H₅	2,4,4-Trimethylcyclopentane-1,3-dione	35	255
Methyl δ-phenyllevulinate	NaOCH₃	2-Phenylcyclopentane-1,3-dione	15	257
Methyl δ-benzyllevulinate	NaOC₂H₅	Cyclization failed		258
Methyl α,δ-diphenyllevulinate	NaOCH₃	1,3-Diphenylcyclopentane-2,5-dione	75	258
Methyl β,δ-diphenyllevulinate	NaOCH₃	2,4-Diphenylcyclopentane-1,3-dione	—	259
α-Angelica lactone	NaOCH₃	1-Hydroxybicyclopentyl-2′,3,5′-trione	—	260
δ-Phenyl-Δ^{α,β}-angelica lactone	NaOCH₃	1-Phenylcyclopentane-2,5-dione	23	258
Phoronic acid dilactone	NaOCH₃	α-(2,5-Diketo-3,3-dimethylcyclopentyl)iso-butyric acid	80	261
Phoronic acid monomethyl ester	NaOCH₃	α-(2,5-Diketo-3,3-dimethylcyclopentyl)iso-butyric acid	50	261
Phoronic acid dimethyl ester	NaOC₂H₅	Methyl α-(2,5-diketo-3,3-dimethylcyclopentyl)-isobutyrate	75	262
α-Phenyl-γ-benzylcrotonolactone	NaOCH₃	2,4-Diphenylcyclopentane-1,3-dione	68	261
Methyl 4-keto-7-α-naphthylheptanoate	NaOC₂H₅	β-(1-Naphthyl)ethylcyclopentane-2,5-dione	—	263
Methyl 4-keto-7-(6-methoxy-1-naphthyl)-heptanoate	NaOC₂H₅	β-(6-Methoxy-1-naphthyl)ethylcyclopentane-2,5-dione	95	264
Ethyl δ-acetyl-n-valerate	NaOC₂H₅	2-Acetylcyclopentanone	90	265, 266
Ethyl δ-propionyl-n-valerate	NaOC₂H₅	2-Propionylcyclopentanone	83	265, 266
Ethyl γ-methyl-δ-acetyl-n-valerate	NaOC₂H₅	3-Methyl-2-acetylcyclopentanone	—	267

Note: References 93–572 are listed on pp. 187–196.

TABLE XII—*Continued*

INTRAMOLECULAR CYCLIZATIONS

Keto Ester	Condensing Agent	Product	Yield %	Reference
Ethyl β-isopropyl-δ-acetyl-n-valerate	Na	4-Isopropyl-2-acetylcyclopentanone	81 *	268
Ethyl β-methyl-δ-isobutyryl-n-valerate	Na	4-Methyl-2-isobutyrylcyclopentanone	67 *	268
Methyl δ-benzoyl-n-valerate	NaNH₂	2-Benzoylcyclopentanone	Good	200
Ethyl δ-benzoyl-n-valerate	NaOC₂H₅	2-Benzoylcyclopentanone	—	269
	NaNH₂	2-Benzoylcyclopentanone	80–90	200
Isoamyl δ-benzoyl-n-valerate	NaNH₂	2-Benzoylcyclopentanone	Good	200
Ethyl propionylpyruvate	NaOC₂H₅	2-Methylcyclopentane-1,3,5-trione	—	270
Ethyl γ-acetylbutyrate	NaOC₂H₅	Cyclohexane-1,3-dione	28	271, 272
Ethyl γ-propionylbutyrate	NaOC₂H₅	2-Methylcyclohexane-1,3-dione	100	273
Ethyl γ-acetylisovalerate	NaOC₂H₅	5-Methylcyclohexane-1,3-dione	80	274
Diethyl methyl-(β-acetyl)ethylmalonate	NaOC₂H₅	4-Methyl-4-carbethoxycyclohexane-1,3-dione	36	275
Diethyl α-acetyl-α′-carbethoxysuccinate	NaOC₂H₅	4,5-Dicarbethoxycyclopentane-1,3-dione	—	276
Diethyl α-carbethoxy-α′-acetyl-β-phenyl-glutarate	KOC₂H₅	5-Phenyl-4,6-dicarbethoxycyclohexane-1,3-dione	—	277
Methyl β,β-dimethyl-γ-acetylbutyrate.	NaOC₂H₅	5,5-Dimethylcyclohexane-1,3-dione		278, 279
Ethyl γ-n-butyrylbutyrate	NaOC₂H₅	2-Ethylcyclohexane-1,3-dione	50	280
Ethyl γ-propionyl-β,β-dimethylbutyrate	NaOC₂H₅	2,5,5-Trimethylcyclohexane-1,3-dione	—	281
Diethyl α-methyl-α′-isobutyrylglutarate	NaOC₂H₅	Cyclization failed		282
Dimethyl meso-α,α′-dimethyl-γ-keto-pimelate	NaOCH₃	α-(2,5-Diketo-3-methylcyclopentyl)propionic acid	38	258
Ethyl γ-acetyl-β-methyl-β-ethylbutyrate	NaOC₂H₅	5-Methyl-5-ethylcyclohexane-1,3-dione	70	283
Ethyl γ-n-butyryl-β,β-dimethylbutyrate	NaOC₂H₅	5,5-Dimethyl-2-ethylcyclohexane-1,3-dione	—	281
Ethyl 2,2,4,6-pentamethyl-3,5-diketo-heptanoate	NaC(C₆H₅)₃	2,2,4,6-Hexamethylcyclohexane-1,3,5-trione	30	10

Ketone	Reagent	Product	Yield (%)	References
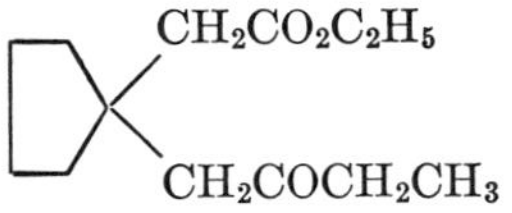 Cyclopentane with $CH_2CO_2C_2H_5$ and $CH_2COCH_2CH_3$	$NaOC_2H_5$	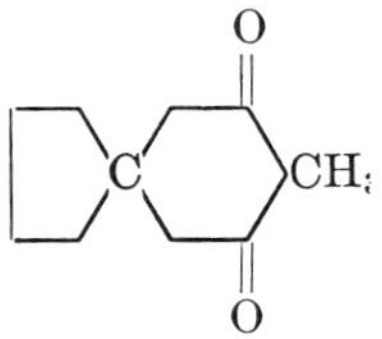 (spiro diketone, CH_3)	Quant.	281
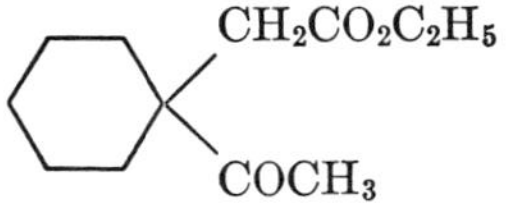 Cyclohexane with $CH_2CO_2C_2H_5$ and $COCH_3$	$NaOC_2H_5$	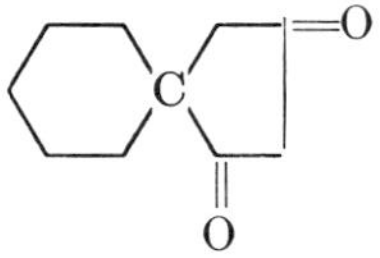 (spiro diketone)	48	256
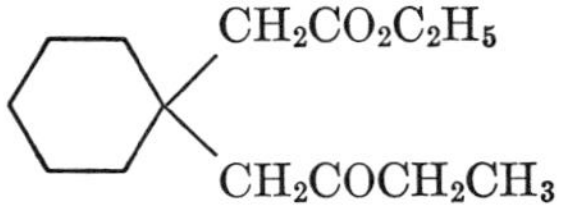 Cyclohexane with $CH_2CO_2C_2H_5$ and $CH_2COCH_2CH_3$	$NaOC_2H_5$	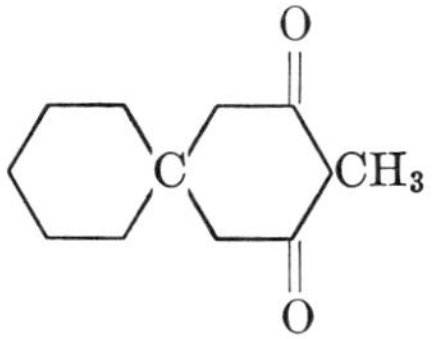 (spiro diketone, CH_3)	100	281
Ethyl β-phenyl-γ-acetylbutyrate	$NaOC_2H_5$	5-Phenylcyclohexane-1,3-dione	—	284
Ethyl α-carbethoxy-β-phenyl-γ-isobutyrylbutyrate	$NaOC_2H_5$	2,2-Dimethyl-4-carbethoxy-5-phenylcyclohexane-1,3-dione	Low	11
Methyl 5-keto-8-(m-methoxyphenyl)-octanoate	$NaOC_2H_5$	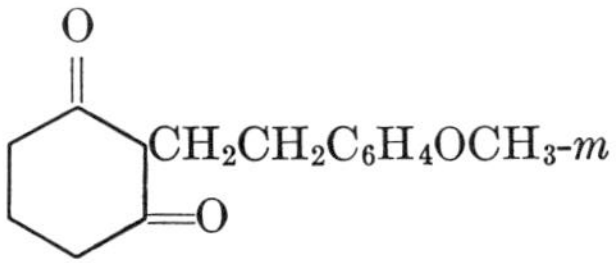 (cyclohexanone with $CH_2CH_2C_6H_4OCH_3$-m)	—	285, 286

Note: References 93–572 are listed on pp. 187–196.
* The product was isolated as the copper derivative.

TABLE XII—*Continued*

INTRAMOLECULAR CYCLIZATIONS

Keto Ester	Condensing Agent	Product	Yield %	Reference
Methyl 5-keto-8-α-naphthyloctanoate	$NaOC_2H_5$	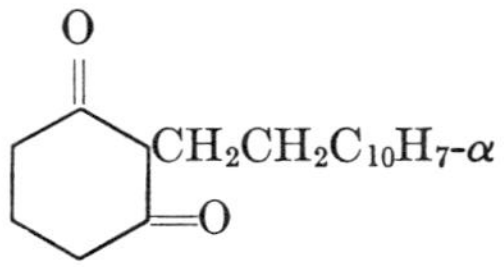	60–63	263, 287
Methyl 5-keto-8-(6-methoxy-1-naphthyl)-octanoate	$NaOC_2H_5$	β-(6-Methoxy-1-naphthyl)ethylcyclohexane-2,6-dione	65	263, 288
Ethyl ε-propionylcaproate	$NaOC_2H_5$	2-Propionylcyclohexanone	83	265, 266
Ethyl ε-benzoylcaproate	$NaNH_2$	2-Benzoylcyclohexanone	60	200
Methyl δ-ketoheneicosanoate	$NaOC_2H_5$	Cyclization failed		258
1-Carbomethoxy-1-methyl-2-(γ-benzoyl-propyl)cyclohexane	$NaOCH_3$	2-Benzoyl-9-methyl-1-decalone	60	288a

Note: References 93–572 are listed on pp. 187–196.

TABLE XIII

MICHAEL CONDENSATIONS ACCOMPANIED BY CLAISEN CYCLIZATIONS *

Unsaturated Carbonyl Compound	Active Hydrogen Compound	Condensing Agent	Product	Yield %	Reference
Mesityl oxide	Diethyl malonate	NaOCH₃	4-Carbethoxy-5,5-dimethylcyclohexane-1,3-dione	65	79, 271
3-Ethyl-3-hexen-5-one	Diethyl malonate	NaOC₂H₅	4-Carbethoxy-5,5-diethylcyclohexane-1,3-dione	81	289
3-Methyl-3-hepten-5-one	Diethyl malonate	NaOC₂H₅	4-Carbethoxy-2,5-dimethyl-5-ethylcyclohexane-1,3-dione	76	290
n-Butylideneacetone	Diethyl malonate	NaOC₂H₅	4-Carbethoxy-5-n-propylcyclohexane-1,3-dione	—	291
Isobutylideneacetone	Diethyl malonate	NaOC₂H₅	4-Carbethoxy-5-isopropylcyclohexane-1,3-dione	70	292
n-Decyl β-n-decylisopropenyl ketone	Diethyl malonate	NaOC₂H₅	4-Carbethoxy-2-n-nonyl-5-methyl-5-n-decylcyclohexane-1,3-dione	—	293
Cyclopentylideneacetone	Diethyl malonate	NaOC₂H₅	5-Cyclopentanespiro-4-carbethoxycyclohexane-1,3-dione	—	279
Cyclohexylideneacetone	Diethyl malonate	NaOC₂H₅	5-Cyclohexanespiro-4-carbethoxycyclohexane-1,3-dione	84	279, 294
1-Cyclopentylidene-2-butanone	Diethyl malonate	NaOC₂H₅	5-Cyclopentanespiro-2-methyl-4-carbethoxycyclohexane-1,3-dione	—	295
1-Cyclohexylidene-2-butanone	Diethyl malonate	NaOC₂H₅	5-Cyclohexanespiro-2-methyl-4-carbethoxycyclohexane-1,3-dione	Good	296
Hexahydrobenzylideneacetone	Diethyl malonate	NaOC₂H₅	4-Carbethoxy-5-cyclohexylcyclohexane-1,3-dione	80	294
Furfuralacetone	Diethyl malonate	NaOC₂H₅	4-Carbethoxy-5-furylcyclohexane-1,3-dione	—	271
Benzylideneacetone	Dimethyl malonate	NaOCH₃	4-Carbomethoxy-5-phenylcyclohexane-1,3-dione	—	271
Benzylideneacetone	Diethyl malonate	NaOC₂H₅	4-Carbethoxy-5-phenylcyclohexane-1,3-dione	—	277, 297, 298, 299, 300
Ethyl α-ethylideneacetoacetate	Diethyl malonate	KOC₂H₅	4,6-Dicarbethoxy-5-methylcyclohexane-1,3-dione	—	277
Ethyl α-benzylideneacetoacetate	Diethyl malonate	(C₂H₅)₂NH, KOC₂H₅	4,6-Dicarbethoxy-5-phenylcyclohexane-1,3-dione	—	277
o-Methoxybenzalacetone	Diethyl malonate	NaOC₂H₅	4-Carbethoxy-5-(o-methoxyphenyl)cyclohexane-1,3-dione	—	301
p-Methoxybenzalacetone	Diethyl malonate	NaOC₂H₅	4-Carbethoxy-5-(p-methoxyphenyl)cyclohexane-1,3-dione	—	271, 301, 302, 303
o-Chlorobenzalacetone	Diethyl malonate	NaOC₂H₅	4-Carbethoxy-5-(o-chlorophenyl)cyclohexane-1,3-dione	—	271, 301
m-Nitrobenzalacetone	Diethyl malonate	NaOC₂H₅	4-Carbethoxy-5-(m-nitrophenyl)cyclohexane-1,3-dione	—	271
p-Nitrobenzalacetone	Diethyl malonate	NaOC₂H₅	4-Carbethoxy-5-(p-nitrophenyl)cyclohexane-1,3-dione	—	271
1-Anisalbutane-2-one	Diethyl malonate	NaOC₂H₅	4-Carbethoxy-5-(p-methoxyphenyl)-2-methylcyclohexane-1,3-dione	75	303

Note: References 93–572 are listed on pp. 187–196.

* In a few reactions the intermediate Michael addition product was isolated, then cyclized by treatment with the basic reagent. Generally, the cyclohexanedione derivative was prepared in one operation involving 1,4-addition to the conjugated system and Claisen cyclization.

TABLE XIII—*Continued*

MICHAEL CONDENSATIONS ACCOMPANIED BY CLAISEN CYCLIZATIONS

Unsaturated Carbonyl Compound	Active Hydrogen Compound	Condensing Agent	Product	Yield %	Reference
Styryl ethyl ketone	Diethyl malonate	$NaOC_2H_5$	4-Carbethoxy-5-phenyl-2-methylcyclohexane-1,3-dione	79	304
	Ethyl phenylacetate	$NaOC_2H_5$	2-Methyl-4,5-diphenylcyclohexane-1,3-dione	21	304
Styryl n-propyl ketone	Diethyl malonate	$NaOC_2H_5$	4-Carbethoxy-5-phenyl-2-ethylcyclohexane-1,3-dione	Good	304
Styryl isopropyl ketone	Diethyl malonate	$NaOC_2H_5$	4-Carbethoxy-5-phenyl-2,2-dimethylcyclohexane-1,3-dione	—	11
Styryl butyl ketone	Diethyl malonate	$NaOC_2H_5$	4-Carbethoxy-5-phenyl-2-n-propylcyclohexane-1,3-dione	35	304
Styryl n-hexyl ketone	Diethyl malonate	$NaOC_2H_5$	4-Carbethoxy-5-phenyl-2-n-amylcyclohexane-1,3-dione	95	304
Styryl phenethyl ketone	Diethyl malonate	$NaOC_2H_5$	4-Carbethoxy-5-phenyl-2-benzylcyclohexane-1,3-dione	60	304
Cinnamalacetone	Diethyl malonate	$NaOC_2H_5$	4-Carbethoxy-5-styrylcyclohexane-1,3-dione	—	271
Mesityl oxide	Diethyl ethoxymalonate	$NaOC_2H_5$	4-Carbethoxy-4-ethoxy-5,5-dimethylcyclohexane-1,3-dione	—	305
Ethyl crotonate	Ethyl acetoacetate	$NaOC_2H_5$	4-Carbethoxy-5-methylcyclohexane-1,3-dione	—	272, 297, 306
Benzalacetone	Ethyl acetoacetate	$NaOC_2H_5$	4-Acetyl-5-phenylcyclohexane-1,3-dione	60	271, 299
Ethyl cinnamate	Ethyl acetoacetate	$NaOC_2H_5$	4-Carbethoxy-5-phenylcyclohexane-1,3-dione	—	307
Ethyl p-methoxycinnamate	Ethyl acetoacetate	$NaOC_2H_5$	4-Carbethoxy-5-(p-methoxyphenyl)cyclohexane-1,3-dione	—	271
Ethyl styrylacetate	Ethyl acetoacetate	$NaOC_2H_5$	4-Carbethoxy-5-benzylcyclohexane-1,3-dione	55	308
Diethyl benzalmalonate	Ethyl acetoacetate	$NaOC_2H_5$	4,6-Dicarbethoxy-5-phenylcyclohexane-1,3-dione	72	309
Diethyl 4-acetoxybenzylidenemalonate	Ethyl acetoacetate	$NaOC_2H_5$	4,6-Dicarbethoxy-5-(p-acetoxyphenyl)cyclohexane-1,3-dione	—	310
1,2-Dihydro-4-carbethoxynaphthalene	Ethyl acetoacetate	$NaOC_2H_5$	1,3-Diketo-4-carbethoxyoctahydrophenanthrene	60	311
p-Methoxybenzalacetone	Ethyl cyanoacetate	$NaOC_2H_5$	4-Cyano-5-(p-methoxyphenyl)cyclohexane-1,3-dione	60-75	312
	1,1,2-Tricarbethoxyethane	$NaOC_2H_5$	4-Carbethoxy-4-carbethoxymethyl-5-(p-methoxyphenyl)-cyclohexane-1,3-dione	40	313
1-(p-Methoxyphenyl)-1-pentene-3-one	Ethyl cyanoacetate	$NaOC_2H_5$	4-Cyano-5-p-methoxyphenyl-2-methylcyclohexane-1,3-dione	54	312
	1,1,2-Tricarbethoxyethane	$NaOC_2H_5$	4-Carbethoxy-4-carbethoxymethyl-5-(p-methoxyphenyl)-2-methylcyclohexane-1,3-dione	25	313
Diethyl benzalmalonate	Ethyl butyrylacetate	Na	4,6-Dicarbethoxy-5-phenyl-2-ethylcyclohexane-1,3-dione	—	314
	Ethyl isobutyrylacetate	Na	4,6-Dicarbethoxy-5-phenyl-2,2-dimethylcyclohexane-1,3-dione	—	282, 314
Diethyl anisalmalonate	Ethyl isobutyrylacetate	$NaOC_2H_5$	4,6-Dicarbethoxy-5-(p-methoxyphenyl)-2,2-dimethylcyclohexane-1,3-dione	—	314
Benzalacetone	Ethyl oxalacetate	$NaOC_2H_5$	4-Ethoxalyl-5-phenylcyclohexane-1,3-dione	—	271
Mesityl oxide	Ethyl phenylacetate	$NaOC_2H_5$	5,5-Dimethyl-6-phenylcyclohexane-1,3-dione	60	315

Note: References 93–572 are listed on pp. 187-196.

TABLE XIV

ACYLATIONS WITH OXALIC ESTERS

(Diethyl oxalate was employed unless otherwise noted.)

Ketone	Condensing Agent	Product	Yield %	Reference
Acetone	NaOC₂H₅	Ethoxalylacetone	70–90	75, 270, 316–319
	NaOC₂H₅	Diethoxalylacetone	85	81, 318, 320–323
Methyl ethyl	NaOC₂H₅	Ethoxalyldiacetone	—	324
	NaOCH₃	Methyl acetopyruvate	70	325
	NaOC₂H₅	Ethyl propionylpyruvate	58	28, 83, 270
	Na	Decane-3,5,6,8-tetraone	70	83
	NaOC₂H₅	Ethyl 5-methylcyclopentane-1,2,4-trione-3-glyoxalate	50	83, 84, 270
	NaOCH₃	Methyl propionylpyruvate	42	325
Methyl β-methoxyethyl	NaOCH₃	Methyl β-methoxypropionylpyruvate *	29	320, 326
Methyl n-propyl	NaOC₂H₅	Ethyl n-butyrylpyruvate	—	327
	NaOC₂H₅	Ethyl 3-ethylcyclopentane-1,2,4-trione-5-glyoxalate	75	328
	NaOCH₃	Methyl n-butyrylpyruvate	52	325
Methyl γ-phenoxypropyl	NaOC₂H₅	Ethyl 5-(β-phenoxyethyl)cyclopentane-1,2,4-trione-3-glyoxalate	75	329
Diethyl	NaOC₂H₅, NaOCH₃	3,5-Dimethylcyclopentane-1,2,4-trione	14	330
Ethylideneacetone	NaOC₂H₅	Ethyl crotonylpyruvate	—	319
Methyl isopropyl	NaOC₂H₅	Ethyl isobutyrylpyruvate	—	327
Methyl isopropenyl	NaOC₂H₅	Ethyl methacrylylpyruvate *	—	319
Methyl n-butyl	NaOC₂H₅	Ethyl n-valerylpyruvate	55–60	331
Methyl isobutyl	NaOCH₃	Methyl isovalerylpyruvate	84	325
	NaOC₂H₅	Ethyl isovalerylpyruvate	91	332, 333
	LiOC₂H₅	Ethyl isovalerylpyruvate	90	332
Methyl t-butyl	NaOCH₃	Methyl trimethylacetopyruvate	75	325
	NaOC₂H₅	Ethyl pivaloylpyruvate	—	319
Methyl benzyl	NaOC₂H₅	Ethyl phenylacetylpyruvate	30	334
	KOC₂H₅	Ethyl 5-phenylcyclopentane-1,2,4-trione-3-glyoxalate	86	335
Benzylacetone	NaOC₂H₅	Ethyl β-phenylpropionylpyruvate	40	334

Note: References 93–572 are listed on pp. 187–196.
* Dimethyl oxalate was employed.

TABLE XIV—Continued

ACYLATIONS WITH OXALIC ESTERS

Ketone	Condensing Agent	Product	Yield %	Reference
Dibenzyl	NaOC2H5	3,5-Diphenylcyclopentane-1,2,4-trione	87	330, 336
Methyl vinyl	NaOC2H5	Ethyl acrylylpyruvate	—	326
2-Methyl-2-hepten-6-one (methyl heptenone)	NaOC2H5	Ethyl 2,4-diketo-8-methyl-7-nonenoate	—	337
Mesityl oxide	Na	Methyl β,β-dimethylacrylylpyruvate *	—	319, 338
	NaOC4H9	n-Butyl β,β-dimethylacrylylpyruvate †	78	339
	Na	Isobutyl β,β-dimethylacrylylpyruvate ‡	68	339
	Na	sec-Butyl β,β-dimethylacrylylpyruvate §	66	339
	NaOC2H5	Ethyl β,β-dimethylacrylylpyruvate	Good	320, 326
	NaOCH3	Ethyl β,β-dimethylacrylylpyruvate	—	333
Crotylideneacetone	NaOC2H5	Ethyl sorbitoylpyruvate	—	333
Isoamylideneacetone	NaOC2H5	Ethyl 2,4-diketo-8-methyl-5-nonenoate	—	333
Methyl pentadecyl	NaOC2H5	Ethyl palmitoylpyruvate	—	333
Cyclopentanone	NaOC2H5	Ethyl cyclopentanone-2-glyoxalate	70	195, 340
	NaOC2H5	Diethyl cyclopentanone-2,5-diglyoxalate	—	195
3-Methylcyclopentanone	NaOC2H5	Ethyl 3-methylcyclopentanone-5-glyoxalate	57-60	195
2,2-Dimethylcyclopentanone	NaOC2H5	Ethyl 2,2-dimethylcyclopentanone-5-glyoxalate	63	341
Thujone	NaOC2H5	Ethyl thujone-2-glyoxalate	—	340
Isothujone	NaOC2H5	Ethyl isothujone-2-glyoxalate	62	340
Cyclohexanone	NaOC2H5	Ethyl cyclohexanone-2-glyoxalate	80-85	82, 342-345
2-Cyclohexen-1-one	NaOC2H5	Ethyl 2-cyclohexen-1-one-6-glyoxalate	—	346
2-Methylcyclohexanone	NaOC2H5	Ethyl 2-methylcyclohexanone-6-glyoxalate	33	317, 345, 347
3-Methylcyclohexanone	Na	Ethyl 3-methylcyclohexanone-6-glyoxalate	70-80	348
	NaOC2H5	Ethyl 3-methylcyclohexanone-6-glyoxalate	63 ‖	317, 345, 348
4-Methylcyclohexanone	NaOC2H5	Ethyl 4-methylcyclohexanone-2-glyoxalate	—	345, 349
2,2-Dimethylcyclohexanone	Na	Ethyl 2,2-dimethylcyclohexanone-6-glyoxalate	37	350
2,5-Dimethylcyclohexanone	NaOC2H5	Ethyl 2,5-dimethylcyclohexanone-6-glyoxalate	—	347
1,3-Dimethyl-3-cyclohexen-5-one	NaOC2H5	Ethyl 1,3-dimethyl-3-cyclohexen-5-one-6-glyoxalate	—	195
2-Methoxycyclohexanone	NaOC2H5	Ethyl 2-methoxycyclohexanone-6-glyoxalate	—	347
4-Methoxycyclohexanone	NaOC2H5	Ethyl 4-methoxycyclohexanone-2-glyoxalate	—	351
2-Methyl-2-phenylcyclohexanone	NaOCH3	Methyl 2-methyl-2-phenylcyclohexanone-6-glyoxalate *	82	352
2-Methyl-2-carbethoxycyclohexanone	NaOC2H5	Ethyl 2-methyl-2-carbethoxycyclohexanone-6-glyoxalate	35	343
3-Methyl-4-carbethoxycyclohexanone	NaOC2H5	Ethyl 3-methyl-4-carbethoxycyclohexanone-6-glyoxalate	Good	353
2,2,3-Trimethyl-4-carbethoxycyclohexanone	NaOC2H5	Ethyl 2,2,3-trimethyl-4-carbethoxycyclohexanone-6-glyoxalate	58	354

Ketone	Base	Product	Yield (%)	References
2-(β-Carbethoxyethyl)-2-methyl-5-isopropenyl-cyclohexanone	NaOC$_2$H$_5$	Ethyl 2-(β-carbethoxyethyl)-2-methyl-5-isopropenylcyclohexanone-6-glyoxalate	—	355
Cycloheptanone	NaOC$_2$H$_5$	Ethyl cycloheptanone-2-glyoxalate	—	347
Camphor	Na	Camphor-3-glyoxylic acid *	40–45	356
	Na	Ethyl camphor-3-glyoxalate	63 ¶	192, 220, 357
	NaOC$_2$H$_5$	Ethyl camphor-3-glyoxalate	10 ¶	357
	Ca	Camphor-3-glyoxylic acid	50	192
	NaNH$_2$	Camphor-3-glyoxylic acid	19	192
	Na	Isoamyl camphor-3-glyoxalate **	60	356
Acetophenone	Na	Ethyl benzoylpyruvate	—	198
	NaOC$_2$H$_5$	Ethyl benzoylpyruvate	70–78	125, 319, 358, 359
	NaOC$_2$H$_5$	Oxalyldiacetophenone	30	125, 358
2-Methylacetophenone	NaOC$_2$H$_5$	2-Methylbenzoylpyruvate	30	360
2,4-Dimethylacetophenone	NaOCH$_3$	1,6-Di-(2,4-dimethylphenyl)hexane-1,3,4,6-tetraone	43	361
2-Hydroxyacetophenone	NaOC$_2$H$_5$	Ethyl 2-hydroxybenzoylpyruvate	98 ¶	320
4-Methoxyacetophenone	NaOC$_2$H$_5$	1,6-Di-(p-methoxyphenyl)hexane-1,3,4,6-tetraone	—	361
	Na	Ethyl anisoylpyruvate	70	362
2,4-Dimethoxyacetophenone	KOC$_2$H$_5$	Ethyl 2,4-dimethoxybenzoylpyruvate	58	363
3,4-Dimethoxyacetophenone	Na	Ethyl 3,4-dimethoxybenzoylpyruvate	—	364
2,4-Diethoxyacetophenone	Na	Ethyl 2,4-diethoxybenzoylpyruvate	—	365
2,5-Diethoxyacetophenone	Na	Ethyl 2,5-diethoxybenzoylpyruvate	—	365
4-Ethoxy-2-hydroxyacetophenone	Na	Ethyl 4-ethoxy-2-hydroxybenzoylpyruvate	—	365
2,4,6-Trimethoxyacetophenone	NaOC$_2$H$_5$	Ethyl 2,4,6-trimethoxybenzoylpyruvate	—	365
3,4-Dimethoxy-6-nitroacetophenone	Na	3,4-Dimethoxy-6-nitrobenzoylpyruvic acid	88	366
Benzalacetone	NaOC$_2$H$_5$	Methyl cinnamoylpyruvate *	64	151
Benzalacetone	Na	Ethyl cinnamoylpyruvate	68	334, 366
4-Methoxybenzalacetone	Na	Methyl 4-methoxycinnamoylpyruvate *	44	151
3,4-Dimethoxybenzalacetone	Na	Methyl 3,4-dimethoxycinnamoylpyruvate *	—	367
3,4-Methylenedioxybenzalacetone	Na	Methyl 3,4-methylenedioxycinnamoylpyruvate *	—	367
1-Phenyl-2-methyl-1-buten-3-one	NaOC$_2$H$_5$	Ethyl (α-methylcinnamoyl)pyruvate	—	368

Note: References 93–572 are listed on pp. 187–196.

* Dimethyl oxalate was employed.
† Di-n-butyl oxalate was employed.
‡ Diisobutyl oxalate was employed.
§ Di-sec-butyl oxalate was employed.
‖ The product was isolated as the copper derivative.
¶ The product was isolated as the sodium derivative.
** Diisoamyl oxalate was employed.

TABLE XIV—Continued

ACYLATIONS WITH OXALIC ESTERS

Ketone	Condensing Agent	Product	Yield %	Reference
4,6-Diacetylresorcinol dimethyl ether	Na	[structure: OCH₃, COCH₂COCO₂CH₃ *, CH₃O]	—	150
	Na	[structure: COCH₂COCO₂CH₃, OCH₃, CH₃O, COCH₂COCO₂C₂H₅]	—	150
Phenyl propenyl	KOC$_2$H$_5$	Ethyl 6-phenyl-2,6-diketo-4-hexenoate	81	30
Mesityl propenyl	KOC$_2$H$_5$	Ethyl 6-mesityl-2,6-diketo-4-hexenoate	90	30
1-Hydrindone	NaOC$_2$H$_5$	Ethyl 1-hydrindone-2-glyoxalate	—	195
5,6-Methylenedioxy-1-hydrindone	NaOC$_2$H$_5$	Ethyl 5,6-methylenedioxy-1-hydrindone-2-glyoxalate	79	195
5,6-Dimethoxy-1-hydrindone	NaOC$_2$H$_5$	Ethyl 5,6-dimethoxy-1-hydrindone-2-glyoxalate	—	201
1-Tetralone	NaOCH$_3$	Methyl 1-tetralone-2-glyoxalate *	91	369, 370
7-Ethyl-1-tetralone	NaOC$_2$H$_5$	Methyl 7-ethyl-1-tetralone-2-glyoxalate *	82	371
6-Methoxy-1-tetralone	NaOCH$_3$	Methyl 6-methoxy-1-tetralone-2-glyoxalate *	92	372
5-Methoxy-1-tetralone	NaOCH$_3$	Methyl 5-methoxy-1-tetralone-2-glyoxalate *	93	370
5-Methyl-6-methoxy-1-tetralone	NaOCH$_3$	Methyl 5-methyl-6-methoxy-1-tetralone-2-glyoxalate *	93–94	373
4,6,7-Trimethyl-1-tetralone	NaOCH$_3$	Methyl 4,6,7-trimethyl-1-tetralone-2-glyoxalate *	91	374
3-Benzyl-1-tetralone	NaOCH$_3$	Methyl 3-benzyl-1-tetralone-2-glyoxalate *	70	375
cis-2-Decalone	NaOC$_2$H$_5$	Ethyl cis-2-decalone-3-glyoxalate	—	376
1-Keto-1,2,3,4,5,6,7,8-octahydrophenanthrene	NaOC$_2$H$_5$	Methyl 1-keto-1,2,3,4,5,6,7,8-octahydrophenanthrene-2-glyoxalate *	89	377
1-Keto-7-methoxy-1,2,3,4,9,10,11,12-octahydrophenanthrene	NaOC$_2$H$_5$	Ethyl 1-keto-7-methoxy-1,2,3,4,9,10,11,12-octahydrophenanthrene-2-glyoxalate	88	285, 378
1-Keto-9-methoxy-s-octahydrophenanthrene	NaOC$_2$H$_5$	Methyl 1-keto-9-methoxy-s-octahydrophenanthrene-2-glyoxalate *	92	379
cis-1-Keto-4b-methyl-Δ$^{4a(10a)}$-dodecahydrophenanthrene *	NaOCH$_3$	Methyl cis-1-keto-4b-methyl-Δ$^{4a(10a)}$-dodecahydrophenanthrene-2-glyoxalate *	95	380
1-Keto-1,2,3,4-tetrahydrophenanthrene	NaOCH$_3$	Methyl 1-keto-1,2,3,4-tetrahydrophenanthrene-2-glyoxalate *	95	381
1-Keto-1,2,3,4-tetrahydrophenanthrene	KOC$_2$H$_5$	Ethyl 1-keto-1,2,3,4-tetrahydrophenanthrene-2-glyoxalate	95	382

Ketone	Reagent	Product	Yield %	References
4-Keto-1,2,3,4-tetrahydrophenanthrene	NaOCH₃	Methyl 4-keto-1,2,3,4-tetrahydrophenanthrene-3-glyoxalate *	85	383
	KOC₂H₅	Ethyl 4-keto-1,2,3,4-tetrahydrophenanthrene-3-glyoxalate	—	382
1-Keto-6-methoxy-1,2,3,4-tetrahydrophenanthrene	NaOCH₃	Methyl 6-methoxy-1-keto-1,2,3,4-tetrahydrophenanthrene-2-glyoxalate *	80–96	384
1-Keto-7-methoxy-1,2,3,4-tetrahydrophenanthrene	NaOCH₃	Methyl 1-keto-7-methoxy-1,2,3,4-tetrahydrophenanthrene-2-glyoxalate *	96	29
1-Keto-7-methoxy-1,2,3,4,9,10-hexahydrophenanthrene	NaOC₂H₅	Ethyl 1-keto-7-methoxy-1,2,3,4,9,10-hexahydrophenanthrene-2-glyoxalate	—	385
1-Keto-9-methoxy-1,2,3,4-tetrahydrophenanthrene	NaOCH₃	Methyl 1-keto-9-methoxy-1,2,3,4-tetrahydrophenanthrene-2-glyoxalate *	95	386
1-Keto-9-ethyl-1,2,3,4-tetrahydrophenanthrene	NaOCH₃	Methyl 1-keto-9-ethyl-1,2,3,4-tetrahydrophenanthrene-2-glyoxalate *	57	387
4'-Ketotetrahydro-3,4-benzpyrene	NaOCH₃	Methyl 4'-ketotetrahydro-3,4-benzpyrene-3'-glyoxalate *	96	388
2'-Keto-2-methyl-3,4-dihydro-1,2-cyclopentenophenanthrene	NaOCH₃	Methyl 2'-keto-2-methyl-3,4-dihydro-1,2-cyclopentenophenanthrene-3'-glyoxalate *	92	389
Methyl 2,4-dimethoxybenzoylpropionate	Na	Ethyl 1-carbomethoxymethyl-2,4-dimethoxybenzoylpyruvate lactone	—	363
2-Acetylpyrrole	NaOC₂H₅	Ethyl 4-(2-pyrryl)-2,4-diketobutanoate	—	755, 390
2,4-Dimethyl-3-acetylpyrrole	NaOC₂H₅	Ethyl 4-(2,4-dimethyl-3-pyrryl)-2,4-diketobutanoate	80	755, 391
2,3-Dimethyl-4-acetylpyrrole	NaOC₂H₅	Ethyl 4-(2,3-dimethyl-4-pyrryl)-2,4-diketobutanoate	—	755, 391
2,4-Dimethyl-5-carbethoxy-3-acetylpyrrole	NaOC₂H₅	Ethyl 4-(2,4-dimethyl-5-carbethoxy-3-pyrryl)-2,4-diketobutanoate	98	391
3-Hydroxy-4-carbethoxy-5-methylpyrrole	NaOC₂H₅	Ethyl 4-(3-hydroxy-4-carbethoxy-5-methyl-2-pyrryl)-2,4-diketobutanoate	Almost quant.	392
2-Hydroxy-4-carbethoxy-5-methylpyrrole	NaOC₂H₅	Ethyl 2-hydroxy-4-carbethoxy-5-methylpyrrole-3-glyoxalate	83	391
(quinolinone structure)	NaOC₂H₅	(quinolinone structure, COCO₂C₂H₅)	76	393
	NaOC₅H₁₁-i	(quinolinone structure, COCO₂C₅H₁₁-i †)	60	393
1-Keto-1,2,3,4-tetrahydrocarbazole	NaOC₂H₅	Ethyl 1-keto-1,2,3,4-tetrahydrocarbazole-2-glyoxalate	75	393
5-Styryl-3-acetylisoxazole	Na	Ethyl 4-(5-styryl-3-isoxazolyl)-2,4-diketobutyrate	—	247

Note: References 93–572 are listed on pp. 187–196.

* Dimethyl oxalate was employed.

† Diisoamyl oxalate was employed.

TABLE XV

ACYLATIONS WITH FORMIC ESTERS

(Ethyl formate was employed unless otherwise noted.)

Ketone	Product	Condensing Agent	Yield %	Reference
Acetone	Acetoacetaldehyde	NaOC$_2$H$_5$	54 *	32, 394, 395
	Acetoacetaldehyde	Na	— *	33, 394, 395, 396
Methyl ethyl	1,3,5-Triacetylbenzene	NaOC$_2$H$_5$	30–38	34
	3-Formyl-2-butanone	NaOC$_2$H$_5$	—	32, 37
	3-Formyl-2-butanone	Na	75	33, 35, 36, 397
Methyl n-propyl	n-Butyrylacetaldehyde(?)	NaOC$_2$H$_5$	—	32
	n-Butyrylacetaldehyde(?)	Na	—	397
Methyl cyclopropyl	n-Butyrylacetaldehyde(?)	NaOC$_2$H$_5$	—	398

$$\text{CH}_2$$
(△ = CH$_2$CH—, cyclopropyl)

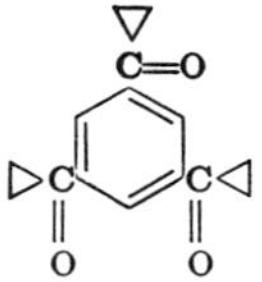

Ketone	Product	Condensing Agent	Yield %	Reference
Methyl γ-ethoxypropyl	5-Ethoxy-3-formyl-2-pentanone	Na	20	35
Methyl isobutyl	Isovalerylacetaldehyde	Na	80 *	38, 399
Methyl t-butyl	Pivaloylacetaldehyde	Na	—	399
Methyl t-butyl	Pivaloylacetaldehyde	NaNH$_2$	50	14
Methyl isoamyl	Isocaproylacetaldehyde(?)	Na	—	399
Methyl n-hexyl	3-Formyl-2-octanone	Na	Good	400
6-Methyl-2-heptanone	8-Methyl-1,3-nonanedione(?)	Na	—	401
3-Ethyl-2-pentanone	Diethylacetylacetaldehyde	Na	—	399
Mesityl oxide	Isopropylideneacetoacetaldehyde	Na	52 †	401
	Isopropylideneacetoacetaldehyde	NaOCH$_3$	—	396
Allylacetone	6-Heptene-1,3-dione	Na	—	401
6-Methyl-3-hepten-2-one	7-Methyl-6-octene-1,3-dione	NaOC$_2$H$_5$	—	401, 402
β-Ionone	Formyl-β-ionone	Na	84 *	403
Diethyl	α-Propionylpropionaldehyde	NaOC$_2$H$_5$	58 †	394, 404
Cyclopentanone	2-Formylcyclopentanone	NaOCH$_3$	10–20	405

Ketone	Base	Product	Yield (%)	References
	NaOC$_2$H$_5$	2-Formylcyclopentanone	59	393, 406
	Na	2-Formylcyclopentanone	15–20	405, 408
	Na	2-Formylcyclopentanone ‡	—	407
Cyclohexanone	Na	2-Formylcyclohexanone	60	409, 410
	Na	2-Formylcyclohexanone ‡	62	118, 407
3-Methylcyclopentanone	Na	5-Formyl-3-methylcyclopentanone ‡	—	407
2-Methylcyclohexanone	Na	6-Formyl-2-methylcyclohexanone	—	410
3-Methylcyclohexanone	Na	6-Formyl-3-methylcyclohexanone ‡	—	407, 410
4-Methylcyclohexanone	Na	2-Formyl-4-methylcyclohexanone	46	410, 411
2,4-Dimethylcyclohexanone	NaNH$_2$	6-Formyl-2,4-dimethylcyclohexanone ‡	—	349
4-Methoxycyclohexanone	NaOC$_2$H$_5$	2-Formyl-4-methoxycyclohexanone §	—	411
1,3-Dimethyl-3-cyclohexen-5-one	NaOC$_2$H$_5$	6-Formyl-1,3-dimethyl-3-cyclohexen-5-one	—	412
Dihydroisophorone	NaOC$_2$H$_5$	2-Formyl-3,3,5-trimethylcyclohexanon ‡	49	413
Menthone	Na	2-Formylmenthone ‡	—	414
	Na	2-Formylmenthone	55–65	410
(−)-Menthone	NaNH$_2$	Formyl-(−)-menthone	85	415
Cycloheptanone	NaOCH$_3$	2-Formylcycloheptanone	86	405
	NaOCH$_3$	2-Formylcycloheptanone ‡	—	415a
Carvomenthone	Na	2-Formylcarvomenthone	—	407
Thujamenthone	Na	2-Formylthujamenthone	—	407
Dihydrocarvone	Na	Formyldihyrocarvone ‡	—	416
Tetrahydrocarvone	Na	Formyltetrahydrocarvone ‡	—	407
Isothujone	Na	Formylisothujone ‡	—	407
Thujone	Na	Formylthujone ‡	—	416
Carvone	Na	Formylcarvone ‡	—	416
Cyclooctanone	NaOCH$_3$	2-Formylcyclooctanone	81	415a
2-Methylbicyclo-1,2,3-octan-4-one	Na	2-Methyl-3-formylbicyclo-1,2,3-octan-4-one §	—	417
Cyclodecanone	NaOCH$_3$	2-Formylcyclodecanone	86	415a
Cyclododecanone	NaOCH$_3$	2-Formylcyclododecanone	68	415a
Cyclohexadecanone	NaOCH$_3$	2-Formylcyclohexadecanone	90	415a
β-Dihydroumbellulone	Na	Formyl-β-dihydroumbellulone §	—	418
Camphor	Na	3-Formylcamphor	Fair	192, 394, 404, 414

Note: References 93–572 are listed on pp. 187–196.

* The product was isolated as the sodium derivative.
† The product was isolated as the copper derivative.
‡ Amyl formate was employed.
§ Isoamyl formate was employed.

TABLE XV—Continued

ACYLATIONS WITH FORMIC ESTERS

Ketone	Condensing Agent	Product	Yield %	Reference
Camphor—Continued	NaOC5H11	3-Formylcamphor	—	414
	NaNH2	3-Formylcamphor	—	22
	Na	3-Formylcamphor ‡	70	394, 414
	NaNH2	3-Formylcamphor	59-63	22
Phenylacetone	NaOC2H5	4-Phenyl-3-ketobutanal	—	419
Benzylacetone	Na	5-Phenyl-3-ketopentanal	—	36
	NaOC2H5	2-Benzyl-3-ketobutanal	80 *	419, 420
		5-Phenyl-3-ketopentanal	15 *	
3-Methyl-4-phenylbutan-2-one	NaOC2H5	4-Methyl-5-phenyl-3-ketopentanal	82	420
Isopropyl benzyl	NaOC2H5	2-Phenyl-4-methyl-3-ketopentanal	—	421
Acetophenone	NaOC2H5	Benzoylacetaldehyde	40-47	394, 420, 422, 423, 424
	Na	Benzoylacetaldehyde	—	33, 396
p-Methoxyacetophenone	NaOC2H5	p-Methoxybenzoylacetaldehyde	95 †	425
	Na	p-Methoxybenzoylacetaldehyde	—	397
p-Methylacetophenone	NaOC2H5	p-Methylbenzoylacetaldehyde	—	397
2-Hydroxyacetophenone	Na	Chromone	—	426
2-Hydroxy-5-chloroacetophenone	Na	2-Hydroxy-5-chlorobenzoylacetaldehyde	50	134
Acetomesitylene	NaOCH3	Mesitoylacetaldehyde	80-99	405
	C2H5MgBr	Mesitoylacetaldehyde	33	129
ω-Methoxyacetophenone	NaOC2H5	2-Methoxy-3-phenyl-3-ketopropanal	16 †	427
ω-Methoxy-p-methoxyacetophenone	NaOC2H5	α-Methoxyanisoylacetaldehyde	81 †	427
2,4,6-Trihydroxy-α-(4-methoxyphenyl)acetophenone	Na	5,7-Dihydroxy-4'-methoxyisoflavone	29	428
Propiophenone	NaOC2H5	α-Benzoylpropionaldehyde	—	394, 404
2-Hydroxypropiophenone	Na	3-Methylchromone	87	426
2-Hydroxy-5-methylpropiophenone	Na	3,6-Dimethylchromone	—	426
Butyrophenone	NaOC2H5	α-Benzoylbutyraldehyde	—	394, 404
	Na	α-Benzoylbutyraldehyde	—	414
2-Hydroxy-5-methylbutyrophenone	Na	3-Ethyl-6-methylchromone	—	426
Isobutyrophenone	NaOC2H5	Condensation failed	—	404

Desoxybenzoin	Formyldesoxybenzoin			394, 404
		NaOC₂H₅		
2-Hydroxyphenyl benzyl	Isoflavone	Na	40	430
2-Hydroxy-4-methoxyphenyl benzyl	7-Methoxyisoflavone	Na	60	431
2-Hydroxy-4-benzyloxyphenyl benzyl	7-Benzyloxyisoflavone	Na	70	431
2,4-Dihydroxyphenyl 4'-hydroxybenzyl	7-Hydroxy-4'-hydroxyisoflavone (daidzein)	Na	6	432
2,4-Dihydroxyphenyl 4'-methoxybenzyl	7-Hydroxy-4'-methoxyisoflavone	Na	20	432
2,4-Dihydroxyphenyl 3',4'-methylenedioxybenzyl (pseudobaptigenitin)	7-Hydroxy-3',4'-methylenedioxyisoflavone (pseudobaptigenin)	Na	—	433
2-Hydroxy-4-methoxyphenyl 3',4'-methylenedioxy-benzyl (pseudobaptigenitin methyl ether)	7-Methoxy-3',4'-methylenedioxyisoflavone (pseudobaptigenin methyl ether)	Na	—	433
2-Hydroxy-4-benzyloxyphenyl 4-methoxybenzyl	7-Benzyloxy-4'-methoxyisoflavone	Na	46	434
2-Hydroxy-4-benzyloxyphenyl 3,4-methylenedioxy-benzyl	7-Benzyloxy-3',4'-methylenedioxyisoflavone	Na	93	434
2,4-Dihydroxy-3-methyl-6-methoxyphenyl 4'-methoxybenzyl	7-Hydroxy-8-methyl-4',5-dimethoxyisoflavone	Na	39	435
2,6-Dihydroxy-4,5-dimethoxyphenyl 4'-methoxy-benzyl	5-Hydroxy-4',6,7-trimethoxyisoflavone	Na	14	436
Osajetin dimethyl ether	2-Hydroxy-2,3-dihydroösajin dimethyl ether	Na	40	437
Tetrahydroösajetin dimethyl ether	2-Hydroxyhexahydroösajin dimethyl ether	Na	75	437
Pomiferitin trimethyl ether	2-Hydroxy-2,3-dihydropomiferin trimethyl ether	Na	40	438
Tetrahydropomiferitin trimethyl ether	2-Hydroxyhexahydropomiferin trimethyl ether	Na	35	438
1-Acetonaphthone	1-Formylacetonaphthone	Na	—	397
1-Phenylacetyl-2-naphthol	2-Phenyl-1,4-β-naphthapyrone	Na	30	431
2-Phenylacetyl-1-naphthol	3-Phenyl-1,4-α-naphthapyrone	Na	30	431
1-Hydroxy-2-β-phenylpropionaphthone	3-Benzyl-1,4-α-naphthapyrone and 2-hydroxy-3-benzyl-2,3-dihydro-1,4-α-naphthapyrone	Na	—	439
1-Tetralone	2-Formyl-1-tetralone	Na	70–75	440
	2-Formyl-1-tetralone	NaOCH₃	94	405
1-Hydrindone	2-Formyl-1-hydrindone	Na	Good	441
	2-Formyl-1-hydrindone	NaOC₂H₅		412
	2-Formyl-1-hydrindone	NaOCH₃	89	405
5-Methoxy-1-hydrindone	2-Formyl-5-methoxy-1-hydrindone	NaOCH₃	98	85

Note: References 93–572 are listed on pp. 187–196.
* The product was isolated as the sodium derivative‡
† The product was isolated as the copper derivative.
‡ Amyl formate was employed.

TABLE XV—Continued

ACYLATIONS WITH FORMIC ESTERS

Ketone	Condensing Agent	Product	Yield %	Reference
6-Methoxy-1-hydrindone	NaOCH₃	2-Formyl-6-methoxy-1-hydrindone	100	405
5,6-Methylenedioxy-1-hydrindone	NaOC₂H₅	2-Formyl-5,6-methylenedioxy-1-hydrindone	—	412
3-Phenyl-1-hydrindone	NaOCH₃	2-Formyl-3-phenyl-1-hydrindone	93	405
1-Keto-1,2,3,4-tetrahydrophenanthrene	NaOCH₃	2-Formyl-1-keto-1,2,3,4-tetrahydrophenanthrene	94	405
4-Keto-1,2,3,4-tetrahydrophenanthrene	NaOCH₃	3-Formyl-4-keto-1,2,3,4-tetrahydrophenanthrene	96	405
1-Keto-7-methoxy-1,2,3,4-tetrahydrophenanthrene	NaOCH₃	2-Formyl-1-keto-7-methoxy-1,2,3,4-tetrahydrophenanthrene	97–99	86
3'-Keto-1,2,3,4-tetrahydrocyclopentenophenanthrene	Na	3'-Keto-4'-formyl-1,2,3,4-tetrahydrocyclopentenophenanthrene	Good	441
4,7-Dimethoxy-3'-keto-1,2-cyclopentenophenanthrene	NaOC₂H₅ (pyridine)	4,7-Dimethoxy-2'-formyl-3'-keto-1,2-cyclopentenophenanthrene	97	39
Estrone methyl ether	Na	Formyl estrone methyl ether	Quant.	442
α-(2-Hydroxy-3-ketocyclohexyl)propionic acid lactone	Na	α-(2-Hydroxy-3-keto-4-formylcyclohexyl)propionic acid lactone	—	443
Dihydrolanostenone	NaOC₂H₅	Formyldihydrolanestenone ‡	92	444
Tropinone	NaOC₂H₅	Formyltropinone ‡	40	156
Ethyl α,α-diethylacetoacetate	Na	Ethyl γ-formyl-α,α-diethylacetoacetate	—	397
Methyl 2-hydroxy-4-methoxybenzoylpropionate	Na	Methyl ester of anhydrobrazilic acid	—	363

Note: References 93–572 are listed on pp. 187–196.
‡ Amyl formate was employed.

TABLE XVI

REARRANGEMENT OF 2-ACYLOXY AND 2-AROYLOXY KETONES

Ketone	Base	Product	Yield %	Reference
2,4-Diacetoxyacetophenone	K₂CO₃	Rearrangement failed		40
2-Acetoxy-4-benzoyloxyacetophenone	K₂CO₃	Rearrangement failed		40
1-Acetoxy-2-acetylnaphthalene	Na	1-Hydroxy-2-naphthoylacetone	50	445
2-Benzoyloxyacetophenone	Li	2-Hydroxydibenzoylmethane	40–48	446
	Na	2-Hydroxydibenzoylmethane	50–62	445, 446
	K	2-Hydroxydibenzoylmethane	52–70	446

Reactant	Reagent	Product	Yield (%)	References
	Rb	2-Hydroxydibenzoylmethane	52–69	446
	Li_2CO_3	Rearrangement failed		446
	Na_2CO_3	2-Hydroxydibenzoylmethane	65	446
	K_2CO_3	2-Hydroxydibenzoylmethane	74	40, 446
	Rb_2CO_3	2-Hydroxydibenzoylmethane	82	446
	Cs_2CO_3	2-Hydroxydibenzoylmethane	75	446
	o-$CH_3COC_6H_4ONa$	2-Hydroxydibenzoylmethane	80	446
	KOH	2-Hydroxydibenzoylmethane	83	446
	NaOH	2-Hydroxydibenzoylmethane	74	446
	$NaOC_6H_5$	2-Hydroxydibenzoylmethane	70	446
	Na_2O_2	2-Hydroxydibenzoylmethane	40–64	446
	$NaC(C_6H_5)_3$	2-Hydroxydibenzoylmethane	64	446
	$NaOC_2H_5$	2-Hydroxydibenzoylmethane	31–60	446
	$NaOCH_3$	2-Hydroxydibenzoylmethane	18–50	446
	$NaNH_2$	2-Hydroxydibenzoylmethane	17–56	446, 447
	Ethyl sodioaceto-acetate	2-Hydroxydibenzoylmethane	15–50	446
	C_6H_5MgBr	2-Hydroxydibenzoylmethane	15	446
	CH_3MgI	2-Hydroxydibenzoylmethane	8	446
	$NaAlO_2$	2-Hydroxydibenzoylmethane	41	446
	CH_3CO_2K	2-Hydroxydibenzoylmethane	24	446
	$C_6H_5CO_2K$	2-Hydroxydibenzoylmethane	10	446
2-Benzoyloxy-4-acetoxyacetophenone	K_2CO_3	2-Hydroxy-4-benzoyloxydibenzoylmethane	—	40
2-Benzoyloxy-4-methoxyacetophenone	Na	2-Hydroxy-4-methoxydibenzoylmethane	—	448
2-Benzoyloxy-5-methoxyacetophenone	Na_2O_2	2-Hydroxy-5-methoxydibenzoylmethane	76	446
2-Benzoyloxy-3,5-dimethoxyacetophenone	$NaOCH_3$	Rearrangement failed		238
2-Benzoyloxy-3,6-dimethoxyacetophenone	$NaNH_2$	2-Hydroxy-3,6-dimethoxydibenzoylmethane	64	238, 449
2-Benzoyloxy-4,6-dimethoxyacetophenone	$NaNH_2$	2-Hydroxy-4,6-dimethoxydibenzoylmethane	40	450
2-Benzoyloxy-5,6-dimethoxyacetophenone	$NaNH_2$	2-Hydroxy-5,6-dimethoxydibenzoylmethane	75	451
2-Benzoyloxy-3,4,5-trimethoxyacetophenone	$NaNH_2$	2-Hydroxy-3,4,5-trimethoxydibenzoylmethane	—	452
2-Benzoyloxy-3,4,6-trimethoxyacetophenone	$NaNH_2$	2-Hydroxy-3,4,6-trimethoxydibenzoylmethane	—	453
2-Benzoyloxy-4,5,6-trimethoxyacetophenone	$NaNH_2$	2-Hydroxy-4,5,6-trimethoxydibenzoylmethane	60	454
2-Benzoyloxy-5-benzyloxyacetophenone	$NaNH_2$	2-Hydroxy-5-benzyloxydibenzoylmethane	—	447
2,4-Dibenzoyloxyacetophenone	K_2CO_3	2-Hydroxy-4-benzoyloxydibenzoylmethane	40	40
2,6-Dibenzoyloxyacetophenone	K_2CO_3	5-Hydroxy-3-benzoylflavone	20	455
2,5-Dibenzoyloxy-6-methoxyacetophenone	$NaNH_2$	2-Hydroxy-5-benzoyloxy-6-methoxydibenzoylmethane	50	456

Note: References 93–572 are listed on pp. 187–196.

TABLE XVI—*Continued*

REARRANGEMENT OF 2-ACYLOXY AND 2-AROYLOXY KETONES

Ketone	Base	Product	Yield %	Reference
2,4-Dibenzoyloxy-3,6-dimethoxyacetophenone	NaNH$_2$	2-Hydroxy-4-benzoyloxy-3,6-dimethoxydibenzoyl-methane and 2,4-dihydroxy-3,6-dimethoxydibenzoylmethane	—	453
2,3,4-Tribenzoyloxyacetophenone	K$_2$CO$_3$	2-Hydroxy-3,4-dibenzoyloxydibenzoylmethane	45	40
2,4-Dibenzoyloxyphenyl benzyl	K$_2$CO$_3$	7-Hydroxy-3-phenylflavone	—	40
2-Benzoyloxy-4-methoxy-5-nitroacetophenone	Na	Rearrangement failed		457
1-Benzoyloxy-2-acetylnaphthalene	NaNH$_2$	1-Hydroxy-2-naphthoylbenzoylmethane	30	458, 459
2-Benzoyloxy-1-acetylnaphthalene	NaOC$_2$H$_5$	2-Hydroxy-1-naphthoylbenzoylmethane	85	460
	NaNH$_2$	2-Hydroxy-1-naphthoylbenzoylmethane	—	447
2-Benzoyloxy-3-acetylnaphthalene	NaOC$_2$H$_5$	2-Hydroxy-3-naphthoylbenzoylmethane	—	461
2-(4-Methoxybenzoyloxy)-3,6-dimethoxyacetophenone	NaNH$_2$	2-Hydroxy-3,4',6-trimethoxydibenzoylmethane	60	453, 462, 463
2-(4-Methoxybenzoyloxy)-5,6-dimethoxyacetophenone	NaNH$_2$	2-Hydroxy-4',5,6-trimethoxydibenzoylmethane	72	462, 463
2-(4-Methoxybenzoyloxy)-3,4,5-trimethoxyacetophenone	NaNH$_2$	2-Hydroxy-3,4,4',5-tetramethoxydibenzoylmethane	—	452
2-(4-Methoxybenzoyloxy)-4,5,6-trimethoxyacetophenone	NaNH$_2$	2-Hydroxy-4,4',5,6-tetramethoxydibenzoylmethane	60	454
2-(4-Methoxybenzoyloxy)-4-benzoyloxyacetophenone	K$_2$CO$_3$	2-Hydroxy-4'-methoxy-4-(4-methoxybenzoyloxy)-dibenzoylmethane	—	40
2,4-Di-(4-methoxybenzoyloxy)acetophenone	K$_2$CO$_3$	2-Hydroxy-4'-methoxy-4-(4-methoxybenzoyloxy)-dibenzoylmethane	—	40
2,5-Di-(4-methoxybenzoyloxy)-6-methoxyacetophenone	NaNH$_2$	2-Hydroxy-4',6-dimethoxy-4-(4-methoxybenzoyl-oxy)dibenzoylmethane	—	462
2-(4-Methoxybenzoyloxy)-1-acetonaphthone	NaOC$_2$H$_5$	2-Hydroxy-1-naphthoyl-4-methoxybenzoylmethane	Almost quant.	460
2-(2-Methoxybenzoyloxy)acetophenone	K$_2$CO$_3$	2-Hydroxy-2'-methoxydibenzoylmethane	39	464
2-(2-Methoxybenzoyloxy)-5-methylacetophenone	K$_2$CO$_3$	2-Hydroxy-5-methyl-2'-methoxydibenzoylmethane	75	464
1-(2-Methoxybenzoyloxy)-2-acetylnaphthalene	NaNH$_2$	1-(2-Hydroxynaphthoyl)-2-methoxybenzoylmethane	25	458
2-(2-Methoxybenzoyloxy)-1-acetylnaphthalene	NaNH$_2$	1-(2-Hydroxynaphthoyl)-2-methoxybenzoylmethane and 2'-methoxy-β-naphthaflavone	—	447
2,4-Di-(2,4-dimethoxybenzoyloxy)acetophenone	K$_2$CO$_3$	2-Hydroxy-2',4'-dimethoxy-4-(2,4-dimethoxyben-zoyloxy)dibenzoylmethane	57	40
1-(2,4-Dimethoxybenzoyloxy)-2-acetylnaphthalene	NaNH$_2$	2-(1-Hydroxynaphthoyl)-2,4-dimethoxybenzoyl-methane	28	458

Ketone	Reagent	Product	Yield (%)	Reference
2-(3,4-Dimethoxybenzoyloxy)-3,4,5,6-tetramethoxyacetophenone	NaNH₂	2-Hydroxy-3,4,5,6,3',4'-hexamethoxydibenzoylmethane	73	465
1-(3,4,5-Trimethoxybenzoyloxy)-2-acetylnaphthalene	NaNH₂	2-(1-Hydroxynaphthoyl)-3,4,5-trimethoxybenzoylmethane	40	458
2-(2-Nitrobenzoyloxy)acetophenone	NaOH	2-Hydroxy-2'-nitrodibenzoylmethane	36	446
	NaH	2-Hydroxy-2'-nitrodibenzoylmethane	80	446
	Ethyl sodioacetoacetate	2-Hydroxy-2'-nitrodibenzoylmethane	50	446
	Na₂O₂	2-Hydroxy-2'-nitrodibenzoylmethane	60	446
2-(3-Nitrobenzoyloxy)acetophenone	Na	2-Hydroxy-3'-nitrodibenzoylmethane	54	457
	o-CH₃COC₆H₄ONa	2-Hydroxy-3'-nitrodibenzoylmethane	60	446
2-(4-Nitrobenzoyloxy)acetophenone	Ethyl sodioacetoacetate	2-Hydroxy-4'-nitrodibenzoylmethane	47	446
2-(3,5-Dinitrobenzoyloxy)acetophenone	o-CH₃COC₆H₄ONa	2-Hydroxy-3',5'-dinitrodibenzoylmethane	70	446
	NaH	2-Hydroxy-3',5'-dinitrodibenzoylmethane	—	446
	Ethyl sodioacetoacetate	2-Hydroxy-3',5'-dinitrodibenzoylmethane	—	446
2-(4-Nitrobenzoyloxy)-5-methoxyacetophenone	Ethyl sodioacetoacetate	2-Hydroxy-5-methoxy-4'-nitrodibenzoylmethane	30	446
	NaOCH₃	2-Hydroxy-5-methoxy-4'-nitrodibenzoylmethane	12	446
1-(2-Nitrobenzoyloxy)-2-acetylnaphthalene	KOH	2-(1-Hydroxynaphthoyl)-2-nitrobenzoylmethane	26	461
1-(3-Nitrobenzoyloxy)-2-acetylnaphthalene	KOH	2-(1-Hydroxynaphthoyl)-3-nitrobenzoylmethane	22	461
	Na	2-(1-Hydroxynaphthoyl)-3-nitrobenzoylmethane	—	457
1-(4-Nitrobenzoyloxy)-2-acetylnaphthalene	KOH	2-(1-Hydroxynaphthoyl)-4-nitrobenzoylmethane	58	461
	Na	2-(1-Hydroxynaphthoyl)-4-nitrobenzoylmethane	—	457
2-(2-Nitrobenzoyloxy)-1-acetylnaphthalene	KOH	1-(2-Hydroxynaphthoyl)-2-nitrobenzoylmethane	Low	461
2-(3-Nitrobenzoyloxy)-1-acetylnaphthalene	KOH	3'-Nitro-5,6-benzflavone	21	461
2-(4-Nitrobenzoyloxy)-1-acetylnaphthalene	KOH	1-(2-Hydroxynaphthoyl)-4-nitrobenzoylmethane	28	461
2-(2-Nitrobenzoyloxy)-3-acetylnaphthalene	KOH	3-(2-Hydroxynaphthoyl)-2-nitrobenzoylmethane	30	461
2-(3-Nitrobenzoyloxy)-3-acetylnaphthalene	KOH	3-(2-Hydroxynaphthoyl)-3-nitrobenzoylmethane	30	461
2-(4-Nitrobenzoyloxy)-3-acetylnaphthalene	KOH	3-(2-Hydroxynaphthoyl)-4-nitrobenzoylmethane	46	461
1-(3,5-Dinitrobenzoyloxy)-2-acetylnaphthalene	KOH	Rearrangement failed		461
2-(3,5-Dinitrobenzoyloxy)-1-acetylnaphthalene	KOH	3',5'-Dinitro-3-(3,5-dinitrobenzoyl)-5,6-benzflavone	50	461
2-(3,5-Dinitrobenzoyloxy)-3-acetylnaphthalene	KOH	3',5'-Dinitro-6,7-benzflavone	3	461
2-(1-Naphthoyloxy)acetophenone	Na	2-Hydroxybenzoyl-1-naphthoylmethane	67	448
2-(2-Naphthoyloxy)acetophenone	Na	2-Hydroxybenzoyl-2-naphthoylmethane	53	448
2-(1-Naphthoyloxy)-4-benzoyloxyacetophenone	Na	2-(1-Naphthyl)-7-hydroxychromone	77	448

Note: References 93–572 are listed on pp. 187–196.

TABLE XVI—Continued

REARRANGEMENT OF 2-ACYLOXY AND 2-AROYLOXY KETONES

Ketone	Base	Product	Yield %	Reference
2-(2-Naphthoyloxy)-4-benzoyloxyacetophenone	Na	2-Hydroxy-4-benzoyloxybenzoyl-2-naphthoyl-methane	—	448
1-(1-Naphthoyloxy)-2-acetylnaphthalene	Na	1-Naphthoyl-2-(1-hydroxynaphthoyl)methane	40	445
2-(1-Naphthoyloxy)-1-acetylnaphthalene	$NaOC_2H_5$	1-Naphthoyl-1-(2-hydroxynaphthoyl)methane	Almost quant.	460
1-(2-Naphthoyloxy)-2-acetylnaphthalene	Na	2-Naphthoyl-2-(1-hydroxynaphthoyl)methane	—	445
2-(2-Naphthoyloxy)-1-acetylnaphthalene	$NaOC_2H_5$	2-Naphthoyl-1-(2-hydroxynaphthoyl)methane	Almost quant.	460
2-(1-Methoxy-2-naphthoyloxy)-1-acetylnaphthalene	$NaOC_2H_5$	1-(2-Hydroxynaphthoyl)-2-(1-methoxynaphthoyl)-methane	Almost quant.	460
2-(3-Methoxy-2-naphthoyloxy)-1-acetylnaphthalene	$NaOC_2H_5$	1-(2-Hydroxynaphthoyl)-2-(3-methoxynaphthoyl)-methane	Almost quant.	460
2-(2-Methoxy-3-naphthoyloxy)-3-acetylnaphthalene	$NaOC_2H_5$	2-(3-Methoxynaphthoyl)-3-(2-hydroxynaphthoyl)-methane	—	461
2-Cinnamoyloxyacetophenone	$NaOC_2H_5$	2-Hydroxybenzoylcinnamoylmethane	25	446
2-Cinnamoyloxy-4-methoxyacetophenone	$NaOC_2H_5$	2-Hydroxy-4-methoxybenzoylcinnamoylmethane	Almost quant.	460
2,4-Dicinnamoyloxyacetophenone	K_2CO_3	2-Styryl-7-cinnamoyloxychromone	—	40
2-(3-Nitrocinnamoyloxy)acetophenone	$o\text{-}CH_3COC_6H_4ONa$	2-Hydroxybenzoyl-3-nitrocinnamoylmethane	70	446
2-Cinnamoyloxy-5-methoxyacetophenone	$NaOCH_3$	2-Hydroxy-5-methoxybenzoylcinnamoylmethane	60	446
1-Cinnamoyloxy-2-acetylnaphthalene	$NaNH_2$	1-Hydroxy-2-naphthoylcinnamoylmethane	—	447
2-Cinnamoyloxy-3-acetylnaphthalene	$NaOC_2H_5$	2-Hydroxy-3-naphthoylcinnamoylmethane	—	461
1-p-Methoxycinnamoyloxy-2-acetylnaphthalene	$NaNH_2$	2-(1-Hydroxynaphthoyl)-p-methoxycinnamoyl-methane and 2-p-methoxystyryl-1,4-α-naphtha-pyrone	—	447
2-Palmitoyloxy-1-acetylnaphthalene	$NaOC_2H_5$	1-(2-Hydroxynaphthoyl) palmitoylmethane	Almost quant.	460
5-Benzoyloxy-4-acetylindane	KOH	5-Hydroxy-4-benzoylacetylindane	—	461
5-Benzoyloxy-6-acetylindane	KOH	5-Hydroxy-6-benzoylacetylindane	—	461
5-(4-Nitrobenzoyloxy)-6-acetylindane	KOH	5-Hydroxy-6-(4-nitrobenzoylacetyl)indane	—	461

Note: References 93–572 are listed on pp. 187–196.

TABLE XVII

KOSTANECKI REACTION

(The condensing agent in these reactions was the sodium salt of the acid corresponding to the anhydride, unless otherwise specified.)

Anhydride	Ketone	Product	Yield %	Reference
Acetic	2-Hydroxyacetophenone	2-Methyl-3-acetylchromone	52	134
		4-Methylcoumarin	5	
	2-Hydroxy-3-methylacetophenone	2,8-Dimethylchromone	35	134
		4,8-Dimethylcoumarin	15	
	2-Hydroxy-4-methylacetophenone	2,7-Dimethylchromone	20	134
		4,7-Dimethylcoumarin	12	
	2-Hydroxy-5-methylacetophenone	2,6-Dimethyl-3-acetylchromone	52	134, 136
		2,6-Dimethylchromone	16	
		4,6-Dimethylcoumarin	24	
	2-Hydroxy-3,5-dimethylacetophenone	2,6,8-Trimethylchromone	78	137
		4,6,8-Trimethylcoumarin	Low	
	2-Hydroxy-4,6-dimethylacetophenone	2,5,7-Trimethyl-3-acetylchromone	47	134
	2-Hydroxy-5-phenylacetophenone	2-Methyl-3-acetyl-6-phenylchromone	—	152
	2,4-Dihydroxyacetophenone	2-Methyl-3-acetyl-7-acetoxychromone	—	466
	2,5-Dihydroxyacetophenone	2-Methyl-3-acetyl-6-acetoxychromone	Good	467
	2,6-Dihydroxyacetophenone	2-Methyl-3-acetyl-5-hydroxychromone	70	468
	2,3,4-Trihydroxyacetophenone	2-Methyl-7,8-dihydroxychromone	40	469, 470
	2,4,6-Trihydroxyacetophenone	2-Methyl-3-acetyl-5,7-diacetoxychromone	—	471
	2,6-Dihydroxy-4-methylacetophenone	2,7-Dimethyl-3-acetyl-5-acetoxychromone and 4,6-dimethyl-5-acetoxycoumarin	—	472
	2,4-Dihydroxy-5-ethylacetophenone	2-Methyl-3-acetyl-6-ethyl-7-acetoxychromone	31	473
	2-Hydroxy-4,6-dimethoxyacetophenone	2-Methyl-3-acetyl-5,7-dimethoxychromone	—	474
	2-Hydroxy-4-benzyloxyacetophenone	2-Methyl-7-benzyloxychromone	35	471
	2,5-Diacetoxyacetophenone	2-Methyl-3-acetyl-6-acetoxychromone	50	134
	2-Hydroxy-5-chloroacetophenone	2-Methyl-6-chlorochromone	18	136
		4-Methyl-6-chlorocoumarin	—	42
	2-Hydroxy-3-methyl-5-chloroacetophenone	2,8-Dimethyl-3-acetyl-6-chlorochromone	41	136
	2-Hydroxy-4-methyl-5-chloroacetophenone	4,7-Dimethyl-6-chlorocoumarin	12	

Note: References 93–572 are listed on pp. 187–196

TABLE XVII—*Continued*

KOSTANECKI REACTION

Anhydride	Ketone	Product	Yield %	Reference
Acetic—*Continued*				
	2-Hydroxy-5-methyl-3-chloroacetophenone	2,6-Dimethyl-3-acetyl-8-chlorochromone	—	42
	2-Hydroxy-3-nitro-5-methylacetophenone	2,6-Dimethyl-3-acetyl-8-nitrochromone	25	134
	4,6-Diacetylresorcinol	3,3′-Diacetyl-2,2′-dimethyldichromone	4	475
		2-Methyl-6-acetyl-7-hydroxychromone	25	
	1-Hydroxy-2-acetylnaphthalene	2-Methyl-3-acetyl-1,4-α,β-naphthapyrone and 2-methyl-1,4-α,β-naphthapyrone	64	134, 476
	2-Hydroxy-1-acetylnaphthalene	3-Methyl-2-acetyl-1,4-β,α-naphthapyrone	48	134, 477
	1-Hydroxy-4-chloro-2-acetylnaphthalene	2-Methyl-3-acetyl-6-chloro-1,4-α,β-naphthapyrone	—	478
	4,7-Dimethoxy-5-acetyl-6-hydroxybenzofuran	3-Acetylkellin	—	479
	2-Methyl-7-hydroxy-8-acetylchromone	α,α′-Dimethyl-β-acetyl[benzo-1,2,5,6-di-(γ-pyrone)]	35	134
	4-Methyl-6-acetyl-7-hydroxy-8-ethylcoumarin	2′,4-Dimethyl-3′-acetyl-8-ethyl-7,6-coumarin-γ-pyrone	—	480
	2-Hydroxypropiophenone	2,3-Dimethylchromone	46	481
	2-Hydroxy-5-methylpropiophenone	2,3,6-Trimethylchromone	—	481
	2-Hydroxy-4-methylpropiophenone	2,3,7-Trimethylchromone	22	482
	2-Hydroxy-6-methylpropiophenone	2,3,5-Trimethylchromone	—	482
	2-Hydroxy-3,5-dimethylpropiophenone	2,3,6,8-Tetramethylchromone	47	137
	2,4-Dihydroxypropiophenone	2,3-Dimethyl-7-hydroxychromone	65	483, 484, 485
	2,5-Dihydroxypropiophenone	2,3-Dimethyl-6-acetoxychromone	53	481
	2,6-Dihydroxypropiophenone	2,3-Dimethyl-5-hydroxychromone	87	486
	2,4-Dihydroxy-6-methylpropiophenone	2,3,5-Trimethyl-7-acetoxychromone	55	145
	2,6-Dihydroxy-4-methylpropiophenone	2,3,7-Trimethyl-5-hydroxychromone	Good	487
	2,3,4-Trihydroxypropiophenone	2,3-Dimethyl-7,8-diacetoxychromone	31	470
	2,4,6-Trihydroxypropiophenone	2,3-Dimethyl-5,7-diacetoxychromone	94	484
	2-Hydroxy-4-ethoxypropiophenone	2,3-Dimethyl-7-ethoxychromone	—	149
	2-Hydroxy-4,6-dimethoxypropiophenone	2,3-Dimethyl-5,7-dimethoxychromone	—	474
	2-Hydroxy-3-methyl-4-methoxypropiophenone	2,3,8-Trimethyl-7-methoxychromone	44	488
	2-Hydroxy-5-chloropropiophenone	2,3-Dimethyl-6-chlorochromone	95	42, 134
	2-Hydroxy-3-methyl-5-chloropropiophenone	2,3,8-Trimethyl-6-chlorochromone	—	42
	2-Hydroxy-5-methyl-3-chloropropiophenone	2,3,6-Trimethyl-8-chlorochromone	—	42

Ketone	Product	Yield	References
2-Hydroxy-5-bromopropiophenone	2,3-Dimethyl-6-bromochromone	—	42
1-Hydroxy-2-propionaphthone	2,3-Dimethyl-1,4-α,β-naphthapyrone	55	135, 481, 489
1-Hydroxy-4-chloro-2-propionaphthone	2,3-Dimethyl-6-chloro-1,4-α,β-naphthapyrone	—	478
4,6-Dipropionylresorcinol	2,2′,3,3′-Tetramethyldichromone	78	483
7-Hydroxy-6-propionyl-2,3-dimethylchromone	2,2′,3,3′-Tetramethyldichromone	95	483
2-Hydroxy-4-methylbutyrophenone	2,7-Dimethyl-3-ethylchromone	35	482
2-Hydroxy-5-methylbutyrophenone	2,6-Dimethyl-3-ethylchromone	—	490
2-Hydroxy-3,5-dimethylbutyrophenone	2,6,8-Trimethyl-3-ethylchromone	—	137
2,4-Dihydroxybutyrophenone	2-Methyl-3-ethyl-7-acetoxychromone	—	484
2,6-Dihydroxybutyrophenone	2-Methyl-3-ethyl-5-hydroxychromone	—	486
2,4,6-Trihydroxybutyrophenone	2-Methyl-3-ethyl-5,7-diacetoxychromone	52	484
2,6-Dihydroxy-4-methylbutyrophenone	5-Hydroxy-2,7-dimethyl-3-ethylchromone	—	487
2-Hydroxy-3-methyl-4-methoxybutyrophenone	2,8-Dimethyl-3-ethyl-7-methoxychromone	—	488
2-Hydroxy-4,6-dimethoxybutyrophenone	2-Methyl-3-ethyl-5,7-dimethoxychromone	—	474
2-Hydroxy-3-methyl-4-methoxy-6-ethoxy-butyrophenone	2,8-Dimethyl-3-ethyl-7-methoxy-5-ethoxy-chromone	—	491
2-Hydroxy-3-methyl-4,6-dimethoxybutyro-phenone	2,8-Dimethyl-3-ethyl-5,7-dimethoxychromone	—	491
2-Hydroxy-3-methyl-4,6-diethoxybutyrophe-none	2,8-Dimethyl-3-ethyl-5,7-diethoxychromone	—	491
2-Hydroxy-5-chlorobutyrophenone	2-Methyl-3-ethyl-6-chlorochromone	95	134
2,6-Dihydroxy-n-valerophenone	2-Methyl-3-n-propyl-5-hydroxychromone	42	492
5-Hydroxy-6-isovaleryl-4-methylcoumarin	Reaction failed	—	41
5-Hydroxy-6-lauryl-4-methylcoumarin	2′,4-Dimethyl-3′-decylcoumarin-6,5-γ-pyrone	—	41
4-Palmitoylresorcinol	2-Methyl-3-tetradecyl-7-acetoxychromone	—	493
4-Palmitoylpyrogallol	2-Methyl-3-tetradecyl-7,8-diacetoxychromone	—	493
5-Hydroxy-6-palmitoyl-4-methylcoumarin	2′,4-Dimethyl-3′-tetradecylcoumarin-6,5-γ-pyrone	—	41
4-Stearoylresorcinol	2-Methyl-3-hexadecyl-7-acetoxychromone	—	493
4-Stearoylpyrogallol	2-Methyl-3-hexadecyl-7,8-diacetoxychromone	—	493
2-Hydroxyphenyl benzyl	2-Methylisoflavone	36	489
2-Hydroxy-5-methylphenyl benzyl	2,6-Dimethylisoflavone	80	134
2,4-Dihydroxyphenyl benzyl	2-Methyl-7-acetoxyisoflavone	90	494
2,4-Dihydroxyphenyl benzyl ketone 4-glucoside	7-Hydroxy-2-methylisoflavone-7-glucoside	—	495
2,3,4-Trihydroxyphenyl benzyl	2-Methyl-7,8-diacetoxyisoflavone	—	496
2,4,6-Trihydroxyphenyl benzyl	2-Methyl-5,7-diacetoxyisoflavone	—	494

Note: References 93–572 are listed on pp. 187–196.

TABLE XVII—Continued

KOSTANECKI REACTION

Anhydride	Ketone	Product	Yield %	Reference
Acetic—Continued	2-Hydroxy-4-methoxyphenyl benzyl	2-Methyl-7-methoxyisoflavone	85	185
	2-Hydroxy-3-methyl-4-methoxyphenyl benzyl	2,8-Dimethyl-7-methoxyisoflavone	46	488
	2-Hydroxy-4,6-dimethoxy-β-phenylpropiophenone	2-Methyl-3-benzyl-5,7-dimethoxychromone	—	497
	2,4-Dihydroxyphenyl 3,4-methylenedioxybenzyl	2-Methyl-7-acetoxy-3',4'-methylenedioxyisoflavone	88	498
	2,4,6-Trihydroxyphenyl 2,4-dimethoxybenzyl	2-Methyl-5,7-diacetoxy-2',4'-dimethoxyisoflavone	—	499
	2-Hydroxy-5-chlorophenyl benzyl	2-Methyl-6-chloroisoflavone	100	134
	1-Hydroxy-2-phenylacetylnaphthalene	2-Methyl-3-phenyl-1,4-α,β-naphthapyrone *	—	439
	2-Hydroxy-1-phenylacetylnaphthalene	2-Methyl-3-phenyl-1,4-β,α-naphthapyrone *	—	489
	4-β-Phenylpropionylresorcinol	2-Methyl-3-benzyl-7-acetoxychromone	—	489, 500
	2-β-Phenylpropionylorcinol	2-Methyl-3-benzyl-5-methyl-7-acetoxychromone	—	496
	4-β-Phenylpropionylpyrogallol	2-Methyl-3-benzyl-7,8-diacetoxychromone	—	496
	2-β-Phenylpropionylphloroglucinol	2-Methyl-3-benzyl-5,7-diacetoxychromone	—	496
	2-β-(4-Hydroxyphenyl)propionylphloroglucinol	2-Methyl-3-benzyl-4',5,7-triacetoxychromone	—	497
	1-Hydroxy-2-β-phenylpropionylnaphthalene	2-Methyl-3-benzyl-1,4-α,β-naphthapyrone	39	439
	2,4-Dihydroxy-ω-methoxyacetophenone	2-Methyl-3-methoxy-7-acetoxychromone	51	501
	2,4,5-Trihydroxy-ω-methoxyacetophenone	2-Methyl-3-methoxy-6,7-dihydroxychromone	78	502
	2,4,6-Trihydroxy-ω-methoxyacetophenone	2-Methyl-3-methoxy-5,7-dihydroxychromone	—	503
	2-Hydroxy-5-methyl-ω-chloroacetophenone	2,6-Dimethyl-3-chlorochromone	62	134
	2-Hydroxy-5-methyl-ω-bromoacetophenone	2,6-Dimethyl-3-bromochromone	—	134
	2-Hydroxy-ω,5-dichloroacetophenone	2-Methyl-3,6-dichlorochromone	—	134
Chloroacetic	2-Hydroxy-5-chloropropiophenone	2-Chloromethyl-3-methyl-6-chlorochromone	50	134
Propionic	2,5-Dihydroxyacetophenone	2-Ethyl-3-propionyl-6-hydroxychromone	—	467
	2,5-Dihydroxy-4-methylacetophenone	2-Ethyl-5-hydroxy-7-methyl-3-propionylchromone	—	467
	2-Hydroxy-3,5-dimethylacetophenone	2-Ethyl-6,8-dimethylchromone and 3,4,6,8-tetramethylcoumarin	—	137
	2-Hydroxy-4-methoxyacetophenone	2-Ethyl-7-methoxychromone	27	185
		3,4-Dimethyl-7-methoxycoumarin	40	134
	2-Acetoxy-5-chloroacetophenone	2-Ethyl-6-chlorochromone and 3,4-dimethyl-6-chlorocoumarin	—	134
	2,4-Dihydroxy-6-methylpropiophenone	2-Ethyl-3,5-dimethyl-7-propionoxychromone	33	145

	Ketone	Product	Yield	References
	2-Hydroxy-4-methoxypropiophenone	2-Ethyl-3-methyl-7-methoxychromone	Low	504
		3-Methyl-4-ethyl-7-methoxycoumarin	19	42, 134
	2-Hydroxy-5-chloropropiophenone	2-Ethyl-3-methyl-6-chlorochromone	95	42
	2-Hydroxy-5-chloro-3-methylpropiophenone	2-Ethyl-3,8-dimethyl-6-chlorochromone	—	42
	2-Hydroxy-3-chloro-5-methylpropiophenone	2-Ethyl-3,6-dimethyl-8-chlorochromone	—	42
	2-Hydroxy-5-bromopropiophenone	2-Ethyl-3-methyl-6-bromochromone	—	185
	2-Hydroxy-4-methoxyphenyl benzyl	2-Ethyl-3-phenyl-7-methoxychromone	70	134
Butyric	2-Hydroxy-5-chloroacetophenone	2-Propyl-6-chlorochromone and 3-ethyl-4-methyl-6-chlorocoumarin	—	
	2,5-Dihydroxyacetophenone	2-Propyl-3-butyryl-6-hydroxychromone	—	467
	2,6-Dihydroxy-4-methylacetophenone	2-Propyl-3-butyryl-5-hydroxy-7-methylchromone	—	467
	2,4-Dihydroxy-6-methylpropiophenone	2-Propyl-3,5-dimethyl-7-butyroxychromone	53	145
	2-Hydroxy-4-methoxypropiophenone	2-Propyl-3-methyl-7-methoxychromone	26	504
		2-Propyl-3-methyl-7-hydroxychromone	Very low	
		3,4-Diethyl-7-methoxycoumarin	—	
	2-Hydroxy-5-chloropropiophenone	2-Propyl-3-methyl-6-chlorochromone	—	42
	2-Hydroxy-3-methyl-5-chloropropiophenone	2-Propyl-3,8-dimethyl-6-chlorochromone	—	42
	2-Hydroxy-5-methyl-3-chloropropiophenone	2-Propyl-3,6-dimethyl-8-chlorochromone	—	42
	2-Hydroxy-5-bromopropiophenone	2-Propyl-3-methyl-6-bromochromone	—	185
Phenylacetic	2-Hydroxy-4-methoxypropiophenone	2-Benzyl-3-methyl-7-methoxychromone	5	
		3-Phenyl-4-ethyl-7-methoxycoumarin	55	
Benzoic	2-Hydroxyacetophenone	Flavone	9	505
	2-Hydroxy-4-methylacetophenone	7-Methylflavone	17	482
	2-Hydroxy-5-methylacetophenone	6-Methylflavone	30	134, 428, 490
	2-Hydroxy-3,5-dimethylacetophenone	3-Benzoyl-6,8-dimethylflavone	71	137
	2,4-Dihydroxyacetophenone	7-Hydroxyflavone	27	91, 506
	2,5-Dihydroxyacetophenone	6-Hydroxyflavone	15	505
	2,6-Dihydroxyacetophenone	3-Benzoyl-5-benzoyloxyflavone	41	506, 507
	2,3,4-Trihydroxyacetophenone	7,8-Dihydroxyflavone	—	469
	2,4,5-Trihydroxyacetophenone	6,7-Dihydroxyflavone	99 (crude)	505
	2,4,6-Trihydroxyacetophenone	5,7-Dihydroxyflavone (chrysin)	—	91, 450, 506, 508
	2,4-Dihydroxy-3-methylacetophenone	3-Benzoyl-7-hydroxy-8-methylflavone	—	509

Note: References 93–572 are listed on pp. 187–196.

* The same product was obtained in unspecified yield using sodium phenylacetate as the condensing agent.[489]

TABLE XVII—*Continued*

KOSTANECKI REACTION

Anhydride	Ketone	Product	Yield %	Reference
Benzoic—*Continued*				
	2,4-Dihydroxy-3-allylacetophenone	3-Benzoyl-7-hydroxy-8-allylflavone	—	509
	2,4-Dihydroxy-6-methylacetophenone	3-Benzoyl-7-benzoyloxy-5-methylflavone	—	510
	2,6-Dihydroxy-4-methylacetophenone	3-Benzoyl-5-hydroxy-7-methylflavone	—	467
	2-Hydroxy-4-methoxy-6-methylacetophenone	3-Benzoyl-7-methoxy-5-methylflavone	—	510
	2,6-Dihydroxy-3-methoxyacetophenone	5-Hydroxy-8-methoxyflavone	—	511
	2,3-Dihydroxy-4-methoxyacetophenone	8-Hydroxy-7-methoxyflavone	27	451
	2,3-Dihydroxy-5-methoxyacetophenone	Reaction failed		238
	2,3-Dihydroxy-6-methoxyacetophenone	8-Hydroxy-5-methoxyflavone	45	512
	2,5-Dihydroxy-6-methoxyacetophenone	6-Hydroxy-5-methoxyflavone	9	449
	2,4-Dihydroxy-3,6-dimethoxyacetophenone	7-Hydroxy-5,8-dimethoxyflavone	36	513
	2,5-Dihydroxy-4,6-dimethoxyacetophenone	6-Hydroxy-5,7-dimethoxyflavone (baicalein dimethyl ether)	—	454
	2-Hydroxy-3,4,6-trimethoxyacetophenone	5,7,8-Trimethoxyflavone	—	514
	2,5-Dihydroxy-3,4,6-trimethoxyacetophenone	6-Hydroxy-5,7,8-trimethoxyflavone	—	515
	2-Hydroxy-3,4-dimethoxy-6-ethoxyacetophenone	7,8-Dimethoxy-5-ethoxyflavone	—	215
	4,6-Diacetylresorcinol	7-Hydroxy-6-acetylflavone	17	475, 516
		Diflavone	16	
	2-Hydroxy-5-chloroacetophenone	3-Benzoyl-6-chloroflavone	38	134
	1-Hydroxy-2-acetylnaphthalene	2-Phenyl-1,4-α,β-naphthapyrone and 2-phenyl-3-benzoyl-1,4-α,β-naphthapyrone	—	476
	2-Hydroxy-1-acetylnaphthalene	2-Phenyl-1,4-β,α-naphthapyrone	31	477
	1-Hydroxy-2-acetyl-4-chloronaphthalene	2-Phenyl-3-benzoyl-6-chloro-1,4-α,β-naphthapyrone	—	478
	2-Hydroxy-5-methylpropiophenone	3,6-Dimethylflavone	86	134
	2,4-Dihydroxypropiophenone	7-Hydroxy-3-methylflavone	55	484
	2,4,6-Trihydroxypropiophenone	5,7-Dihydroxy-3-methylflavone	—	484
	2-Hydroxy-4,6-dimethoxypropiophenone	5,7-Dimethoxy-3-methylflavone	—	474
	4,6-Dipropionylresorcinol	3,3'-Dimethyldiflavone	70	483
	2-Hydroxy-5-methylbutyrophenone	3-Ethyl-6-methylflavone	70	134
	2,4,6-Trihydroxybutyrophenone	3-Ethyl-5,7-dihydroxyflavone	—	484
	2-Hydroxy-5-methyl-n-valerophenone	3-n-Propyl-6-methylflavone	85	134
	2-Hydroxy-5-methylisovalerophenone	3-Isopropyl-6-methylflavone	85	134

Ketone	Product	Yield (%)	References
2-Hydroxyphenyl benzyl	3-Phenylflavone	36	489
2-Hydroxy-5-methylphenyl benzyl	3-Phenyl-6-methylflavone	95	134, 517
2,4-Dihydroxyphenyl benzyl	3-Phenyl-7-hydroxyflavone	—	494
2,4-Dihydroxyphenyl 4-methoxybenzyl	3-(4-Methoxyphenyl)-7-hydroxyflavone	—	518
2,5-Dihydroxyphenyl benzyl	3-Phenyl-6-hydroxyflavone	—	518
2,3,4-Trihydroxyphenyl benzyl	3-Phenyl-7,8-dihydroxyflavone	—	496
2,4,6-Trihydroxyphenyl benzyl	3-Phenyl-5,7-dihydroxyflavone	—	518
2,4,6-Trihydroxyphenyl 4-methoxybenzyl	3-(4-Methoxyphenyl)-5,7-dihydroxyflavone	95	518
2-Hydroxy-5-chlorophenyl benzyl	3-Phenyl-6-chloroflavone	—	134
2-Hydroxy-1-phenylacetylnaphthalene	2,3-Diphenyl-1,4-β,α-naphthapyrone	—	489
4-β-Phenylpropionylresorcinol	3-Benzyl-7-hydroxyflavone	—	496
4-β-Phenylpropionylpyrogallol	3-Benzyl-7,8-dihydroxyflavone	—	496
2-β-Phenylpropionylphloroglucinol	3-Benzyl-5,7-dihydroxyflavone	—	496
1-Hydroxy-2-β-phenylpropionylnaphthalene	2-Phenyl-3-benzyl-1,4-α,β-naphthapyrone	44	439
2-Hydroxy-ω,3-dimethoxyacetophenone	3,8-Dimethoxyflavone	—	518a
2-Hydroxy-ω,4,6-trimethoxyacetophenone	3,5,7-Trimethoxyflavone	—	519
2-Hydroxy-ω,4,6-trimethoxyacetophenone	5-Hydroxy-3,7-dimethoxyflavone	—	520
2-Hydroxy-ω,4,6-trimethoxyacetophenone	6-Hydroxy-3,5,7-trimethoxyflavone	—	521
2-Hydroxy-3-methyl-ω,4-dimethoxyacetophenone	3,7-Dimethoxy-8-methylflavone	—	522
2-Hydroxy-ω,3,4,6-tetramethoxyacetophenone	3,5,7,8-Tetramethoxyflavone	—	523
2-Hydroxy-ω,3,5,6-tetramethoxyacetophenone	3,5,6,8-Tetramethoxyflavone	—	524
2-Hydroxy-ω,3,4,5,6-pentamethoxyacetophenone	3,5,6,7,8-Pentamethoxyflavone	—	525
2,4-Dihydroxy-ω-methoxyacetophenone	3-Methoxy-7-hydroxyflavone	80	501
2,4-Dihydroxy-3-methyl-ω-methoxyacetophenone	3-Methoxy-7-hydroxy-8-methylflavone	—	522
2,4-Dihydroxy-ω,3,6-trimethoxyacetophenone	7-Benzoyloxy-3,5,8-trimethoxyflavone	—	523
2,5-Dihydroxy-ω,3,4,6-tetramethoxyacetophenone	6-Hydroxy-3,5,7,8-tetramethoxyflavone	—	526
2,5-Dihydroxy-ω,3,6-trimethoxy-4-benzyloxyacetophenone	6-Hydroxy-3,5,8-trimethoxy-7-benzyloxyflavone	—	527
2,4,5-Trihydroxy-ω-methoxyacetophenone	6,7-Dihydroxy-3-methoxyflavone	90	528
2,4,6-Trihydroxy-ω-methoxyacetophenone	5,7-Dihydroxy-3-methoxyflavone	—	529
ω,2,4,5-Tetramethoxyacetophenone	3,6,7-Trimethoxyflavone	—	528
3-Methyl-4-hydroxy-5-methoxyacetylcoumarone	7,8-(3-Methylfuro)-3-methoxyflavone	—	530

Note: References 93–572 are listed on pp. 187–196.

TABLE XVII—*Continued*
KOSTANECKI REACTION

Anhydride	Ketone	Product	Yield %	Reference
Benzoic—*Continued*	2,4-Dihydroxy-ω-benzoyloxyacetophenone	3,7-Dihydroxyflavone	24	508
	2,4,6-Trihydroxy-ω-benzoyloxyacetophenone	3,5,7-Trihydroxyflavone	34	508
4-Methoxybenzoic	2,4-Dihydroxyacetophenone	7-Hydroxy-4'-methoxyflavone	55	91
	2,5-Dihydroxyacetophenone	6-Hydroxy-4'-methoxyflavone	24	505
	2,4,6-Trihydroxyacetophenone	5,7-Dihydroxy-4'-methoxyflavone	69	91, 531
	2,3,4-Trihydroxyacetophenone	7,8-Dihydroxy-4'-methoxyflavone	Poor	235
	2,4-Dihydroxy-3,6-dimethoxyacetophenone	7-Hydroxy-4',5,8-trimethoxyflavone	12 †	532, 533
	2,5-Dihydroxy-4,6-dimethoxyacetophenone	6-Hydroxy-4',7-dimethoxyflavone and 6-hydroxy-4',5,7-trimethoxyflavone	—	454
	2-Hydroxy-3,4,6-trimethoxyacetophenone	4',5,7,8-Tetramethoxyflavone	27	215
	4,6-Diacetylresorcinol	4',4''-Dimethoxydiflavone	4	475, 516
	1-Hydroxy-2-acetylnaphthalene	7-Hydroxy-4'-methoxy-6-acetylflavone	—†	476
		3-Anisoyl-4'-methoxy-1,4-α,β-naphthaflavone and 4'-methoxy-1,4-α,β-naphthaflavone		
	2-Hydroxy-1-acetylnaphthalene	4'-Methoxy-1,4-β,α-naphthaflavone	Poor	477
	2,4-Dihydroxyphenyl benzyl	7-Hydroxy-3-phenyl-4'-methoxyflavone	—	518
	2,4,6-Trihydroxyphenyl benzyl	5,7-Dihydroxy-3-phenyl-4'-methoxyflavone	—	518
	2,4-Dihydroxyphenyl 4-methoxybenzyl	7-Hydroxy-4'-methoxy-3-(4-methoxyphenyl)flavone	—	518
	2,5-Dihydroxy-ω,4-dimethoxyacetophenone	6-Hydroxy-3,4',7-trimethoxyflavone	—	528
	2,4,6-Trihydroxy-ω-methoxyacetophenone	5,7-Dihydroxy-3,4'-dimethoxyflavone	—	534
	2,4-Dihydroxy-ω,3,6-trimethoxyacetophenone	7-Hydroxy-3,4',5,8-tetramethoxyflavone	—	535
	2,5-Dihydroxy-ω,4,6-trimethoxyacetophenone	6-Hydroxy-3,4',5,7-tetramethoxyflavone	—	521
	2,6-Dihydroxy-ω,4,5-trimethoxyacetophenone	5-Hydroxy-3,4',6,7-tetramethoxyflavone and 5-hydroxy-3,4',7,8-tetramethoxyflavone	89	536
	2-Hydroxy-ω,3,4,5,6-pentamethoxyacetophenone	3,4',5,6,7,8-Hexamethoxyflavone	—	525
	2,5-Dihydroxy-ω,3,4,6-tetramethoxyacetophenone	6-Hydroxy-3,4',5,7,8-pentamethoxyflavone	—	526
	2-Hydroxy-ω,4,6-trimethoxy-3-(γ,γ-dimethylallyl)acetophenone	3,4',5,7-Tetramethoxy-8-(γ,γ-dimethylallyl)flavone	27	537
4-Ethoxybenzoic	2,4-Dihydroxy-ω-benzoyloxyacetophenone	3,7-Dihydroxy-4'-methoxyflavone	30	508
	2,4,6-Trihydroxy-ω-benzoyloxyacetophenone	3,5,7-Trihydroxy-4'-methoxyflavone	29	508
	2-Hydroxy-3-methoxy-ω,4,6-triethoxyacetophenone	3,4',5,7-Tetraethoxy-8-methoxyflavone	—†	538

Acid	Ketone	Product	Yield (%)	Reference
4-Benzyloxybenzoic	2,4,6-Trihydroxyacetophenone	5,7-Dihydroxy-4'-benzyloxyflavone	62	539
	2-Hydroxy-ω,4,6-trimethoxyacetophenone	4'-Hydroxy-3,5,7-trimethoxyflavone	—†	540
	2-Hydroxy-ω,3,4,5,6-pentamethoxyacetophenone	4'-Hydroxy-3,5,6,7,8-pentamethoxyflavone	—†	541
	2,4,6-Trihydroxy-ω-methoxyacetophenone	4',5,7-Trihydroxy-3-methoxyflavone	—†	540
2-Methoxybenzoic	2,4,6-Trihydroxy-ω-methoxyacetophenone	5,7-Dihydroxy-2'-methoxyflavone	—	539
2-Acetoxybenzoic	2,4,6-Trihydroxy-ω-methoxyacetophenone	2-Methyl-3-methoxy-5,7-dihydroxychromone	—	503
3,4-Methylenedioxybenzoic	2,4-Dihydroxy-ω-ethoxyacetophenone	7-Hydroxy-3-ethoxy-3',4'-methylenedioxyflavone	—†	542
	2-Hydroxy-ω,4,6-trimethoxyacetophenone	3,5,7-Trimethoxy-3',4'-methylenedioxyflavone	—†	542
3,4-Dimethoxybenzoic	2,3,4-Trihydroxyacetophenone	7,8-Dihydroxy-3',4'-dimethoxyflavone	Poor	235
	2,4-Dihydroxy-6-methoxyacetophenone	7'-Hydroxy-3',4',5-trimethoxyflavone	—	543
	4,6-Diacetylresorcinol	7-Hydroxy-3',4'-dimethoxy-6-acetylflavone	49	475
	2,4,6-Trihydroxypropiophenone	5,7-Dihydroxy-3',4'-dimethoxy-3-methylflavone	70	544
	2,4-Dihydroxyphenyl benzyl	7-Hydroxy-3',4'-dimethoxy-3-phenylflavone	35	518
	2,4-Dihydroxy-ω-methoxyacetophenone	7-Hydroxy-3,3',4'-trimethoxyflavone	91†	545
	2,4,6-Trihydroxy-ω-methoxyacetophenone	5,7-Dihydroxy-3,3',4'-tetramethoxyflavone	94†	545
	2,5-Dihydroxy-ω,4-dimethoxyacetophenone	6-Hydroxy-3,3',4',7-tetramethoxyflavone	Good	546
	2,4-Dihydroxy-ω,3,6-trimethoxyacetophenone	7-Hydroxy-3,3',4',5,8-pentamethoxyflavone	22†	547
	2,5-Dihydroxy-ω,4,6-trimethoxyacetophenone	6-Hydroxy-3,3',4',5,7-pentamethoxyflavone	—	521
	2,6-Dihydroxy-ω,4,5-trimethoxyacetophenone	5-Hydroxy-3,3',4',6,7-pentamethoxyflavone	63	547
	2-Hydroxy-ω,3,4,5,6-pentamethoxyacetophenone	3,3',4',5,6,7,8-Heptamethoxyflavone and 3,3',4',6,7,8-hexamethoxyflavone	—	525
	2,4-Dihydroxy-6-methoxy-ω-benzoyloxyacetophenone	3,7-Dihydroxy-3',4',5-trimethoxyflavone	9†	548
	2,6-Dihydroxy-4-methoxy-ω-benzoyloxyacetophenone	3,5-Dihydroxy-3',4',7-trimethoxyflavone	20†	548
2,4-Dimethoxybenzoic	2,4,6-Trihydroxyacetophenone	5,7-Dihydroxy-2',4'-dimethoxyflavone	21	549
	2,4,6-Trihydroxy-ω-methoxyacetophenone	5,7-Dihydroxy-2',3,4'-trimethoxyflavone	70	549
3-Benzyloxy-4-methoxybenzoic	2,4,6-Trihydroxyacetophenone	5,7-Dihydroxy-3'-benzyloxy-4'-methoxyflavone	—	550
4-Benzyloxy-3-methoxybenzoic	2,4,6-Trihydroxyacetophenone	5,7-Dihydroxy-4'-benzyloxy-3'-methoxyflavone	48 (crude)	550
	2,4-Dihydroxy-ω,6-dimethoxyacetophenone	4',7-Dihydroxy-3',3,5-trimethoxyflavone	16†	548
	2,6-Dihydroxy-ω,4-dimethoxyacetophenone	4',5-Dihydroxy-3',3,7-trimethoxyflavone	26‡	548
	2,4,6-Trihydroxy-ω-benzoyloxyacetophenone	3,4',5,7-Tetrahydroxy-3'-methoxyflavone	10†	551
	2,4,6-Trihydroxy-ω-benzoyloxyacetophenone	3,4',5,7-Tetrahydroxy-3'-methoxyflavone	30‡	551

Note: References 93–572 are listed on pp. 187–196.
† The potassium salt of the acid was used as the condensing agent.
‡ Triethylamine was used as the condensing agent.

TABLE XVII—*Continued*

KOSTANECKI REACTION

Anhydride	Ketone	Product	Yield %	Reference
4-Benzoyloxy-3-methoxybenzoic— *Continued*	2-Hydroxy-ω,4,6-trimethoxyacetophenone	4'-Hydroxy-3,3',5,7-tetramethoxyflavone	—	552
3-Benzoyloxy-2-methoxybenzoic	2,4,6-Trihydroxy-ω-benzoyloxyacetophenone	3,3',5,7-Tetrahydroxy-2'-methoxyflavone	—	508
4-Benzoyloxy-3-methoxybenzoic	2,6-Dihydroxy-4-methoxy-ω-benzoyloxyacetophenone	3,4',5-Trihydroxy-3',7-dimethoxyflavone (rhamnazin)	26‡	553
	2-Hydroxy-4,6-dimethoxy-ω-benzoyloxyacetophenone	3,4'-Dihydroxy-3',5,7-trimethoxyflavone	8	548
	2-Hydroxy-4,6-dimethoxy-ω-benzoyloxyacetophenone	3,4'-Dihydroxy-3',5,7-trimethoxyflavone	35‡	548
3,4-Dibenzoyloxybenzoic	2,4,6-Trihydroxy-ω-methoxyacetophenone	3',4',5,7-Tetrahydroxy-3-methoxyflavone (quercetin-3-methyl ether)	28‡	553
	2,4-Dihydroxy-6-methoxy-ω-benzoyloxyacetophenone	3,3',4',7-Tetrahydroxy-5-methoxyflavone (quercetin-5-methyl ether)	7‡	553
	2,6-Dihydroxy-4-methoxy-ω-benzoyloxyacetophenone	3,3',4',5-Tetrahydroxy-7-methoxyflavone (rhamnetin)	11‡	553
3,4,5-Trimethoxybenzoic	2-Hydroxyacetophenone	3',4',5'-Trimethoxyflavone	Low	505
	2,5-Dihydroxyacetophenone	6-Hydroxy-3',4',5'-trimethoxyflavone	4	505
	2,3,4-Trihydroxyacetophenone	6,7-Dihydroxy-3',4',5'-trimethoxyflavone	Poor	235
	2,4,6-Trihydroxyacetophenone	5,7-Dihydroxy-3',4',5'-trimethoxyflavone	18	554
	2,4,6-Trihydroxyacetophenone	5,7-Dihydroxy-3',4',5'-trimethoxy-3-(3,4,5-trimethoxybenzoyl)flavone	41	235
	2,4-Dihydroxy-3,6-dimethoxyacetophenone	7-Hydroxy-3',4',5',5,8-pentamethoxyflavone	40†	555
	4,6-Diacetylresorcinol	7-Hydroxy-3',4',5'-trimethoxy-6-acetylflavone	—†	475
	2-Hydroxy-1-acetylnaphthalene	3',4',5'-Trimethoxy-1,4-β,α-naphthaflavone	17	477
	2,4-Dihydroxy-ω-methoxyacetophenone	7-Hydroxy-3,3',4',5'-tetramethoxyflavone	—	556
	2,4-Dihydroxy-ω-methoxyacetophenone	7-Hydroxy-3,3',4',5'-tetramethoxyflavone	69	235
	2-Hydroxy-ω,4,6-trimethoxyacetophenone	3,3',4',5,5',7-Hexamethoxyflavone	43†	557
	2,5-Dihydroxy-ω,4-dimethoxyacetophenone	6-Hydroxy-3,3',4',5',7-pentamethoxyflavone	—§	528
	2,4-Dihydroxy-ω,3,6-trimethoxyacetophenone	7-Hydroxy-3,3',4',5,5',8-hexamethoxyflavone (hexamethylhibiscetin)	—	558

Acid	Ketone	Product	Yield (%)	Reference
4-Benzyloxy-3,5-dimethoxybenzoic	2,5-Dihydroxy-ω,4,6-trimethoxyacetophenone	6-Hydroxy-3,3',4',5,5',7-hexamethoxyflavone	—	521
	2-Hydroxy-ω,3,5,6-tetramethoxyacetophenone	5-Hydroxy-3,3',4',5',6,8-hexamethoxyflavone	—	524
	2-Hydroxy-ω,3,4,5,6-pentamethoxyacetophenone	5-Hydroxy-3,3',4',5',6,7,8-heptamethoxyflavone	†	525
	2,4,6-Trihydroxy-ω-methoxyacetophenone	5,7-Dihydroxy-3,3',4',5'-tetramethoxyflavone	96	529
	2,4,6-Trihydroxy-ω-benzoyloxyacetophenone	3,5,7-Trihydroxy-3',4',5'-trimethoxyflavone	59	559
	2,4,6-Trihydroxy-ω-benzoyloxyacetophenone	3,5,7-Trihydroxy-4'-benzyloxy-3',5'-dimethoxy-flavone	34	559
Cinnamic	2,4,6-Trihydroxyacetophenone	5,7-Dicinnamoyloxy-2-styrylchromone	18	135
	2,4-Dihydroxypropiophenone	7-Cinnamoyloxy-2-styryl-3-methylchromone	—	135
	1-Hydroxy-2-propionylnaphthalene	2-Styryl-3-methyl-1,4-α,β-naphthapyrone	40	135
	2-Hydroxy-5-methylphenyl benzyl	2-Styryl-6-methylisoflavone	—	134
	2,4-Dihydroxyphenyl benzyl	7-Cinnamoyloxy-2-styrylisoflavone	—	494
	2,4-Dihydroxyphenyl 4-methoxybenzyl	7-Hydroxy-2-styryl-4'-methoxyisoflavone	63	518
	1-Hydroxy-2-phenylacetylnaphthalene	3-Phenyl-2-styryl-1,4-α,β-naphthapyrone	66	439
	1-Hydroxy-2-β-phenylpropionylnaphthalene	3-Benzyl-2-styryl-1,4-α,β-naphthapyrone	70	439
	2,4-Dihydroxy-ω-methoxyacetophenone	7-Hydroxy-3-methoxy-2-styrylchromone	—	534
	2,4,6-Trihydroxy-ω-methoxyacetophenone	5,7-Dihydroxy-3-methoxy-2-styrylchromone	—	534
	2,4,6-Trihydroxyphenyl benzyl	5,7-Dihydroxy-3-phenyl-2-styrylbenzo-γ-pyrone	—	518
	2,4,6-Trihydroxyacetophenone	5,7-Di-(4-methoxycinnamoyloxy)-4'-methoxy-2-styrylchromone	—	135
4-Methoxycinnamic	2,4-Dihydroxypropiophenone	7-(4-Methoxycinnamoyloxy)-3-methyl-4'-methoxy-2-styrylchromone	—	135
	2,4,6-Trihydroxy-ω-methoxyacetophenone	5,7-Dihydroxy-3,4'-dimethoxy-2-styrylchromone	90	534
	1-Hydroxy-2-propionaphthone	2-Styryl-3-methyl-4'-methoxy-1,4-α,β-naphtha-pyrone	—	135
3,4-Dimethoxycinnamic	2,4,6-Trihydroxy-ω-methoxyacetophenone	5,7-Dihydroxy-3,3',4'-trimethoxy-2-styrylchro-mone	—	534
β-Phenylpropionic	2,4-Dihydroxy-ω-methoxyacetophenone	7-Hydroxy-3-methoxy-2-phenethylchromone	—	534

Note: References 93–572 are listed on pp. 187–196.
† The potassium salt of the acid was used as the condensing agent.
‡ Triethylamine was used as the condensing agent.
§ The condensing agent used was not specified.

TABLE XVIII

ACYLATIONS WITH ACID CHLORIDES

Acid Chloride	Ketone	Condensing Agent	Product	Yield %	Reference
Acetyl	Ethyl 2,2,4-trimethyl-3-ketovalerate	$(C_6H_5)_3CNa$	Ethyl 2,2,4,4-tetramethyl-3,5-diketocaproate	52	10
Isobutyryl	Ethyl 2,2,4-trimethyl-3-ketovalerate	$(C_6H_5)_3CNa$	Ethyl 2,2,4,4,6-pentamethyl-3,5-diketoheptanoate	46	10
Pivaloyl	Pentamethylacetone	$NaNH_2$	2,2,4,6,6-Hexamethylheptane-3,5-dione	—	560
Benzoyl	Pentamethylacetone	$NaNH_2$	1-Phenyl-2,2,4,4-tetramethylpentane-1,3-dione	—	560
	1-Hydrindone	$NaNH_2$	2-Benzoyl-1-hydrindone	Low	201
	Cyclohexanone	$NaNH_2$	Enol benzoate of benzoylcyclohexanone		200
	Acetophenone	Na	Tribenzoylmethane	10	561
Cinnamoyl	Acetophenone	$NaNH_2$	Benzoyldicinnamoylmethane	66	18
Benzoyl	α-Methoxyacetophenone	$NaNH_2$	2-Methoxy-1,3-diphenylpropane-1,3-dione	11	168
	Phenyl isopropyl	$NaNH_2$	2,2-Dimethyl-1,3-diphenylpropane-1,3-dione	—	560
	Phenyl benzyl	$NaNH_2$	Phenyldibenzoylmethane or phenyltribenzoylmethane	—	562
	α,α-Diphenylacetophenone	Pyridine	Benzoyloxytriphenylethylene	—	563
Acetyl	Methyl methyl-t-butylneopentylcarbinyl	C_2H_5MgBr	Acetyl(methyl-t-butylneopentylacetyl)methane	70	564
	Acetomesitylene	C_2H_5MgBr	Acetylacetomesitylene	69	565
	Acetomesitylene	C_2H_5MgBr	Diacetylacetomesitylene	—	566
Methyl-t-butylneopentylacetyl	Methyl triethylcarbinyl	C_2H_5MgBr	Triethylacetyl(methyl-t-butylneopentylacetyl)methane	25	564
	Methyl methyl-t-butylneopentylcarbinyl	C_2H_5MgBr	Bis(methyl-t-butylneopentylacetyl)methane	23	564
	Methyl dineopentylcarbinyl	C_2H_5MgBr	Dineopentylacetyl(methyl-t-butylneopentylacetyl)methane	—	564
Dineopentylacetyl	Methyl methyl-t-butylneopentylcarbinyl	C_2H_5MgBr	Dineopentylacetyl(methyl-t-butylneopentylacetyl)methane	42	564
	Methyl dineopentylcarbinyl	C_2H_5MgBr	Bis(dineopentylacetyl)methane	68	567
	Ethyl dineopentylcarbinyl	C_2H_5MgBr	1,1-Bis(dineopentylacetyl)ethane	49	567
Benzoyl	Methyl methyl-t-butylneopentylcarbinyl	C_2H_5MgBr	Benzoyl(methyl-t-butylneopentylacetyl)methane	61	564

Methyl dineopentylcarbinyl	C_2H_5MgBr	Benzoyl(dineopentylacetyl)methane	41	567
Ethyl dineopentylcarbinyl	C_2H_5MgBr	1-Benzoyl-1-(dineopentylacetyl)ethane	39	567
Ethyl methyl-t-butylneopentylcarbinyl	C_2H_5MgBr	1-Benzoyl-1-(methyl-t-butylneopentylacetyl)ethane	43	564
Isopropyl methyl-t-butylneopentylcarbinyl	C_2H_5MgBr	Enol benzoate	72	564
Acetomesitylene	C_2H_5MgBr	Benzoylmesitoylmethane	75	565, 568
Acetomesitylene	C_2H_5MgBr	Dibenzoylmesitoylmethane	85	566
α,α-Dibromoacetomesitylene	C_2H_5MgBr	1-Benzoyloxy-1-mesityl-2,2-dibromoethylene	—	569
Propiomesitylene	C_2H_5MgBr	Enol benzoate of α-benzoylpropiomesitylene	65	565, 569
Isobutyromesitylene	C_2H_5MgBr	1-Benzoyloxy-1-mesityl-2-methyl-1-propene	—	569
3,5-Dibromoisobutyromesitylene	C_2H_5MgBr	1-Benzoyloxy-1-(2,4,6-trimethyl-3,5-dibromo)phenyl-2-methyl-1-propene	72	569
β,β-Diphenylpropiophenone	C_2H_5MgBr	Diphenylmethylenedibenzoylmethane	—	568
α,β,β-Triphenylpropiophenone	C_2H_5MgBr	1-Benzoyloxy-1,2,3,3-tetraphenyl-1-propene	—	568
β-Phenylpropiomesitylene	C_2H_5MgBr	Benzylbenzoylacetomesitylene and 1-benzoyloxy-1-mesityl-3-phenyl-1-propene	—	568
β-Phenylbutyromesitylene	C_2H_5MgBr	α-Methylbenzylbenzoylacetomesitylene and 1-benzoyloxy-1-mesityl-3-phenyl-1-butene	—	568
β,β-Diphenylpropiomesitylene	C_2H_5MgBr	Benzhydrylbenzoylacetomesitylene and 1-benzoyloxy-1-mesityl-3,3-diphenyl-1-propene	—	568
2,4,6-Trimethyl-benzoyl β,β-Diphenylpropiophenone	C_2H_5MgBr	Benzhydrylbenzoylacetomesitylene and 1-(2,4,6-tri-methyl)benzoyloxy-1-mesityl-3,3-diphenyl-1-propene	—	568
2,4,6-Triethylben-zoyl Acetomesitylene	C_2H_5MgBr	Dimesitoylmethane	64 *	565
Acetomesitylene	C_2H_5MgBr	2,4,6-Trimethyl-2',4',6'-triethyldibenzoylmethane	49 *	565
2,4,6-Trichloroben-zoyl 2,4,6-Trichloroacetophenone	C_2H_5MgBr	Di(2,4,6-trichlorobenzoyl)methane	40	570

Note: References 93–572 are listed on pp. 187–196.
* The product was isolated as the copper derivative.

TABLE XIX

ACYLATIONS WITH ANHYDRIDES BY BORON TRIFLUORIDE

Anhydride	Ketone	Product	Yield %	Reference
Acetic	Acetone	Acetylacetone	80–86	53, 92
	Methyl ethyl	3-Methylpentane-2,4-dione	32	51
	Methyl n-propyl	3-Ethylpentane-2,4-dione	31	51
		n-Butyrylacetone	3	
	Methyl isopropyl	3,3-Dimethylpentane-2,4-dione	19	51
		Isobutyrylacetone	9	
	Methyl isobutyl	3-Isopropylpentane-2,4-dione	16–21	50a,
		Isovalerylacetone	25–42	51
	Methyl t-butyl	Pivaloylacetone	45	54
	Methyl n-amyl	3-n-Butylpentane-2,4-dione	53–62	50a
		Caproylacetone	6–16	51
	Methyl isoamyl	3-Isobutylpentane-2,4-dione	46	50a
		7-Methyloctane-2,4-dione	7	
	Methyl n-hexyl	3-n-Amylpentane-2,4-dione	48	51
		Decane-2,4-dione	5	
	Methyl cyclohexyl	Hexahydrobenzoylacetone	27	50a
	Cyclohexylacetone	3-Cyclohexylpentane-2,4-dione	23	50a
		1-Cyclohexylpentane-2,4-dione	25	
	Diethyl	3-Methylhexane-2,4-dione	62	53
	Diisopropyl	Acylation failed		54
	Diisobutyl	3-Isopropyl-6-methylheptane-2,4-dione	45–78	52b, 54
	Mesityl oxide	Acylation failed		53
	Cyclopentanone	2-Acetylcyclopentanone	59–76	52b, 72
	Cyclohexanone	2-Acetylcyclohexanone	35–86	52b, 53, 54
	2-Methylcyclohexanone	2-Acetyl-2-methylcyclohexanone	17	51
		6-Acetyl-2-methylcyclohexanone	17	
	Acetophenone	Benzoylacetone	50–83	52b, 54, 53, 571
	p-Methylacetophenone	p-Methylbenzoylacetone	62	72
	p-Chloroacetophenone	p-Chlorobenzoylacetone	—	72
	p-Methoxyacetophenone	p-Methoxybenzoylacetone	—	72
	o-Nitroacetophenone	o-Nitrobenzoylacetone	68	58
	m-Nitroacetophenone	m-Nitrobenzoylacetone	64	58
	p-Nitroacetophenone	p-Nitrobenzoylacetone	66	58
	Phenylacetone	3-Phenylpentane-2,4-dione	41–63	54, 92a
		1-Phenylpentane-2,4-dione	1	
	p-Nitrophenylacetone	3-(p-Nitrophenyl)pentane-2,4-dione	49	50a
	Benzalacetone	Cinnamoylacetone	22	53
	Propiophenone	α-Methylbenzoylacetone	25	50a
	α-Methoxyacetophenone	2-Methoxy-1-phenylbutane-1,3-dione	10	168
	1-Tetralone	2-Acetyl-1-tetralone	83	53
Propionic	Acetone	Propionylacetone	46	54
	Methyl ethyl	3-Methylhexane-2,4-dione	31	54
	Methyl isobutyl	7-Methyloctane-3,5-dione	26	54
		3-Isopropylhexane-2,4-dione	17	
	Methyl n-amyl	3-n-Butylhexane-2,4-dione	47	54
		Decane-3,5-dione	4	
	Methyl neopentyl	7,7-Dimethyloctane-3,5-dione	38	50a
	Cyclohexanone	2-Propionylcyclohexanone	35–79	52b, 54
	Acetophenone	ω-Propionylacetophenone	30–67	52b, 54
	Methyl benzyl	3-Phenylhexane-2,4-dione	40	572
		1-Phenylhexane-2,4-dione	Trace	
n-Butyric	Acetone	Butyrylacetone	48	54
	Methyl ethyl	3-Methylheptane-2,4-dione	44	54

Note: References 93–572 are listed on pp. 187–196.

TABLE XIX—*Continued*

ACYLATIONS WITH ANHYDRIDES BY BORON TRIFLUORIDE

Anhydride	Ketone	Product	Yield %	Reference
n-Butyric— *Continued*	Methyl isobutyl	2-Methylnonane-4,6-dione	26	54
		3-Isopropylheptane-2,4-dione	18	
	Methyl n-amyl	3-n-Butylheptane-2,4-dione	38	54
		Undecane-4,6-dione	4	
	Diethyl	4-Methyloctane-3,5-dione	46	54
	Cyclopentanone	2-Butyrylcyclopentanone	54–88	52b
	Cyclohexanone	2-Butyrylcyclohexanone	34–83	52b, 54
	Acetophenone	1-Phenylhexane-1,3-dione	63–81	52b, 54
Isobutyric	Methyl n-amyl	3-n-Butyl-5-methylhexane-2,4-dione	29	54
		2-Methyldecane-3,5-dione	3	
Caproic	Methyl ethyl	3-Methylnonane-2,4-dione	64	54
	Methyl n-amyl	Tridecane-6,8-dione and 3-n-butylnonane-2,4-dione	22	50a
	Cyclohexanone	2-Caproylcyclohexanone	37–68	52b
Diethylacetic	Cyclohexanone	2-(ω,ω-Diethylacetyl)cyclohexanone	68	52b
2-Ethylhexanoic	Cyclohexanone	2-(2-Ethylhexanoyl)cyclohexanone	56	52b
Succinic	Acetophenone	Acylation failed		54
Benzoic	Acetophenone	Acylation failed		53
Phenylacetic	Acetone	Acylation failed		54
Phthalic	Acetophenone	Acylation failed		54

TABLE XX

ACETOACETYLATION OF AROMATIC COMPOUNDS WITH ACETIC ANHYDRIDE BY BORON TRIFLUORIDE [52a]

Aromatic Compound	β-Diketone *	Yield %
Benzene	Benzoylacetone	2
Toluene	p-Methylbenzoylacetone	43–53
Anisole	p-Methoxybenzoylacetone	51
Mesitylene	2,4,6-Trimethylbenzoylacetone	57
Chlorobenzene	p-Chlorobenzoylacetone	0

Note: References 93–572 are listed below.
* Varying amounts of intermediate ketones have been isolated.

REFERENCES TO TABLES VIII–XX

[93] Claisen and Ehrhardt, *Ber.*, **22**, 1009 (1889).
[94] Claisen and Feyerabend, *Ber.*, **38**, 693 (1905).
[95] Zellars and Levine, *J. Org. Chem.*, **13**, 160 (1948).
[96] Hansley, U. S. pat. 2,158,071 [*C. A.*, **33**, 6342 (1939)].
[97] Hansley, U. S. pat. 2,218,026 [*C. A.*, **35**, 1066 (1941)].
[98] Weygand and Baumgartel, *Ber.*, **62**, 574 (1929).
[99] Morgan and Reeves, *J. Chem. Soc.*, **123**, 444 (1923).
[100] Powell and Seymour, *J. Am. Chem. Soc.*, **53**, 1049 (1931).
[101] Morgan, Drew, and Ackermann, *J. Chem. Soc.*, **125**, 740 (1924).
[102] Pannizi, *Gazz. chim. ital.*, **71**, 216 (1941).

[103] Morgan, Drew, and Porter, *J. Chem. Soc.*, **125**, 737 (1924).
[104] Fittig, *Ann.*, **353**, 35 (1907).
[105] Bouveault and Bongert, *Compt. rend.*, **132**, 701 (1901).
[106] Kutz and Adkins, *J. Am. Chem. Soc.*, **52**, 4042 (1930).
[107] Dewar, *J. Chem. Soc.*, **1944**, 615.
[108] Balbianó, *Gazz. chim. ital.*, **23**, 323 (1893).
[109] Morgan and Holmes, *J. Chem. Soc.*, **125**, 760 (1924).
[110] Morgan and Drew, *J. Chem. Soc.*, **121**, 922 (1922).
[111] Couturier, *Compt. rend.*, **150**, 928 (1910).
[112] Kramers, *Rec. trav. chim.*, **16**, 109 (1897).
[113] Wild, *Ann.*, **414**, 111 (1918).
[114] Leser, *Bull. soc. chim. France*, [3] **27**, 64 (1902).
[115] Morgan and Holmes, *J. Chem. Soc.*, **127**, 2891 (1925).
[116] Morgan and Taylor, *J. Chem. Soc.*, **127**, 2620 (1925).
[117] Barbier and Leser, *Bull. soc. chim. France*, [3] **17**, 748 (1897).
[118] Borsche, *Ann.*, **377**, 70 (1910).
[119] Leser, *Ann. chim. phys.*, [8] **26**, 227 (1912.)
[120] Leser, *Bull. soc. chim. France*, [3] **25**, 196 (1901).
[121] Leser, *Bull. soc. chim. France*, [3] **23**, 370 (1900).
[122] Brühl, *Ber.*, **37**, 746 (1904).
[123] Harris and Levine, *J. Am. Chem. Soc.*, **70**, 3360 (1948).
[124] Hickinbottom, *Reactions of Organic Compounds*, 2nd ed., p. 271, Longmans, Green and Co., 1936.
[125] Beyer and Claisen, *Ber.*, **20**, 2178 (1887).
[126] Claisen, *Ann.*, **291**, 25 (1896).
[127] Gattermann-Wieland, *Laboratory Methods of Organic Chemistry*, 24th ed., p. 253, The Macmillan Co., 1937.
[128] Basu, *J. Indian Chem. Soc.*, **8**, 119 (1931).
[129] Fuson, Fugate, and Fischer, *J. Am. Chem. Soc.*, **61**, 2362 (1939).
[130] Fuson and Woodward, *J. Am. Chem. Soc.*, **55**, 3474 (1933).
[131] Hanus, Jilek, and Lukas, *Collection Czechoslov. Chem. Communs.*, **1**, 392 (1929) [*C. A.*, **23**, 5175 (1929)].
[132] Auwers and Heimke, *Ann.*, **458**, 186 (1927).
[133] Banchetti, *Gazz. chim. ital.*, **70**, 134 (1940).
[134] Wittig, Bangert, and Richter, *Ann.*, **446**, 155 (1926).
[135] Cheema, Gulati, and Venkataraman, *J. Chem. Soc.*, **1932**, 925.
[136] Wittig, *Ber.*, **57**, 88 (1924).
[137] Flynn and Robertson, *J. Chem. Soc.*, **1936**, 215.
[138] Jones and Robertson, *J. Chem. Soc.*, **1932**, 1689.
[139] Adams and Mecornay, *J. Am. Chem. Soc.*, **66**, 802 (1944).
[140] Tasaki, *Acta Phytochim. Japan*, **3**, 259 (1927) [*Chem. Zentr.*, **1927**, II, 1949; *C. A.*, **23**, 125 (1929)].
[141] Auwers and Lammerhirt, *Ann.*, **421**, 1 (1920).
[142] Zaki and Azzam, *J. Chem. Soc.*, **1943**, 434.
[143] Sachs and Herold, *Ber.*, **40**, 2714 (1907).
[144] Sethna and Shah, *J. Indian Chem. Soc.*, (a) **17**, 211 (1940); (b) **17**, 487 (1940).
[145] Trivedi, Sethna, and Shah, *J. Univ. Bombay*, **11**, Pt. 3, 144 (1942) [*C. A.*, **37**, 2375 (1943)].
[146] Blumberg and Kostanecki, *Ber.*, **36**, 2191 (1903).
[147] Block and Kostanecki, *Ber.*, **33**, 471 (1900).
[148] Crivelli and Kostanecki, *Ber.*, **33**, 2512 (1900).
[149] Kostanecki and Lloyd, *Ber.*, **34**, 2942 (1901).
[150] Algar, *Proc. Roy. Irish Acad.*, **33B**, 86 (1916) [*C. A.*, **10**, 2577 (1916)].
[151] Ryan and Dunlea, *Proc. Roy. Irish Acad.*, **32B**, 1 (1913); *J. Chem. Soc.*, **104**, I, 1067 (1913) [*C. A.*, **8**, 1106 (1914)].
[152] Cheetham and Hey, *J. Chem. Soc.*, **1937**, 770.

[153] Wittig and Blumenthal, *Ber.*, **60**, 1085 (1927).
[154] Mosettig and Stuart, *J. Am. Chem. Soc.*, **61**, 1 (1939).
[155] Curd and Robertson, *J. Chem. Soc.*, **1933**, 1173.
[156] Willstätter and Iglauer, *Ber.*, **33**, 359 (1900).
[157] Sommelet, *Bull. soc. chim. France*, [4] **1**, 377 (1907).
[158] Henne, Newman, Quill, and Staniforth, *J. Am. Chem. Soc.*, **69**, 1819 (1947).
[159] Renard and Maquinoy, *Bull. soc. chim. Belge*, **55**, 98 (1946).
[160] Harris and Wilson, *J. Am. Chem. Soc.*, **63**, 2526 (1941).
[161] Walther, *J. prakt. Chem.*, [2] **83**, 171 (1911).
[162] Panizzi, *Gazz. chim. ital.*, **73**, 99 (1943).
[163] Panizzi, *Gazz. chim. ital.*, **72**, 99 (1942).
[164] Fischer and Bartholomaus, *Ber.*, **45**, 1983 (1912).
[165] Auwers and Jacobsen, *Ann.*, **426**, 161 (1922).
[166] Heilbron, Hey, and Lowe, *J. Chem. Soc.*, **1934**, 1311.
[167] Kostanecki and Tambor, *Ber.*, **34**, 1693 (1901).
[168] Munch-Petersen and Hauser, *J. Am. Chem. Soc.*, **71**, 770 (1949).
[169] Musante, *Gazz. chim. ital.*, **70**, 685 (1940).
[170] Oroshnik and Spoerri, *J. Am. Chem. Soc.*, **67**, 721 (1945).
[171] Fischer and Baer, *Helv. Chim. Acta*, **16**, 534 (1933).
[172] Morgan and Thomason, *J. Chem. Soc.*, **125**, 754 (1924).
[173] Fischer, Berg, and Schormuller, *Ann.*, **480**, 150 (1930).
[174] Smith and King, *J. Am. Chem. Soc.*, **65**, 441 (1943).
[175] Morgan and Taylor, *J. Chem. Soc.*, **127**, 797 (1925).
[176] Man, Swamer, and Hauser, *J. Am. Chem. Soc.*, **73**, 901 (1951).
[177] Baumgarten and Hauser, unpublished work.
[178] Diels and Schrum, *Ann.*, **530**, 68 (1937).
[179] Green and LaForge, *J. Am. Chem. Soc.*, **70**, 2287 (1948).
[180] Morgan and Porter, *J. Chem. Soc.*, **125**, 1269 (1924).
[181] Kohler and Rao, *J. Am. Chem. Soc.*, **41**, 1697 (1919).
[182] Hauser and Tompkins, unpublished work.
[183] Becker, *Helv. Chim. Acta*, **32**, 1114 (1949).
[184] Bulow and Grotowsky, *Ber.*, **34**, 1479 (1901).
[185] Heilbron, Hey, and Lythgoe, *J. Chem. Soc.*, **1936**, 295.
[186] Hauser, Walker, and Sanderson, unpublished work.
[187] Morgan and Jones, *J. Chem. Soc.*, **127**, 2619 (1925).
[188] Rupe and Kloppenburg, *Helv. Chim. Acta*, **2**, 363 (1919).
[189] Robinson and Seijo, *J. Chem. Soc.*, **1941**, 582.
[190] Daub and Johnson, *J. Am. Chem. Soc.*, **72**, 501 (1950).
[191] Johnson, Johnson, and Petersen, *J. Am. Chem. Soc.*, **68**, 1926 (1946).
[192] Tingle and Gorsline, *Am. Chem. J.*, **40**, 46 (1908).
[193] Ruhemann, *J. Chem. Soc.*, **93**, 431 (1908).
[194] Ruhemann, *J. Chem. Soc.*, **93**, 1281 (1908).
[195] Ruhemann, *J. Chem. Soc.*, **101**, 1729 (1912).
[196] Ruhemann, *J. Chem. Soc.*, **97**, 457 (1910).
[197] Claisen, *Ber.*, **20**, 655 (1887).
[198] Tingle and Gorsline, *J. Am. Chem. Soc.*, **30**, 1874 (1908).
[199] Michael and Hibbert, *Ann.*, **390**, 68 (1912).
[200] Bauer, *Ann. chim.*, [9] **1**, 393 (1914).
[201] Robinson and Shah, *J. Chem. Soc.*, **1933**, 610.
[202] Bulow and Sicherer, *Ber.*, **34**, 2372 (1901).
[203] Pascual, *Anales soc. españ. fís. y quím.*, **27**, 668 (1929) [*C. A.*, **24**, 358 (1930)].
[204] Mozingo and Adkins, *J. Am. Chem. Soc.*, **60**, 669 (1938).
[205] Bradley and Robinson, *J. Chem. Soc.*, **129**, 2356 (1926).
[206] Kostanecki and Tambor, *Ber.*, **33**, 330 (1900).
[207] Robinson and Turner, *J. Chem. Soc.*, **113**, 874 (1918).
[208] Tambor, *Ber.*, **41**, 793 (1908).

[209] Ludwinowsky and Tambor, *Ber.*, **39**, 4037 (1906).

[210] Emilwicz, Kostanecki, and Tambor, *Ber.*, **32**, 2448 (1899).

[211] Kimura and Hosi, *J. Pharm. Soc. Japan*, **57**, 163 (1937) [*C. A.*, **33**, 602 (1939)].

[212] Reigrodski and Tambor, *Ber.*, **43**, 1964 (1910).

[213] Hattori, *Acta Phytochim. Japan*, **6**, 131 (1932) [*C. A.*, **26**, 4816 (1932)].

[214] Bargellini, *Gazz. chim. ital.*, **49**, II, 47 (1919).

[215] Hattori, *Acta Phytochim. Japan*, **5**, 219 (1931) [*C. A.*, **26**, 1282 (1932)].

[216] Baker, *J. Chem. Soc.*, **1941**, 662.

[217] Abell, *J. Chem. Soc.*, **101**, 989 (1912).

[218] Smedley, *J. Chem. Soc.*, **97**, 1492 (1910).

[219] Weygand, Forkel, and Bischoff, *Ber.*, **61**, 687 (1928).

[220] Tingle and Gorsline, *Am. Chem. J.*, **37**, 483 (1907).

[221] Rupe and Hirschmann, *Helv. Chim. Acta*, **11**, 1180 (1928).

[222] Tambor, *Ber.*, **41**, 787 (1908).

[223] Czajkowski, Kostanecki, and Tambor, *Ber.*, **33**, 1988 (1900).

[224] Bargellini and Grippa, *Gazz. chim. ital.*, **57**, 605 (1927).

[225] Bargellini, *Gazz. chim. ital.*, **45**, I, 69 (1915).

[226] Block and Kostanecki, *Ber.*, **33**, 1998 (1900).

[227] Pistermann and Tambor, *Ber.*, **45**, 1239 (1912).

[228] Kostanecki and Tambor, *Ber.*, **34**, 1690 (1901).

[229] Grossman and Kostanecki, *Ber.*, **33**, 2515 (1900).

[230] Kostanecki and Steuermann, *Ber.*, **34**, 109 (1901).

[231] Burgess, *J. Chem. Soc.*, **1927**, 2017.

[232] Gulland and Robinson, *J. Chem. Soc.*, **127**, 1493 (1925).

[233] Perkin and Weizmann, *J. Chem. Soc.*, **89**, 1649 (1906).

[234] Kostanecki, Rozycki, and Tambor, *Ber.*, **33**, 3410 (1900).

[235] Badhwar, Kang, and Venkataraman, *J. Chem. Soc.*, **1932**, 1107.

[236] Bulow and Riess, *Ber.*, **35**, 3900 (1902).

[237] Perkin and Schiess, *J. Chem. Soc.*, **85**, 159 (1904).

[238] Baker, Brown, and Scott, *J. Chem. Soc.*, **1939**, 1922.

[239] Bargellini and Monti, *Gazz. chim. ital.*, **45**, I, 64 (1915).

[240] Mahal and Venkataraman, *J. Chem. Soc.*, **1936**, 569.

[241] Virkar and Wheeler, *J. Chem. Soc.*, **1939**, 1681.

[242] Schwerim, *Ber.*, **27**, 104 (1894).

[243] Berend and Herms, *J. prakt. Chem.*, [2] **74**, 131 (1906).

[244] Smedley, *J. Chem. Soc.*, **97**, 1484 (1910).

[245] Semmler and Ascher, *Ber.*, **42**, 2355 (1909).

[246] Musante, *Gazz. chim. ital.*, **71**, 172 (1941).

[247] Musante, *Gazz. chim. ital.*, **72**, 242 (1942).

[248] Micko, *Monatsh.*, **17**, 442 (1896).

[249] Ferenczy, *Monatsh.*, **18**, 673 (1897).

[250] Gough and King, *J. Chem. Soc.*, **1933**, 350.

[251] Tscherne, *Monatsh.*, **22**, 615 (1901).

[252] Weidel, *Monatsh.*, **17**, 401 (1896).

[253] Linnell and Rigby, *Quart. J. Pharm. Pharmacol.*, **11**, 722 (1938) [*C. A.*, **33**, 3524 (1939)].

[254] Shivers and Hauser, *J. Am. Chem. Soc.*, **70**, 437 (1948).

[255] Peletier de Rosanbo, *Ann. chim.*, [9] **19**, 327 (1923).

[256] Rothstein and Thorpe, *J. Chem. Soc.*, **129**, 2011 (1926).

[257] Eskola, *Suomen Kemistilehti*, **11B**, 9 (1938) [*C. A.*, **32**, 3359 (1938)].

[258] Eskola, *Ann. Acad. Sci. Fennicae*, Ser. A, II, Chem. No. 18 [*C. A.*, **41**, 949 (1947)].

[259] Maeder, *Helv. Chim. Acta*, **29**, 120 (1946).

[260] Eskola, Udd, Leppanen, and Stjernvall, *Suomen Kemistilehti*, **20B**, 13 (1947) [*C. A.*, **42**, 1192 (1948)].

[261] Eskola, *Suomen Kemistilehti*, **15B**, 17 (1942) [*C. A.*, **38**, 6277 (1944)].

[262] Toivonen, *Ann. Acad. Sci. Fennicae*, Ser. A, **28**, Chem. No. 11 (*Chem. Zentr.*, **1928**, II, 39).
[263] Robinson and Thompson, *J. Chem. Soc.*, **1939**, 1739.
[264] Chuang, Ma, Tien, and Huang, *Ber.*, **72**, 949 (1939).
[265] Blaise and Kohler, *Compt. rend.*, **148**, 1401 (1909).
[266] Blaise and Kohler, *Bull. soc. chim. France*, [4] **7**, 710 (1910).
[267] Godchot, *Compt. rend.*, **176**, 1151 (1923).
[268] Baeyer and Oehler, *Ber.*, **29**, 27 (1896).
[269] Grateau, *Compt. rend.*, **191**, 947 (1930).
[270] Kotz and Lemien, *J. prakt. Chem.*, [2] **90**, 382 (1914).
[271] Vorländer, *Ann.*, **294**, 253 (1897).
[272] Schilling and Vorländer, *Ann.*, **308**, 184 (1899).
[273] Blaise and Marie, *Bull. soc. chim. France*, [4] **3**, 425 (1908); *Compt. rend.*, **144**, 572 (1907).
[274] Knoevenagel and Brunswig, *Ber.*, **35**, 2172 (1902).
[275] Lin and Robinson, *J. Chem. Soc.*, **1938**, 2005.
[276] Michael and Ross, *J. Am. Chem. Soc.*, **53**, 2394 (1931).
[277] Knoevenagel, *Ber.*, **27**, 2337 (1894).
[278] Vorländer and Gartner, *Ann.*, **304**, 20 (1899).
[279] Norris and Thorpe, *J. Chem. Soc.*, **119**, 1199 (1921).
[280] Robinson and Shah, *J. Chem. Soc.*, **1934**, 1491.
[281] Desai, *J. Chem. Soc.*, **1932**, 1079.
[282] Cox, Kroecker, and McElvain, *J. Am. Chem. Soc.*, **56**, 1173 (1934).
[283] Quadrat-I-Khuda, *J. Chem. Soc.*, **1929**, 1913.
[284] Vorländer and Knotzsch, *Ann.*, **294**, 323 (1897).
[285] Robinson and Walker, *J. Chem. Soc.*, **1936**, 747.
[286] Robinson and Schlittler, *J. Chem. Soc.*, **1935**, 1288.
[287] Chang, Huang, and Ma, *Ber.*, **72**, 713 (1939).
[288] Chang, Tien, and Huang, *Ber.*, **70**, 858 (1937).
[288a] Johnson, *J. Am. Chem. Soc.*, **65**, 1317 (1943).
[289] Kon and Linstead, *J. Chem. Soc.*, **127**, 815 (1925).
[290] Becker and Thorpe, *J. Chem. Soc.*, **121**, 1303 (1922).
[291] Eccott and Linstead, *J. Chem. Soc.*, **1930**, 905.
[292] Crossley, *J. Chem. Soc.*, **81**, 675 (1902); Crossley and Pratt, *ibid.*, **107**, 171 (1915).
[293] Birch and Robinson, *J. Chem. Soc.*, **1942**, 488.
[294] Kon, *J. Chem. Soc.*, **1926**, 1792.
[295] Dickens, Hugh, and Kon, *J. Chem. Soc.*, **1929**, 572.
[296] Dickens, Hugh, and Kon, *J. Chem. Soc.*, **1928**, 1630.
[297] Crossley and Renouf, *J. Chem. Soc.*, **107**, 602 (1915).
[298] Boyd, Clifford, and Probert, *J. Chem. Soc.*, **117**, 1383 (1920).
[299] Vorländer, *Ber.*, **27**, 2053 (1894).
[300] Michael, *Ber.*, **27**, 2126 (1894).
[301] Hinkel, Ayling, and Dippy, *J. Chem. Soc.*, **1935**, 539.
[302] Chaudhuri, *J. Indian Chem. Soc.*, **21**, 341 (1944).
[303] Friedmann, *J. prakt. Chem.*, [2] **146**, 65 (1936).
[304] Mattar, Hastings, and Walker, *J. Chem. Soc.*, **1930**, 2455.
[305] Meyer, *Compt. rend.*, **205**, 920 (1937).
[306] Gilling, *J. Chem. Soc.*, **103**, 2029 (1913).
[307] Michael and Freer, *J. prakt. Chem.*, [2] **43**, 390 (1891).
[308] Linstead and Williams, *J. Chem. Soc.*, **1926**, 2735.
[309] Bredt, *Ber.*, **24**, 603 (1891).
[310] Papadakis, *J. Am. Chem. Soc.*, **67**, 1799 (1945).
[311] Rabe, *Ber.*, **31**, 1896 (1898).
[312] Friedmann, *J. prakt. Chem.*, [2] **146**, 71 (1936).
[313] Friedmann, *J. prakt. Chem.*, [2] **146**, 79 (1936).

[314] Dieckmann and Kron, *Ber.*, **41**, 1260 (1908).
[315] Borsche, *Ber.*, **42**, 4496 (1909).
[316] Lehninger and Witzemann, *J. Am. Chem. Soc.*, **64**, 874 (1942).
[317] Kotz and Blendermann, *J. prakt. Chem.*, [2] **88**, 257 (1913).
[318] Claisen and Stylos, *Ber.*, **20**, 2188 (1887).
[319] Rinderknecht, Ward, Bergel, and Morrison, *Biochem. J.*, **41**, 463 (1947).
[320] Puetzer, Nield, and Barry, *J. Am. Chem. Soc.*, **67**, 832 (1945).
[321] Ruzicka and Fornasir, *Helv. Chim. Acta*, **3**, 806 (1920).
[322] Rimini, *Gazz. chim. ital.*, **26**, 375 (1896).
[323] Claisen, *Ber.*, **24**, 111 (1891).
[324] Claisen and Stylos, *Ber.*, **21**, 1141 (1888).
[325] Royals, *J. Am. Chem. Soc.*, **67**, 1508 (1945).
[326] Puetzer, Nield, and Barry, *Science*, **101**, 307 (1945) [*C. A.*, **39**, 2290 (1945)].
[327] Lapworth and Hann, *J. Chem. Soc.*, **81**, 1485 (1902).
[328] Koenigs and Ottmann, *Ber.*, **54**, 1343 (1921).
[329] Robinson and Watt, *J. Chem. Soc.*, **1934**, 1536.
[330] Claisen and Ewan, *Ann.*, **284**, 247 (1895).
[331] Lehninger, *J. Biol. Chem.*, **153**, 561 (1944).
[332] Swamer and Hauser, unpublished observations.
[333] Keskin, *Rev. faculté sci. univ. Istanbul*, **9A**, 64 (1944) [*C. A.*, **40**, 1822 (1946)].
[334] Keskin, *Rev. faculté sci. univ. Istanbul*, **11A**, 143 (1946) [*C. A.*, **41**, 3785 (1947)].
[335] Wislicenus and Melms, *Ann.*, **436**, 101 (1924).
[336] Ruggli and Schmidlin, *Helv. Chim. Acta*, **27**, 499 (1944).
[337] Leser, *Compt. rend.*, **127**, 763 (1898).
[338] Claisen, *Ann.*, **291**, 125 (1896).
[339] Ford, U. S. pat. 2,138,540 [*C. A.*, **33**, 1759 (1939)].
[340] Kotz, Bieber, and Schuler, *Ann.*, **348**, 111 (1906).
[341] Cohen, Cook, and Hewett, *J. Chem. Soc.*, **1935**, 445.
[342] Pandya, Nargund, and Bokil, *J. Univ. Bombay*, **10**, Pt. 5, 114 (1942) [*C. A.*, **37**, 614 (1943)].
[343] Kotz and Michels, *Ann.*, **350**, 204 (1906).
[344] Kon and Nandi, *J. Chem. Soc.*, **1933**, 1628.
[345] Jaeger and van Dijk, *Proc. Acad. Sci. Amsterdam*, **39**, 384 (1936) [*C. A.*, **30**, 6341 (1936)].
[346] Kotz, *J. prakt. Chem.*, [2] **80**, 506 (1909).
[347] Kotz and Meyer, *J. prakt. Chem.*, [2] **88**, 261 (1913).
[348] Kotz and Hesse, *Ann.*, **342**, 306 (1905).
[349] Cornubert and Maurel, *Bull. soc. chim. France*, [4] **49**, 1525 (1931).
[350] Fischer and Wunderlich, *Ber.*, **74**, 1544 (1941).
[351] Cook and Lawrence, *J. Chem. Soc.*, **1938**, 58.
[352] Newman and Farbman, *J. Am. Chem. Soc.*, **66**, 1550 (1944).
[353] Chakravarti, *J. Indian Chem. Soc.*, **21**, 322 (1944).
[354] Chakravarti, *J. Indian Chem. Soc.*, **20**, 301 (1943).
[355] Adamson, McQuillin, Robinson, and Simonsen, *J. Chem. Soc.*, **1937**, 1576.
[356] Tingle, *Am. Chem. J.*, **20**, 318 (1898).
[357] Tingle, *Am. Chem. J.*, **19**, 393 (1897).
[358] Bromme and Claisen, *Ber.*, **21**, 1131 (1888).
[359] Wislicenus, *Ber.*, **28**, 811 (1895).
[360] Haworth, Jones, and Way, *J. Chem. Soc.*, **1943**, 10.
[361] Widman and Virgin, *Ber.*, **42**, 2794 (1909).
[362] Robinson and Schwartzenbach, *J. Chem. Soc.*, **1930**, 822.
[363] Perkin and Robinson, *J. Chem. Soc.*, **93**, 489 (1908).
[364] Haworth and Kelly, *J. Chem. Soc.*, **1937**, 1645.
[365] Kostanecki, Paul, and Tambor, *Ber.*, **34**, 2475 (1901).
[366] Lawson, Perkin, and Robinson, *J. Chem. Soc.*, **125**, 626 (1924).
[367] Ryan and Plunkett, *Proc. Irish Acad.*, **32B**, 199 (1916) [*C. A.*, **10**, 1849 (1916)].

[368] Panizzi and Benati, *Gazz. chim. ital.*, **76**, 66 (1946).
[369] Bachmann and Thomas, *J. Am. Chem. Soc.*, **63**, 598 (1941).
[370] Bachmann and Wendler, *J. Am. Chem. Soc.*, **68**, 2580 (1946).
[371] Bachmann and Edgerton, *J. Am. Chem. Soc.*, **62**, 2219 (1940).
[372] Bachmann and Thomas, *J. Am. Chem. Soc.*, **64**, 94 (1942).
[373] Martin and Robinson, *J. Chem. Soc.*, **1943**, 491.
[374] Campbell and Soffer, *J. Am. Chem. Soc.*, **64**, 417 (1942).
[375] Geissman and Tulagin, *J. Am. Chem. Soc.*, **66**, 719 (1944).
[376] Cook and Lawrence, *J. Chem. Soc.*, **1937**, 817.
[377] Bachmann and Morin, *J. Am. Chem. Soc.*, **66**, 553 (1944).
[378] Robinson and Walker, *J. Chem. Soc.*, **1938**, 183.
[379] Bachmann and Ness, *J. Am. Chem. Soc.*, **64**, 536 (1942).
[380] Bachmann and Dreiding, *J. Org. Chem.*, **13**, 317 (1948).
[381] Bachmann and Wilds, *J. Am. Chem. Soc.*, **62**, 2084 (1940).
[382] Haworth, *J. Chem. Soc.*, **1932**, 1125.
[383] Bachmann and Cortes, *J. Am. Chem. Soc.*, **65**, 1329 (1943).
[384] Bachmann and Horton, *J. Am. Chem. Soc.*, **69**, 58 (1947).
[385] Robinson and Walker, *J. Chem. Soc.*, **1937**, 60.
[386] Bachmann and Holmes, *J. Am. Chem. Soc.*, **62**, 2750 (1940).
[387] Bachmann and Anderson, *J. Org. Chem.*, **13**, 297 (1948).
[388] Bachmann and Carmack, *J. Am. Chem. Soc.*, **63**, 2494 (1941).
[389] Wilds and Beck, *J. Am. Chem. Soc.*, **66**, 1688 (1944).
[390] Angeli, *Ber.*, **23**, 1793 (1890).
[391] Fischer and Müller, *Z. physiol. Chem.*, **132**, 72 (1924).
[392] Fischer and Loy, *Z. physiol. Chem.*, **128**, 59 (1923).
[393] Elks, Elliott, and Hems, *J. Chem. Soc.*, **1944**, 624.
[394] Claisen, *Bull. soc. chim. France*, [3] **1**, 496 (1889).
[395] Claisen and Roosen, *Ann.*, **278**, 274 (1894).
[396] Panizzi and Monti, *Gazz. chim. ital.*, **77**, 556 (1947).
[397] Benary, Meyer, and Charisium, *Ber.*, **59**, 108 (1926).
[398] Chelintsev, *J. Gen. Chem. U.S.S.R.*, **14**, 1070 (1944) [*C. A.*, **41**, 101 (1947)].
[399] Couturier and Vignon, *Compt. rend.*, **140**, 1695 (1905).
[400] Caldwell, Kornfeld, and Donrell, *J. Am. Chem. Soc.*, **63**, 2188 (1941).
[401] Couturier, *Compt. rend.*, **150**, 705 (1910).
[402] Leser, *Bull. soc. chim. France*, [3] **21**, 969 (1899); *Compt. rend.*, **128**, 110 (1899).
[403] Shantz, *J. Am. Chem. Soc.*, **68**, 2553 (1948).
[404] Claisen and Meyerowitz, *Ber.*, **22**, 3273 (1889).
[405] Johnson and Shellberg, *J. Am. Chem. Soc.*, **67**, 1745 (1945).
[406] King and Robinson, *J. Chem. Soc.*, **1941**, 465.
[407] Wallach and Steindorff, *Ann.*, **329**, 109 (1903).
[408] Thompson, *J. Am. Chem. Soc.*, **53**, 3160 (1931).
[409] Auwers, Buschmann, and Heidenrich, *Ann.*, **435**, 277 (1924).
[410] Sen-Gupta, *J. Chem. Soc.*, **107**, 1347 (1915).
[411] Helfer, *Helv. Chim. Acta*, **7**, 950 (1924).
[412] Ruhemann and Levy, *J. Chem. Soc.*, **101**, 2542 (1912).
[413] Meister, Lucius, and Brüning, Ger. pat. 119,862 [*Chem. Zentr.*, **1901**, I, 1024].
[414] Bishop, Claisen, and Sinclair, *Ann.*, **281**, 314 (1894).
[415] Rupe and Gubler, *Helv. Chim. Acta*, **9**, 582 (1926).
[415a] Prelog, Ruzicka, and Metzler, *Helv. Chim. Acta*, **30**, 1883 (1947).
[416] Wallach, *Ber.*, **28**, 31 (1895).
[417] Semmler and Bartelt, *Ber.*, **40**, 4844 (1907).
[418] Semmler, *Ber.*, **40**, 5017 (1907).
[419] Roch, *Compt. rend.*, **220**, 322 (1945).
[420] Rupe and Müller, *Helv. Chim. Acta*, **4**, 841 (1921).
[421] Knorr, *Ber.*, **28**, 699 (1895).
[422] Claisen and Fischer, *Ber.*, **21**, 1135 (1888).

[423] Bulow and Sicherer, *Ber.*, **34**, 3889 (1901).

[424] Claisen and Fischer, *Ber.*, **20**, 2191 (1887).

[425] Pratt, Robinson, and Williams, *J. Chem. Soc.*, **125**, 199 (1924).

[426] Mentzer and Meunier, *Bull. soc. chim. France*, [5] **11**, 302 (1944).

[427] Malkin and Robinson, *J. Chem. Soc.*, **127**, 1190 (1925).

[428] Shriner and Hull, *J. Org. Chem.*, **10**, 288 (1945).

[429] Shriner and Hull, *J. Org. Chem.*, **10**, 228 (1945).

[430] Joshi and Venkataraman, *J. Chem. Soc.*, **1934**, 513.

[431] Mahal, Rai, and Venkataraman, *J. Chem. Soc.*, **1934**, 1120.

[432] Wessely, Kornfeld, and Lechner, *Ber.*, **66**, 685 (1933).

[433] Späth and Lederer, *Ber.*, **63**, 743 (1930).

[434] Mahal, Rai, and Venkataraman, *J. Chem. Soc.*, **1934**, 1769.

[435] Shriner and Hull, *J. Org. Chem.*, **10**, 228 (1945).

[436] Shriner and Stephenson, *J. Am. Chem. Soc.*, **64**, 2737 (1942).

[437] Wolfrom, Mohan, Morgan, and Johnson, *J. Am. Chem. Soc.*, **63**, 1248 (1941).

[438] Wolfrom and Mohan, *J. Am. Chem. Soc.*, **63**, 1253 (1941).

[439] Cheema and Venkataraman, *J. Chem. Soc.*, **1932**, 918.

[440] Auwers and Wiegand, *J. prakt. Chem.*, [2] **134**, 82 (1932).

[441] Birch, Jaeger, and Robinson, *J. Chem. Soc.*, **1945**, 582.

[442] Bardhan, *J. Chem. Soc.*, **1936**, 1848.

[443] Paranjpe, Phalnikar, Bhide, and Nargund, *Rasāyanam*, **1**, 233 (1943) [*C. A.*, **37**, 6671 (1943)].

[444] Ruzicka, Rey, and Muhr, *Helv. Chim. Acta*, **27**, 472 (1944).

[445] Virkar and Wheeler, *J. Chem. Soc.*, **1939**, 1679.

[446] Doyle, Gogan, Gowan, Keane, and Wheeler, *Sci. Proc. Roy. Dublin Soc.*, **24** (N. S.), 291 (1948) [*C. A.*, **43**, 2620 (1949)].

[447] Bhala, Mahal, and Venkataraman, *J. Chem. Soc.*, **1935**, 868.

[448] Virkar and Shah, *J. Univ. Bombay*, **11**, Pt. 3, 140 (1942) [*C. A.*, **37**, 2374 (1943)].

[449] Horii, *J. Pharm. Soc. Japan, Trans.*, **59**, 209 (1939) [*C. A.*, **34**, 3270 (1940)].

[450] Gulati and Venkataraman, *J. Chem. Soc.*, **1936**, 267.

[451] Baker, *J. Chem. Soc.*, **1939**, 956.

[452] Sastri and Seshadri, *Proc. Indian Acad. Sci.*, **23A**, 134 (1946) [*C. A.*, **41**, 120 (1947)].

[453] Sastri and Seshadri, *Proc. Indian Acad. Sci.*, **24A**, 243 (1946) [*C. A.*, **41**, 2417 (1947)].

[454] Sastri and Seshadri, *Proc. Indian Acad. Sci.*, **23A**, 262 (1946) [*C. A.*, **41**, 449 (1947)].

[455] Baker, *J. Chem. Soc.*, **1934**, 1953.

[456] Nakazawa, *J. Pharm. Soc. Japan, Trans.*, **59**, 194 (1939) [*C. A.*, **34**, 106 (1940)].

[457] Virkar, *J. Univ. Bombay*, **11**, Pt. 3, 136 (1942) [*C. A.*, **37**, 2358 (1943)].

[458] Mahal and Venkataraman, *J. Chem. Soc.*, **1934**, 1767.

[459] Mahal and Venkataraman, *Current Sci.*, **2**, 214 (1933) [*C. A.*, **28**, 2715 (1934)].

[460] Ullal, Shah, and Wheeler, *J. Chem. Soc.*, **1940**, 1499.

[461] Nowlan, Slavin, and Wheeler, *J. Chem. Soc.*, **1950**, 340.

[462] Horii, *J. Pharm. Soc. Japan, Trans.*, **60**, 81 (1940) [*C. A.*, **34**, 6277 (1940)].

[463] Baker and Simmonds, *J. Chem. Soc.*, **1940**, 1370.

[464] Baker and Besly, *J. Chem. Soc.*, **1940**, 1103.

[465] Horii, *J. Pharm. Soc. Japan, Trans.*, **60**, 246 (1940) [*C. A.*, **35**, 7964 (1941)].

[466] Kostanecki and Rozycki, *Ber.*, **34**, 102 (1901).

[467] Desai and Mavani, *Proc. Indian Acad. Sci.*, **25A**, 353 (1947) [*C. A.*, **42**, 1914 (1948)].

[468] Limaye and Kelkar, *J. Indian Chem. Soc.*, **12**, 788 (1935).

[469] Venkataraman, *J. Chem. Soc.*, **1929**, 2219.

[470] Canter, Martin, and Robertson, *J. Chem. Soc.*, **1931**, 1877.

[471] Gulati, Seth, and Venkataraman, *J. Chem. Soc.*, **1934**, 1765.

[472] Desai and Vakil, *Proc. Indian Acad. Sci.*, **12A**, 357 (1940) [*C. A.*, **35**, 3639 (1941)].

[473] Desai and Hamid, *Proc. Indian Acad. Sci.*, **6A**, 287 (1937) [*C. A.*, **32**, 2119 (1938)].

[474] Canter, Curd, and Robertson, *J. Chem. Soc.*, **1931**, 1245.

[475] Gulati and Venkataraman, *J. Chem. Soc.*, **1931**, 2376.

[476] Bhullar and Venkataraman, *J. Chem. Soc.*, **1931**, 1165.

[477] Menon and Venkataraman, *J. Chem. Soc.*, **1931**, 2591.
[478] Chakravarti and Bagchi, *J. Indian Chem. Soc.*, **13**, 689 (1936).
[479] Späth and Gruber, *Ber.*, **71**, 106 (1938).
[480] Limaye and Ghate, *Rasāyanam*, **1**, 169 (1939) [*C. A.*, **34**, 5072 (1940)].
[481] Robertson, Sandrock, and Hendry, *J. Chem. Soc.*, **1931**, 2426.
[482] Robertson, Waters, and Jones, *J. Chem. Soc.*, **1932**, 1681.
[483] Wittig and Richter, *Ber.*, **59**, 117 (1926).
[484] Canter, Curd, and Robertson, *J. Chem. Soc.*, **1931**, 1255.
[485] Chakravarti, *J. Indian Chem. Soc.*, **8**, 129 (1931).
[486] Limaye, Shenolikar, and Talwalder, *Rasāyanam*, **1**, 217 (1941) [*C. A.*, **36**, 1039 (1942)].
[487] Desai and Gaitonde, *Proc. Indian Acad. Sci.*, **25A**, 351 (1947) [*C. A.*, **42**, 1914 (1948)].
[488] Shah and Shah, *J. Indian Chem. Soc.*, **17**, 32 (1940).
[489] Chadha, Mahal, and Venkataraman, *J. Chem. Soc.*, **1933**, 1459.
[490] Robertson and Sandrock, *J. Chem. Soc.*, **1932**, 1180.
[491] Robertson and Sandrock, *J. Chem. Soc.*, **1933**, 819.
[492] Bhagwat and Shahane, *Rasāyanam*, **1**, 220 (1941) [*C. A.*, **36**, 1039 (1942)].
[493] Desai and Waravdekar, *Proc. Indian Acad. Sci.*, **13A**, 177 (1941) [*C. A.*, **36**, 90 (1942)].
[494] Baker and Robinson, *J. Chem. Soc.*, **127**, 1981 (1925).
[495] Zemplen, Farkas, and Bien, *Ber.*, **77**, 452 (1944).
[496] Baker, *J. Chem. Soc.*, **127**, 2349 (1925).
[497] King and Robertson, *J. Chem. Soc.*, **1934**, 403.
[498] Baker, Robinson, and Simpson, *J. Chem. Soc.*, **1937**, 805.
[499] Mitter and Maitra, *J. Indian Chem. Soc.*, **13**, 236 (1936).
[500] Crabtree and Robinson, *J. Chem. Soc.*, **113**, 859 (1918).
[501] Allan and Robinson, *J. Chem. Soc.*, **125**, 2192 (1924).
[502] Healy and Robinson, *J. Chem. Soc.*, **1934**, 1625.
[503] Kalff and Robinson, *J. Chem. Soc.*, **127**, 1968 (1925).
[504] Heilbron, Hey, and Lythgoe, *J. Chem. Soc.*, **1934**, 1581.
[505] Chadha and Venkataraman, *J. Chem. Soc.*, **1933**, 1073.
[506] Trivedi, Sethna, and Shah, *J. Indian Chem. Soc.*, **20**, 171 (1943).
[507] Sugasawa, *Proc. Imp. Acad. (Tokyo)*, **10**, 338 (1934) [*C. A.*, **28**, 6717 (1934)].
[508] Heap and Robinson, *J. Chem. Soc.*, **1926**, 2336.
[509] Rangaswami and Seshadri, *Proc. Indian Acad. Sci.*, **9A**, 1 (1939) [*C. A.*, **33**, 4244 (1939)].
[510] Sethna and Shah, *J. Indian Chem. Soc.*, **17**, 601 (1940).
[511] Sugasawa, *J. Chem. Soc.*, **1933**, 1621.
[512] Nakazawa, *J. Pharm. Soc. Japan, Trans.*, **59**, 199 (1939) [*C. A.*, **34**, 1017 (1940)].
[513] Shah, Mehta, and Wheeler, *J. Chem. Soc.*, **1938**, 1555.
[514] Hattori, *J. Chem. Soc. Japan*, **51**, 472 (1930) [*C. A.*, **26**, 714 (1932)].
[515] Murti, Rao, and Seshadri, *Proc. Indian Acad. Sci.*, **26A**, 183 (1948) [*C. A.*, **42**, 5909 (1948)].
[516] Algar, McCarthy, and Dick, *Proc. Roy. Irish Acad.*, **41B**, 155 (1933) [*C. A.*, **27**, 3935 (1933)].
[517] Shriner and Moffett, *J. Am. Chem. Soc.*, **63**, 1694 (1941).
[518] Baker and Eastwood, *J. Chem. Soc.*, **1929**, 2897.
[518a] Aso, *J. Agr. Chem. Soc. Japan*, **15**, 59 (1939) [*C. A.*, **33**, 4992 (1939)].
[519] Kimura and Hoshi, *J. Pharm. Soc. Japan*, **55**, 229 (1935) [*C. A.*, **31**, 6654 (1937)].
[520] Rao and Seshadri, *Proc. Indian Acad. Sci.*, **22A**, 383 (1945) [*C. A.*, **40**, 4061 (1946)].
[521] Row and Seshadri, *Proc. Indian Acad. Sci.*, **23A**, 23 (1946) [*C. A.*, **40**, 5050 (1946)].
[522] Rangaswami and Seshadri, *Proc. Indian Acad. Sci.*, **8A**, 214 (1938) [*C. A.*, **33**, 2122 (1939)].
[523] Rao and Seshadri, *Proc. Indian Acad. Sci.*, **22A**, 157 (1945) [*C. A.*, **40**, 1832 (1946)].
[524] Balakrishna and Seshadri, *Proc. Indian Acad. Sci.*, **27A**, 91 (1948) [*C. A.*, **42**, 5454 (1948)].
[525] Seshadri and Venkateswarlu, *Proc. Indian Acad. Sci.*, **23A**, 192 (1946) [*C. A.*, **40**, 5431 (1946)].

[526] Murti, Row, and Seshadri, *Proc. Indian Acad. Sci.*, **24A**, 233 (1946) [*C. A.*, **41**, 2417 (1947)].

[527] Sastri and Seshadri, *Proc. Indian Acad. Sci.*, **24A**, 238 (1946) [*C. A.*, **41**, 2417 (1947)].

[528] Rao, Row, and Seshadri, *Proc. Indian Acad. Sci.*, **22A**, 297 (1945) [*C. A.*, **40**, 3756 (1946)].

[529] Kalff and Robinson, *J. Chem. Soc.*, **127**, 181 (1925).

[530] Limaye and Limaye, *Rasāyanam*, **1**, 161 (1939) [*C. A.*, **33**, 7793 (1939)].

[531] Robinson and Venkataraman, *J. Chem. Soc.*, **1926**, 2348.

[532] Wessely and Moser, *Monatsh.*, **56**, 97 (1930).

[533] Furukawa and Tamaki, *Bull. Inst. Phys. Chem. Research (Tokyo)*, **10**, 732 (1931) [*C. A.*, **26**, 142 (1932)].

[534] Robinson and Shinoda, *J. Chem. Soc.*, **127**, 1973 (1925).

[535] Goldsworthy and Robinson, *J. Chem. Soc.*, **1938**, 56.

[536] Goldsworthy and Robinson, *J. Chem. Soc.*, **1937**, 46.

[537] Akai and Nakazawa, *J. Pharm. Soc. Japan*, **55**, 135 (1935) [*C. A.*, **29**, 7982 (1935)].

[538] Rao and Seshadri, *Proc. Indian Acad. Sci.*, **25A**, 292 (1947) [*C. A.*, **42**, 6812 (1948)].

[539] Tseng, *J. Pharm. Soc. Japan*, **55**, 30 (1935) [*C. A.*, **29**, 7981 (1935)].

[540] Rao and Seshadri, *J. Chem. Soc.*, **1947**, 122.

[541] Seshadri and Venkateswarlu, *Proc. Indian Acad. Sci.*, **24A**, 349 (1946) [*C. A.*, **41**, 2735 (1947)].

[542] Rao and Seshadri, *Proc. Indian Acad. Sci.*, **23A**, 147 (1946) [*C. A.*, **41**, 448 (1947)].

[543] Shinoda and Sato, *J. Pharm. Soc. Japan*, **48**, 220 (1928) [*C. A.*, **22**, 2947 (1928)].

[544] Shinoda and Sato, *J. Pharm. Soc. Japan*, No. 541, 191 (1927) [*C. A.*, **21**, 2270 (1927)].

[545] Allan and Robinson, *J. Chem. Soc.*, **1926**, 2334.

[546] Row and Seshadri, *Proc. Indian Acad. Sci.*, **21A**, 155 (1945) [*C. A.*, **39**, 4325 (1945)].

[547] Baker, Nodzu, and Robinson, *J. Chem. Soc.*, **1929**, 74.

[548] Kuhn, Low, and Trischmann, *Ber.*, **77**, 202 (1944).

[549] Robinson and Venkataraman, *J. Chem. Soc.*, **1929**, 61.

[550] Lovecy, Robinson, and Sugasawa, *J. Chem. Soc.*, **1930**, 817.

[551] Kuhn and Low, *Ber.*, **77**, 196 (1944).

[552] Rao and Seshadri, *J. Chem. Soc.*, **1946**, 771.

[553] Kuhn, Low, and Trischmann, *Ber.*, **77**, 211 (1944).

[554] Anderson, *Can. J. Res.*, **7**, 285 (1932).

[555] Gakhokidze, *J. Applied Chem. U.S.S.R.*, **20**, 904 (1947) [*C. A.*, **42**, 4174 (1948)].

[556] Charlesworth and Robinson, *J. Chem. Soc.*, **1933**, 268.

[557] Seshadri and Venkateswarlu, *Proc. Indian Acad. Sci.*, **23A**, 296 (1946) [*C. A.*, **40**, 6447 (1946)].

[558] Rao, Rao, and Seshadri, *Proc. Indian Acad. Sci.*, **19A**, 88 (1944) [*C. A.*, **39**, 301 (1945)].

[559] Heap and Robinson, *J. Chem. Soc.*, **1929**, 67.

[560] Haller and Bauer, *Compt. rend.*, **153**, 145 (1912).

[561] Freer and Lachman, *Am. Chem. J.*, **19**, 878 (1897).

[562] Meisenheimer and Weibezahn, *Ber.*, **54**, 3195 (1921).

[563] Biltz, *Ber.*, **32**, 655 (1899).

[564] Whitmore and Randall, *J. Am. Chem. Soc.*, **64**, 1242 (1942).

[565] Fuson, Fugate, and Fisher, *J. Am. Chem. Soc.*, **61**, 2362 (1939).

[566] Kohler and Baltzly, *J. Am. Chem. Soc.*, **54**, 4015 (1932).

[567] Whitmore and Lester, *J. Am. Chem. Soc.*, **64**, 1251 (1942).

[568] Kohler, Tishler, and Potter, *J. Am. Chem. Soc.*, **57**, 2517 (1935).

[569] Fuson, Fisher, Ullyott, and Fugate, *J. Org. Chem.*, **4**, 111 (1939).

[570] Ross and Fuson, *J. Am. Chem. Soc.*, **59**, 1508 (1937).

[571] Breslow and Hauser, *J. Am. Chem. Soc.*, **62**, 2385 (1940).

[572] Hauser and Ringler, unpublished work.

CHAPTER 4

THE SOMMELET REACTION

S. J. Angyal

The New South Wales University of Technology, Sydney, Australia

CONTENTS

INTRODUCTION

The Sommelet reaction is the process whereby aldehydes are produced from alkyl (usually arylmethyl) halides by the action of hexamine (hexamethylenetetramine). The reaction is essentially a conversion of an amine into an aldehyde, a process that is not in itself particularly useful, because aldehydes are frequently more readily available than the corresponding primary amines. It is fortunate therefore that the required amines can be prepared by the interaction of alkyl halides with hexamine, i.e., with the same reagent that serves to convert the amines into aldehydes; it is in this combined form that the reaction was discovered by Sommelet.[1]

Alkyl halides form quaternary salts ("hexaminium salts") with hexamine;[2] these salts are readily isolated when the reaction is conducted in non-hydroxylic solvents. In a hydroxylic medium these salts are hydrolyzed to products the nature of which depends on the pH of the solution. Strong acids produce salts of primary amines[3] (see p. 204); alkalies or ammonia[4] give the corresponding methyleneamines; and at intermediate pH's an equilibrium mixture of the two is obtained. At these intermediate pH's, however, particularly at about pH 3.0–6.5, the mixture reacts with hexamine to yield an aldehyde. These reactions may be illustrated by the diagram; a fuller discussion of the last step is given in the following section.

$$RCH_2X + C_6H_{12}N_4$$

$$\downarrow \qquad\qquad (1)$$

$$[RCH_2 \cdot C_6H_{12}N_4]^+X^-$$

$$\overset{H^+}{\swarrow} \quad \Big\downarrow H_2O \quad \overset{OH^-}{\searrow} \qquad (2)$$

$$RCH_2NH_3^+ + CH_2O \rightleftharpoons RCH_2NH_2 + CH_2O \rightleftharpoons RCH_2N{=}CH_2$$

$$\Big\downarrow \begin{smallmatrix}\text{Hexamine}\\ pH\ 3\text{–}6.5\end{smallmatrix} \qquad (3)$$

RCHO

The Sommelet reaction, when started with a halide, proceeds therefore in three stages:[5] (1) formation of a hexaminium salt; (2) hydrolysis

[1] Sommelet, *Compt. rend.*, **157**, 852 (1913); *Bull. soc. chim. France*, [4], **13**, 1085 (1913).

[2] Wohl, *Ber.*, **19**, 1840 (1886); Delépine and Jaffeux, *Bull. soc. chim. France*, [4], **31**, 108 (1922).

[3] Delépine, *Bull. soc. chim. France*, [3], **13**, 358 (1895); [3], **17**, 290 (1897); [4], **31**, 108 (1922); *Compt. rend.*, **120**, 501 (1895); **124**, 292 (1897); Mannich and Hahn, *Ber.*, **44**, 1542 (1911).

[4] Graymore, *J. Chem. Soc.*, **1947**, 1117.

[5] Angyal and Rassack, *J. Chem. Soc.*, **1949**, 2700.

of this salt to an amine and its methylene derivative; and (3) formation of an aldehyde (the Sommelet reaction proper). Frequently these steps can be performed in one operation without isolation of the intermediates.

CHARACTER AND MECHANISM

At the time of its discovery Sommelet recognized [1] that the reaction took place in three stages but did not understand the nature of the third stage. Tentatively, he suggested that the reaction occurred by shift of the double bond in methylenebenzylamine to give benzylidenemethylamine, which, in turn, was hydrolyzed to benzaldehyde and methylamine.

$$C_6H_5CH_2N{=}CH_2 \rightarrow C_6H_5CH{=}NCH_3 \rightarrow C_6H_5CHO + CH_3NH_2$$

Further research proved that this suggestion was untenable and led to the recognition of the reaction as an oxidation-reduction process. Sommelet announced his views in two lectures [6] but did not publish them and they therefore remained largely unknown. The course of the reaction has now been re-investigated by Angyal and Rassack,[5, 7] whose conclusions are similar to those reached by Sommelet.

It was previously known [8] that benzaldehyde is formed from methylenebenzylamine even in the absence of hexamine, but in low yield. The study of this simple reaction provided the clue to the understanding of the course followed by the Sommelet reaction.[5, 7] Methylamine was *not* found among the products of the reaction, thus providing definite evidence against the mechanism involving a shift of the double bond. The reason for the low yield of benzaldehyde became apparent when it was found that a large proportion of methylenebenzylamine was converted to methylbenzylamine. This reaction is a hydrogenation, and benzylamine was recognized as the source of hydrogen by the isolation, in equivalent amounts, of benzaldehyde and *ammonia*. Presumably benzylamine is dehydrogenated to the imine, $C_6H_5CH{=}NH$, which is then hydrolyzed. The overall reaction can be represented by equation 4. In the absence of hexamine, therefore, not more than half

$$C_6H_5CH_2NH_2 + C_6H_5CH_2N{=}CH_2 + H_2O \rightarrow$$

$$C_6H_5CHO + NH_3 + C_6H_5CH_2NHCH_3 \quad (4)$$

of a given amount of an amine can be converted into the corresponding aldehyde.

[6] Sommelet, *Bull. soc. chim. France*, [4], **17**, 82 (1915); [4], **23**, 95 (1918).

[7] Angyal and Rassack, *Nature*, **161**, 723 (1948).

[8] Graymore and Davies, *J. Chem. Soc.*, **1945**, 293.

When hexamine is added to the reaction mixture, only small amounts of methylbenzylamine are formed and there is a corresponding increase in the yield of aldehyde. In these circumstances methylamine is present at the end of the reaction and must have been derived from the hexamine that acts as a hydrogen acceptor. Being in equilibrium with its hydrolysis products and intermediates at the pH required for the Sommelet reaction, hexamine reacts as the methylene derivative of ammonia, $CH_2{=}NH$, in being hydrogenated to methylamine. The reaction is shown in equation 5, which represents the fundamental process

$$C_6H_5CH_2NH_2 + CH_2{=}NH + H_2O \rightarrow C_6H_5CHO + NH_3 + CH_3NH_2 \quad (5)$$

of the Sommelet reaction.

The methylation of benzylamine (equation 4) and of ammonia (equation 5) are competitive processes: therefore, increasing the proportion of hexamine, the source of ammonia, should reduce the amount of methylbenzylamine formed and thereby improve the yield of benzaldehyde. This effect has been verified by experiment.[5]

The Sommelet reaction is the ammono analog of the interaction between carbonyl compounds and alcoholic alkali which is generally believed to occur by the transfer of a hydride ion.[9]

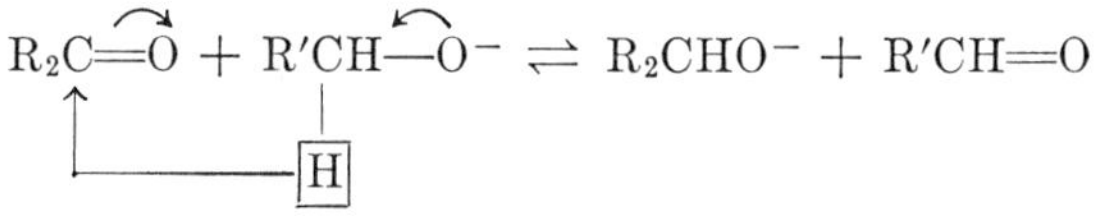

$$R_2C{=}\overset{\frown}{O} + R'CH\overset{\frown}{—}O^- \rightleftharpoons R_2CHO^- + R'CH{=}O$$

Angyal, Penman, and Warwick [10] have suggested that the Sommelet reaction similarly proceeds by a hydride-ion transfer, the acceptor being the conjugate acid of a Schiff base.

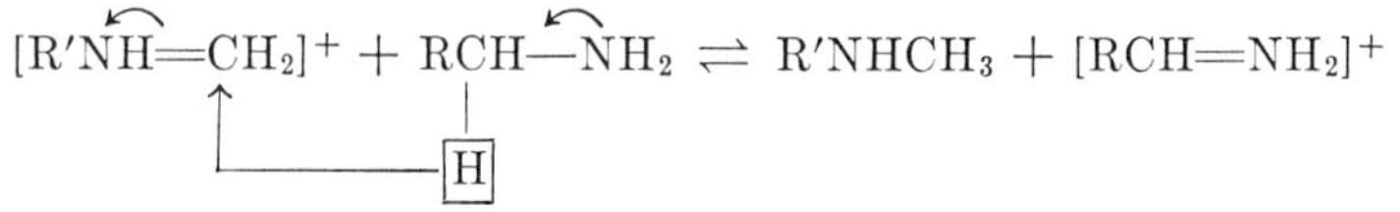

$$[R'\overset{\frown}{N}H{=}CH_2]^+ + RCH\overset{\frown}{—}NH_2 \rightleftharpoons R'NHCH_3 + [RCH{=}NH_2]^+$$

A similar mechanism has been proposed for other related reductions of Schiff bases.[11]

A completely different course for the Sommelet reaction has been postulated by Hartough and Dickert [12] in the formation of thiophene-

[9] Alexander, *Principles of Ionic Organic Reactions*, pp. 167–170, John Wiley & Sons, New York, 1950.

[10] Angyal, Penman, and Warwick, *J. Chem. Soc.*, **1953**, 1742.

[11] McLaughlin and Wagner, *J. Am. Chem. Soc.*, **66**, 251 (1944); Staple and Wagner, *J. Org. Chem.*, **14**, 559 (1949).

[12] Hartough and Dickert, *J. Am. Chem. Soc.*, **71**, 3922 (1949).

carboxaldehydes, but their proposal appears to lack experimental foundation.[10]

SCOPE AND LIMITATIONS

Aromatic Aldehydes. The Sommelet reaction is best suited and most frequently used for the preparation of aromatic aldehydes. The halides that are employed are readily available, either by chloromethylation,[13] or by the halogenation of substituted toluenes. In either case the Sommelet reaction has the advantage that the often lachrymatory or unstable halomethyl compounds need not be purified, since the isolation of their hexaminium salts separates them from impurities; or, alternatively, the reaction can be carried out with impure halomethyl compounds since the aldehydes are readily purified. Substituted benzylamines can, of course, be used as starting materials if they are available. The yield of aromatic aldehydes is usually between 50% and 80% of the theoretical; yields over 80% are seldom attainable because of inevitable side reactions.

Several limitations apply to the preparation of aromatic aldehydes. First, the reaction is subject to steric hindrance: [14, 15] if both *ortho* positions are substituted the reaction fails. Even one *ortho* substituent frequently lowers the yield.[14] Furthermore, accumulation of strongly electron-attracting substituents may prevent the reaction. Thus 2,4-dinitrobenzaldehyde could not be prepared by the Sommelet reaction.[16] Finally, phenolic aldehydes are not readily obtainable by this method because the aromatic ring, when activated by hydroxyl groups, tends to condense with formaldehyde. Phenolic aldehydes can, however, often be prepared by the related Duff reaction (p. 204). If electron-attracting substituents are also present, they may counterbalance the effect of the hydroxyl group; e.g., nitrohydroxybenzaldehydes can be prepared. The deactivating effect of one chlorine atom is not sufficient, 3-Chloro-4-hydroxybenzaldehyde is obtained in low yield and in a very impure state from *o*-chlorophenol. The two chlorine atoms in 2,4-dichlorophenol, however, permit the preparation of 3,5-dichloro-2-hydroxybenzaldehyde in good yield. The hydroxyl groups can be blocked by ether or ester formation,[17–19] and the Sommelet reaction then becomes feasible. The acyl group is removed during the reaction.

[13] Fuson and McKeever, *Org. Reactions*, **1**, 63 (1942).
[14] Angyal, Morris, Rassack, and Waterer, *J. Chem. Soc.*, **1949**, 2704.
[15] Fuson and Denton, *J. Am. Chem. Soc.*, **63**, 654 (1941).
[16] Angyal, Morris, Tetaz, and Wilson, *J. Chem. Soc.*, **1950**, 2141.
[17] Fabriques de Produits de Chimie Organique de Laire, Ger. pat. 268,786 [*Frdl.*, **11**, 197 (1915)].
[18] Sommelet, *Compt. rend.*, **197**, 256 (1933).
[19] Sommelet and Marszak, *Compt. rend.*, **198**, 2258 (1934).

Heteroaromatic Aldehydes. The thiophenecarboxaldehydes are readily prepared by the Sommelet reaction.[20] Most workers in this field used a technique (steam distillation, p. 207) that does not result in the best yields; but the example of thiophene-2-carboxaldehyde [10] shows that the yields of thiophenecarboxaldehydes can be as good as those of the benzaldehydes.

N-Heteroaromatic aldehydes have also been prepared by the Sommelet method.[21] The scope of the reaction is rather limited, for the aldehyde group cannot be introduced into the α- and γ-positions relative to the nitrogen atom (exception: 2-phenylthiazole-4-carboxaldehyde). The heteroaromatic halomethyl compounds, being difficult to prepare and unstable, are not convenient starting materials, and the aminomethyl compounds are employed instead. Thus pyridine-3-carboxaldehyde is obtained from nicotinonitrile through 3-aminomethylpyridine in good yield.

Aliphatic Aldehydes. Aliphatic aldehydes that contain a hydrogen atom attached to the α-carbon atom are not stable under the conditions of the Sommelet reaction and are rapidly converted into polymeric nitrogenous material.[22] However, if the aldehydes are removed by steam distillation as fast as they are formed, they can be so obtained. The reaction is probably of little preparative value since the yields are not particularly good and the aldehydes are usually obtainable by other methods. Isovaleraldehyde, n-hexaldehyde, and n-heptaldehyde have been prepared in 40–50% yield; the more reactive n-butyraldehyde and phenylacetaldehyde, in much smaller yield.[22] Unsaturated aldehydes have also been prepared, but most yields were poor or were not stated.[23-25] Trimethylacetaldehyde, which has no hydrogen atoms on the α-carbon atom, is stable under the Sommelet conditions and can be prepared in good yield.[22]

Dialdehydes. Starting from bis-halomethyl compounds, dialdehydes can be obtained, but the yields in such double Sommelet reactions are usually less than in the simple ones.[16, 26] Here again at least one position *ortho* to each halomethyl group must be unsubstituted. *Ortho* dialdehydes are not obtainable; nitrogen-containing compounds are formed instead, probably by cyclization involving ammonia and form-

[20] Hartough, "Thiophene and Its Derivatives," in Weissberger's *The Chemistry of Heterocyclic Compounds*, p. 310, Interscience, New York, 1952.

[21] Angyal, Barlin, and Wailes, *J. Chem. Soc.*, **1953**, 1740.

[22] Angyal, Penman, and Warwick, *J. Chem. Soc.*, **1953**, 1737.

[23] Bert, *Compt. rend.*, **214**, 230 (1942).

[24] Delaby, *Compt. rend.*, **194**, 1249 (1932), and private communication.

[25] Young and Linden, *J. Am. Chem. Soc.*, **69**, 2913 (1947).

[26] Wood, Tung, Perry, and Gibson, *J. Am. Chem. Soc.*, **72**, 2992 (1950).

aldehyde. A similar side reaction may be responsible for the failure to obtain biphenyl-2,2'-dicarboxaldehyde.[16]

Ketones. Ketones can be obtained from secondary halides or from the corresponding amines, but the reaction has not been extensively studied. Acetophenone has been prepared from α-phenylethylamine (30%),[8] benzophenone from benzhydryl bromide (6%), and fluorenone from 9-bromofluorene (45%).[27] Unsaturated alicyclic ketones have also been prepared in low yield.[28]

RELATED REACTIONS

There are two other reactions by which halomethyl groups are converted into aldehyde groups. In the first, discovered by Hass and Bender,[29] a substituted benzyl halide reacts with the sodium salt of 2-nitropropane.

$$\text{ArCH}_2\text{X} + [(\text{CH}_3)_2\text{C}{=}\text{NO}_2]^-\text{Na}^+ \rightarrow \text{ArCHO} + (\text{CH}_3)_2\text{C}{=}\text{NOH} + \text{NaX}$$

The reaction has been used only for the preparation of substituted benzaldehydes, which are obtained in good yield. It is not suitable for the preparation of nitrobenzaldehydes and was shown to fail with several polysubstituted aldehydes.[16] Since the reaction involves the use of metallic sodium and the maintenance of anhydrous conditions, it seems less convenient than the Sommelet reaction.

In the second reaction, discovered by Kröhnke,[30] the halide is first converted into the pyridinium salt, which is then allowed to react with p-nitrosodimethylaniline to give a nitrone; this, in turn, gives an aldehyde on acid hydrolysis.

$$\text{RCH}_2\text{X} \xrightarrow{\text{C}_5\text{H}_5\text{N}} [\text{RCH}_2\text{NC}_5\text{H}_5]^+\text{X}^- \xrightarrow[\text{NaOH}]{p\text{-ONC}_6\text{H}_4\text{N(CH}_3)_2}$$

$$\text{RCH}{=}\overset{\overset{\text{O}}{\uparrow}}{\text{N}}\text{C}_6\text{H}_4\text{N(CH}_3)_2 \xrightarrow[\text{H}^+]{\text{H}_2\text{O}} \text{RCHO}$$

The Kröhnke reaction is capable of wide application, giving good yields of aromatic, unsaturated, and α-keto aldehydes, and also of dialdehydes and of aromatic ketones, but not of saturated aliphatic aldehydes. The Sommelet reaction, being simpler and more economical,

---

[27] Angyal and Tetaz, unpublished work.
[28] Bowman, Joffe, Rinne, and Wilkes, *Trans. Kentucky Acad. Sci.*, **13**, 78 (1950) [*C. A.*, **45**, 2880g (1951)].
[29] Hass and Bender, *J. Am. Chem. Soc.*, **71**, 1767 (1949); *Org. Syntheses*, **30**, 99 (1950).
[30] Kröhnke and Börner, *Ber.*, **69**, 2006 (1936); Kröhnke, *Ber.*, **71**, 2583 (1938); Kröhnke and Schmeiss, *Ber.*, **72**, 440 (1939).

is probably preferable for the synthesis of most aromatic aldehydes; but the Kröhnke method, since it utilizes very mild conditions, is particularly suitable for the preparation of sensitive aldehydes. It has found application in the field of steroids [31] and of isoprenoid compounds.[32] In contrast to the Sommelet reaction, the Kröhnke reaction is favored by electron-attracting substituents; even dinitrobenzaldehydes are readily obtained.[30]

Closely related to the Sommelet reaction is the Duff reaction [33] for the preparation of o-hydroxy aromatic aldehydes. This process consists in the treatment of phenols with hexamine in glyceroboric acid or glacial acetic acid, and it results in the introduction of an aldehyde group into a position *ortho* to the hydroxyl group. The course of the reaction has not yet been fully clarified, but it appears [34] to involve an aminomethylation to the secondary amine, HOArCH$_2$NHCH$_2$ArOH, followed by a Sommelet reaction. This method has been extensively and successfully used on flavones by Seshadri and his associates.[35] The reaction has been extended to dialkylanilines, the aldehyde group entering the *para* position.[36]

As mentioned in the Introduction, acid hydrolysis of hexaminium salts gives the corresponding primary amines.[3] This reaction, named after Delépine, is an excellent method for the preparation of primary amines from alkyl halides without the formation of secondary amines.[37] It is comparable to, and sometimes more convenient than, the more popular Gabriel synthesis. The hydrolysis is best effected by a mixture of ethanol and concentrated hydrochloric acid, which removes the formaldehyde as the volatile diethyl formal.

When a hexaminium salt is heated with formic acid, the corresponding fully methylated amine is obtained, e.g., dimethylbenzylamine from benzylhexaminium chloride.[38, 39] This is essentially an Eschweiler-Clarke methylation [40] for which the hexaminium salt supplies both the

[31] Reich and Reichstein, *Helv. Chim. Acta*, **22**, 1124 (1939); Ruzicka, Prelog, and Wieland, *ibid.*, **26**, 2050 (1943); Ruzicka, Jeger, and Norymberski, *ibid.*, **27**, 1185 (1944); Reichstein, *ibid.*, **23**, 219 (1940).

[32] Karrer and Epprecht, *Helv. Chim. Acta*, **24**, 1039 (1941).

[33] Duff, *J. Chem. Soc.*, **1941**, 547; Duff and Bills, *ibid.*, **1934**, 1305.

[34] Duff and Furness, *J. Chem. Soc.*, **1951**, 1512.

[35] Seshadri et al., *Proc. Indian Acad. Sci.*, **9A**, 7 (1939); **28A**, 210 (1948); **29A**, 168, 223 (1949); **30A**, 13, 111, 116, 125, 345 (1949); **31A**, 33 (1950) [*C. A.*, **33**, 4244 (1939); **44**, 3984g, 3986, 3987b, 5875, 5876e, 9960 (1950)].

[36] Duff, *J. Chem. Soc.*, **1945**, 276; Duff and Furness, *ibid.*, **1952**, 1159.

[37] Galat and Elion, *J. Am. Chem. Soc.*, **61**, 3585 (1939).

[38] Sommelet and Guioth, *Compt. rend.*, **174**, 687 (1922).

[39] Sommelet, *Compt. rend.*, **175**, 1149 (1923).

[40] Moore, *Org. Reactions*, **5**, 307 (1949).

amine and the formaldehyde. When hexaminium salts prepared from aliphatic halides are thus methylated, the addition of formaldehyde is necessary.[22]

CHOICE OF EXPERIMENTAL CONDITIONS

Preparation from Halides

Situations Requiring Isolation of the Hexaminium Salt. The fortunate circumstance that hexamine is the essential reagent for both step 1 and step 3 of the Sommelet reaction, though its function is very different in these steps, usually makes it possible to carry out the reaction without the isolation of any intermediates. However, this is practicable only when the first step is fast compared with the last one. Benzyl halides react vigorously with hexamine at 100°; the reaction is usually complete in five to fifteen minutes, and, when the Sommelet reaction employing such halides is run in the usual way, refluxing for one to two hours, the aldehydes are not contaminated by unchanged halide. Electron-attracting substituents, however, make the reaction slower.[16] Aliphatic halides react very sluggishly.[22] In these cases some of the halide would remain unchanged, or the reaction would have to be much prolonged to the detriment of the more sensitive aldehydes.

It is imperative therefore to conduct the first step separately, and to isolate the hexaminium salt, in the following cases: (1) benzyl halides with electron-attracting substituents, such as the nitrobenzyl chlorides; (2) aliphatic halides; (3) bis-halomethyl compounds. It is also desirable to isolate the salt when unpurified halomethyl compounds are used as starting materials (p. 201); the isolation then serves as a purification step. When in doubt it is safer to isolate the quaternary salt.

Preparation of the Hexaminium Salt. The usual procedure is to heat the halomethyl compound, under refluxing conditions, with an excess (about 10%) of hexamine in chloroform solution on the steam bath until salt formation is complete.[41] It is important to use sufficient solvent to dissolve all the hexamine (about 100 ml. for each 15 g.), for otherwise the precipitated salt will cover some of the base and prevent complete reaction. For the same reason it is advisable to dissolve the hexamine completely before adding the halide. Benzyl halides require one to two hours' heating, aliphatic halides often as many as twenty-four; boiling can be continued for long periods without fear of side reactions. After cooling, the precipitated salt is separated by filtration and washed with chloroform. Most hexaminium salts are very slightly

[41] Jacobs and Heidelberger, *J. Biol. Chem.*, **20**, 659, 685 (1915).

soluble in chloroform; but if the yield is poor even after long heating, indicating that the salt is soluble in the solvent as are the nitrobenzyl-hexaminium chlorides, it is best to evaporate some of the chloroform and add ether or acetone.[16,41] The yields are usually nearly quantitative. Benzyl iodides and hydroxyl substituted benzyl halides react with hexamine even at room temperature.

Chloroform seems to be the only satisfactory solvent for this reaction. For industrial practice chlorobenzene has been recommended;[42] but at its boiling point the hexaminium salts decompose and therefore the reaction has to be conducted with temperature control and with stirring.[22] Chlorobenzene has the further disadvantage that it will dissolve less hexamine than chloroform will; it is therefore not recommended for laboratory operations. p-Sulfamylbenzyl chloride is insoluble in chloroform. This halide was converted to the hexaminium salt in ethanol, but without heating.[43]

Most of the hexaminium salts cannot be satisfactorily recrystallized, but they are pure enough as prepared for further reaction.

Choice of Solvent. Any hydroxylic solvent appears to be a suitable medium for the Sommelet reaction. Water itself can be used if the starting materials and the intermediates have sufficient solubility in water. Benzaldehyde, for example, is readily prepared in this medium in good yield.[1,5] Water is also a satisfactory solvent for the preparation of many dialdehydes.[26] However, when water is the solvent an insoluble intermediate may precipitate and prevent the reaction from going to completion. For example, von Braun and Engel obtained and erroneously described [44] as fluorene-2-carboxaldehyde the intermediate 2-methyleneaminomethylfluorene.[45] It is better therefore to add an organic solvent, but it is not necessary to add sufficient to make the solution homogeneous.

Aqueous ethanol (50–80%) was the solvent favored by early workers. The amount of solvent employed was often far in excess of that required, thereby slowing down the reaction; fairly concentrated solutions are preferable. Dilute ethanol has the advantage that on concentrating the solution the solubility of the aldehyde decreases and its isolation is easier.

Hewett [46] introduced glacial acetic acid as a solvent for the Sommelet reaction. With concentrated solutions, good yields of aldehydes may sometimes be obtained from bromomethyl compounds where heating

[42] Long and Troutman, *J. Am. Chem. Soc.*, **71**, 2473 (1949).

[43] Angyal and Jenkin, *Australian J. Sci. Research*, **3A**, 463 (1950) [*C. A.*, **45**, 7040 (1951)]. Compare ref. 37.

[44] von Braun and Engel, *Ber.*, **57**, 191 (1924).

[45] Angyal, Barlin, and Wailes, *J. Chem. Soc.*, **1951**, 3512.

[46] Hewett, *J. Chem. Soc.*, **1940**, 297.

for only one minute is necessary.[47]   The method is not always successful, as the boiling point of the mixture can be so high (over 150°) that
the aldehydes decompose when longer heating is required, e.g., with
chloromethyl compounds.[16]   When benzaldehyde was heated under reflux for one hour with a concentrated solution of hexamine in acetic
acid only a third of it remained unchanged.   Glacial acetic acid as a
solvent should therefore be used with care; the solution should contain
at least 5 parts of solvent for each part of hexamine, and the time of
boiling should be as short as possible.   Nevertheless, there are cases in
which glacial acetic acid is superior to other solvents.

As a solvent for the Sommelet reaction 50% acetic acid seems to com-
bine a suitable boiling point with good solvent power and with a desirable acidity.[16]   In many cases in which comparative runs were made
using several solvents, 50% acetic acid proved to be the best.   It is
worth mentioning that, under otherwise identical conditions, the reaction is faster in glacial than in dilute acetic acid, and faster in 50%
acetic acid than in 80% ethanol.   Dilute acetic acid has the disadvantage that it rapidly hydrolyzes hexamine.   In order to assure complete
reaction of the halide, it is necessary to use an excess of hexamine (up
to 2 moles) even if the quaternary salt formation is fairly rapid.   If
the hexaminium salt forms slowly it must be prepared in chloroform
before 50% acetic acid can be employed.   When the reaction is conducted with the isolated hexaminium salt or with an amine as the
starting material, the hydrolysis of hexamine is not a disadvantage
because it is not hexamine itself but its hydrolysis products that react
in step 3.

Whatever solvent is used, the solution is usually heated under reflux
for one-half hour to two hours.   Some aldehydes containing electron-
attracting substituents, such as p-nitrobenzaldehyde, are slowly destroyed by a side reaction; the yield reaches a maximum at a particular
time and decreases on longer heating.[16]   It may then be necessary to
establish by trial and error the optimum reaction time.   Most of the
aromatic aldehydes, however, are not affected by heating under the
conditions of the reaction.

Aliphatic aldehydes are so sensitive to the conditions of the Sommelet
reaction that they must be removed continuously by passing steam
through the reaction mixture.[22]   The same method has been used in the
preparation of various thiophenecarboxaldehydes,[12, 20, 48-52] though these

[47] Badger, *J. Chem. Soc.*, **1941**, 536.
[48] Campaigne and LeSuer, *J. Am. Chem. Soc.*, **70**, 1557 (1948).
[49] Campaigne and LeSuer, *J. Am. Chem. Soc.*, **71**, 333 (1949).
[50] King and Nord, *J. Org. Chem.*, **13**, 639 (1948).
[51] Dunn, Waugh, and Dittmer, *J. Am. Chem. Soc.*, **68**, 2118 (1946).
[52] Wiberg, *Org. Syntheses*, **29**, 87 (1949).

aldehydes are quite stable under the conditions of the reaction. The steam removes not only the desired aldehyde but also formaldehyde and ammonia and thereby reduces the yield. This is clearly seen in a comparison of the preparation of thiophene-2-carboxaldehyde by the steam-distillation technique (48–53% yield),[52] with its preparation by refluxing in 50% acetic acid (71–74% yield).[10]

At the end of the refluxing period, excess of hydrochloric acid should be added and the boiling continued for about five minutes; this serves to hydrolyze the Schiff bases present.[16] If this precaution is not taken the bases are removed with the aldehyde into an extracting solvent; or, if the aldehyde is separated by steam distillation, the bases will cause cloudiness of the distillate for a long time after all the aldehyde has distilled. If acid is added at this stage it is usually not necessary to purify the aldehydes by conversion into bisulfite compounds. The addition of mineral acid is advisable even when acetic acid is used as a solvent because acetic acid does not fully hydrolyze the Schiff bases (cf. footnote, p. 211).

An important factor affecting the Sommelet reaction is the acidity of the solution. The reaction proceeds at a reasonable rate only in the pH range of 3.0 to 6.5.[5,7] There is, however, usually no need to control the acidity, because it adjusts itself. Solutions of the hexaminium salts are fairly acidic (pH about 3), and the ammonia formed by the hydrolysis of hexamine gradually buffers them until, at the end of the reaction, the pH is usually 6.0 to 6.5. Some workers prefer to add mineral acid at the beginning; this is neutralized by the hydrolysis of hexamine. In fact, considerable amounts of acid can be added to the Sommelet reaction. Acetic acid is ideal in this respect since it forms with hexamine a buffer system which keeps the pH well within the optimum range. If any difficulty is experienced with a Sommelet reaction it is advisable to check the pH of the solution.

Side Reactions. The most important side reaction is the formation of the methylated amine according to equation 4 (p. 199), which is the main reaction when hexamine is not present. It can be suppressed by using an excess of hexamine and by adding the halide or the amine dropwise to a boiling solution of hexamine.[5] The gain in yield by this latter procedure, however, seldom warrants the extra labor involved. This applies also to the oxidation of the aldehydes by air which can be prevented by working in an atmosphere of carbon dioxide, but the small increase in yield usually will not make such a procedure worth while.

Recommended Procedure. The optimum conditions (solvent, concentration, time) for the reaction naturally vary from aldehyde to aldehyde. However, the following experimental conditions have been effectively used by the present writer for trial runs.

With isolation of the hexaminium salt: 0.1 mole of halomethyl compound and 15.5 g. of hexamine in 100 ml. of chloroform are heated under reflux for four hours. The hexaminium salt is then boiled for one to two hours with 90 ml. of 50% acetic acid or 60% ethanol.

Without isolation of the hexaminium salt: 0.1 mole of halomethyl compound is heated under reflux for one to two hours with 30 g. of hexamine in 90 ml. of 50% acetic acid, or with 16.5 g. of hexamine in 90 ml. of 60% ethanol.

Preparation from Amines

When an amine is employed as the starting material for the Sommelet reaction, the choice of experimental conditions is simpler since a hexaminium salt is not prepared. All that has been said above about the choice of solvent and about the practical details of the reaction applies in this case as well. Some attention should be given to the pH of the solution. When the amine is available as the free base it must be neutralized with a mineral acid; a slight excess will assure the required acid reaction. When a salt of the amine is used, 1 mole of formaldehyde is frequently added: this causes the pH to drop to about 3, because a small amount of Schiff base is formed and an equivalent amount of acid liberated. When acetic acid is used as a solvent it is not necessary to add formaldehyde or an excess of mineral acid.

Secondary amines give aldehydes in the Sommelet reaction although in poor yields; [5, 34] tertiary amines do not react.

Recommended Procedure. One-tenth mole of amine and 12 ml. of concentrated hydrochloric acid, or 0.1 mole of a salt of the amine and 10 ml. of 40% formaldehyde solution, are heated under reflux for one to two hours with 16.5 g. of hexamine in 90 ml. of 50% acetic acid or 60% ethanol.

EXPERIMENTAL PROCEDURES

o-Tolualdehyde.[53] (Preparation from a halomethyl compound without isolation of the hexaminium salt.) To a mixture of 60 g. of ω-bromo-*o*-xylene and 250 ml. of ethanol are added, with shaking, 48 g. of hexamine and 50 ml. of water. The mixture becomes warm as the hexamine dissolves, and the odor of the bromoxylene disappears in about five minutes. An additional 200 ml. of water is added, and the mixture is heated under reflux for two hours. The product is distilled with steam

[53] Weygand, *Organic Preparations*, p. 156, Interscience, New York, 1945.

until the condensate, though still cloudy,* no longer smells of aldehyde (after about 1.5 l. has been collected). The distillate is extracted with ether; the ethereal solution is washed with water, dried, and fractionated to give 27 g. (70%) of o-tolualdehyde, b.p. 86–88°/19 mm.

The preparation of 1-naphthaldehyde in *Organic Syntheses*[54] is another good example of the Sommelet reaction without the isolation of the hexaminium salt. The solvent in this preparation is 50% acetic acid, and the yield is 77–82%.

p-Nitrobenzaldehyde.[16] (Preparation from a halomethyl compound with isolation of the hexaminium salt.) To a solution of 11 g. of hexamine in 70 ml. of chloroform is added 11.4 g. of *p*-nitrobenzyl chloride. The mixture is heated under reflux on a steam bath for four hours, during which time a precipitate separates. The reflux condenser is replaced by a condenser set for distillation, and heating is continued until 35 ml. of solvent has distilled. After the addition of 35 ml. of acetone, the mixture is cooled in ice, and the precipitate collected on a Büchner funnel and dried in air. The salt is heated under reflux for one hour with 100 ml. of 50% acetic acid; 100 ml. of water and 25 ml. of concd. hydrochloric acid are then added, and the boiling is continued for five minutes. On being cooled in an ice bath the solution deposits 6.3 g. (63%) of the aldehyde, m.p. 105°.

o-Iodobenzaldehyde.[55] (Preparation from a substituted toluene without isolation of the halomethyl compound.) A gently refluxing mixture of 218 g. of *o*-iodotoluene, 600 ml. of carbon tetrachloride, and 200 ml. of water containing a little iodine, irradiated by three 75-watt lamps, is treated during two hours with a solution of 160 g. of bromine in 300 ml. of carbon tetrachloride. After heating under reflux for one additional hour, the solvents are removed as completely as possible by distilling from a steam bath. The organic layer is separated from the water, diluted with 150 ml. of chloroform, and then heated in a boiling-water bath under reduced pressure (water pump) until all the chloroform and water are removed. After cooling, a solution of 200 g. of hexamine in 2 l. of chloroform is added to the residue and the mixture is allowed to stand overnight. The separated hexaminium salt is collected on a Büchner funnel, washed with a little chloroform, and dried in air for about one hour. The salt is then dissolved in a mixture of 300 ml. of glacial acetic acid and 300 ml. of water and heated under reflux for one

---

* The cloudiness is caused by Schiff bases. It can be eliminated, and the end of the steam distillation more readily distinguished, if hydrochloric acid is added to the mixture before steam distillation.

[54] Angyal, Tetaz, and Wilson, *Org. Syntheses*, **30**, 67 (1950).

[55] Anet, Hughes, Marmion, and Ritchie, *Australian J. Sci. Research*, **3A**, 333 (1950) [*C. A.*, **45**, 5162 (1951)].

and one-half hours. The mixture is cooled, diluted with water, and extracted several times with ether. The ethereal extracts are washed with sodium carbonate solution, then with water, dried, and distilled in a stream of nitrogen. The pale yellow distillate (81 g.), b.p. 143–148°/28 mm., completely solidifies to a colorless solid melting at 35°.*

From the mother liquor of the hexaminium salt 76 g. of o-iodotoluene is recovered by washing with water, evaporating, and distilling. Allowing for this recovery, the overall yield of o-iodobenzaldehyde is 54%.

Pyridine-3-carboxaldehyde.[21] (Preparation of an aldehyde from an amine.) A mixture of 11.4 g. of 3-aminomethylpyridine, 26 ml. of 10 N hydrochloric acid, 4 ml. of glacial acetic acid, 18 g. of hexamine, and 24 ml. of water is heated under reflux for six hours. The mixture is saturated with sodium nitrate, adjusted to pH 5 with a little hydrochloric acid, and extracted several times with chloroform (200 ml. in all). The solvent is removed through a short fractionating column and the residue distilled under reduced pressure to give 6.4 g. (57%) of colorless aldehyde, b.p. 95–97°/15 mm.

The basic character of this aldehyde prevents acid hydrolysis. The pH chosen for the extraction is the lowest at which the aldehyde can be extracted. However, at this pH considerable amounts of Schiff bases are still present and the yield is thereby reduced.

n-Heptaldehyde.[22] (Preparation of an aliphatic aldehyde.) To a solution of 20 g. of hexamine in 150 ml. of chloroform is added 30 g. of n-heptyl iodide. The mixture is boiled on a steam bath for six hours. Half of the solvent is then removed by distillation, and heating under reflux is resumed for an additional sixteen hours. After cooling, the salt is collected on a filter and dried in air; it is thus obtained in 90% yield.

One hundred and twenty milliliters of 50% acetic acid is placed in a flask equipped for steam distillation and fitted with a dropping funnel having a wide-bore stopcock. The salt, suspended in 150 ml. of water, is introduced in portions over thirty minutes into the flask, through which steam is being passed. Distillation is continued until no more aldehyde comes over (test with semicarbazide); approximately 150 ml. of distillate is collected. The distillate is made strongly acid with hydrochloric acid and is extracted three times with 50-ml. portions of ether. The extracts are washed with sodium carbonate solution, dried, and evaporated. Distillation of the residue yields 6.5 g. (46%) of n-heptaldehyde, b.p. 152–154°.

4-Methoxyisophthalaldehyde.[26] (Preparation of a dialdehyde.) Twenty-five grams of 2,4-bis(chloromethyl)anisole and 37 g. of hex-

* The distillation residue, which crystallizes, consists mainly of o-iodomethylenebenzylamine (E. Ritchie, private communication), indicating that hydrolysis by a mineral acid would be advisable before extraction with ether.

amine are dissolved separately in a small excess of dry chloroform. After the two solutions have been brought together, the mixture is heated under reflux for three hours. The salt is removed by filtration, dried, and then heated under reflux with 500 ml. of water for four hours. The hot solution is filtered and the filtrate is cooled in an ice bath to give 14 g. (70%) of white needles, m.p. 117–118°. One crystallization from 60% ethanol gives 12.6 g. of the pure aldehyde, m.p. 119–120°.

TABULAR SURVEY OF THE SOMMELET REACTION

An attempt has been made to collect in the following tables all examples of the Sommelet reaction published before January, 1953. A few later preparations also are included. ·The compounds are listed in order of increasing substitution, the substituents being arranged in the conventional order. In the column headed "Starting Material" the group is shown which, during the reaction, is replaced by the —CHO group; when there are other changes in the molecule the full name or formula of the starting material is given. In those experiments in which the hexaminium salt was isolated, this is indicated by giving its yield when known, or by "Yes" if the yield was not stated; "No" indicates that the salt was not isolated. The yields in the penultimate column are calculated on the basis of the starting material (and not of the hexaminium salts).

Certain of the aldehydes, indicated by appropriate footnotes in the tables, were prepared without the knowledge of optimal experimental conditions which is now available; some yields could be improved by following one of the procedures given in the preceding section. In particular the yields of the thiophenecarboxaldehydes prepared by the steam-distillation method should be improved by using the reflux procedure, and the preparations carried out in very dilute ethanolic solution should be improved by employing less solvent.

TABLE I

ALIPHATIC AND ARYLALIPHATIC ALDEHYDES

Aldehyde	Starting Material *	Hexaminium Salt Isolated %	Solvent	Yield %	Ref
n-Butyraldehyde	—CH$_2$NH$_2$	—	H$_2$O †	16	22
Isovaleraldehyde	—CH$_2$I	82	50% CH$_3$CO$_2$H †	37	22
Trimethylacetaldehyde	—CH$_2$NH$_2$	—	50% CH$_3$CO$_2$H	80 ‡	22
n-Hexaldehyde	—CH$_2$NH$_2$ or —CH$_2$Br	78	50% CH$_3$CO$_2$H †	42	22
n-Heptaldehyde	—CH$_2$I	90	50% CH$_3$CO$_2$H †	46	22
Phenylacetaldehyde	—CH$_2$NH$_2$	—	50% CH$_3$CO$_2$H †	12	22
β-Methylcrotonaldehyde	—CH$_2$Cl	Nearly quantitative	H$_2$O †	35	25
β-n-Heptylacrolein	—CH$_2$Br	81	H$_2$O	20	56
β-n-Nonylacrolein	—CH$_2$Br	90	H$_2$O	9	56
Cinnamaldehyde	—CH$_2$Br	Yes	H$_2$O	38	24
β-o-Tolylacrolein	—CH$_2$Br	Yes	H$_2$O	30	24
β-p-Tolylacrolein	—CH$_2$Br	Yes	H$_2$O	45	24
β-Phenethylacrolein	—CH$_2$Br	Yes	H$_2$O	20	24
β-(γ-Phenylpropyl)acrolein	—CH$_2$Br	Yes	H$_2$O	20	24
β-(o-Methoxyphenyl)-acrolein	—CH$_2$Cl	—	H$_2$O—C$_2$H$_5$OH	—	23
β-(2,4-Dimethoxyphenyl)acrolein	—CH$_2$Cl	—	H$_2$O—C$_2$H$_5$OH	—	23
β-(2,4,5-Trimethoxyphenyl)acrolein	—CH$_2$Cl	—	H$_2$O—C$_2$H$_5$OH	—	23

* The group is shown which, during the reaction, is replaced by the —CHO group.
† Steam was passed through the reaction mixture.
‡ Allowance was made for recovered starting material.

TABLE II

SUBSTITUTED BENZALDEHYDES

Benzaldehyde	Starting Material	Hexaminium Salt Isolated %	Solvent	Yield %	Ref.
Unsubstituted	—CH$_2$Cl	No	H$_2$O	70–82	1, 5
	—CH$_2$NH$_2$	—	H$_2$O	66	8
m-Fluoro-	—CH$_2$Cl	No	60% C$_2$H$_5$OH	57 *	57
p-Fluoro-	—CH$_2$Cl	No	60% C$_2$H$_5$OH	61 *	57
o-Chloro-	—CH$_2$Cl	No	60% C$_2$H$_5$OH	—	58
	—CH$_2$NH$_2$	—	H$_2$O	38 †	8
m-Chloro-	—CH$_2$NH$_2$	—	H$_2$O	50 †	8
p-Chloro-	—CH$_2$Cl	No	60% C$_2$H$_5$OH	73 *	57
	—CH$_2$Cl	No	60% C$_2$H$_5$OH	32 †	58
	—CH$_2$NH$_2$	—	H$_2$O	50 †	8
o-Bromo-	—CH$_2$Br	95	50% CH$_3$CO$_2$H	47	14
	—CH$_2$Br	No	66% C$_2$H$_5$OH	50	14
m-Bromo-	—CH$_2$Br	94	50% CH$_3$CO$_2$H	69	14
	—CH$_2$Br	No	66% C$_2$H$_5$OH	60	14

[56] Delaby, *Bull. soc. chim. France*, [5], **3**, 2375 (1936).

TABLE II—*Continued*

Substituted Benzaldehydes

Benzaldehyde	Starting Material	Hexaminium Salt Isolated %	Solvent	Yield %	Ref.
p-Bromo-	—CH_2Br	98	50% CH_3CO_2H	73	14
	—CH_2Br	No	66% C_2H_5OH	69	14
	—CH_2Br	No	60% C_2H_5OH	77 *	57
o-Iodo-	—CH_2Br	95	50% CH_3CO_2H	76	14
	—CH_3	Yes	50% CH_3CO_2H	54 ‡	55
m-Iodo-	—CH_2Br	No	60% C_2H_5OH	58 *	57
p-Iodo-	—CH_2Br	No	60% C_2H_5OH	73 *	57
o-Nitro-	—CH_2Cl	89	50% CH_3CO_2H	36	16
m-Nitro-	—CH_2Cl	89	50% CH_3CO_2H	45	16
p-Nitro-	—CH_2Cl	91	50% CH_3CO_2H	59	16
o-Hydroxy-	$CO(OC_6H_4CH_2Cl)_2$	No	70% C_2H_5OH	55	17
p-Hydroxy-	$C_2H_5OCO_2C_6H_4CH_2Cl$	No	H_2O—C_2H_5OH	—	18
p-Methoxy-	—CH_2Cl	—	—	—	19
p-Sulfamyl-	—CH_2Cl	96	50% CH_3CO_2H	21	16
	—CH_2NH_2	--	50% CH_3CO_2H	19	16
o-Methyl-	—CH_2Br	Yes	H_2O	Excellent	1
	—CH_2Br	No	H_2O—C_2H_5OH	66–75	17
	—CH_2Br	70	H_2O	46	17
	—CH_2Br	No	H_2O—C_2H_5OH	70	53
m-Methyl-	—CH_2Br	Yes	H_2O	Excellent	1
p-Methyl-	—CH_2Br	Yes	H_2O	Excellent	1
o-Ethyl-	—CH_2Br	No	60% C_2H_5OH	34 †	58
p-Carbomethoxy-	—CH_2Br	No	62% CH_3OH	57	58a
p-Methoxymethyl-	—CH_2Cl	No	80% C_2H_5OH	40 †	59
3-Chloro-4-hydroxy-	—CH_2Cl	Quantitative	CH_3CO_2H	22 §	16
3-Nitro-4-hydroxy-	—CH_2Cl	No	CH_3CO_2H	70	16
	—CH_2Cl	No	50% CH_3CO_2H	41	16
3-Nitro-6-hydroxy-	—CH_2Cl	No	CH_3CO_2H	57	16
	—CH_2Cl	No	50% CH_3CO_2H	37	16
4-Nitro-6-hydroxy-	—CH_2Cl	Nearly quantitative	50% CH_3CO_2H	45	60
2-Methoxy-5-acetyl-	—CH_2Cl	No	60% C_2H_5OH	28	16
2-Methylmercapto-5-methyl-	—CH_2Cl	Yes	20% HCl	50	61
3,5-Dichloro-2-hydroxy-	—CH_2Cl	93	CH_3CO_2H	66	16
	—CH_2Cl	No	CH_3CO_2H	55	16

* The yield refers to aldehyde purified through the bisulfite compound but not distilled or recrystallized. All steps of this preparation were carried out in a stream of carbon dioxide.

† The yield in this preparation would probably be improved by following one of the procedures given in the preceding section.

‡ This yield was calculated allowing for recovered o-iodotoluene.

§ The product was very impure.

[57] J. W. Baker, private communication; Baker and Hopkins, *J. Chem. Soc.*, **1949**, 1096.

[58] Mayer and English, *Ann.*, **417**, 74 (1918).

[58a] Fuson and Cooke, *J. Am. Chem. Soc.*, **62**, 1180 (1940).

[59] Quelet, *Bull. soc. chim. France*, [4], **53**, 233 (1933).

[60] N. Gill and F. Lions, private communication.

[61] Howard, Campaigne, and Shriner, *J. Am. Chem. Soc.*, **70**, 4251 (1948).

TABLE III

POLYCYCLIC ALDEHYDES

Aldehyde	Starting Material	Hexaminium Salt Isolated %	Solvent	Yield %	Ref.
1-Naphthaldehyde	—CH₂Br	No	60% C₂H₅OH	68	62
	—CH₂Cl	No	60% C₂H₅OH	48–64	63, 64, 65, 66,
	—CH₂Cl	No	95% C₂H₅OH	60	67
	—CH₂Br	No	CH₃CO₂H	67	47
	Naphthalene	No	CH₃CO₂H	34–40	68
	—CH₂Cl	No	50% CH₃CO₂H	75–82	16, 54
	Naphthalene	No	50% CH₃CO₂H	52	54
2-Naphthaldehyde	—CH₂Br	No	60% C₂H₅OH	70–80	62
	—CH₂Br	No	CH₃CO₂H	52	47
4-Bromo-1-naphthaldehyde	—CH₂Br	No	60% C₂H₅OH	29 *	62
1-Bromo-2-naphthaldehyde	—CH₂Br	No	60% C₂H₅OH	—	62
	—CH₂Br	No	CH₃CO₂H	40 *	46
	—CH₂Cl	No	96% C₂H₅OH	20 *	69
Fluorene-2-carboxaldehyde	—CH₂NH₂	—	50% C₂H₅OH	77	45
	—CH₂Cl	Quantitative	5% HCl	78	70

$$\text{The aldehyde structures are drawn as: CH}_3 \text{ / CHO / H}_3\text{C / CH(CH}_3)_2 \text{ naphthalene; and CHO CH}_2 \text{ / O / CH}_2 \text{ / O / Cl benzene}$$

* The yield in this preparation would probably be improved by following one of the procedures given in the preceding section.

[62] Mayer and Sieglitz, *Ber.*, **55**, 1835 (1922).

[63] Coles and Dodds, *J. Am. Chem. Soc.*, **60**, 853 (1938).

[64] Gaylord and Becker, *J. Org. Chem.*, **15**, 312 (1950).

[65] Ruggli and Preuss, *Helv. Chim. Acta*, **24**, 1350 (1941).

[66] Rupe and Brentano, *Helv. Chim. Acta*, **19**, 586 (1936).

[67] Anderson and Short, *J. Chem. Soc.*, **1933**, 485.

[68] Price and Voong, *J. Org. Chem.*, **14**, 115 (1949).

[69] Briggs, Gill, Lions, and Taylor, *J. Chem. Soc.*, **1949**, 1100.

[70] S. F. Lawson, B.Sc. Thesis, Sydney University, **1949**.

TABLE IV

Heteroaromatic Aldehydes

Aldehyde	Starting Material	Hexaminium Salt Isolated %	Solvent	Yield %	Ref.
Thiophene-2-	—CH$_2$Cl	94–98	H$_2$O *	48–53 †	51, 52
	—CH$_2$Cl	No	50% CH$_3$CO$_2$H	71–74	10
	Thiophene	Yes	H$_2$O *	50 †	12, 20
Thiophene-3-	—CH$_2$Br	Quantitative	H$_2$O *	49 †	48
2-Chlorothiophene-3-	—CH$_2$Br	84	H$_2$O *	25 †	49
2-Bromothiophene-3-	—CH$_2$Br	75	H$_2$O *	15 †	49
5-Chlorothiophene-2-	2-Chlorothiophene ‡	—	H$_2$O *	37 †	12
	—CH$_2$Br	66	50% CH$_3$CO$_2$H *	33 †	70a
5-Bromothiophene-2-	—CH$_2$Cl	Yes	50% CH$_3$CO$_2$H *	32 †	70a
3-Methylthiophene-2-	3-Methylthiophene ‡	—	H$_2$O *	42 †	12
5-Methylthiophene-2-	2-Methylthiophene‡	—	H$_2$O *	48 †	12
4- or 5-t-Butylthiophene-2-	t-Butylthiophene ‡§	—	H$_2$O *	44 †	12
2,5-Dichlorothiophene-3-	—CH$_2$Br	90	H$_2$O *	59	70a
Thianaphthene-3-	—CH$_2$Cl	Yes	H$_2$O *	31 †	50
Pyridine-3-	—CH$_2$NH$_2$	—	10% CH$_3$CO$_2$H	57	21
(pyridine structure: HO, CH$_3$, CHO, H$_3$C substituents)	—CH$_2$Cl	No	60% C$_2$H$_5$OH	34 ‖	71
Isoquinoline-4-	—CH$_2$NH$_2$	—	50% CH$_3$CO$_2$H	56	21
2-Phenylthiazole-4-	—CH$_2$Br	No	50% CH$_3$CO$_2$H	55	21

* Steam was passed through the reaction mixture.

† The yield in this preparation would probably be improved by following one of the procedures given in the preceding section.

‡ The thiophene was converted into the aminomethyl compound, which was then used in the Sommelet reaction.

§ The starting material was a mixture of the 2- and 3-isomers.

‖ The product was isolated as the thiosemicarbazone.

70a Campaigne, Monroe, Arnwine, and Archer, *J. Am. Chem. Soc.*, **75**, 989 (1953).

71 Gardner, Smith, Wenis, and Lee, *J. Org. Chem.*, **16**, 1124 (1951).

TABLE V
DIALDEHYDES

Aldehyde	Starting Material	Hexaminium Salt Isolated %	Solvent	Yield %	Ref.
4 Hydroxyisophthal-aldehyde	CH₂Cl (structure)	No	50% CH_3CO_2H	63	16
	CHO (structure) CH₂Cl OH	No No	50% CH_3CO_2H 60% C_2H_5OH	25 30	16 16
4-Methoxyisophthal-aldehyde	1,3-di-CH₂Cl	Nearly quantitative	H_2O	70	26
4-Methylmercapto-isophthalaldehyde	1,3-di-CH₂Cl	Nearly quantitative	H_2O	24	26
4,6-Dimethoxyiso-phthalaldehyde	1,3-di-CH₂Cl	Nearly quantitative	H_2O	—	26
Terephthalaldehyde	1,4-di-CH₂Cl	90	50% CH_3CO_2H	34	16
2,5-Dimethoxytere-phthalaldehyde	1,4-di-CH₂Cl 1,4-di-CH₂Cl	99 Nearly quantitative	50% CH_3CO_2H H_2O	32 63	16 26
2,5-Dimethylterephthal-aldehyde	1,4-di-CH₂Cl	No	60% C_2H_5OH	57	26
CHO HO—CHO H₃C—N (structure)	4,5-di-CH₂Cl	Yes	60% C_2H_5OH	9 *	71

* The product was isolated as the bis-thiosemicarbazone and its identity was not conclusively established.

TABLE VI
UNSUCCESSFUL SOMMELET REACTIONS

Starting Material	Ref.
2,4-Dinitrobenzyl chloride	16
2,6-Dichlorobenzyl bromide	14
2,4,6-Trimethylbenzyl chloride	14, 15
2-Chloro-6-nitrobenzyl bromide	14
2-Methyl-1-chloromethylnaphthalene	14
2,2′-Bis(bromomethyl)biphenyl	16
Bis(chloromethyl)mesitylene	26
o-Xylylene bromide	16, 26
4,5-Bis(chloromethyl)-o-xylene	26
4,5-Bis(chloromethyl)veratrole	26
3,4-Bis(chloromethyl)veratrole	26
5-Nitro-2-chloromethylthiophene	70a, 72
2-Aminomethylpyridine	21
4-Aminomethylpyridine	21
2-Bromomethylquinoline	21
4-Phenyl-2-bromomethylthiazole	21
2-Aminomethylfuran	21
β-Methoxyethylamine	22

[72] Dullaghan, Owen, and Nord, *J. Am. Chem. Soc.*, **74**, 2676 (1952).

CHAPTER 5

THE SYNTHESIS OF ALDEHYDES FROM CARBOXYLIC ACIDS

Erich Mosettig

National Institutes of Health, U. S. Public Health Service, Department of Health, Education, and Welfare

CONTENTS

INTRODUCTION

The Rosenmund reduction of acid chlorides to the corresponding aldehydes was discussed in Vol. IV of *Organic Reactions*. There are a number of other, less direct methods by which carboxylic acids can be converted into aldehydes, and it is the purpose of the present chapter to consider the more useful of these procedures.

Three of these methods, the hydrolytic decomposition of Reissert's compounds, the method of Grundmann, and the reductive desulfurization of thiol esters, require acid chlorides as intermediates and in this respect are competitive with the Rosenmund reduction of acid chlorides. In the fourth method, the McFadyen and Stevens synthesis, acid chlorides may be used for the preparation of the intermediate acyl hydrazides although the common practice is to use esters for this purpose. Two additional procedures, the method of Sonn and Müller and that of Stephen, are based upon the use of intermediate imido chlorides, which may be prepared from the corresponding anilides or toluides via the acid chlorides or, in the latter instance, from the nitriles.

It is obvious that the above six methods, seven if the Rosenmund reduction of acid chlorides is included, do not represent the only ways by which aldehydes can be synthesized from the corresponding carboxylic acids. However, the methods listed above appear to be the only ones that have been developed to the point where further discussion is profitable. A new method, which has not been exploited to a large extent, consists in the controlled reduction of cyanides and acid amides with lithium aluminum hydride. It is dealt with briefly at the end of this chapter.

THE HYDROLYTIC DECOMPOSITION OF REISSERT'S COMPOUNDS

A mixture of quinoline and benzoyl chloride in aqueous potassium cyanide gives 1-benzoyl-2-cyano-1,2-dihydroquinoline (1-benzoyl-1,2-di-hydroquinaldonitrile I, R = C_6H_5) in excellent yield.[1] This addition product, generally referred to as Reissert's compound,[2] can be hydrolyzed with strong mineral acids to give almost quantitative yields of benzaldehyde and quinoline-2-carboxylic acid, the latter arising from the intermediate 2-cyanoquinoline (III).

McEwen and his coworkers [3,4,5] have proposed that the acid-catalyzed cleavage of the Reissert compounds (I) proceeds by the attack of a proton on the amide oxygen and (over-all) migration of a proton from the 2-position of the quinoline ring to the amide carbon atom. The resulting intermediate complex II then decomposes to the nitrile III (which is hydrolyzed to the corresponding acid), the aldehyde IV, and a proton.

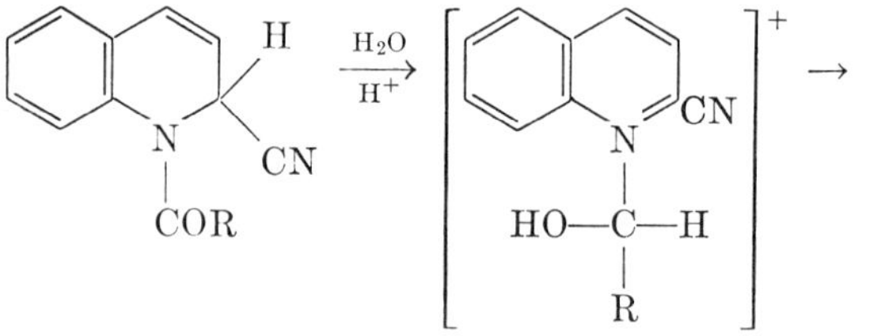

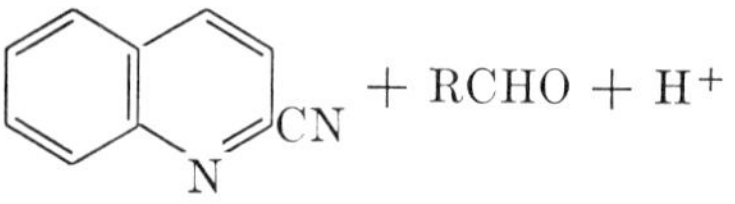

The Reissert's compound from *p*-chlorobenzoyl chloride and isoquinoline yields *p*-chlorobenzaldehyde on acid hydrolysis. The *alkylated* Reissert compounds of *isoquinoline* (see below) yield 1-alkyliso-quinolines on *alkaline hydrolysis.*[6,7] According to Boekelheide and his

[1] Reissert, *Ber.*, **38**, 1603 (1905).

[2] Migrdichian, *The Chemistry of Organic Cyanogen Compounds*, pp. 131, 144–145, 164, Am. Chem. Soc. Monograph Series 105, Reinhold, New York, 1947.

[3] McEwen and Hazlett, *J. Am. Chem. Soc.*, **71**, 1949 (1949).

[4] McEwen, Kindall, Hazlett, and Glazier, *J. Am. Chem. Soc.*, **73**, 4591 (1951).

[5] McEwen, Terss, and Elliott, *J. Am. Chem. Soc.*, **74**, 3605 (1952).

[6] Boekelheide and Ainsworth, *J. Am. Chem. Soc.*, **72**, 2134 (1950).

[7] Boekelheide and Weinstock, *J. Am. Chem. Soc.*, **74**, 660 (1952).

collaborators, the reaction is induced by the attack of hydroxyl ion on the amide carbon atom, resulting in the shift of a pair of electrons to the nitrile group, which separates as the ion.

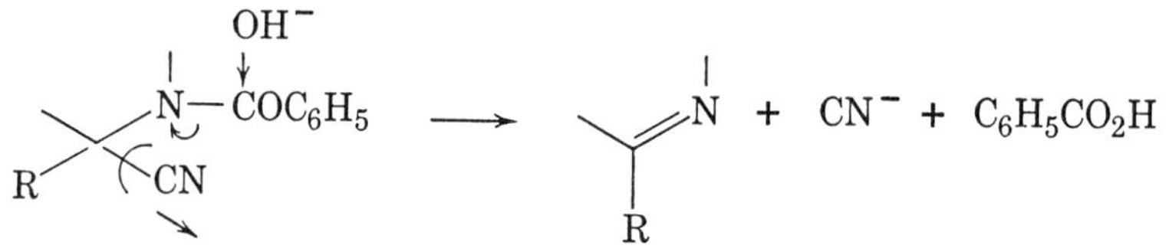

$$
\underset{R}{\overset{OH^-}{\underset{CN}{\overset{\downarrow}{N-COC_6H_5}}}} \longrightarrow \underset{R}{N} + CN^- + C_6H_5CO_2H
$$

Scope and Limitations

Attempts [8] to utilize the acid-catalyzed decomposition of Reissert's compounds as a general method for the synthesis of aldehydes from acid chlorides by replacing the benzoyl group by other acyl groups have been only moderately successful. Although two aromatic aldehydes and cinnamaldehyde were obtained in fair yields, the method failed completely in the aliphatic series. However, by working in non-aqueous media, Grosheintz and Fischer [9] succeeded in preparing the Reissert's compounds from aliphatic as well as from aromatic acid chlorides. The yields of a limited number of acyl dihydroquinaldonitriles were generally high, and their decomposition into the corresponding aldehydes proceeded nearly quantitatively. The authors observed, however, that some acid chlorides when brought into reaction with quinoline and hydrocyanic acid formed intractable resinous oils. It is noteworthy that o-nitrobenzoyl chloride and 2-nitro-3,4,5-trimethoxybenzoyl chloride were converted into the corresponding aldehydes in 60–70% yields.[10] In attempting to prepare unsaturated aldehydes from the corresponding acids, Wittig et al.[11] modified the Reissert method by using phenanthridine in place of quinoline to form the addition product, and dilute phosphoric acid instead of dilute sulfuric acid to decompose the addition product. 5-Cinnamoyl-6-cyano-5,6-dihydrophenanthridine and cinnamaldehyde were obtained in excellent yields (86% and 97%, respectively), but the yields of the next higher vinylogous compounds were considerably lower (64% for the addition product and 35% for the 5-phenylpentadienal). The decomposition of 5-(7-phenylheptatrienoyl)-6-cyano-5,6-dihydrophenanthridine did not yield any of the expected aldehyde.

[8] Sugasawa and Tsuda, J. Pharm. Soc. Japan, **56**, 557 (Transactions 103) (1936) [C. A., **32**, 5836 (1938)].

[9] Grosheintz and Fischer, J. Am. Chem. Soc., **63**, 2021 (1941).

[10] Buchanan, Cook, and Loudon, J. Chem. Soc., **1944**, 325.

[11] Wittig, Jesaitis, and Glos, Ann., **577**, 1 (1952).

Reissert's compounds obtained from quinoline, 6-methoxyquino-
line,[12] isoquinoline (2-benzoyl-1-cyano-1,2-dihydroisoquinoline),[13,14] and
phenanthridine (5-benzoyl-6-cyano-5,6-dihydrophenanthridine)[11] are
of incidental usefulness in the preparation of quinoline-2-carboxylic
acid,[1] 6-methoxyquinoline-2-carboxylic acid,[12] isoquinoline-1-carboxylic
acid,[13,15,16] phenanthridine-6-carboxylic acid,[11] and aminomethyl derivatives of tetrahydroquinoline[12,17] and tetrahydroisoquinoline.[14]

Reissert's compounds have been utilized for the preparation of a
series of otherwise not readily accessible quinoline and isoquinoline
derivatives.[6,7] Thus 1-skatylisoquinoline (VII) was obtained by alkaline
hydrolysis of the alkylation product VI obtained from V. Under

proper conditions Reissert's compounds could be smoothly alkylated
by various alkyl halides, and 1-methyl-, 1-benzyl-, and 1-n-butyl-
isoquinoline, respectively, were obtained in yields ranging from 41 to
78%. Methylation of the Reissert compound derived from quinoline,
followed by alkaline hydrolysis, gave lepidine, although quinaldine
might have been expected. With sodium hydride in benzene, 1-acyl-
2-cyano-1,2-dihydroquinolines and 2-acyl-1-cyano-1,2-dihydroisoquino-
lines (acyl = acetyl, benzoyl) were converted to the corresponding
2-acylquinolines and 1-acylisoquinolines in yields ranging from 30 to
70%.

Experimental Conditions and Reagents

Preparation of Reissert's Compounds.[9,17,18] Two to three milliliters
of anhydrous hydrogen cyanide is poured, at about −5°, into 14 g. (0.1
mole) of freshly distilled quinoline. With further cooling, a solution of

[12] Gassmann and Rupe, *Helv. Chim. Acta*, **22**, 1241 (1939).
[13] Reissert, *Ber.*, **38**, 3415 (1905).
[14] Rupe and Frey, *Helv. Chim. Acta*, **22**, 673 (1939).
[15] Padbury and Lindwall, *J. Am. Chem. Soc.*, **67**, 1268 (1945).
[16] Solomon, *J. Chem. Soc.*, **1947**, 129.
[17] Rupe, Paltzer, and Engel, *Helv. Chim. Acta*, **20**, 209 (1937).
[18] von Bidder and Rupe, *Helv. Chim. Acta*, **22**, 1268 (1939).

0.05 mole of acid chloride in 10–20 ml. of absolute benzene is added through a dropping funnel during a period of ten minutes. After about sixteen hours at room temperature, the separation of quinoline hydrochloride is complete. The reaction mixture is then treated with 100–200 ml. of ether, and the resulting solution is successively washed, three times with 10 ml. of water, three times with 20 ml. of 5 N sulfuric acid, several times with 10 ml. of saturated sodium bicarbonate solution until no further evolution of carbon dioxide occurs, and twice with 10 ml. of water. If the 1-acyl-2-cyano-1,2-dihydroquinoline is not readily soluble in ether, it may partially crystallize during the washings. After evaporation of the solvent the residue is crystallized from aqueous ethanol.

Hydrolysis of Reissert's Compounds. The hydrolysis of the 1-acyl-2-cyano-1,2-dihydroquinolines is ordinarily carried out with 5–10 N sulfuric acid. The nitrile (0.01 mole) and the acid (30 ml.) are boiled to effect hydrolysis, and the resulting aldehyde is isolated by filtration, extraction, distillation, or steam distillation. For the preparation of aldehydes, the intermediary nitrile need not be isolated. The reaction mixture may be steam-distilled in the presence of sulfuric acid, thus giving the aldehyde in one operation.

Experimental Procedure

o-**Nitrobenzaldehyde.**[10] To a solution of 3 ml. of anhydrous hydrogen cyanide in 14 g. of quinoline protected from moisture and cooled to −10° is added during ten minutes a solution of 10 g. of *o*-nitrobenzoyl chloride in 10 ml. of benzene. After twelve hours at room temperature, during which interval some crystals form, 130 ml. of benzene is added. The resulting mixture is washed successively with water, 5 N sulfuric acid, sodium bicarbonate, and water, then dried and concentrated. The 1-*o*-nitrobenzoyl-2-cyano-1,2-dihydroquinoline thus obtained in 80% yield melts at 173° after recrystallization from ethanol.

One gram of the above product is hydrolyzed by boiling for three hours in 250 ml. of 15 N sulfuric acid. The *o*-nitrobenzaldehyde, identified by a mixed melting point and as the 2,4-dinitrophenylhydrazone, is obtained in a yield of 73% by extracting the hydrolysate with ether, washing the extract with sodium bicarbonate, and evaporating the solvent.

Table I. Aldehydes Prepared from Acid Chlorides via a Reissert's Compound

In Table I are listed aldehydes which have been prepared from acid chlorides via the 1-acyl-2-cyano-1,2-dihydroquinolines. The literature has been surveyed through 1952.

TABLE I

ALDEHYDES PREPARED FROM ACID CHLORIDES VIA A REISSERT'S COMPOUND *

Aldehyde	Acid Chloride	Reissert's Compound Yield %	Aldehyde Yield %	Over-all Yield %	Reference
Acetaldehyde	Acetyl	74	99 a	73 a	9
Propionaldehyde	Propionyl	10	92 a	9,a 36 b	9
n-Butyraldehyde	Butyryl	64	97 a	62 a	9
Isobutyraldehyde	Isobutyryl	28	98 a	27,a 56 b	9
n-Valeraldehyde	Valeryl			42 b,c	9
Isovaleraldehyde	Isovaleryl	64	98 a	63 a	9
Cinnamaldehyde	Cinnamoyl	34,d 91, 77,e 86 f	30, 82, 97 a	10, 75, 83 a	8, 9, 19, 11
5-Phenyl-2,4-pentadienal	5-Phenyl-2,4-pentadienoyl	64 f	35 a	22 a	11
Benzaldehyde	Benzoyl	96, 86,e,g 94 f	98, 97 a	94, 90 a	9, 19, 11
p-Tolualdehyde	p-Toluyl			96 e	20
o-Chlorobenzaldehyde	o-Chlorobenzoyl	80	94	75	9
m-Chlorobenzaldehyde	m-Chlorobenzoyl	28	96	27, 65 b	9
p-Chlorobenzaldehyde	p-Chlorobenzoyl	77	92	71, 50 c,h	9, 20
o-Nitrobenzaldehyde	o-Nitrobenzoyl	80	73	58 i	10
m-Nitrobenzaldehyde	m-Nitrobenzoyl				10
2-Nitro-3,4,5-trimethoxybenzaldehyde	2-Nitro-3,4,5-trimethoxybenzoyl	80	60–70	48–56	10
o-Methoxybenzaldehyde	o-Methoxybenzoyl	66	97	64	9
p-Methoxybenzaldehyde	p-Methoxybenzoyl	51,d 88	57, 98	29, 86	8, 9
3,4-Dimethoxybenzaldehyde	3,4-Dimethoxybenzoyl	36 d	56	21	8
3,4,5-Trimethoxybenzaldehyde	3,4,5-Trimethoxybenzoyl	Poor			8, 10

* The following aldehydes could not be prepared by this method: heptanal,[8] phenylacetaldehyde,[8] 7-phenylheptatrienal,[11] p-nitrobenzaldehyde,[10] 2,4-dinitrobenzaldehyde,[10] and 3,5-dinitrobenzaldehyde.[10]

a The yield refers to the p-nitrophenylhydrazone.
b In this experiment the aldehyde was prepared without isolating the acyl dihydroquinaldonitrile.
c The yield refers to the 2,4-dinitrophenylhydrazone.
d The reaction was carried out in aqueous medium.
e The addition product was obtained by allowing the acid chloride, quinoline, and potassium cyanide to react in liquid sulfur dioxide.
f Phenanthridine was used for the preparation of the addition product.
g For the preparation in aqueous medium, cf. refs. 1, 17, 18.
h The isoquinoline addition product was used in this preparation.
i An unusually large amount of hydrolyzing agent is required (for 0.01 mole of nitrile, 750 ml. of 15 N H_2SO_4).

19 Woodward, J. Am. Chem. Soc., **62**, 1626 (1940).

20 McEwen and Glazier, Abstracts, 123rd ACS National Meeting, 11M, 1953.

THE METHOD OF GRUNDMANN

This method consists of a combination of well-established synthetic procedures. An acid chloride is converted to a diazo ketone, which by treatment with glacial acetic acid gives an acetoxy ketone. By reduction of the keto group and simultaneous hydrolysis, the corresponding glycol is obtained. Oxidative cleavage of the glycol yields the aldehyde containing the same number of carbon atoms as the starting material, i.e., the acid or acid chloride. The entire process may be depicted as follows.

$$RCOCl \rightarrow RCOCHN_2 \rightarrow RCOCH_2OCOCH_3 \rightarrow RCHOHCH_2OH \rightarrow RCHO$$

Scope and Limitations

In spite of the complexity of this method, the yield of aldehyde is generally satisfactory since the intermediates are formed in good yields. The method can be applied equally well to the aliphatic and to the aromatic series. It has not been utilized, as yet, in the preparation of heterocyclic aldehydes. The particular value of the method lies in its applicability to aldehydes of sensitive nature such as olefinic aldehydes [21] and phenylacetaldehydes.[22] The method does not allow the preparation of α,β-unsaturated aldehydes since, in the treatment of the corresponding acid chlorides with diazomethane, a second mole of diazomethane adds to the double bond with the formation of pyrazoline derivatives.[21, 23, 24]

$$C_6H_5CH{=}CHCOCl \rightarrow \quad
\begin{array}{c}
H_5C_6CH{-\!\!\!-\!\!\!-}CHCOCHN_2 \\
| \qquad\quad | \\
CH \quad\; NH \\
\diagdown \;\; \diagup \\
N
\end{array}$$

Thus, this method complements the von Braun and Rudolph modification of the Sonn and Müller procedure (see p. 241) (reduction of imido chlorides with chromous chloride [25, 26, 27]) by which those olefinic aldehydes in which the double bond is in the α,β-position can be prepared. Attention is also drawn to the method of Hershberg [28a, b] by which the

[21] Grundmann, *Ann.*, **524**, 31 (1936).
[22] Schöpf, Brass, Jacobi, Jorde, Mocnik, Neuroth, and Salzer, *Ann.*, **544**, 30 (1940).
[23] Dane and Höss, *Ann.*, **552**, 113 (1942).
[24] Codington and Mosettig, *J. Org. Chem.*, **17**, 1027 (1952).
[25] von Braun and Rudolph, *Ber.*, **67**, 269 (1934).
[26] von Braun and Rudolph, *Ber.*, **67**, 1735 (1934).
[27] von Braun and Kurtz, *Ber.*, **70**, 1009 (1937).
[28a] Hershberg, *Helv. Chim. Acta.*, **17**, 351 (1934).
[28b] Jensen and Dynesen, *Acta Chem. Scand.*, **4**, 692 (1950) [*C. A.*, **45**, 798 (1951)].

synthesis of an unstable aldehyde is accomplished according to the following scheme.

$$RBr \rightarrow RMgBr \rightarrow RCH_2CH{=}CH_2 \rightarrow$$

$$\underset{\underset{C_6H_5COO}{|}}{RCH_2CH}{\rule{1cm}{0.4pt}}\underset{\underset{OCOC_6H_5}{|}}{CH_2} \quad \rightarrow RCH_2CHOHCH_2OH \rightarrow RCH_2CHO$$

Experimental Conditions

Two of the preparative procedures embodied in this method, the preparation of the diazo ketone [29] and the reduction with aluminum isopropoxide,[30] are dealt with in previous chapters of *Organic Reactions*. It may be ventured that lithium aluminum hydride [31] will advantageously replace aluminum isopropoxide. For the preparation of the acetoxy ketones the following general procedure is recommended.[21] The diazo ketone is introduced in small portions, not exceeding 5 g., into glacial acetic acid (500–700 ml. for 1 mole of diazo ketone) warmed to 60–70°. The lively evolution of gas which immediately takes place may be facilitated by adding coarsely powdered clay plate chips. The reaction is exothermic, and cooling with an ice bath may be necessary to keep the temperature below 70°. After all the diazo ketone has been introduced and the nitrogen evolution begins to slacken, the solution is heated slowly to the boiling point. If crude diazo ketone, which always contains chloro ketone, was used, 0.1 mole of potassium acetate is added and boiling is continued for one hour. After cooling, the acetoxy ketone is isolated in an appropriate manner.

The final step, the glycol cleavage with lead tetraacetate, has been reviewed.[32] The preparation of this oxidizing agent has been described on various occasions. Complete directions are found in Fieser's laboratory manual [33] and in *Inorganic Syntheses*.[34] It is obvious that it will be possible in many instances to replace the lead tetraacetate used in Grundmann's procedure by periodic acid. The periodic acid oxidation is the subject of a previous chapter of *Organic Reactions*.[35]

[29] Bachmann and Struve, in Adams, *Org. Reactions*, **1**, 38–62, Wiley, New York, 1942.

[30] Wilds, in Adams, *Org. Reactions*, **2**, 178–223, Wiley, New York, 1944.

[31] Brown, in Adams, *Org. Reactions*, **6**, 469–509, Wiley, New York, 1951.

[32] *Newer Methods of Preparative Organic Chemistry*, pp. 1–17, Interscience Publishers, New York, 1948.

[33] Fieser, *Experiments in Organic Chemistry*, 2nd ed., pp. 436–438, Heath and Co., Boston, 1941.

[34] Bailar, *Inorg. Syntheses*, **1** (1939).

[35] Jackson, in Adams, *Org. Reactions*, **2**, 341–375, Wiley, New York, 1944.

Experimental Procedures

3-Benzyloxy-4-methoxyphenylacetaldehyde.[22]   A solution of 13.5 g. of 3-benzyloxy-4-methoxyphenylacetic acid in 100 ml. of dry benzene is distilled until the last traces of water are removed. To the ice-cooled solution 11 g. (5% excess) of phosphorus pentachloride is added in small portions, and the mixture is allowed to stand at 0° for one-half hour. The benzene and phosphorus oxychloride are removed by distillation in vacuum, dry benzene is added to the residue, and the solvent is again removed. The process is repeated three times, whereupon a crystalline acid chloride is obtained. This compound is dissolved, without further purification, in dry ether and added dropwise at 0° to an ethereal solution of 7 g. of diazomethane; the diazo ketone precipitates immediately. The precipitate is collected after seven hours, and the mother liquor is concentrated. More diazo ketone precipitates, and the total amount of pure reaction product of m.p. 84–86° is 12 g. (81%). After recrystallization from methanol the product is obtained as yellow needles melting at 86°.

Ten grams of the diazo ketone is introduced into 20 ml. of warmed (60–70°) glacial acetic acid at such rate that the nitrogen evolution proceeds at a moderate rate and the temperature remains at about 60°. Finally the mixture is heated briefly to 100°, and cooled, whereupon 8.5 g. (77%) of practically pure acetoxy ketone of m.p. 101° precipitates from the reaction mixture. After recrystallization from methanol the acetoxy ketone melts at 106°.

A mixture of 4.5 g. of acetoxy ketone and 9 g. of aluminum isopropoxide in 100 ml. of dry isopropyl alcohol is heated so that 70 ml. of solvent is distilled in four and one-half hours, after which the distillate is free of acetone. To the residual mixture is added 2 N hydrochloric acid, and the precipitated glycol is extracted with ether. The product thus obtained is very pure; m.p. 110°, yield 3.7 g. (94%). High-vacuum distillation (215–220°/0.04 mm.) does not change the melting point of the product.

To a hot solution of 1.5 g. of glycol in 75 ml. of dry benzene is added, in small portions, 2.2 g. of lead tetraacetate. After cooling, 75 ml. of dry ether is added, the lead acetate is removed by filtration, and the filtrate is washed twice with sodium bicarbonate and once with water, and then dried over sodium sulfate. Evaporation under nitrogen leaves an almost quantitative yield of viscous oil. The aldehyde distils at 155°/0.01 mm. as a colorless oil which does not crystallize. It resinifies after a few days. The yield exceeds 90%.

The corresponding 3-hydroxy-4-methoxyphenylacetaldehyde, obtained by catalytic debenzylation with palladium, was also obtained as an oil.

10-Hendecenal.[21] A mixture of 40 g. of 10-hendecenoic acid, m.p. 24°, and 20 ml. of thionyl chloride is heated at 60–80° until gas evolution has ceased. The acid chloride is purified by vacuum distillation, b.p. 119°/10 mm. The yield is 41.5 g. (94%).

Forty-one grams of the acid chloride is introduced into a cooled ethereal solution of 19 g. of diazomethane. After evaporation of the ether, the diazo ketone is obtained as a yellow oil which solidifies on cooling and melts at about 16°. This product is added in small portions to about 100 ml. of glacial acetic acid at 60–70°. After nitrogen evolution has ceased, 2 g. of potassium acetate is added and the mixture is gently boiled for one hour. The mixture is cooled, an equal volume of water is added, and 43 g. of crystalline acetoxy ketone precipitates. From the mother liquor an additional 3.5 g. of nearly pure product is obtained. The yield based on the acid is 90%. The acetoxy ketone crystallizes from glacial acetic acid in white felted needles melting at 52°.

To a solution of 27 g. of acetoxy ketone in 150 ml. of dry isopropyl alcohol is added 45 ml. of a saturated solution of aluminum isopropoxide in isopropyl alcohol. About 150 ml. of solvent is distilled from the reaction mixture, isopropyl alcohol being added from time to time. When the distillate is free of acetone, the reaction mixture is poured into excess 10% sulfuric acid, and the precipitated glycol is extracted with ether. It is obtained as a thick yellowish oil which becomes completely crystalline; yield 21 g. (94%). The glycol crystallizes from benzene in white hexagonal leaflets of m.p. 48°.

To a solution of 20 g. of the glycol in 100 ml. of glacial acetic acid is added 50 g. of lead tetraacetate (10% excess), the temperature being maintained below 50°. After the reaction mixture has been kept for one-half hour at this temperature, the excess oxidizing agent is removed by the dropwise addition of ethylene glycol (test with potassium iodide-starch paper). The reaction mixture is then diluted with 500 ml. of water and extracted with ether. The combined ethereal extracts are washed with aqueous sodium bicarbonate and water, and dried. The aldehyde is recovered and purified by vacuum distillation. The yield of product boiling at 102–105°/12 mm. is 11 g. (64%); n_D^{18} 1.4491, d_4^{18} 0.8609. The aldehyde is stable when sealed in an evacuated tube. It polymerizes when exposed to air, forming a solid of m.p. 26° which is probably a dimer.

Table II. Aldehydes Prepared from Acids by the
Method of Grundmann

In Table II are listed the aldehydes which have been prepared from acids by the method of Grundmann. The yields of intermediates and of end products given in the table are for individual steps unless indicated otherwise. The literature has been reviewed through 1952.

TABLE II

ALDEHYDES PREPARED FROM ACIDS BY THE METHOD OF GRUNDMANN [21]

Aldehyde	Acid	Diazo Ketone Yield %	Acetoxy Ketone Yield %	Glycol Yield %	Aldehyde Yield %	Over-all Yield %
Stearaldehyde	Stearic	88	89	80	90	56
cis-9-Octadecenal	Oleic	a	75 [b]		74	
trans-9-Octadecenal	Elaidic	83	94	ca. 95		
10-Hendecenal	10-Hendecenoic	a	90 [b]	94	64	54 [c]
(+)-Citronellal	(+)-Citronellic	a	67	82	76	42
3-Hexen-1-al	3-Hexenoic	a	70 [d]	45 [e]	40	13
3-Hexene-1,6-dial	3-Hexenedioic (β-Hydromuconic)	82	65	e		
Benzaldehyde	Benzoic	a	81	76	78	48
3-Benzyloxy-4-methoxyphenylacetaldehyde	3-Benzyloxy-4-methoxyphenylacetic	81	77	94	ca. 95	ca. 56 [f]

[a] The diazo ketone obtained in the Arndt-Eistert reaction was converted without further purification to the acetoxy ketone.

[b] This is the over-all yield from the acid.

[c] Attempts to prepare this aldehyde by the Rosenmund reduction were unsuccessful.[36]

[d] This is the over-all yield from the acid chloride.

[e] In the reduction 3% sodium amalgam was used.

This preparation was described by Schöpf et al.[22]

THE REDUCTIVE DESULFURIZATION OF THIOL ESTERS

The ingenious method of reductive desulfurization with Raney nickel catalyst discovered by Bougault, Cattelain, and Chabrier,[37-42] led Wolfrom and Karabinos [43-45] to devise a method for reducing carbonyl groups by hydrogenolysis of the corresponding thioacetals.

[36] Mosettig and Mozingo, in Adams, *Org. Reactions*, **4**, 362–377, Wiley, New York, 1948.

[37] Bougault, Cattelain, and Chabrier, *Bull. soc. chim. France*, [5], **5**, 1699 (1938).

[38] Bougault, Cattelain, and Chabrier, *Bull. soc. chim. France*, [5], **6**, 34 (1939).

[39] Bougault, Cattelain, and Chabrier, *Compt. rend.*, **208**, 657 (1939).

[40] Bougault, Cattelain, and Chabrier, *Bull. soc. chim. France*, [5], **7**, 781 (1940).

[41] du Vigneaud, Melville, Folkers, Wolf, Mozingo, Keresztesy, and Harris, *J. Biol. Chem.*, **146**, 475 (1942).

[42] Mozingo, Wolf, Harris, and Folkers, *J. Am. Chem. Soc.*, **65**, 1013 (1943).

[43] Wolfrom and Karabinos, *J. Am. Chem. Soc.*, **66**, 909 (1944).

[44] Bernstein and Dorfman, *J. Am. Chem. Soc.*, **68**, 1152 (1946).

[45] Woodward and Brehm, *J. Am. Chem. Soc.*, **70**, 2107 (1948).

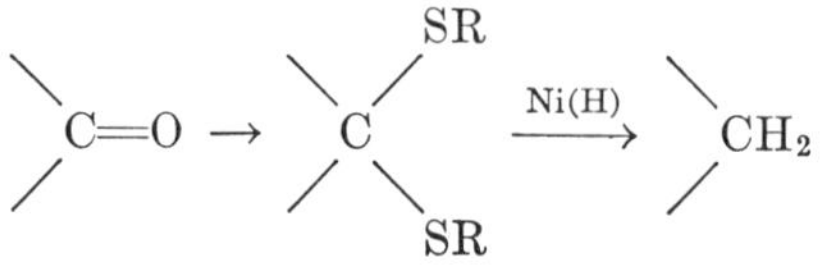

$$\begin{array}{c} \diagdown \\ \diagup \end{array} C=O \ \rightarrow \ \begin{array}{c} \diagdown \diagup \\ C \\ \diagup \diagdown \end{array} \overset{SR}{\underset{SR}{}} \ \overset{Ni(H)}{\longrightarrow} \ \begin{array}{c} \diagdown \\ \diagup \end{array} CH_2$$

By application of this mode of hydrogenolysis to thiol esters, the latter authors expected to arrive at a new general method for converting carboxylic acids, through the acid chlorides and thiol esters, to the corresponding aldehydes, according to the following scheme.

$$RCOCl \ \rightarrow \ RCOSR \ \overset{Ni(H)}{\longrightarrow} \ RCHO$$

The successful preparation of benzaldehyde, propionaldehyde, and aldehydo-D-ribose tetraacetate from the corresponding thiol esters realized this expectation.* [46, 47]

Contemporaneous and independent experiments by Prelog and co-workers,[48, 49] who were attempting to develop an aldehyde synthesis through hydrogenolysis of thiol esters, led exclusively to the formation of the corresponding alcohols. Subsequently this reaction was shown to be an efficient and convenient way to convert acids to the corresponding alcohols under very mild conditions.†[50-56]

The more recent investigations by Levin and co-workers corroborate these latter findings. The reductive desulfurization of thiol esters leads under the usual conditions, i.e., with a standard Raney nickel catalyst, to the corresponding alcohols. If, however, the Raney nickel catalyst is partially deactivated, e.g., by boiling with acetone, the aldehydes are obtained in satisfactory yields.[54-56] Thus, this new method is reminiscent of the Rosenmund reduction of acid chlorides.[36]

---

* It must be pointed out that Bougault and his co-workers observed the formation of acetaldehyde when an ethanolic solution of thioacetic acid was treated with the Raney nickel catalyst. This observation, however, becomes inconclusive when the dehydrogenating effect of the catalyst upon ethanol is considered. See refs. 43, 47, and 48.

† The advantages of this method of preparing alcohols are the following: olefinic double bonds are not attacked; acetoxy groups are not hydrolyzed; the pyridine nucleus is not reduced, ethyl thiolnicotinate furnishes pyridyl-3-carbinol,[48] and ethyl thiolisonicotinate furnishes pyridyl-4-carbinol[53] in excellent yields; and a single carboxyl group may be reduced in an ester acid chloride, e.g., $CH_3CO_2(CH_2)_{14}COCl \rightarrow CH_3CO_2(CH_2)_{14}CH_2OH$.[48]

[46] Wolfrom and Karabinos, J. Am. Chem. Soc., 68, 724 (1946).
[47] Wolfrom and Karabinos, J. Am. Chem. Soc., 68, 1455 (1946).
[48] Jeger, Norymberski, Szpilfogel, and Prelog, Helv. Chim. Acta, 29, 684 (1946).
[49] Prelog, Norymberski, and Jeger, Helv. Chim. Acta, 29, 360 (1946).
[50] Jeger, Nisoli, and Ruzicka, Helv. Chim. Acta, 29, 1183 (1946).
[51] Heer and Miescher, Helv. Chim. Acta, 30, 777 (1947).
[52] Sorkin, Krähenbühl, and Erlenmeyer, Helv. Chim. Acta, 31, 65 (1948).
[53] Prijs, Lutz, and Erlenmeyer, Helv. Chim. Acta, 31, 571 (1948).
[54] Spero, McIntosh, Jr., and Levin, J. Am. Chem. Soc., 70, 1907 (1948).
[55] McIntosh, Jr., Meinzer, and Levin, J. Am. Chem. Soc., 70, 2955 (1948).
[56] McIntosh, Jr., Searcy, Meinzer, and Levin, J. Am. Chem. Soc., 71, 3317 (1949).

Experimental Conditions and Reagents

The thiol esters are usually prepared by one of two methods: [47, 48, 57] (a) the acid chloride is allowed to react with the appropriate mercaptan, generally in a solvent such as benzene or ether, in the presence of pyridine or, less frequently, a tertiary aliphatic amine such as tributylamine or triisoamylamine; (b) the acid chloride as such or in ethereal solution is added to the lead alkylmercaptide covered with ether. With both methods the yields are generally high.

The course of the reductive desulfurization, whether leading to alcohols or to aldehydes, depends upon the quality of the Raney nickel catalyst. Standard Raney nickel catalyst,[42, 58] catalyst W-1,[59] and the more active catalyst W-4 [60] result in reduction to the alcohol, irrespective of whether 60% or 90% ethanol is employed as a solvent.[47, 54] A commercial active Raney nickel was equal in activity to the catalysts just mentioned, while a commercial pelleted Raney catalyst was found to be entirely inactive.[55, 56] The temperature of the reaction mixture may vary from room temperature to the boiling point of the mixture.

The partial deactivation of the catalyst is accomplished by refluxing it with acetone for one to two hours. The ratio of catalyst to thiol ester should be approximately 10:1; a ratio of 20:1 may bring about the formation of alcohol even with a deactivated catalyst.[55, 56]

Experimental Procedures

3β-Acetoxy-5-cholen-24-al.[55] A suspension of 40 g. of W-1 Raney nickel catalyst in 120 ml. of acetone is heated under reflux with stirring for one hour. A solution of 4 g. of ethyl 3β-acetoxy-5-thiolcholenate [57] in 80 ml. of acetone is added, followed by 80 ml. of water. The mixture is again heated as before for one hour. The Raney nickel is then separated by filtration and washed with hot acetone. The filtrate and washings are combined and evaporated under reduced pressure until a heavy white precipitate forms. The mixture is then diluted with an equal amount of water, and the precipitate is recovered by filtration and air-dried to give 3.3 g. of a powder melting at 115–133°. This crude aldehyde is dissolved in 110 ml. of ether and shaken with 90 ml. of 40% aqueous sodium bisulfite for fifteen minutes. Water is then added and the bisulfite addition compound is collected by centrifuging. The wet solid is suspended in 75 ml. of 10% sodium carbonate in a

[57] Levin, McIntosh, Jr., Spero, Rayman, and Meinzer, *J. Am. Chem. Soc.*, **70**, 511 (1948).
[58] Adkins, *Reactions of Hydrogen*, p. 20, University of Wisconsin Press, Madison, 1937.
[59] Adkins and Pavlic, *J. Am. Chem. Soc.*, **69**, 3039 (1947).
[60] Pavlic and Adkins, *J. Am. Chem. Soc.*, **68**, 1471 (1946).

separatory funnel, ether is added, and the mixture is agitated for two hours by a current of nitrogen. The ether layer is separated and evaporated, to give 2.2 g. (63%) of aldehyde melting at 139–147°. After recrystallization from aqueous acetic acid and from hexane, the aldehyde melts at 148–152°; $[\alpha]_D^{25}$ −52° (chloroform).

3α,12α-Diacetoxynorcholan-23-al.[56] A suspension of 30 g. of commercial active Raney nickel (washed, alkali free) in 90 ml. of acetone was stirred and heated under reflux for an hour, then 30 ml. of water was added, followed by a solution of 3.0 g. of ethyl 3α,12α-diacetoxynorthiolcholanate in 60 ml. of acetone. The reaction mixture was heated an hour, then was filtered hot. The Raney nickel was washed with hot acetone and the filtrate and washings concentrated under reduced pressure until a heavy precipitate formed. The precipitate (2.67 g.) was dissolved in a mixture of 45 ml. of ether and 40 ml. of methanol, then 100 ml. of 40% aqueous sodium bisulfite was added, and the mixture was shaken for ten minutes. On standing three layers separated (some water may be required). The aldehyde bisulfite compound was present in largest amount in the middle layer. The two lower layers combined were brought to pH 10 by addition of saturated aqueous sodium carbonate and extracted with ether to give 1.76 g. of crystalline aldehyde. The ether layer, extracted a second time with bisulfite, gave 0.36 g. of aldehyde. A residue of 0.61 g. remained after evaporation of the ether. The crude aldehyde was crystallized from aqueous acetic acid to give 1.82 g. (69%) of 3α,12α-diacetoxynorcholan-23-al, m.p. 115–121°. After crystallization from light petroleum (Skellysolve "B") the aldehyde melted at 128–131°; $[\alpha]_D^{25}$ +88° (chloroform).

Table III. Aldehydes Prepared by Reductive Desulfurization of Thiol Esters

In Table III are listed the aldehydes prepared by reductive desulfurization of the corresponding thiol esters. The literature has been surveyed through 1952.

THE METHOD OF McFADYEN AND STEVENS *

McFadyen and Stevens [62] found that aldehydes can be obtained by the alkaline decomposition of 1-acyl-2-arylsulfonylhydrazines.

$$RCONHNHSO_2Ar + OH^- \rightarrow RCHO + ArSO_2^- + N_2 + H_2O$$

* The author wishes to thank Dr. Edward Caflisch for his helpful comments on the section dealing with the McFadyen-Stevens method and for calling attention to examples of the reaction which had not been located in the original search of the literature.

[62] McFadyen and Stevens, *J. Chem. Soc.*, **1936**, 584.

TABLE III

Aldehydes Prepared from Thiol Esters by Reductive Desulfurization *

Aldehyde	Thiol Ester	Yield of Aldehyde %	Reference
Propionaldehyde	Ethyl thiolpropionate	73 [d]	47
aldehydo-D-Ribose tetraacetate	Ethyl thiol-D-ribonate tetraacetate	22	47
Benzaldehyde	Ethyl thiolbenzoate	62 [a, b]	47
3β-Acetoxy-bisnor-5-cholen-22-al	Ethyl 3β-acetoxy-5-bisnorthiolcholenate [c]	50–55 [d]	55
3α,12α-Diacetoxynorcholan-23-al	Ethyl 3α,12α-diacetoxynorthiolcholanate [c]	69	56
3β-Hydroxy-5-cholen-24-al	Ethyl 3β-hydroxy-5-thiolcholenate [c]	55 [e]	55
3β-Formoxy-5-cholen-24-al	Ethyl 3β-formoxy-5-thiolcholenate [c]	78	56
3β-Acetoxy-5-cholen-24-al	Ethyl 3β-acetoxy-5-thiolcholenate [c]	63 [f]	55
3α-Acetoxy-11-cholen-24-al	Ethyl 3α-acetoxy-11-thiolcholenate	49	56
3α-Formoxycholan-24-al	Ethyl 3α-formoxythiolcholanate [c]	62	56
3α-Acetoxycholan-24-al	Ethyl 3α-acetoxythiolcholanate	39	56
12α-Acetoxycholan-24-al	Ethyl 12α-acetoxythiolcholanate	60	56
3α,12α-Diformoxycholan-24-al	Ethyl 3α,12α-diformoxythiolcholanate [c]	60–80 [g]	54
Succindialdehyde	Diphenyl dithiolsuccinate	25 [h]	61

* The desulfurization of phenyl β-(2-piperidyl)thiolpropionate did not yield any of the expected β-(2-piperidyl)propionaldehyde. The only product isolated in the reaction was 3-ketoöctahydropyrrocoline.[61] (See also ref. 164.)

[a] The yield refers to the sodium bisulfite complex.

[b] Following the directions of Wolfrom and Karabinos,[47] Spero et al.[54] obtained only traces of benzaldehyde. Jeger et al.[48] observed the formation of benzyl alcohol only. The discrepancy in results may be accounted for by assuming that Wolfrom and Karabinos worked with a catalyst which had become sufficiently deactivated.

[c] For the preparation and properties of the thiol ester see ref. 57.

[d] The benzyl thiol ester gave slightly higher yields.

[e] The yield refers to the 2,4-dinitrophenylhydrazone.

[f] 3β-Acetoxy-5-cholen-24-al 2,4-dinitrophenylhydrazone was obtained in 68% yield from benzyl 3β-acetoxy-5-thiolcholenate, in 62% and 49% yield from the corresponding phenyl and isopropyl [57] thiol esters, respectively.

[g] The yield refers to the crude semicarbazone, apparently a mixture of mono- and di-formoxy compounds. The benzyl thiol ester was desulfurized with similar results.

[h] The yield refers to the bis-2,4-dinitrophenylhydrazone.

It is likely that the above reaction proceeds via a bimolecular elimination [63] and subsequent decomposition of the intermediate $RCON{=}NH$.

$$RCONHNHSO_2Ar + OH^- \rightarrow [RCON{=}NH] + ArSO_2^- + H_2O$$

A method closely related to that of McFadyen and Stevens has been applied to the preparation of a limited number of aldehydes by Kalb and Gross.[64-67] It consists in the alkaline oxidation of an acylhydrazine.

$$RCONHNH_2 \xrightarrow{-H_2} [RCON{=}NH] \rightarrow RCHO + N_2$$

The method has had only very limited study and deserves further investigation.

[61] King, Hofmann, and McMillan, J. Org. Chem., 16, 1100 (1951).

[63] Dhar, Hughes, Ingold, Mandour, Maw, and Woolf, J. Chem. Soc., 1948, 2093.

[64] Kalb and Gross, Ber., 59, 727 (1926).

[65] Weygand, Organic Preparations, p. 57, Interscience Publishers, New York, 1945.

[66] Niemann and Hays, J. Am. Chem. Soc., 65, 482 (1943).

[67] Wingfield, Harlan, and Hanmer, J. Am. Chem. Soc., 74, 5796 (1952)

Scope and Limitations

The method of McFadyen and Stevens is not applicable to the preparation of aliphatic aldehydes.[62] It has given good yields of a variety of substituted benzaldehydes containing hydroxyl, alkoxyl, and alkyl groups and halogen atoms as substituents. A number of heterocyclic aldehydes have also been prepared in fair yields.

The reaction has been applied successfully to the replacement by hydrogen of a reactive halogen in a benzene ring [62] and of the methoxyl group in two tropolone methyl ethers.[68] Thus 1,3,5-trinitrobenzene is readily prepared from picryl chloride, and 2-methoxy-6-methylcyclo-

$$C_6H_2(NO_2)_3Cl \rightarrow C_6H_2(NO_2)_3NHNHSO_2C_6H_5 \rightarrow C_6H_3(NO_2)_3$$

heptatrienone (I, R = OCH_3) and 2-methoxy-4-methylcycloheptatrienone (II, R = OCH_3) may be converted via the hydrazino compounds (I and II, R = $NHNH_2$) and their benzenesulfonyl derivatives to 3- and 4-methylcycloheptatrienone (I and II, R = H).

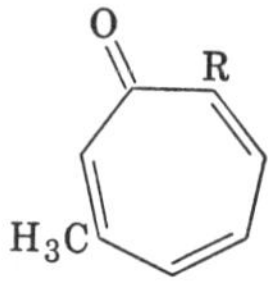

I 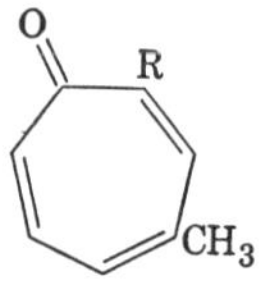   II

In both the Kalb-Gross and the McFadyen-Stevens methods there appear to be two reaction paths, one leading as shown above to an aldehyde, the other to a 1,2-diacylhydrazine.[66]

$$2RCONHNH_2 + 4OH^- - 4e \rightarrow RCONHNHCOR + N_2 + 4H_2O$$

$$2RCONHNHSO_2Ar + 2OH^- \rightarrow$$

$$RCONHNHCOR + 2ArSO_2^- + N_2 + H_2O$$

The substituent R in the acyl group appears to determine the course of the principal reaction. When R is an aromatic or heterocyclic group, an aldehyde results; when R is aliphatic or aromatic with an electronegative substituent in the ortho or para position no aldehyde is formed.

Experimental Conditions and Reagents

The hydrazides are generally prepared from the corresponding esters by reaction with hydrazine hydrate. It is not necessary to use highly purified hydrazides for the next step in the procedure.

[68] Akroyd, Haworth, and Hobson, *J. Chem. Soc.*, **1951**, 3427.

The symmetrical 1-acyl-2-arylsulfonylhydrazines are prepared by adding the arylsulfonyl chloride (benzene-, p-toluene-, or 2,5-dichloro-benzene-sulfonyl chloride) in small portions to the cooled solution of the appropriate acid hydrazide in dry pyridine. The mixture is allowed to stand at room temperature and is then poured into a slight excess of ice-cold dilute hydrochloric acid. The precipitate is collected, washed with dilute hydrochloric acid and water, and recrystallized from an appropriate solvent.

For conversion into the aldehyde, the 1-acyl-2-arylsulfonylhydrazine is heated in ethylene glycol (which has a high boiling point and is a solvent for alkali carbonates) at about 150–160°, and 4–6 equivalents of anhydrous sodium or potassium carbonate is added in one portion, causing rapid decomposition. The aldehyde is isolated from the reaction mixture by extraction with a suitable solvent. If the aldehyde is volatile with steam and insoluble in alkali, and if the decomposition of the 1-acyl-2-arylsulfonylhydrazine takes place readily, it is convenient to add the hydrazine to aqueous sodium carbonate solution and steam-distil.

Experimental Procedures

Benzaldehyde.[62] To a cooled and stirred solution of 4 g. of benzhydrazide in 25 ml. of pyridine is slowly added 3.8 ml. (5.2 g.) of benzene-sulfonyl chloride. After two hours the solution is poured into a mixture of ice and hydrochloric acid; the pale yellow precipitate is recovered, washed with dilute hydrochloric acid and water, and crystallized from 80 ml. of ethanol to give 7 g. (86%) of 1-benzoyl-2-benzenesulfonyl-hydrazine as colorless prismatic needles, m.p. 192–194° (dec.). The 1-benzoyl-2-benzenesulfonylhydrazine is dissolved in 5–20 parts of ethylene glycol and heated to 160°. Five equivalents of anhydrous sodium carbonate is added in one portion, causing brisk effervescence. After seventy-five seconds, the reaction is stopped by the addition of hot water. The washed and dried ethereal extract of the resulting solution is evaporated. The yield of redistilled benzaldehyde is about 70%.

The quantity of solvent (5–20 parts) has little effect on the yield. Sodium carbonate gives slightly better results than potassium carbonate. Lower or higher temperatures, prolonged heating, and lesser amounts of alkali give poorer results. 1-Benzoyl-2-(2,5-dichlorophenyl)-sulfonylhydrazine decomposes at a lower temperature (110°), giving a yield of about 70%. This decomposition can also be effected by steam distillation from aqueous sodium carbonate.

p-(p′-Methoxyphenoxy)benzaldehyde.[69] A solution of 25.8 g. of crude p-(p-methoxyphenoxy)benzhydrazide in 200 ml. of dry pyridine

[69] Harington and Rivers, *J. Chem. Soc.*, **1940**, 1101.

is cooled in an ice bath and treated with 20 g. of p-toluenesulfonyl chloride in small portions. The mixture is kept at room temperature for two hours and then poured into a slight excess of ice-cold 5 N hydrochloric acid; the yield of 1-acyl-2-arylsulfonylhydrazine is 34 g. (88%). After two crystallizations from acetic acid the compound melts at 172–173°. Thirty-three and eight-tenths grams of 1-p-(p'-methoxyphenoxy)benzoyl-2-(p-tolylsulfonyl)hydrazine and 150 ml. of ethylene glycol are heated in a metal bath to 160°. To the hot solution is added 17.5 g. of anhydrous sodium carbonate. Vigorous effervescence sets in and lasts for about thirty seconds. Heating is continued for an additional thirty seconds, and the solution is then rapidly cooled to about 100° and diluted with 1.2 l. of hot water. The mixture is extracted with ether, and the extract is dried over sodium sulfate and evaporated. The crystalline residue is practically pure aldehyde (15.7 g., 80%). After crystallization from petroleum ether (b.p. 60–80°), the aldehyde melts at 60.5°.

4-Amino-2-methylpyrimidine-5-carboxaldehyde.[70] To a suspension of 4 g. of the hydrazide of 4-amino-2-methylpyrimidine-5-carboxylic acid in 80 ml. of dry pyridine, 4.32 g. of benzenesulfonyl chloride is added dropwise and with stirring during fifteen minutes, the temperature being maintained at 17–18°. Simultaneously with the disappearance of the hydrazide, finely divided pyridine hydrochloride separates. The stirring is continued for three and one-half hours while the reaction mixture is allowed to come to room temperature. Evaporation of the solvent under reduced pressure leaves a semisolid mass which becomes crystalline on treatment with water; yield, 5.3 g. (73%). The product can be crystallized from 95% ethanol to give slender, white needles, m.p. 228.5–229° (dec.). Five and three-tenths grams of the preceding hydrazine derivative is suspended in 60 ml. of ethylene glycol, the mixture is heated at 160° in a bath maintained at 157–160°, and 4.8 g. of sodium carbonate is then added to the solution. When the brisk evolution of gas ceases, at the end of about three to five minutes, water is added. The solution is cooled and extracted with 200 ml. of chloroform in six portions. After the solution is dried and the chloroform removed, the residual yellow solid is taken up in the minimal amount of 95% ethanol from which it crystallizes. The yield is 1.05 g. (44%). After a second crystallization, using animal charcoal, the aldehyde separates in the form of fine, white needles, m.p. 195–196°.

1-(4-Hydroxy-2-methyl-5-pyrimidylacetyl)-2-(benzenesulfonyl)hydrazine, prepared and decomposed like the 1-(4-amino-2-methyl-5-pyrimidylcarbonyl)-2-(benzenesulfonyl)hydrazine, gave reaction products from which no trace of aldehyde could be isolated.[70]

[70] Price, May, and Pickel, *J. Am. Chem. Soc.*, **62**, 2818 (1940).

TABLE IV

ALDEHYDES PREPARED BY THE DECOMPOSITION OF 1-ACYL-2-ARYLSULFONYLHYDRAZINES *

Aldehyde	Hydrazine [a]	Yield of Aldehyde, %	Reference
Cyclopropanecarboxaldehyde	1-(Cyclopropanecarbonyl)-2-phenylsulfonyl	16 [b]	70a
Benzaldehyde	1-Benzoyl-2-phenylsulfonyl	ca. 70	62
m-Methylbenzaldehyde	1-(m-Methylbenzoyl)-2-p-tolylsulfonyl	73 (crude)	70b
o-Hydroxybenzaldehyde	1-(o-Hydroxybenzoyl)-2-phenylsulfonyl	55 [c]	62
p-Methoxybenzaldehyde	1-(p-Methoxybenzoyl)-2-phenylsulfonyl	77	62
3,5-Dimethoxybenzaldehyde	1-(3,5-Dimethoxybenzoyl)-2-phenylsulfonyl [d]	68	71, 71a
3,4-Methylenedioxybenzaldehyde	1-(3,4-Methylenedioxybenzoyl)-2-phenylsulfonyl	87	62
2-Methoxy-3-methylbenzaldehyde	1-(2-Methoxy-3-methylbenzoyl)-2-phenylsulfonyl	66	72
2-Ethyl-3-methoxybenzaldehyde	1-(2-Ethyl-3-methoxybenzoyl)-2-phenylsulfonyl	86	72a
3,4,5-Trimethoxybenzaldehyde	1-(3,4,5-Trimethoxybenzoyl)-2-phenylsulfonyl	84	10, 72b
3,4,5-Tribenzyloxybenzaldehyde	1-(3,4,5-Tribenzyloxybenzoyl)-2-phenylsulfonyl	94	73
p-Chlorobenzaldehyde	1-(p-Chlorobenzoyl)-2-(2,5-dichlorophenylsulfonyl)	77	62
o-Fluorobenzaldehyde	1-(o-Fluorobenzoyl)-2-phenylsulfonyl	50	73a
m-Fluorobenzaldehyde	1-(m-Fluorobenzoyl)-2-phenylsulfonyl	50	73a
p-Fluorobenzaldehyde	1-(p-Fluorobenzoyl)-2-phenylsulfonyl	42	73a
4-Bromo-2-methylbenzaldehyde	1-(4-Bromo-2-methylbenzoyl)-2-phenylsulfonyl	61	74
3-Fluoro-4-methoxybenzaldehyde	1-(3-Fluoro-4-methoxybenzoyl)-2-phenylsulfonyl	67 (crude)	75
3,5-Difluoro-4-methoxybenzaldehyde	1-(3,5-Difluoro-4-methoxybenzoyl)-2-phenylsulfonyl	62 (crude)	75
m-Nitrobenzaldehyde	1-(m-Nitrobenzoyl)-2-phenylsulfonyl	42	62
2-Biphenylcarboxaldehyde	1-(2-Biphenylcarbonyl)-2-phenylsulfonyl	55 [e]	75a
2'-Carboxy-2-biphenylcarboxaldehyde (diphenaldehydic acid)	1-(2'-Carboxy-2-biphenylcarbonyl)-2-phenylsulfonyl	40	75a
3',4,5,6-Tetramethoxy-2-biphenylcarboxaldehyde	1-(3',4,5,6-Tetramethoxy-2-biphenylcarbonyl)-2-phenyl-sulfonyl		75a
4',4,5,6-Tetramethoxy-2-biphenylcarboxaldehyde	1-(4',4,5,6-Tetramethoxy-2-biphenylcarbonyl)-2-phenyl-sulfonyl	67-78	75b

TABLE IV—*Continued*

ALDEHYDES PREPARED BY THE DECOMPOSITION OF 1-ACYL-2-ARYLSULFONYLHYDRAZINES *

Aldehyde	Hydrazine [a]	Yield of Aldehyde, %	Reference
p-Benzylthiobenzaldehyde	1-(p-Benzylthiobenzoyl)-2-p-tolylsulfonyl	80 (crude)	75c
p-(o′-Methoxyphenoxy)benzaldehyde	1-[p-(o′-Methoxyphenoxy)benzoyl]-2-p-tolylsulfonyl	79 (crude)	76
p-(p′-Methoxyphenoxy)benzaldehyde	1-[p-(p′-Methoxyphenoxy)benzoyl]-2-p-tolylsulfonyl	80	69
3,5-Diiodo-4-(4′-methoxyphenoxy)benzaldehyde	1-[3,5-Diiodo-4-(4′-methoxyphenoxy)benzoyl]-2-p-tolylsulfonyl	35 [b]	76a
N-Phenyl-o-aminobenzaldehyde	1-(N-Phenyl-o-aminobenzoyl)-2-p-tolylsulfonyl	80	76b
o-Styrylbenzaldehyde	1-(o-Styrylbenzoyl)-2-p-tolylsulfonyl [d]	79	77
3,4-Dimethoxy-9-phenanthraldehyde	1-(3,4-Dimethoxy-9-phenanthroyl)-2-phenylsulfonyl	79	78
2,3,4,5-Tetramethoxy-9-phenanthraldehyde	1-(2,3,4,5-Tetramethoxy-9-phenanthroyl)-2-phenylsulfonyl		10
2,3,4,6-Tetramethoxy-9-phenanthraldehyde	1-(2,3,4,6-Tetramethoxy-9-phenanthroyl)-2-phenylsulfonyl		10
2,3,4,7-Tetramethoxy-9-phenanthraldehyde	1-(2,3,4,7-Tetramethoxy-9-phenanthroyl)-2-phenylsulfonyl		10
2,3,4,7-Tetramethoxy-10-phenanthraldehyde	1-(2,3,4,7-Tetramethoxy-10-phenanthroyl)-2-phenylsulfonyl		78a
3-Thianaphthenecarboxaldehyde	1-(3-Thianaphthenecarbonyl)-2-p-tolylsulfonyl	63	75c
Picolinaldehyde	1-(2-Pyridylcarbonyl)-2-phenylsulfonyl [d, f]	20, 46 [g]	79, 80
Nicotinaldehyde	1-(3-Pyridylcarbonyl)-2-phenylsulfonyl [d]	22, 36, 36	79, 81, 82
Isonicotinaldehyde	1-(4-Pyridylcarbonyl)-2-phenylsulfonyl [f]	31 [g, h]	79, 80
2-Methylpyridine-3-carboxaldehyde	1-(2-Methyl-3-pyridylcarbonyl)-2-phenylsulfonyl [d]	31	83
4,6-Dimethyl-2-pyridone-3-carboxaldehyde	1-(4,6-Dimethyl-2-pyridone-3-carbonyl)-2-phenylsulfonyl	56	83a
o-3-Pyridylbenzaldehyde	1-(o-3-Pyridylbenzoyl)-2-p-tolylsulfonyl	67	83b
3-Quinolinecarboxaldehyde	1-(3-Quinolylcarbonyl)-2-p-tolylsulfonyl	33	84
5-Quinolinecarboxaldehyde	1-(5-Quinolylcarbonyl)-2-p-tolylsulfonyl	13	84
6-Quinolinecarboxaldehyde	1-(6-Quinolylcarbonyl)-2-p-tolylsulfonyl	45	84
8-Quinolinecarboxaldehyde	1-(8-Quinolylcarbonyl)-2-p-tolylsulfonyl	25	84

Aldehyde	Hydrazide	Yield (%)	Ref.
7,8-Dimethoxy-2-methylquinoline-3-carboxaldehyde	1-(7,8-Dimethoxy-2-methyl-3-quinolylcarbonyl)-2-phenylsulfonyl		84a
6,7-Dimethoxy-1-methylisoquinoline-3-carboxaldehyde	1-(6,7-Dimethoxy-1-methyl-3-isoquinolylcarbonyl)-2-phenylsulfonyl	70 [i]	84b
6,7-Methylenedioxy-1-methylisoquinoline-3-carboxaldehyde	1-(6,7-Methylenedioxy-1-methyl-3-isoquinolylcarbonyl)-2-phenylsulfonyl	35 [i]	84b
4-Amino-2-methylpyrimidine-5-carboxaldehyde	1-(4-Amino-2-methyl-5-pyrimidylcarbonyl)-2-phenylsulfonyl	44	70
2,3-Dimethyl-1-phenyl-5-pyrazolone-4-carboxaldehyde	1-(2,3-Dimethyl-1-phenyl-5-pyrazolone-4-carbonyl)-2-phenylsulfonyl	50	84c
1-Methylimidazole-5-carboxaldehyde	1-(1-Methyl-5-imidazolylcarbonyl)-2-phenylsulfonyl	60–66	85
1-Isopropylimidazole-5-carboxaldehyde	1-(1-Isopropyl-5-imidazolylcarbonyl)-2-phenylsulfonyl	58	85
1-Phenylimidazole-5-carboxaldehyde	1-(1-Phenyl-5-imidazolylcarbonyl)-2-phenylsulfonyl	51	85
1-Cyclohexylimidazole-5-carboxaldehyde	1-(1-Cyclohexyl-5-imidazolylcarbonyl)-2-phenylsulfonyl	61	85
4-Methylimidazole-5-carboxaldehyde	1-(4-Methyl-5-imidazolylcarbonyl)-2-phenylsulfonyl [j]	20	86
4-Thiazolecarboxaldehyde	1-(4-Thiazolylcarbonyl)-2-phenylsulfonyl	25	87
5-Thiazolecarboxaldehyde	1-(5-Thiazolylcarbonyl)-2-phenylsulfonyl	30	87
4-Methylthiazole-5-carboxaldehyde	1-(4-Methyl-5-thiazolylcarbonyl)-2-phenylsulfonyl	40 (crude)	88

* The following aldehydes could not be prepared by this method: acetaldehyde, isobutyraldehyde, cinnamaldehyde,[62] o- and p-nitrobenzaldehyde,[62, 66] diphenylacetaldehyde,[62] 4-nitro-2-(N-phenylamino)benzaldehyde,[76b] 4-hydroxy-2-methylpyrimidine-5-carboxaldehyde,[83a] 4-hydroxy-2-methyl-5-pyrimidylacetaldehyde,[70] pyrazinealdehyde,[88a] 4(5)-imidazolecarboxaldehyde,[85] and 4-methyl-5-thiazolylacetaldehyde.[70]

a Ethylene glycol was used as solvent for the thermal decomposition of the hydrazines unless stated otherwise.
b The yield refers to the 2,4-dinitrophenylhydrazone.
c The salicylaldehyde was steam-distilled from the acidified reaction mixture.
d Glycerol was used in place of ethylene glycol.
e The yield is based on acid.
f The hydrazine was decomposed in ethylene glycol in the presence of thiosemicarbazide.
g The yield refers to the thiosemicarbazone.
h The aldehyde is unstable under the conditions of the decomposition of the hydrazine.
i The yield refers to the semicarbazone.
j The decomposition was effected with dried borax. By using alkali carbonate the yield was decreased.

REFERENCES TO TABLE IV

[70a] Roberts, *J. Am. Chem. Soc.*, **73**, 2959 (1951).

[70b] Hey and Kohn, *J. Chem. Soc.*, **1949**, 3177.

[71] Adams, MacKenzie, Jr., and Loewe, *J. Am. Chem. Soc.*, **70**, 664 (1948).

[71a] Adams, U. S. pat. 2,509,387 [*C. A.*, **44**, 9485 (1950)].

[72] Hill and Short, *J. Chem. Soc.*, **1937**, 260.

[72a] Richtzenhain and Meyer-Delius, *Ber.*, **81**, 81 (1948).

[72b] Dornow and Petsch, *Arch. Pharm.*, **284**, 160 (1951).

[73] Clinton and Geissman, *J. Am. Chem. Soc.*, **65**, 85 (1943).

[73a] Bennett and Niemann, *J. Am. Chem. Soc.*, **72**, 1800 (1950).

[74] Harris, *J. Chem. Soc.*, **1947**, 690.

[75] Niemann, Benson, and Mead, *J. Am. Chem. Soc.*, **63**, 2204 (1941).

[75a] Cook, Dickson, Jack, Loudon, McKeown, MacMillan, and Williamson, *J. Chem. Soc.*, **1950**, 139.

[75b] Barton, Cook, Loudon, and MacMillan, *J. Chem. Soc.*, **1949**, 1079.

[75c] Elliott and Harington, *J. Chem. Soc.*, **1949**, 1374.

[76] Ungnade, *J. Am. Chem. Soc.*, **63**, 2091 (1941).

[76a] Borrows, Clayton, and Hems, *J. Chem. Soc.*, **1949**, S 185.

[76b] Albert, *J. Chem. Soc.*, **1948**, 1225.

[77] Natelson and Gottfried, *J. Am. Chem. Soc.*, **63**, 487 (1941).

[78] Holmes, Lee, and Mooradian, *J. Am. Chem. Soc.*, **69**, 1998 (1947).

[78a] Cook, Jack, Loudon, Buchanan, and MacMillan, *J. Chem. Soc.*, **1951**, 1397.

[79] Niemann, Lewis, and Hays, *J. Am. Chem. Soc.*, **64**, 1678 (1942).

[80] Fox, *J. Org. Chem.*, **17**, 555 (1952).

[81] Panizzon, *Helv. Chim. Acta*, **24**, 24E (1941).

[82] Dornow and Schacht, *Ber.*, **80**, 505 (1947).

[83] Dornow and Bormann, *Ber.*, **82**, 216 (1949).

[83a] Geissman, Schlatter, Webb, and Roberts, *J. Org. Chem.*, **11**, 741 (1946).

[83b] Hey and Williams, *J. Chem. Soc.*, **1951**, 1527.

[84] Cook, Heilbron, and Steger, *J. Chem. Soc.*, **1943**, 413.

[84a] Ried, Berg, and Schmidt, *Ber.*, **85**, 204 (1952).

[84b] Ohara, *J. Pharm. Soc. Japan*, **72**, 145 (1952) [*C. A.*, **46**, 11207 (1952)].

[84c] Winternitz, Ledrut, and Combes, *Bull. soc. chim. France*, **1952**, 398.

[85] Jones and McLaughlin, *J. Am. Chem. Soc.*, **71**, 2444 (1949).

[86] Tamamushi, *J. Pharm. Soc. Japan*, **60**, 184 (Transactions, 92) (1940) [*C. A.*, **34**, 5447 (1940)].

[87] Erne, Ramirez, and Burger, *Helv. Chim. Acta*, **34**, 143 (1951).

[88] Buchman and Richardson, *J. Am. Chem. Soc.*, **61**, 891 (1939).

[88a] Fand and Spoerri, *J. Am. Chem. Soc.*, **74**, 1345 (1952).

Table IV. Aldehydes Prepared from 1-Acyl-2-arylsulfonylhydrazines

In Table IV, above, are listed the aldehydes prepared by the decomposition of 1-acyl-2-arylsulfonylhydrazines. The literature has been reviewed through 1952.

THE METHOD OF SONN AND MÜLLER

The preparation of aldehydes by the method of Sonn and Müller [89] involves three steps. An acid anilide or toluide is converted to an imido

[89] Sonn and Müller, *Ber.*, **52**, 1927 (1919).

chloride by reaction with phosphorus pentachloride, the imido chloride is reduced with stannous chloride, and the anil (Schiff's base) so formed is hydrolyzed to the aldehyde and aniline. The reactions may be represented by the following equations.

$$ArCONHC_6H_5 + PCl_5 \rightarrow ArCCl{=}NC_6H_5 + HCl + POCl_3$$

$$ArCCl{=}NC_6H_5 + SnCl_2 + 2HCl \rightarrow ArCH{=}NC_6H_5 \cdot HCl + SnCl_4$$

$$ArCH{=}NC_6H_5 + H_2O \rightarrow ArCHO + C_6H_5NH_2$$

The method is not applicable to simple aliphatic anilides, for the imido chlorides obtained from them are unstable and undergo spontaneous decomposition, the first step of which is the formation of the corresponding enamine.[90, 91]

$$-CH{-}C(Cl){=}NC_6H_5 \rightarrow -C{=}CClNHC_6H_5$$

Imido chlorides from α,β-unsaturated anilides are more stable; cinnamaldehyde has been prepared in 92% yield from cinnamanilide,[89] and the α,β-unsaturated aldehydes have been prepared in 50% yield from 2-hexenoic o-toluide and 2-nonenoic anilide using chromous chloride as the reducing agent.[25] Stannous chloride is ineffective in the reduction of the imido chlorides of purely aliphatic α,β-unsaturated anilides like the two just mentioned. Although chromous chloride promises to be a valuable reagent for this purpose, the directions for its preparation and use are not clear in certain respects,* and it has had only limited

---

* According to von Braun and Rudolph,[25] the success of the method depends upon the quality of the reducing agent, chromous chloride, which must be prepared freshly from chromous acetate. While these authors are indefinite about the composition of the latter salt, whether water free or hydrated, Kuhn and Morris [92, 93] describe the salt as a dihydrate without substantiating this statement with analytical values. It appears now quite certain that the chromous acetate described more than one hundred years ago by Peligot,[94-97] and more recently by Balthis and Bailar,[98] is the monohydrate. From this the anhydrous compound may be obtained by heating for six hours at 100° in vacuum over phosphorus pentoxide.[99]

[90] von Braun, Jostes, and Heymons, Ber., **60**, 92 (1927).

[91] von Braun, Jostes, and Münch, Ann., **453**, 113 (1927).

[92] Kuhn and Morris, Ber., **70**, 853 (1937).

[93] Weygand, Organic Preparations, pp. 45–46, Interscience Publishers, New York, 1945.

[94] Peligot, Ann. chim. phys., [3], **12**, 541 (1844).

[95] Moissan, Ann. chim. phys., [5], **25**, 416 (1882).

[96] von der Pfordten, Ann., **228**, 112 (1885).

[97] Vanino, Handbuch der präparativen Chemie, I, 3rd ed., p. 710, Edwards Brothers, Ann Arbor, Michigan, 1943.

[98] Balthis and Bailar, Inorg. Syntheses, **1**, 122 (1939).

[99] King and Garner, J. Chem. Phys., **18**, 689 (1950).

use.[92, 26] An attempt to reduce the imido chloride from 2-tridecenoic
o-toluide with chromous chloride failed completely.[100]

The Sonn and Müller method appears to be applicable to the preparation of aromatic aldehydes which do not contain substituents affected by phosphorus pentachloride or stannous chloride. o-Tolualdehyde has been prepared in about 80% yield,[101] and 3,5-dimethoxy- [102] and 3,4,5-trimethoxy-benzaldehyde [103–105] have been prepared in 85% and 70% yields, respectively. The 1-, 2-, 3-, and 9-phenanthraldehydes have been prepared in yields of 75–85%.[106–109]

Attempts to extend the Sonn and Müller procedure to the preparation of heterocyclic aldehydes have been only partially successful.[110] Cinchoninic anilide and 6-chlorocinchoninic anilide furnish the secondary amines resulting from reduction of the CO group in the amide to CH_2. The ethyl amide of nicotinic acid yields a mixture of the secondary amine and the desired aldehyde.

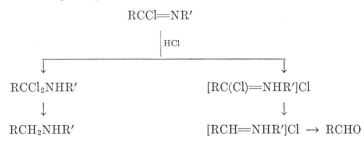

As an explanation of the difference in behavior of the heterocyclic and aromatic anilides it has been assumed that the reduction proceeds through the hydrogen chloride addition product of the imido chloride; depending upon whether this addition product is a covalent or an electrovalent compound, an amine or an anil will be formed.

$$RCCl{=}NR'$$

$$\downarrow HCl$$

RCCl$_2$NHR'   [RC(Cl)=NHR']Cl

$$\downarrow \qquad\qquad\qquad\qquad\qquad \downarrow$$

RCH$_2$NHR'   [RCH=NHR']Cl $\rightarrow$ RCHO

[100] Stoll, Helv. Chim. Acta, 30, 991 (1947).

[101] King, L'Ecuyer, and Openshaw, J. Chem. Soc., 1936, 352.

[102] Asahina and Matsuzaki, J. Pharm. Soc. Japan, No. 509, 527 (1924) [C. A., 19, 51 (1925)].

[103] Cook, Graham, Cohen, Lapsley, and Lawrence, J. Chem. Soc., 1944, 322.

[104] Sonn and Meyer, Ber., 58, 1096 (1925).

[105] Hey, Quart. J. Pharm. Pharmacol., 20, 129 (1947).

[106] Bachmann and Boatner, J. Am. Chem. Soc., 58, 2097 (1936).

[107] Bachmann, J. Am. Chem. Soc., 57, 555 (1935).

[108] Bachmann and Kloetzel, J. Am. Chem. Soc., 59, 2207 (1937).

[109] Shoppee, J. Chem. Soc., 1933, 37.

[110] Work, J. Chem. Soc., 1942, 429.

Since the Sonn and Müller method depends on the reduction of an imido chloride it should be applicable to imido chlorides obtained from other sources than anilides.   Imido chlorides can be isolated from the Beckmann rearrangement of ketoximes prior to the hydrolysis of the reaction products with water.   It is therefore not surprising that there are a few examples on record of the preparation of an aldehyde from a ketoxime by a Beckmann rearrangement with phosphorus pentachloride followed by reduction with stannous chloride.   In this way 1,2,3,4-tetra-hydro-9-phenanthraldehyde has been prepared in 68% yield from 9-benzoyl-1,2,3,4-tetrahydrophenanthrene oxime, and benzaldehyde and p-chlorobenzaldehyde have been prepared in 85% and 81% yields, respectively, from benzophenone oxime and from *anti* phenyl p-chloro-phenyl ketoxime.[111]

Experimental Conditions and Procedures

The anilide is converted to the imido chloride by treatment with an equimolar quantity of phosphorus pentachloride * in the presence of a dry hydrocarbon or halide solvent, such as benzene, toluene, or tetra-chloroethane.   The crude imido chloride, obtained by distillation of the solvent and phosphorus oxychloride under diminished pressure, either alone or in a dry, inert solvent (ether, tetrachloroethane, ethylene dibromide) is added to an excess (3–4 moles) of stannous chloride previously treated with ether and hydrogen chloride.   The mixture is allowed to stand until no further precipitation of the tin complex salt of the anil (apparently $RCH = NC_6H_5 \cdot HCl \cdot SnCl_2$ [89]) occurs.   The reduction is usually complete in two to twelve hours.   The tin salt or the whole reaction mixture is heated with dilute hydrochloric acid, and the aldehyde is isolated by extraction, steam distillation, or as the sodium bisulfite addition product.

Cinnamaldehyde.[89]   To a suspension of 14 g. of powdered cinnam-anilide in 210 ml. of dry toluene is added 14 g. of finely divided phosphorus pentachloride.   The mixture is thoroughly shaken and is then warmed on the steam bath.   Hydrogen chloride is evolved, and a clear red solution is formed.   The flask is placed in a water bath at 50–60°, and the solvent and phosphorus oxychloride are removed by distillation under diminished pressure.   On cooling, the residue hardens to a clear, red mass which cannot be crystallized.

---

* For the preparation of aromatic imido chlorides, thionyl chloride has also been employed.[112]

[111] Coleman and Pyle, *J. Am. Chem. Soc.*, **68**, 2007 (1946).

[112] von Braun and Pinkernelle, *Ber.*, **67**, 1218 (1934).

The crude imido chloride is dissolved in 100 ml. of dry ether, and the solution is added to the freshly prepared reducing mixture obtained from 35 g. of dry stannous chloride, 175 ml. of anhydrous ether, and dry hydrogen chloride. The mixture is shaken, and soon fine, light-brown crystals begin to separate. After several hours, the precipitation is complete. The reaction mixture is then subjected to steam distillation. After two to three hours, a sample of the distillate is found to be clear. The cinnamaldehyde is then collected by extraction of the distillate with ether. After removal of the ether, the residual oil is shaken with twice its volume of saturated aqueous sodium bisulfite. The mixture is allowed to stand for two hours. The crystalline addition product is collected on a filter and washed with ethanol and ether. It is decomposed by gentle warming with dilute sulfuric acid. The regenerated aldehyde is extracted with ether, and the ethereal solution is dried over sodium sulfate. After removal of the ether, 8.9 g. (92%) of cinnamaldehyde is distilled at 120–121°/12 mm.

3-Phenanthraldehyde.[107, 108] A mixture of 30 g. of 3-phenanthroic anilide, 21 g. of phosphorus pentachloride, and 20 ml. of benzene is heated on the steam bath for one-half hour. After removal of the benzene and phosphorus oxychloride by distillation under diminished pressure (oil bath at 140°), the product is dissolved in 40 ml. of ethylene dibromide and the solution is added to an ice-cold solution of 78 g. of anhydrous stannous chloride in 300 ml. of ether saturated with hydrogen chloride. After twelve hours at 0°, cold water is added cautiously to the mixture and the ether is removed by distillation and the ethylene bromide by steam distillation. The residue is then heated with dilute hydrochloric acid to complete the hydrolysis to the aldehyde. The aqueous solution is discarded, and the organic material is digested with 150–200 ml. of carbon tetrachloride in order to dissolve the aldehyde. After removal of the carbon tetrachloride from the filtered solution, the residue is dissolved in a mixture of ether and chloroform and the solution is shaken for thirty-six hours with a saturated aqueous solution of sodium bisulfite. The crystalline addition product is separated, and the organic liquid is shaken four days with a fresh solution of sodium bisulfite. The combined fractions of the addition product are decomposed with dilute hydrochloric acid, and the aldehyde is purified by distillation under reduced pressure, b.p. 198°/2 mm., and by recrystallization from benzene-ligroin, yielding 17.8 g. (85%) of pure 3-phenanthraldehyde, m.p. 79.5–80°.

2-Phenanthraldehyde (m.p. 59–59.5°) may be prepared in yields of 80–85% by the same procedure, except that 300 ml. of ethylene dibromide is necessary to dissolve the crude imido chloride.

TABLE V

ALDEHYDES PREPARED BY THE METHOD OF SONN AND MÜLLER *

Aldehyde	Anilide or Toluidide	Solvents A	Solvents B	Yield of Aldehyde, %	Reference
α-(β-Phenoxyethyl)valeraldehyde	α-(β-Phenoxyethyl)valeranilide a	Benzene	Ether	ca. 65 b (crude)	113
2-Hexenal	2-Hexenoic o-toluide c	Benzene	Ether	50	25
2-Nonenal	2-Nonenoic anilide c, d	Benzene	Ether	50	25
3,7-Dimethyl-2-octenal	3,7-Dimethyl-2-octenoic anilide c	Benzene	Ether	e	25
3-Methyl-4-cyclopentenyl-2-butenal	3-Methyl-4-cyclopentenyl-2-butenoic anilide c	Benzene	Ether	30 e	25
5,9-Dimethyl-2,4,8-decatrienal	5,9-Dimethyl-2,4,8-decatrienoic anilide c	Benzene	Ether	30 e	25, 26
β-Ionylideneacetaldehyde	β-Ionylideneacet-o-toluide c	Benzene	Ether	30?	92, 114, 115, 116
6-Methyl-1-cyclohexenal	6-Methyl-1-cyclohexenoic anilide	Toluene	Ether	60	117
α-Cyclocitrylideneacetaldehyde	α-Cyclocitrylideneacetanilide c	Benzene	Ether		27
β-Cyclocitrylideneacetaldehyde	β-Cyclocitrylideneacetanilide c	Benzene	Ether		27
Atropaldehyde	Atropic anilide c	Benzene	Ether	25–30 f	25
Cinnamaldehyde	Cinnamanilide	Toluene	Ether	92	89
4-Hydroxy-3-methoxycinnamaldehyde	4-Acetoxy-3-methoxycinnamanilide	Toluene	Chloroform	Nearly quantitative g	118
Benzaldehyde	Benzanilide	Toluene	Ether		89
o-Tolualdehyde	o-Toluic anilide	Toluene	Ether	ca. 80	101
p-Hydroxybenzaldehyde	p-(Carbethoxyoxy)benzanilide	Toluene	Ether		89
3,5-Dimethoxybenzaldehyde	3,5-Dimethoxybenzanilide	Toluene	Ether	86	102
2-Methoxy-3-methylbenzaldehyde	2-Methoxy-3-methylbenzanilide	Benzene	Ether h	62	72
3,4,5-Trimethoxybenzaldehyde	3,4,5-Trimethoxybenzanilide	Tetrachloroethane	Ether	65–75 i	103, 104, 105
o-Phenethylbenzaldehyde	o-Phenethylbenzanilide	None	Ether	72	119
p-Phenylsulfonylbenzaldehyde	p-Phenylsulfonylbenzanilide	Tetrachloroethane	Ether	57	120
1-Phenanthraldehyde	1-Phenanthroic anilide	Ether	Ethylene dibromide	75	106
2-Phenanthraldehyde	2-Phenanthroic anilide	Benzene	Ethylene dibromide	80–85	107, 108
3-Phenanthraldehyde	3-Phenanthroic anilide	Benzene	Ethylene dibromide	85	107, 108
9-Phenanthraldehyde	9-Phenanthroic anilide	Tetrachloroethane	Tetrachloroethane	87	109
1,2,3,4-Tetrahydro-9-phenanthraldehyde	1,2,3,4-Tetrahydro-9-phenanthroic anilide	Benzene	Ethylenedichloride	ca. 90	121
3,4-Benzo-1-phenanthraldehyde	3,4-Benzo-1-phenanthroic anilide	Tetrachloroethane	Tetrachloroethane	66	122

* In the attempt to convert 1-tridecenoic o-toluide to the corresponding unsaturated aldehyde only the saturated tridecanol was obtained in small yields.[100]

a In the attempt to prepare α-(β-ethoxyethyl)valeryl chloride, rearrangement to ethyl α-(β-chloroethyl)valerate took place.

b The aldehyde polymerized and was not purified as such.

c Chromous chloride was employed as the reducing agent.

d In the attempted Stephen reduction the corresponding nitrile was attacked neither by stannous chloride nor by chromous chloride.

e The acid employed and the acid obtained were sterically inhomogeneous.

f When stannous chloride was used as reducing agent the yield was about 5%.

g The yield is calculated on the complex tin salt.

h The imido chloride was prepared by digesting the anilide with phosphorus pentachloride in toluene. If the reaction mixture was heated for about 20 minutes after solution had resulted, nuclear chlorination took place and finally a chloro-3,5-dimethoxybenzaldehyde was obtained as the main product.

i Attention is drawn to the difficulties encountered by earlier investigators [89,104] in the preparation of 3,4,5-trimethoxybenzaldehyde by this method.

REFERENCES TO TABLE V

[113] Work, *J. Chem. Soc.*, **1946**, 197.
[114] Karrer and Rüegger, *Helv. Chim. Acta*, **23**, 284 (1940).
[115] Heilbron, Johnson, Jones, and Spinks, *J. Chem. Soc.*, **1942**, 727.
[116] Arens and Van Dorp, *Rec. trav. chim.*, **67**, 973 (1948).
[117] Rapson and Shuttleworth, *J. Chem. Soc.*, **1940**, 636.
[118] Freudenberg and Dillenburg, *Chem. Ber.*, **84**, 67 (1951).
[119] Natelson and Gottfried, *J. Am. Chem. Soc.*, **58**, 1432 (1936).
[120] Burton and Hu, *J. Chem. Soc.*, **1948**, 601.
[121] Bachmann and Cronyn, *J. Org. Chem.*, **8**, 456 (1943).
[122] Hewett, *J. Chem. Soc.*, **1940**, 293.

Table V. Aldehydes Prepared by the Method of Sonn and Müller

In Table V, above, are listed the aldehydes whose preparation by the method of Sonn and Müller is reported in the literature through 1952. The solvents listed in Column A are those in which the anilides were converted to the imido chlorides; the solvents in Column B are those in which the imido chlorides were dissolved before addition to the reducing mixture.

THE METHOD OF STEPHEN

In the method originated by Stephen [123] for the conversion of a nitrile to an aldehyde, an ether solution of the nitrile is added to a solution of stannous chloride in ether saturated with hydrogen chloride. The nitrile combines with a molecule of hydrogen chloride to form an imido chloride which is reduced to an aldimine by stannous chloride. Hydrolysis of the aldimine yields the aldehyde.

$$RCN + HCl \rightarrow RC(Cl){=}NH$$

$$RC(Cl){=}NH + SnCl_2 + 2HCl \rightarrow RCH{=}NH \cdot HCl + SnCl_4$$

$$RCH{=}NH \cdot HCl + H_2O \rightarrow RCHO + NH_4Cl$$

Stephen's method has been applied to aliphatic and to aromatic nitriles and to a few heterocyclic nitriles. An examination of the results reported strongly suggests the desirability of further study of the applicability of the method.

In his original report Stephen implied that the yields of aldehydes from saturated aliphatic nitriles are nearly quantitative, but he gave very few actual yields. Later workers have not always been able to prepare aliphatic aldehydes in the yields to be expected from Stephen's

[123] Stephen, *J. Chem. Soc.*, **127**, 1874 (1925).

report.[124-127]   The purely aliphatic α,β-unsaturated nitrile, 2-nonenoic nitrile, is not converted to an aldehyde.[25]   The two phenyl-substituted nitriles $C_6H_5CH{=}CHCN$ and $C_6H_5CH{=}CHCH{=}CHCN$ gave 40% and 10% yields, respectively, of the corresponding aldehydes with stannous chloride as the reducing agent;[128] replacement of stannous chloride by the bromide increased the yields to 65% and 50%, respectively.   Neither stannous chloride nor bromide gave an appreciable yield of aldehyde from the triply unsaturated nitrile, $C_6H_5CH{=}CHCH{=}CHCH{=}CHCN$.[128,129] β-Hydroxypropionitrile,[125] β-cyanopropiophenone,[130] and α-cyanoacetovanillone acetate [131] gave no aldehyde.

Most aromatic nitriles give good to excellent yields of aldehydes. Among some twenty benzonitriles containing alkyl, alkoxyl, sulfonyl, acetyl, and halogen substituents the only poor yields reported are in the preparation of o-tolualdehyde (9%) [123,101,125] and 3,4,5-trimethoxybenzaldehyde (10–20%).[123,132]   The low yield of o-tolualdehyde and the correspondingly low yield of α-naphthaldehyde [123,101,125] are not necessarily to be interpreted as a simple ortho effect, for o-chlorobenzonitrile is reported to furnish the aldehyde in nearly quantitative yield.[123]

Only a few heterocyclic nitriles, 2-benzyloxazole-4-carbonitrile,[133] 4-methylthiazole-5-carbonitrile,[134] and 3-pyridinecarbonitrile [135] have been successfully subjected to the Stephen reaction.   The reaction failed with 4-pyridinecarbonitrile.[80]   The 2,6-dihalopyridine-4-carbonitriles give the corresponding 2,6-dihalo-4-aminomethylpyridines rather than the aldehydes,[136] a behavior similar to that shown by certain heterocyclic anilides in the Sonn and Müller reaction (p. 242).

Variations in the reducing agent and the experimental conditions have been reported.   Slotta and Kethur [137,128] observed that absolutely water-free stannous chloride does not dissolve in ether saturated with hydrogen chloride, and they obtained very high yields (80–90%) of aldehydes by employing stannous chloride preparations containing

[124] Ralston, *Fatty Acids and Their Derivatives*, pp. 818–819, Wiley, New York, 1948.

[125] Williams, *J. Am. Chem. Soc.*, **61**, 2248 (1939).

[126] Lieber, *J. Am. Chem. Soc.*, **71**, 2862 (1949).

[127] Knight and Zook, *J. Am. Chem. Soc.*, **74**, 4560 (1952).

[128] Wittig and Kethur, *Ber.*, **69**, 2078 (1936).

[129] Wittig and Hartmann, *Ber.*, **72**, 1387 (1939).

[130] Allen, Gilbert, and Young, *J. Org. Chem.*, **2**, 227 (1937).

[131] Brickman, Hawkins, and Hibbert, *Can. J. Research B*, **19**, 24 (1941).

[132] Baker and Robinson, *J. Chem. Soc.*, **1929**, 152.

[133] Cornforth, Fawaz, Goldsworthy, and Robinson, *J. Chem. Soc.*, **1949**, 1549.

[134] Harington and Moggridge, *J. Chem. Soc.*, **1939**, 443.

[135] Gardner, Smith, Wenis, and Lee, *J. Org. Chem.*, **16**, 1121 (1951).

[136] Wibaut and Overhoff, *Rec. trav. chim.*, **52**, 55 (1933).

[137] Slotta and Kethur, *Ber.*, **71**, 335 (1938).

1.4–1.5% of water. Wittig and Hartmann, who used with advantage stannous bromide [129] (see above), also tried chromous chloride, vanadous chloride, and titanous chloride. All were ineffective.

In his original reduction of nitriles Stephen operated at room temperature and considered the precipitation of an aldimine-stannic chloride complex, $(RCH{=}NH \cdot HCl)_2SnCl_4$, a criterion of a successful reaction. Other workers, when they failed to secure a precipitate of the complex at room temperature, heated the reaction mixture in ether or used dioxane as a solvent and heated in order to bring about precipitation of the complex.[101,125,138–140] Precipitation of the complex indicates that reduction has taken place, and filtration of the complex permits hydrolysis of the aldimine in the absence of other organic materials. However, failure to obtain a solid aldimine-stannic chloride complex does not necessarily mean an unsuccessful reduction. Lieber's extensive work with lauronitrile [126] and the ensuing and instructive studies of Knight and Zook [127] with lauronitrile and palmitonitrile show clearly that further investigation, particularly with higher aliphatic nitriles, is needed in order to elucidate the mechanism of the Stephen reaction and to make it uniformly successful as a preparative method.

Experimental Conditions and Reagents

The reducing agent is prepared by suspending anhydrous stannous chloride (1.5 moles [123] to 6 moles [141] for 1 mole of nitrile) in ether and saturating the mixture with dry hydrogen chloride. The nitrile is added, and the mixture is stirred or shaken vigorously for fifteen minutes to half an hour. In many preparations the crystalline complex of the aldimine hydrochloride and stannic chloride, $(RCH{=}NH \cdot HCl)_2SnCl_4$, begins to separate within a few minutes after the addition of the nitrile. The mixture is allowed to stand until the deposition of the salt appears complete (two hours to twenty hours). The salt is then collected by decantation or filtration on a glass filter. It is hydrolyzed by boiling with water, and the aldehyde is isolated by steam distillation or extraction.

If the nitrile is insoluble in ether, it is dissolved in chloroform and this solution is mixed with the ethereal reducing agent. With some nitriles which are only slowly attacked, the mixture is allowed to stand for several hours, cooled, and resaturated with hydrogen chloride. The reducing agent has also been prepared in dioxane. The use of this

[138] King and Robinson, *J. Chem. Soc.*, **1933**, 270.
[139] King, Liguori, and Robinson, *J. Chem. Soc.*, **1933**, 1475.
[140] King, Clifton, and Openshaw, *J. Chem. Soc.*, **1942**, 422.
[141] Harington and Barger, *Biochem. J.*, **21**, 169 (1927).

solvent permits reduction at higher temperatures and may prove to be advantageous with nitriles which are slowly attacked under the ordinary conditions.

Preparation of the Stannous Chloride Reducing Agent.[142,143]   To 194 ml. (210 g., 2.06 moles) of acetic anhydride in a beaker is added gradually, with stirring, 226 g. (1 mole) of stannous chloride dihydrate. Considerable heat is evolved, and the anhydrous salt separates. After the mixture has cooled to room temperature, the liquid is decanted, the precipitate is washed by decantation with dry ether and filtered on a sintered-glass funnel; yield 188 g. (99%). The anhydrous salt does not appear to be hygroscopic and can be preserved indefinitely in a desiccator. It crystallizes in long needles from acetic acid containing a little acetic anhydride. It is readily soluble in acetone and amyl alcohol, insoluble in benzene, toluene, xylene, and chloroform. It dissolves readily in absolute methanol and ethanol, but a trace of water causes immediate hydrolysis with the formation of an opalescent precipitate which is presumably stannous oxychloride.

Experimental Procedures

β-Naphthaldehyde. Detailed directions for the preparation of this aldehyde in 68–75% yield from β-naphthyl cyanide are given in *Organic Syntheses*.[142]

3,5-Diiodo-4-(4′-methoxyphenoxy)benzaldehyde.[141]   Five grams of 3,5-diiodo-4-(4′-methoxyphenoxy)benzonitrile is dissolved in 35 ml. of chloroform and added with vigorous shaking to a solution of 12 g.* of anhydrous stannous chloride in 60 ml. of dry ether saturated with hydrogen chloride. After standing for at least sixteen hours the yellow precipitate is filtered, washed with ether, and heated with water containing a little hydrochloric acid. At the boiling point the hydrolysis is almost instantaneous, the yellow stannic chloride addition compound being replaced by a colorless flocculent precipitate of aldehyde. This is collected, washed with dilute hydrochloric acid and then with water, and dried and crystallized from glacial acetic acid. It forms colorless prisms, m.p. 121°. The yield varies from 70 to 100%.

If, according to Stephen,[123] 1.5 moles of stannous chloride is employed, and the reduction mixture is allowed to stand for only two hours, the aldehyde is obtained in minute yields.

* Twelve grams of stannous chloride for 5 g. of nitrile corresponds to a molar ratio of 6:1.

[142] Williams, *Org. Syntheses*, **23**, 63 (1943).

[143] Stephen, *J. Chem. Soc.*, **1930**, 2786.

TABLE VI

ALDEHYDES PREPARED BY THE METHOD OF STEPHEN

Aldehyde	Nitrile	Yield of Aldehyde, %	Reference
Isocaproaldehyde	Isocapronitrile	31	125
Caprylaldehyde	Caprylonitrile	—	123
Lauraldehyde	Lauronitrile	?	126, 127
Myristaldehyde	Myristonitrile	—	123
Palmitaldehyde	Palmitonitrile	?	123, 127
Stearaldehyde	Stearonitrile	—	123
α-(β-Ethoxyethyl)valeraldehyde	α-(β-Ethoxyethyl)valeronitrile [a]	Poor	113
γ-Phthalimidobutyraldehyde	γ-Phthalimidobutyronitrile	74	101
γ-Phthalimido-α-methylbutyraldehyde	γ-Phthalimido-α-methylbutyronitrile [b,c]	54	139
γ-Phenoxybutyraldehyde	γ-Phenoxybutyronitrile	79	140
γ-Phenoxy-α-methylbutyraldehyde	γ-Phenoxy-α-methylbutyronitrile [c]	46, 51	138, 139
α-(β-Phenoxyethyl)valeraldehyde	α-(β-Phenoxyethyl)valeronitrile [c]	38	113
Phenylacetaldehyde	Phenylacetonitrile	33	123, 125
p-Tolylacetaldehyde	p-Tolylacetonitrile	Nearly quantitative	123
p-Chlorophenylacetaldehyde	p-Chlorophenylacetonitrile	Nearly quantitative	123
β-Phenylpropionaldehyde	β-Phenylpropionitrile	Nearly quantitative	123
Cinnamaldehyde	Cinnamonitrile	40, 65 [d]	1, 128, 129
Cinnamylideneacetaldehyde	Cinnamylideneacetonitrile	10,[e] 50 [d]	128, 129
Malonaldehyde tetraethylacetal	Cyanoacetaldehyde diethylacetal	35 [f]	144
Benzaldehyde	Benzonitrile	97	123, 125, 128, 129
o-Tolualdehyde	o-Tolunitrile	Small, ?	123, 101, 125
p-Tolualdehyde	p-Tolunitrile	Nearly quantitative	123
m-Trifluoromethylbenzaldehyde [g]	m-Trifluoromethylbenzonitrile	—	145
p-Trifluoromethylbenzaldehyde [g]	p-Trifluoromethylbenzonitrile	26	146
o-Chlorobenzaldehyde	o-Chlorobenzonitrile	Nearly quantitative	123
p-Chlorobenzaldehyde	p-Chlorobenzonitrile	Nearly quantitative	123
p-Iodobenzaldehyde	p-Iodobenzonitrile	ca. 70	148
3-Fluoro-4-methoxybenzaldehyde	3-Fluoro-4-methoxybenzonitrile	63	149
3-Acetyl-6-methoxybenzaldehyde	3-Acetyl-6-methoxybenzonitrile	39	150
3,4,5-Trimethoxybenzaldehyde	3,4,5-Trimethoxybenzonitrile	10–20	123, 132
o-Carbomethoxybenzaldehyde	3-Carbomethoxybenzonitrile [h]	84	137
4-Carbomethoxybenzaldehyde	4-Carbomethoxybenzonitrile [h]	90	137
3-Carbethoxybenzaldehyde	3-Carbethoxybenzonitrile [h]	86	137

Aldehyde	Nitrile	Yield (%)	References
4-Carbethoxybenzaldehyde	4-Carbethoxybenzonitrile [h]	86	137
4-β-Chlorocarbethoxybenzaldehyde	4-β-Chlorocarbethoxybenzonitrile [h]	74	137
3-β-Chlorocarbethoxybenzaldehyde	3-β-Chlorocarbethoxybenzonitrile [h]	75	137
4-(3',5'-Diiodo-4'-methoxyphenoxy)benzaldehyde	4-(3',5'-Diiodo-4'-methoxyphenoxy)benzonitrile [b]	55	151
3,5-Diiodo-4-(2'-methoxyphenoxy)benzaldehyde	3,5-Diiodo-4-(2'-methoxyphenoxy)benzonitrile [b]	55	152
3,5-Diiodo-4-(3'-methoxyphenoxy)benzaldehyde	3,5-Diiodo-4-(3'-methoxyphenoxy)benzonitrile [b]	75	153
3,5-Dichloro-4-(4'-methoxyphenoxy)benzaldehyde	3,5-Dichloro-4-(4'-methoxyphenoxy)benzonitrile [b]	75	154
3,5-Dibromo-4-(4'-methoxyphenoxy)benzaldehyde	3,5-Dibromo-4-(4'-methoxyphenoxy)benzonitrile [b]	80–85	154
3,5-Diiodo-4-(4'-methoxyphenoxy)benzaldehyde	3,5-Diiodo-4-(4'-methoxyphenoxy)benzonitrile [b]	70–100	141
3,5-Diiodo-4-(3'-fluoro-4-methoxyphenoxy)benzaldehyde	3,5-Diiodo-4-(3'-fluoro-4'-methoxyphenoxy)benzonitrile [b]	68	155
3,5-Diiodo-4-(3',5'-difluoro-4'-methoxyphenoxy)benzaldehyde	3,5-Diiodo-4-(3',5'-difluoro-4'-methoxyphenoxy)benzonitrile [b]	72	75
p-Sulfamylbenzaldehyde	p-Sulfamylbenzonitrile	—	120
p-Methylsulfonylbenzaldehyde	p-Methylsulfonylbenzonitrile [b]	68	156
p-Phenylsulfonylbenzaldehyde	p-Phenylsulfonylbenzonitrile [b]	82	120
4-(4'-Methylphenylthio)benzaldehyde	4-(4'-Methylphenylthio)benzonitrile [b]	81	157
4-(4'-Ethoxyphenylthio)benzaldehyde	4-(4'-Ethoxyphenylthio)benzonitrile [b]		157
3,5-Diiodo-4-(4'-methoxyphenylthio)benzaldehyde	3,5-Diiodo-4-(4'-methoxyphenylthio)benzonitrile [b]	66	158
α-Naphthaldehyde	α-Naphthonitrile [i]	Small, 7 [i]	123, 101, 125
β-Naphthaldehyde	β-Naphthonitrile [i]	73–80, 75	125, 142, 159
2,7-Naphthalenedicarboxaldehyde	2,7-Naphthalenedicarbonitrile	24	160
Nicotinaldehyde thiosemicarbazone	3-Pyridinecarbonitrile [k]	83	135
4-Ethoxymethyl-2-hydroxy-6-methylpyridine-3-carboxaldehyde thiosemicarbazone	4-Ethoxymethyl-2-hydroxy-6-methylpyridine-3-carbonitrile	ca. 10	135
2-Benzyloxazole-4-carboxaldehyde	2-Benzyloxazole-4-carbonitrile	88 (crude)	133
4-Methylthiazole-5-carboxaldehyde	4-Methylthiazole-5-carbonitrile	40	134

[a] The mixture was shaken overnight and then heated under gentle reflux for seven hours.
[b] The nitrile was dissolved in chloroform.
[c] The reaction mixture was allowed to stand at room temperature for twelve hours, heated for several hours on a steam bath, and resaturated with hydrogen chloride.
[d] Stannous bromide in ether containing hydrogen bromide was used as reducing agent.
[e] The yield rose to 15% when the reaction was carried out in dioxane at 55°.
[f] The β,β-diethoxyiminopropionaldehyde hydrochloride-stannic chloride complex was heated in absolute ethanol at 45° for three and one-half days before ethanolysis was complete.
[g] m-Trifluoromethylbenzaldehyde and the para isomer were prepared in yields of 81% and 72% (crude), respectively, by the Rosenmund reduction.147
[h] To the anhydrous stannous chloride, 10% of crystalline hydrated stannous chloride was added.
[i] Preliminary experiments (unpublished results by Mosettig and Schmelz) indicate that analogous relations exist in the phenanthrene series, the 9-cyanide being decidedly less reactive than the 3-cyanide.
[j] Heating the reaction mixture had no apparent effect.
[k] A solution of the aldimine hydrochloride tin complex was prepared in diethylene glycol diethyl ether. By boiling with water containing thiosemicarbazide, the nicotinaldehyde thiosemicarbazone hydrochloride stannous chloride complex was obtained which on subsequent treatment with hydrogen sulfide gave nicotinaldehyde thiosemicarbazone.

REFERENCES TO TABLE VI

[144] McElvain and Clarke, J. Am. Chem. Soc., **69**, 2657 (1947).
[145] Brown, Suckling, and Whalley, J. Chem. Soc., **1949**, S95.
[146] Bernstein, Yale, Losee, Holsing, Martins, and Lott, J. Am. Chem. Soc., **73**, 906 (1951).
[147] Burger and Hornbaker, J. Org. Chem., **18**, 192 (1953).
[148] Sah, J. Am. Chem. Soc., **64**, 1487 (1942).
[149] English, Mead, and Niemann, J. Am. Chem. Soc., **62**, 350 (1940).
[150] Gray and Bonner, J. Am. Chem. Soc., **70**, 1249 (1948).
[151] Block and Powell, J. Am. Chem. Soc., **64**, 1070 (1942).
[152] Niemann and Mead, J. Am. Chem. Soc., **63**, 2685 (1941).
[153] Niemann and Redemann, J. Am. Chem. Soc., **63**, 1549 (1941).
[154] Schuegraf, Helv. Chim. Acta, **12**, 405 (1929).
[155] Niemann, Mead, and Benson, J. Am. Chem. Soc., **63**, 609 (1941).
[156] Fuller, Tonkin, and Walker, J. Chem. Soc., **1945**, 633.
[157] Law and Johnson, J. Am. Chem. Soc., **52**, 3623 (1930).
[158] Harington, Biochem. J., **43**, 434 (1948).
[159] Fulton and Robinson, J. Chem. Soc., **1939**, 200.
[160] Wood and Stanfield, J. Am. Chem. Soc., **64**, 2343 (1942).

4-Methyl-5-thiazolecarboxaldehyde.[134] Dry hydrogen chloride is passed into a mixture of 10 g. of anhydrous stannous chloride and 50 ml. of anhydrous ether, until solution is attained. An ethereal solution of 2.5 g. of crude 4-methyl-5-thiazolecarbonitrile is then added; the pressure bottle is immediately stoppered and shaken until the solid product first formed is converted into a viscous oil (2.5–3 hours). The ether is decanted, and the oil is taken up in a little water; the solution is cooled to −10°, treated with excess chilled aqueous sodium hydroxide (250 ml. of 40% solution), and rapidly extracted with ether. Evaporation of the dried (calcium chloride) extracts, after treatment with charcoal, gives 1.7 g. (65%) of crude aldehyde. Crystallization from light petroleum ether (b.p. 60–80°) gives 1.0 g. (40%) of the pure aldehyde as colorless plates, m.p. 72.5°.

Table VI. Aldehydes Prepared by the Method of Stephen

In Table VI, above, are listed the aldehydes that have been prepared by the Stephen reaction. Unless otherwise indicated, the reductions were carried out in ether solutions at room temperature. The literature has been reviewed through 1952.

THE CONTROLLED REDUCTION OF NITRILES AND AMIDES WITH LITHIUM ALUMINUM HYDRIDE

Friedman's [161] observation that the lithium aluminum hydride reduction of nitriles and acid amides may be so conducted as to furnish alde-

[161] Friedman, Abstracts, 116th ACS National Meeting, 5M, 1949.

hydes has been mentioned cursorily in a previous chapter.[31] Although no detailed or specific record of this process has been published by Friedman himself, a number of authors have subsequently applied it with success to the preparation of a variety of aldehydes. Used primarily as starting materials are nitriles and tertiary amides, which with $\frac{1}{4}$ mole of lithium aluminum hydride yield aldehydes.

$$RC\!\!\equiv\!\!N \xrightarrow{MH} RCH\!\!=\!\!NM$$
$$RCONR_2 \xrightarrow{MH} RCH(OM)NR_2$$
$$\xrightarrow{H_2O} RCHO$$

$$M = \frac{LiAl}{4}$$

Besides amides and nitriles, acids, ortho esters (leading directly to acetals), lactones, and lactams have been converted into the corresponding aldehydes (see Table VII). When tertiary amides are employed as starting materials the substituents on the nitrogen may have a decisive influence on the reduction. While, e.g., N,N-dimethylcinnamylideneacetamide is not attacked by lithium aluminum hydride, the diphenylene amide, N-cinnamylideneacetylcarbazole, gives a 73% yield of cinnamylideneacetaldehyde.[162] In some instances the nature of the solvent, the concentration of reactants, and, particularly, low temperatures during addition of the lithium reagent are of importance for the success of the reduction. In general, however, no particular precautions need be taken.

Notable achievements in the use of this method are the preparation of the elusive aldehydes $C_6H_5(CH\!\!=\!\!CH)_nCHO$, $n = 2$, 4, and 6,[162] and of the unstable γ-methylaminobutyraldehyde,[163] δ-methylaminovaleraldehyde,[163] and β-(α-piperidyl)propionaldehyde.[164] The variety of aldehydes thus far prepared by the lithium aluminum hydride reduction indicates its wide applicability. The simplicity of operation and the ready availability of the reducing agent make the method particularly attractive. In a comprehensive study of this method, Weygand and co-workers point out that the N-methylanilides are particularly suitable for reduction to aldehydes.[164a]

Experimental Procedures

9-Phenylnonatetraenal.[162] A mixture of 3.75 g. (0.01 mole) of N-(9-phenylnonatetraenoyl)carbazole in 30 ml. of dry tetrahydrofuran

[162] Wittig and Hornberger, Ann., **577**, 11 (1952).

[163] Galinovsky, Wagner, and Weiser, Monatsh., **82**, 551 (1951).

[164] Galinovsky, Vogl, and Weiser, Monatsh., **83**, 114 (1952).

[164a] Weygand, Eberhardt, Linden, Schäfer, and Eigen, Angew. Chem., **65**, 525 (1953).

and 2.5 ml. of M ethereal lithium aluminum hydride solution (0.0025 mole) is allowed to stand at room temperature for fifteen minutes. The solution is shaken with 100 ml. of aqueous dilute hydrochloric acid; the precipitate is filtered, dried, and triturated twice with 15 ml. of chloroform, leaving 1.42 g. of carbazole. The aldehyde obtained by evaporation of the chloroform extract is recrystallized twice from butanol; m.p. 139–141°, 1.7 g. (81%). After sublimation (130°/0.1 mm.) the carmine-red crystals melt at 141–143°.

γ-Dimethylamino-α,α-diphenylvaleraldehyde.[165] To a stirred, boiling solution of 56 g. (0.2 mole) of γ-dimethylamino-α,α-diphenylvaleronitrile in 200 ml. of dry ether is added dropwise in one hour 40 ml. of 1.5 M ethereal lithium aluminum hydride (0.06 mole). The mixture is heated under reflux for another hour, and treated gradually with 24 ml. of water. The ethereal solution is decanted and evaporated. To the residue is added 2.5 N aqueous nitric acid until the solution is acid to Congo. The crystalline nitrate of the amino aldehyde precipitates and is collected after one-half hour; yield 56.3 g. (82%), m.p. 186–188°. After crystallization from water, it melts at 188–190°; the base crystallized from ligroin melts at 77–78°.

Table of Aldehydes Obtained by the Lithium Aluminum Hydride Reduction of Acids and Derivatives

In Table VII are listed the aldehydes obtained by the lithium aluminum hydride reduction of acids and their derivatives. The literature has been surveyed through 1952.

[165] T. D. Perrine and E. L. May, *J. Org. Chem.*, **19**, 775 (1954).

TABLE VII

ALDEHYDES OBTAINED BY LITHIUM ALUMINUM HYDRIDE REDUCTION OF ACIDS AND ACID DERIVATIVES

Aldehyde	Acid or Acid Derivative	Yield of Aldehyde, %	Reference
Acetaldehyde	Acetic acid NMA [a]	68 [b]	164a
Chloroacetaldehyde	Chloroacetic acid NMA [a]	68 [b]	164a
Trifluoroacetaldehyde [c]	Ethyl trifluoroacetate	71,[d] 46,[e] 26 [f]	166a, 166, 168
Perfluoropropionaldehyde	Ethyl perfluoropropionate	75,[d] 20 [f]	166a, 168
Perfluorobutyraldehyde [g]	Ethyl perfluorobutyrate	76,[d] 34 [f]	166a, 168
Trimethylacetaldehyde	Trimethylacetic acid NMA [a]	56 [b, h]	164a
Perfluoroöctanal	Ethyl perfluoroöctanoate	70 [b, d]	166a
β-Methylmercaptopropionaldehyde dimethyl acetal	Methyl β-methylmercaptoörthopropionate	97 [i]	169
Cyclopropanecarboxaldehyde	Cyclopropanecarbonitrile	48 [k]	170
Palmitaldehyde	Palmitic acid NMA [a]	98 [b, h]	164a
γ-Dimethylamino-α,α-diphenylvaleraldehyde	γ-Dimethylamino-α,α-diphenylvaleronitrile	82	165, 171
γ-Dimethylamino-α,α-diphenyl-β-methylbutyraldehyde	γ-Dimethylamino-α,α-diphenyl-β-methyl-butyronitrile	24	171
Phenylacetaldehyde	Phenylacetic acid NMA [a]	70 [b]	164a
β-Phenylpropionaldehyde	β-Phenylpropionic acid NMA [a]	55 [b, h]	164a
Cinnamaldehyde	N-Cinnamylcarbazole [l]	49 [m]	162
Cinnamylideneacetaldehyde	N-Cinnamylideneacetylcarbazole [n]	73 [o]	162
9-Phenylnonatetraenal	N-9-Phenylnonatetraenoylcarbazole	81 [p]	162
13-Phenyltridecahexaenal	N-13-Phenyltridecahexaenoylcarbazole	60	162
γ-Hydroxyvaleraldehyde	γ-Hydroxyvaleric acid NMA [a]	55 [b]	164a
	γ-Valerolactone	58	174
α,γ-Dihydroxy-β,β-dimethylbutyraldehyde	(-)α-Hydroxy-β,β-dimethyl-γ-butyro-lactone(pantoyllactone)		174
α-Methyl-δ-hydroxycaproaldehyde	α-Methyl-δ-caprolactone	64-84	174
γ-Methylaminobutyraldehyde [q]	N-Methyl-α-pyrrolidone	60-70 (estimated)	163

TABLE VII—Continued

ALDEHYDES OBTAINED BY LITHIUM ALUMINUM HYDRIDE REDUCTION OF ACIDS AND ACID DERIVATIVES

Aldehyde	Acid or Acid Derivative	Yield of Aldehyde, %	Reference
δ-Methylaminovaleraldehyde [r]	N-Methyl-α-piperidone [s]	60–70 (estimated)	163
β-(α-Piperidyl)propionaldehyde [t]	3-Ketoöctahydropyrrocoline		164
Glyoxal	Oxalic acid bis-NMA [a]	94 [b,h]	164a
Succinaldehyde	Succinic acid bis-NMA [a]	68 [b,h]	164a
Glutaraldehyde	Glutaric acid bis-NMA [a]	64 [b,h]	164a
Adipaldehyde	Adipic acid bis-NMA [a]	67 [b,h]	164a
Sebacaldehyde	Sebacic acid bis-NMA [a]	78 [b,h]	164a
Brassylaldehyde	Brassylic acid bis-NMA [a]	81 [b,h]	164a
Thiodiacetaldehyde	Thiodiacetic acid bis-NMA [a]	86 [b,h]	164a
(±)-Malaldehyde	(±)-Malic acid bis-NMA [a]	75 [b]	164a
(±)-O-Acetylmalaldehyde	(-)-O-Acetylmalic acid bis-NMA [a]	62 [b,h]	164a
Benzaldehyde	Benzoic acid NMA [a]	68 [b]	164a, 171a
Salicylaldehyde	Salicylic acid NMA [a]	54 [b]	164a
Thiosalicylaldehyde	Thiosalicylic acid NMA [a]	51 [b]	164a
o-Methoxybenzaldehyde	o-Methoxybenzoic acid NMA [a]	30 [b]	164a
Phthalaldehyde	Phthalic acid bis-NMA [a]	60 [b]	164a
	Phthalic acid bis-dimethylamide	70 [u]	172
4,5-Dimethoxyphthalaldehyde	4,5-Dimethoxyphthalic acid bis-NMA [a]	20 [v]	164a
α-Naphthaldehyde	α-Naphthoic acid NMA [a]	(estimated) 42 [w]	164a
2-Hydroxy-3-naphthaldehyde	2-Hydroxy-3-naphthoic acid NMA [a]	50 [b]	164a
2,2'-Diphenyldicarboxaldehyde	2,2'-Diphenyldica:boxylic acid bis-NMA [a]	68 [b]	164a
Nicotinaldehyde	Nicotinic acid NMA [a]	65 [x]	164a
1-Phenazinecarboxaldehyde	N,N-Dimethyl-1-phenazinecarboxamide		173

[a] NMA = N-methylanilide.
[b] The yield refers to the 2,4-dinitrophenylhydrazone.
[c] This aldehyde was obtained in a yield of 64% in the Fröschl and Danoff modification (gas phase) of the Rosenmund reduction.[167]
[d] At −70°.

e In this experiment the nitrile was reduced.

f In this experiment the acid was reduced.

g This aldehyde was also obtained in the (low-pressure) Rosenmund reduction in yields of 32% and 35%.[168]

h The optimal yield in a series of runs.

i The corresponding diethyl acetal was obtained in a yield of 73% from the ethyl ortho ester.

k Cyclopropanecarboxpiperidide gave the aldehyde in a yield of 20%.

l The dimethylamide, N-methylanilide, and diphenylamide of cinnamic acid yielded with lithium borohydride as well as with lithium aluminum hydride oils and resins that were not identified.

m The reduction with lithium borohydride gave a 13% yield of aldehyde.

n The dimethylamide of cinnamylideneacetic acid was not attacked under these conditions.

o The reduction with lithium borohydride gave a 62% yield of aldehyde.

p The reduction with lithium borohydride gave a 69% yield.

q The aldehyde could not be isolated as such, but was converted into hygrine and cuscohygrine.

r The aldehyde could not be isolated as such, but was converted into methylisopelletierine and 1,3-di-(N-methyl-α-piperidyl)propan-2-one.

s The reaction fails with α-piperidone.

t The aldehyde could not be isolated as such, but was characterized through its condensation products with acetonedicarboxylic acid and with benzoylacetic acid.

u The phthalic bis-piperidide gave the aldehyde in a yield of 20%. With either amide an excess of lithium aluminum hydride did not carry the redution beyond the aldehyde stage.

v Estimated from 2,3-dihydroxy-6,7-dimethoxynaphthoquinone (by condensation with glyoxal).

w This yield was obtained using one-third to one-half mole of lithium aluminum hydride at 60–65°; at 0° only 4% of aldehyde was obtained.

x The yield refers to the phenylhydrazone.

166 Henne, Pelley, and Alm, J. Am. Chem. Soc., 72, 3370 (1950).
166a Pierce and Kane, J. Am. Chem. Soc., 76, 300 (1954).
167 Brown and Musgrave, J. Chem. Soc., 1952, 5049.
168 Husted and Ahlbrecht, J. Am. Chem. Soc., 74, 5422 (1952).
169 Claus and Morgenthau, Jr., J. Am. Chem. Soc., 73, 5005 (1951).
170 Smith and Rogier, J. Am. Chem. Soc., 73, 4047 (1951).
171 Yandik and Larsen, J. Am. Chem. Soc., 73, 3534 (1951).
171a Mićović and Mihailović, J. Org. Chem., 18, 1190 (1953).
172 Weygand and Tietjen, Chem. Ber., 84, 625 (1951).
173 Birkofer and Birkofer, Chem. Ber., 85, 286 (1952).
174 Arth, J. Am. Chem. Soc., 75, 2413 (1953).

CHAPTER 6

THE METALATION REACTION WITH ORGANOLITHIUM COMPOUNDS

Henry Gilman

Iowa State College

John W. Morton Jr.

The Procter & Gamble Company

CONTENTS

INTRODUCTION

The term metalation denotes the replacement of hydrogen by metal to yield a true organometallic compound.[1] The replacement of hydrogen by metal in a compound such as acetoacetic ester is not generally classed as a metalation reaction in this sense, because the resulting salt is not a typical organometallic compound. The distinction, however, is one of degree rather than of kind.

The use of organolithium compounds as metalating agents dates from 1928, when it was discovered that ethyllithium reacts with fluorene to produce 9-fluorenyllithium (I), and with several similar hydrocarbons in an analogous manner.[2] Shortly afterward, it was found that organolithium

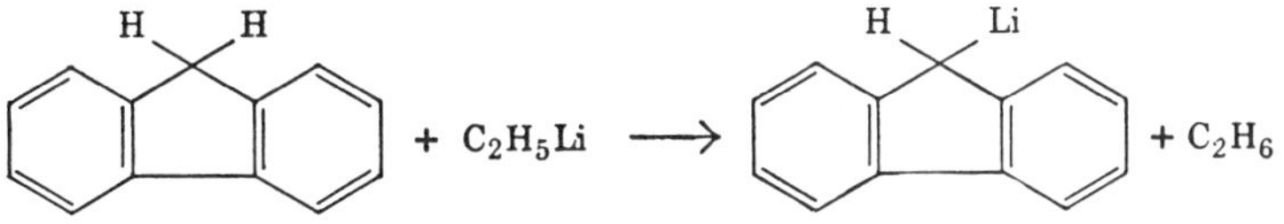

compounds can be used to replace one of the reactive methyl hydrogen atoms of 2-picoline and of quinaldine, with the formation of the organo-metallic products II and III, respectively.[3] In 1934, it was discovered

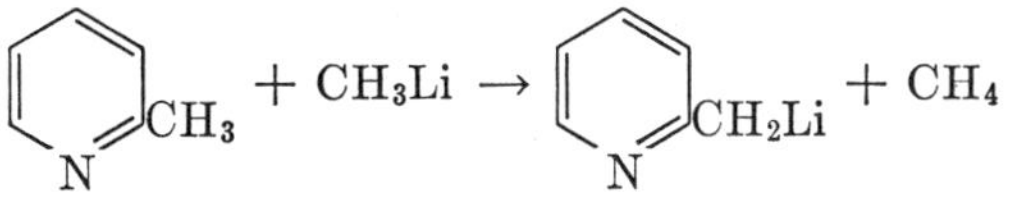

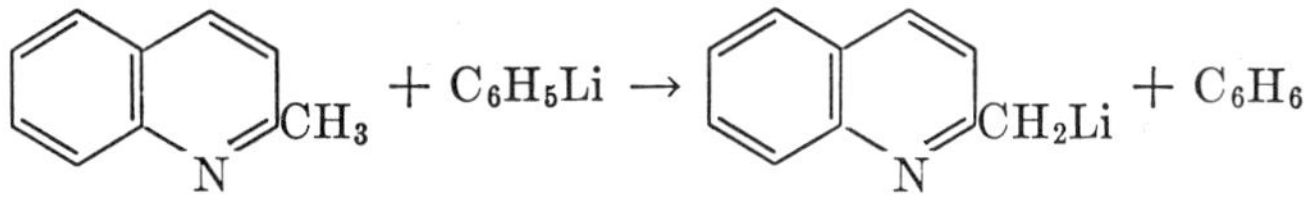

that dibenzofuran, which contains no highly activated hydrogen, reacts with n-butyllithium in diethyl ether to yield 4-dibenzofuryllithium (IV).[4,5] Subsequent studies have made it plain that the organolithium

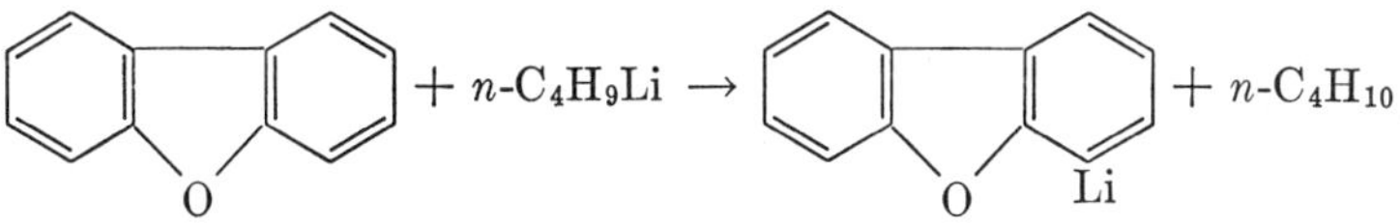

[1] Gilman and Young, *J. Am. Chem. Soc.*, **56**, 1415 (1934).
[2] Schlenk and Bergmann, *Ann.*, **463**, 192 (1928).
[3] Ziegler and Zeiser, *Ann.*, **485**, 174 (1931).
[4] W. G. Bywater, Doctoral Dissertation, Iowa State College, 1934.
[5] D. M. Hayes, M.S. Thesis, Iowa State College, 1934.

compounds are particularly effective in this type of metalation. The formation of the organolithium compound IV is typical of the organolithium metalations with respect to solvent, experimental conditions, and metalating agent. The orientation, too, is typical of organolithium metalations; in such reactions, the entering metal atom shows a strong tendency to replace a nuclear hydrogen atom *ortho* to the hetero atom, or a lateral hydrogen atom (i.e., one attached to a side chain) on a carbon adjacent to the hetero atom. Thus, *n*-butyllithium metalates thiophene in the 2 position,[6] dibenzothiophene in the 4 position,[7] and methyl phenyl sulfide on the methyl carbon atom,[8] to give the organometallic compounds V, VI, and VII, respectively. It is shown in subsequent parts

of this discussion that different hetero atoms and groups have different activating powers in the metalation reaction, and that when a molecule containing two different hetero functions is metalated it is often possible to predict which of the *ortho* positions will be attacked.

This ability to yield *ortho* products, usually unmixed with *para* or other isomers, distinguishes the metalation reaction from the more familiar types of substitution and makes possible the preparation of many products not readily available through other routes. The organolithium compound formed in a metalation reaction may be converted into any of a great number of derivatives (Table II). By appropriate treatment, the lithium atom may be replaced by carboxyl (Table I), hydroxyl,[9] amino,[10, 11] halogen,[12–14] formyl,[15–17] acetyl,[18] benzoyl,[19–21] methyl,[22]

[6] Gilman and Shirley, *J. Am. Chem. Soc.*, **71**, 1870 (1949).

[7] Gilman and Bebb, *J. Am. Chem. Soc.*, **61**, 109 (1939).

[8] Gilman and Webb, *J. Am. Chem. Soc.*, **62**, 987 (1940).

[9] Gilman, Cheney, and Willis, *J. Am. Chem. Soc.*, **61**, 951 (1939).

[10] Gilman and Avakian, *J. Am. Chem. Soc.*, **68**, 1514 (1946).

[11] Willis, *Iowa State Coll. J. Sci.*, **18**, 98 (1943) [*C. A.*, **38**, 739 (1944)].

[12] S. Avakian, Doctoral Dissertation, Iowa State College, 1944.

[13] G. E. Brown, Doctoral Dissertation, Iowa State College, 1941.

[14] Gilman and Nobis, *J. Am. Chem. Soc.*, **67**, 1479 (1945).

[15] Wittig in *Newer Methods of Preparative Organic Chemistry*, Interscience, New York, 1948.

[16] Adams and Carlin, *J. Am. Chem. Soc.*, **65**, 360 (1943).

[17] Adams and Mathieu, *J. Am. Chem. Soc.*, **70**, 2120 (1948).

[18] Miller and Bachman, *J. Am. Chem. Soc.*, **57**, 766 (1935).

[19] Kliegl, Weng, and Wiest, *Ber.*, **63**, 1262 (1930).

[20] M. A. Plunkett, Doctoral Dissertation, Iowa State College, 1947.

[21] Schlenk and Bergmann, *Ber.*, **62**, 748 (1929).

[22] Gilman and Jacoby, *J. Org. Chem.*, **3**, 108 (1938).

benzyl,[3, 23] benzhydryl,[24] allyl,[3] β-hydroxyethyl,[25, 26] hydroxymethyl,[27] substituted hydroxymethyl,[28] or substituted silyl groups.[12, 20, 29, 30] Metalation products have also been converted into other organometallic derivatives by reaction with triphenyltin chloride,[31] germanium tetrabromide,[32] antimony trichloride,[33] and triphenyllead chloride.[34] The RLi compound produced in a metalation may be oxidized to R—R by cupric chloride,[35] or added across the azomethine linkage of a compound such as quinoline.[6, 36] In the metalations with organolithium compounds which have been carried out heretofore the emphasis has usually been on studying the position of substitution rather than on preparing particular compounds. For this reason the derivative most commonly prepared from a metalation product has been the carboxylic acid, made by the reaction of the lithium compound with carbon dioxide. This reaction, carbonation, is useful in the study of metalation products because the usual metalating agents, the alkyllithium compounds, yield volatile acids which are easily separated from the acids of higher molecular weight obtained from the metalated products themselves.

MECHANISM

Two different interpretations of the mechanism of the metalation reaction have been advanced. In one of these,[37, 38] the organometallic ion-pair is pictured as forming a coordinate bond between the metal cation and a pair of electrons belonging to a hetero atom (such as halogen, oxygen, nitrogen, or the like) of the molecule undergoing metalation.

[23] Blum-Bergmann, *Ber.*, **65**, 109 (1932).

[24] Blum-Bergmann, *Ann.*, **484**, 26 (1930).

[25] W. H. Kirkpatrick, Doctoral Dissertation, Iowa State College, 1935.

[26] Mikhailov and Blokhina, *Izvest. Akad. Nauk S.S.S.R., Otdel. Khim. Nauk*, **1949**, 279 [*C. A.*, **44**, 2963 (1950)].

[27] Gaertner and St. John, unpublished studies.

[28] Gilman and Beel, *J. Am. Chem. Soc.*, **71**, 2328 (1949).

[29] L. S. Miller, Doctoral Dissertation, Iowa State College, 1950.

[30] Sunthankar and Gilman, *J. Am. Chem. Soc.*, **72**, 4884 (1950).

[31] T. Goreau, M.S. Thesis, Iowa State College, 1951.

[32] Leeper, *Iowa State Coll. J. Sci.*, **18**, 57 (1943) [*C. A.*, **38**, 726 (1944)].

[33] O'Donnell, *Iowa State Coll. J. Sci.*, **20**, 34 (1945) [*C. A.*, **40**, 4689 (1946)].

[34] Gilman, Bywater, and Parker, *J. Am. Chem. Soc.*, **57**, 885 (1935).

[35] Gilman, Swiss, and Cheney, *J. Am. Chem. Soc.*, **62**, 1963 (1940).

[36] Shirley and Cameron, *J. Am. Chem. Soc.*, **72**, 2788 (1950).

[37] Roberts and Curtin, *J. Am. Chem. Soc.*, **68**, 1658 (1946).

[38] Sunthankar and Gilman, *J. Org. Chem.*, **16**, 8 (1951).

Subsequently or simultaneously, the carbanion portion of the organo-metallic ion-pair attacks an adjacent hydrogen atom, removing it as a proton. The coordination of the metal cation with the hetero element weakens the ionic bond between the metal and the carbanion and at the same time polarizes the adjacent carbon-hydrogen bond so as to facilitate proton removal. This interpretation of the reaction emphasizes the nucleophilic properties of the RLi molecule and pictures metalation as analogous to halogen-metal interconversion.[38, 39] The metalation of compounds like triphenylmethane which contain no hetero atom pre-sumably takes place by direct nucleophilic attack on hydrogen, without preliminary formation of a complex, and would be explained as a simple acid-base reaction. This view of hydrocarbon metalations was taken in early studies by Conant and Wheland [40] and by others.[41, 42]

The other interpretation of the metalation reaction stresses the elec-trophilic properties of the organometallic molecule and pictures the initial coordination with a hetero atom as being followed, or accom-panied, by an electrophilic attack of the metal cation on the carbon atom from which hydrogen is to be removed.[43] The role of the carbanion in removing the proton is pictured as being of secondary importance. This theory is in accord with the view that organoalkali compounds generally function as electrophilic species.[44] However, although some coupling [45] and elimination [46] reactions of organoalkali compounds apparently in-volve clear-cut electrophilic action of the metal cation, it seems doubtful that this interpretation is adequate for all *metalation* reactions. If the metalation of 2-methoxynaphthalene takes place through electrophilic attack on a carbon atom, it would be predicted that the transition state would be more stable when the 1 position is being attacked than when the attack is at the 3 position. In the former case, oxonium structures VIII and IX may contribute to the transition state without damping normal Kekule resonance in the unsubstituted ring; in the latter case, only one

VIII   IX   X

[39] Jones and Gilman in Adams, *Organic Reactions*, Vol. 6, Wiley, New York, 1951.
[40] Conant and Wheland, *J. Am. Chem. Soc.*, **54**, 1212 (1932).
[41] McEwen, *J. Am. Chem. Soc.*, **58**, 1124 (1936).
[42] Wooster and Mitchell, *J. Am. Chem. Soc.*, **52**, 688 (1930).
[43] A. A. Morton, *J. Am. Chem. Soc.*, **69**, 969 (1947).
[44] A. A. Morton, *Chem. Revs.*, **35**, 1 (1944).
[45] Cristol, Overhults, and Meek, *J. Am. Chem. Soc.*, **73**, 813 (1951).
[46] Letsinger and Bobko, *J. Am. Chem. Soc.*, **75**, 2649 (1953).

oxonium structure, X, is possible. However, metalation actually takes place in the 3 position.[38] Similarly, 2-methoxyphenanthrene is metalated in the 3 position, 3-methoxyphenanthrene in the 2 position,[47] and 2,7-dimethoxynaphthalene in the 3 and 6 positions,[38] to give the organometallic compounds XI, XII, and XIII, respectively. In each reaction the *ortho* position attacked is the one that would give rise to the less-stable transition state if the electrophilic view is correct.

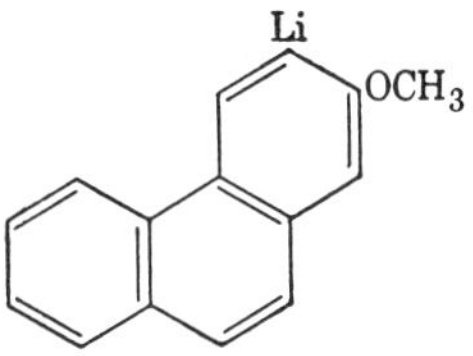

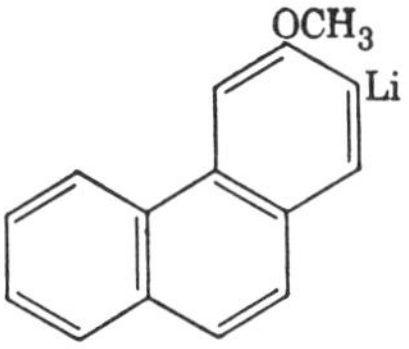

It should be emphasized [48] that both the above-suggested mechanisms are simplified ones; each stresses the action of only one partner of the organometallic ion-pair. In the solvents of low dielectric constant employed in metalation reactions, there can never be any great separation of charge, and reactions in these solvents are probably highly concerted. From this viewpoint, the electrophilic and nucleophilic interpretations of metalation are seen as limiting extremes, with some individual reactions lying nearer to one extreme than to the other.

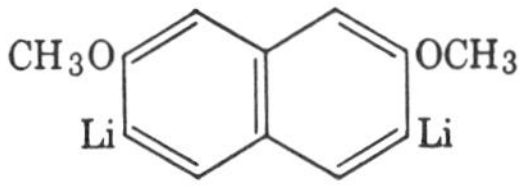

Several metalations by organolithium compounds are not satisfactorily explained by either of the above mechanisms. Triphenylamine is metalated, not in the expected *ortho* position, but in the *meta* position, to give the product XIV,[49] although the closely related 9-phenylcarbazole un-

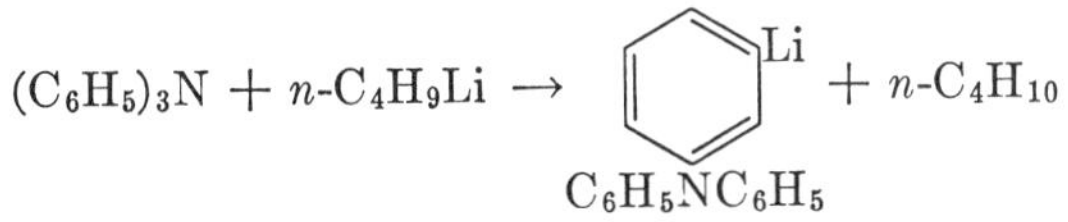

dergoes normal metalation in the 2' position [50a] and dimetalation in the 2' and 6' positions [50b] to yield the products XV and XVI. Triphenylarsine [51] and triphenylphosphine [52] are also anomalously metalated in the *meta* position by *n*-butyllithium.

[47] Gilman and Cook, *J. Am. Chem. Soc.*, **62**, 2813 (1940).
[48] A. A. Morton and Cluff, *J. Am. Chem. Soc.*, **74**, 4056 (1952).
[49] Gilman and Brown, *J. Am. Chem. Soc.*, **62**, 3208 (1940).
[50a] Gilman, Stuckwisch, and Kendall, *J. Am. Chem. Soc.*, **63**, 1758 (1941).
[50b] Gilman and Stuckwisch, *J. Am. Chem. Soc.*, **65**, 1729 (1943).
[51] Gilman and Stuckwisch, *J. Am. Chem. Soc.*, **63**, 3532 (1941).
[52] Gilman and Brown, *J. Am. Chem. Soc.*, **67**, 824 (1945).

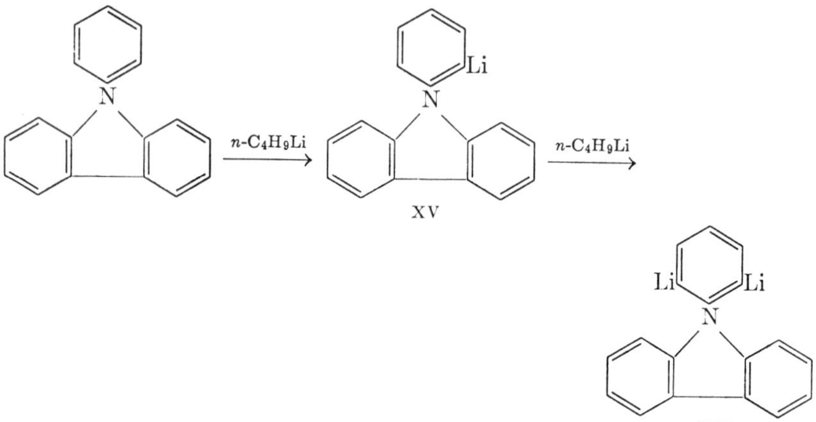

XV

XVI

SCOPE OF THE REACTION

Nature of the RLi Compound

Metalation, like halogen-metal interconversion,[39] is best effected by alkyllithium compounds, and, of these, n-butyllithium is most frequently used. In a comparison of different organolithium compounds, dibenzo-thiophene was allowed to react in diethyl ether with the metalating agent, and the mixture was carbonated after a suitable length of time to give dibenzothiophene-4-carboxylic acid. n-Butyllithium gave a 54% yield of the acid; phenyllithium gave only 12%; 1-naphthyllithium gave 7.6% and p-anisyllithium gave no metalation product.[53] However, some substances can be metalated in appreciable yields by aryllithium compounds. Phenyllithium metalates resorcinol dimethyl ether to give a 55% yield of the aldehyde XVII after treatment of the reaction mixture with N-methylformanilide.[15] Even such sterically hindered aryllithium

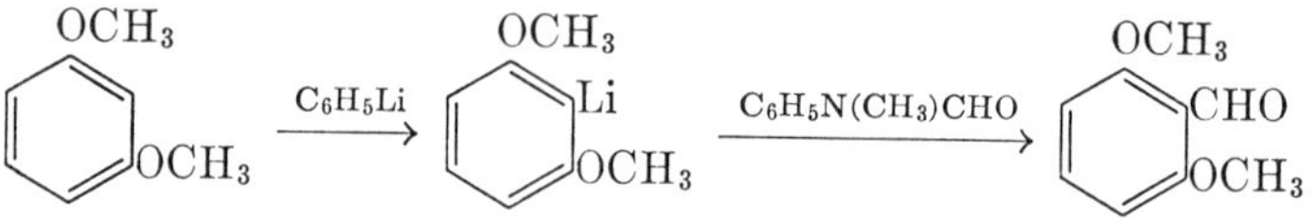

XVII

compounds as mesityllithium (XVIII) and 2, 4, 6-triphenylphenyl-lithium (XIX) can effect certain metalations in satisfactory yields.

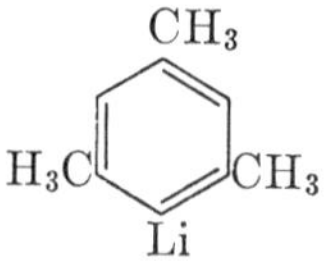

XVIII

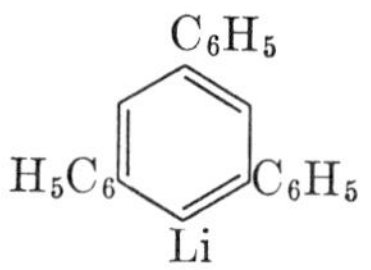

XIX

[53] Jacoby, *Iowa State Coll. J. Sci.*, **13**, 70 (1938) [*C. A.*, **34**, 99 (1940)].

Both these RLi compounds metalate fluorene to give, on carbonation, crude yields of fluorene-9-carboxylic acid in excess of 50%, and mesityllithium will even metalate resorcinol dimethyl ether in the hindered 2 position to an appreciable extent.[54] Organolithium compounds normally react with 2-phenylquinoline (XX) by addition to the azomethine

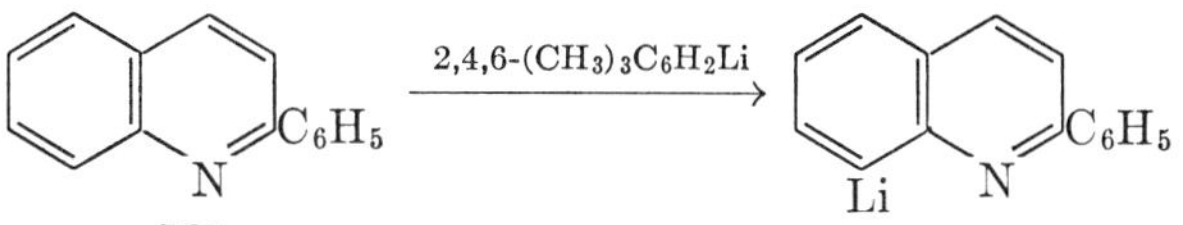

linkage,[55] but mesityllithium metalates 2-phenylquinoline in the 8 position.[56] Presumably the bulky mesityl group retards the normally rapid addition reaction and permits the slower metalation reaction to occur.

In some reactions, the comparative efficacies of different metalating agents depend upon the solvent used in the reaction. This effect will be discussed in the section on Experimental Conditions.

Compounds Metalated by RLi

Hydrocarbons. Few strictly aromatic hydrocarbons have been metalated by organolithium compounds. Benzene is not metalated by a mixture of lithium metal and diethylmercury even after an eight-week period of contact, but is metalated to the extent of about 5% by n-butyllithium in diethyl ether to yield benzoic acid upon carbonation.[57] Naphthalene is metalated in 20% yield by n-butyllithium, giving a mixture of 1- and 2-naphthyllithium in which the 1 isomer predominates.[7]

With the polyarylmethanes, in which the lateral hydrogen atom is activated, the organolithium metalations have been studied in more detail. Fluorene is metalated rapidly and quantitatively by phenyllithium in diethyl ether.[58] The reaction with ethyllithium in benzene is much slower.[2] Triphenylmethane is metalated by organolithium compounds to give the bright red triphenylmethyllithium, and this reaction has found practical application as a color test for reactive organometallic compounds.[59a] Diphenylmethane is metalated in 20% yield, and phenyl-1-naphthylmethane in 80% yield by n-butyllithium, to give the

[54] Gilman and J. W. Morton, Jr., unpublished studies.
[55] Gilman and Gainer, *J. Am. Chem. Soc.*, **69**, 877 (1947).
[56] Gilman and Reid, unpublished studies.
[57] Young, *Iowa State Coll. J. Sci.*, **12**, 177 (1937) [*C. A.*, **32**, 4979 (1938)].
[58] Ziegler and Jakob, *Ann.*, **511**, 45 (1934).
[59a] Gilman and Swiss, *J. Am. Chem. Soc.*, **62**, 1847 (1940).

compounds XXI and XXII, respectively. However, bibenzyl, which is

$(C_6H_5)_2CHLi$

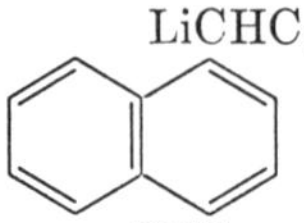
LiCHC6H5

XXI XXII

laterally dimetalated both by *n*-butylsodium and by *n*-butylpotassium to give α,β-diphenylsuccinic acid (XXIII) after carbonation, is metalated in only 1% yield by *n*-butyllithium, and the products of carbonation are the *meta*- and *para*-substituted acids XXIV and XXV.[7]

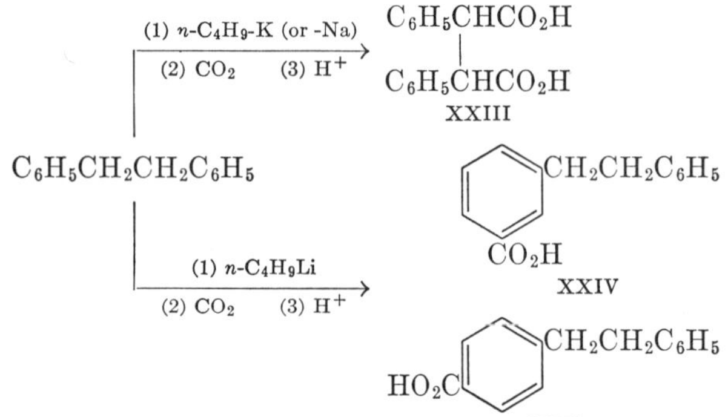
(1) n-C4H9-K (or -Na)
(2) CO2 (3) H+
C6H5CHCO2H
C6H5CHCO2H
XXIII
C6H5CH2CH2C6H5
CH2CH2C6H5
CO2H
XXIV
(1) n-C4H9Li
(2) CO2 (3) H+
CH2CH2C6H5
HO2C

XXV

An interesting study by Talalaeva and Kocheshkov describes the tetrametalation of diphenylmethane, and the tetra- and penta-metalation of toluene, by ethyllithium.[59b] Positions of substitution were not determined. Such polymetalation is in striking contrast to the mono- and di-substitution usually encountered in organolithium metalation.

Replacement of an active hydrogen atom by lithium is sometimes accompanied by rearrangement or by the elimination of lithium hydride, always in such a way as to increase the total conjugation of the molecule. Thus, 1,4-dihydronaphthalene (XXVI) and phenyllithium give after

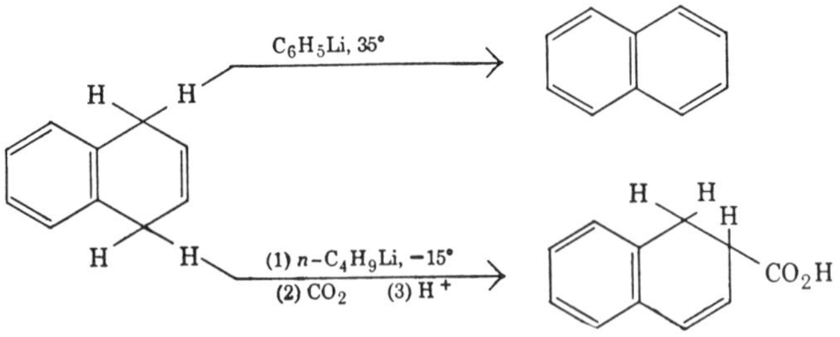
C6H5Li, 35°
H H
H H
(1) n-C4H9Li, −15°
(2) CO2 (3) H+
H H
H
CO2H

XXVI

[59b] Talalaeva and Kocheshkov, *Doklady Akad. Nauk S.S.S.R.*, **77**, 621 (1951) [*C. A.*, **45**, 10191 (1951)].

extended refluxing an 85% yield of naphthalene, while the same hydrocarbon and n-butyllithium at $-15°$ for a shorter time yield 1,2-dihydro-
2-naphthoic acid on carbonation; in similar fashion, 1,4-diphenyl-2-
butene is dehydrogenated by n-butyllithium to yield 1,4-diphenyl-1,3-
butadiene.[60] This type of reaction is not confined to hydrocarbons. 1,4-
Dihydrodibenzofuran (XXVII) can be metalated in such a way as to

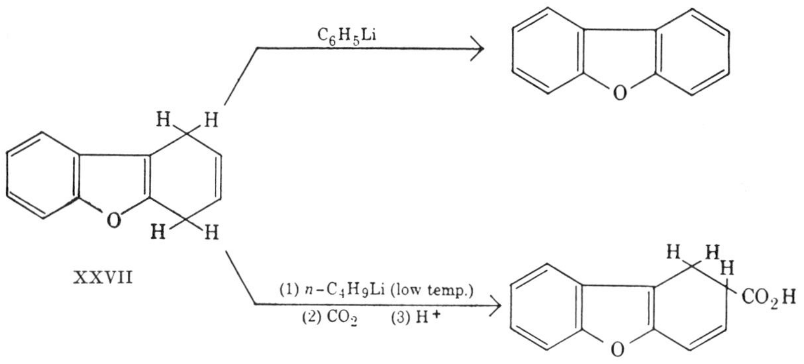

result either in rearrangement or in dehydrogenation,[60] and a similar
dehydrogenation of 1,4-dihydrodibenzothiophene has been reported.[22]
9,10-Dihydroanthracene is metalated by n-butyllithium, without rearrangement or elimination, to yield on carbonation a mixture of the acids
XXVIII and XXIX.[7, 26]

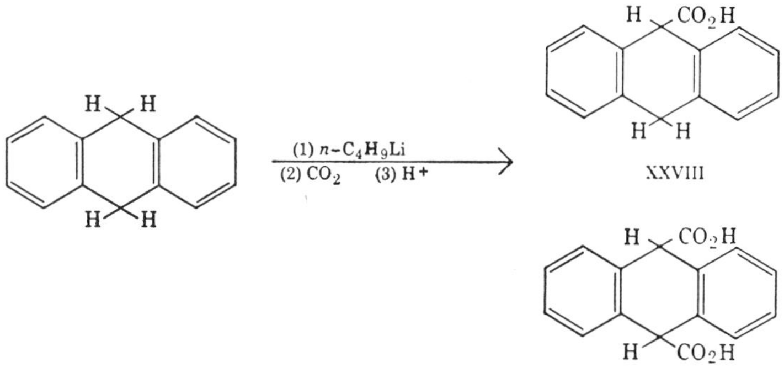

Halides. Some halogen derivatives of hydrocarbons are metalated by
RLi compounds. This metalation has been found to play a surprising
role in certain coupling reactions of the Fittig type. The production of a
biaryl, R—R, from the reaction between the halide RX and the organometallic compound RLi, is usually viewed as taking place by the simple
elimination of LiX and the combination of the R fragments. However,

[60] Gilman and Bradley, *J. Am. Chem. Soc.*, **60**, 2333 (1938).

Wittig and co-workers, in a study of the reaction between phenyllithium and fluorobenzene, demonstrated the presence of *o*-biphenylyllithium in the reaction mixture by isolating the carbinol **XXX** after treatment with

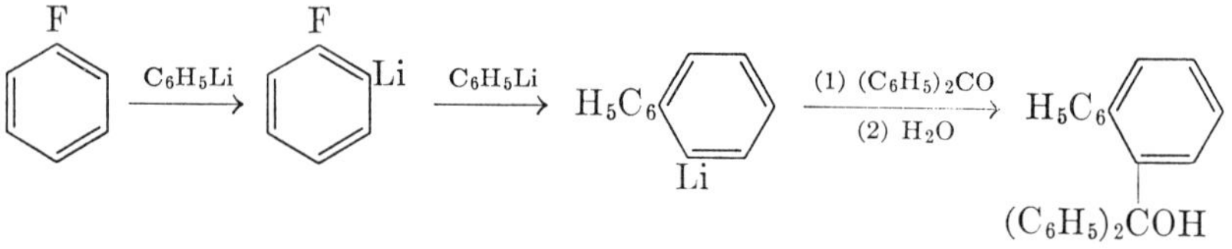

F → F Li → H₅C₆ ... Li → H₅C₆ ... (C₆H₅)₂COH

$$\text{F} \xrightarrow{C_6H_5Li} \text{F,Li} \xrightarrow{C_6H_5Li} H_5C_6\text{—}\text{Li} \xrightarrow[(2)\ H_2O]{(1)\ (C_6H_5)_2CO} H_5C_6\text{—}(C_6H_5)_2\text{COH}$$

XXX

benzophenone. It is postulated that the coupling occurs through *ortho* metalation of the fluorobenzene, giving an activated fluorine atom which is replaced by a phenyl group from another phenyllithium molecule.[61] The production of *m*-terphenyl from *m*-difluorobenzene and phenyllithium has been shown to involve an analogous metalation between the two fluorine atoms, yielding finally 2,6-diphenylphenyllithium (**XXXI**), the presence of which was demonstrated by conversion to a carbinol by

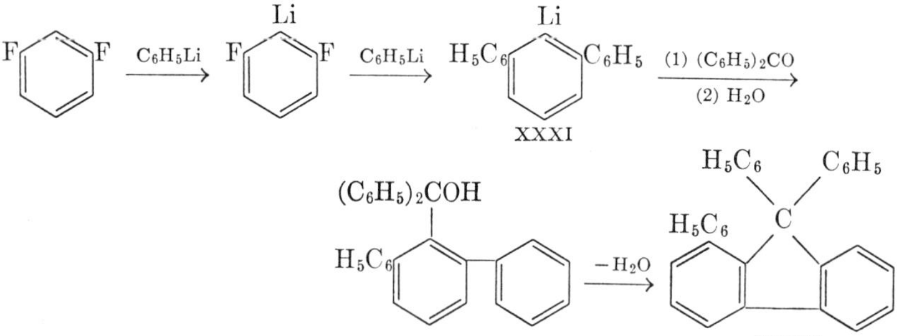

$$\text{F}\underset{\text{F}}{\text{—}} \xrightarrow{C_6H_5Li} \text{F}\underset{\text{F}}{\overset{Li}{\text{—}}} \xrightarrow{C_6H_5Li} H_5C_6\overset{Li}{\underset{}{\text{—}}}C_6H_5 \xrightarrow[(2)\ H_2O]{(1)\ (C_6H_5)_2CO}$$

XXXI

$$\underset{H_5C_6}{\overset{(C_6H_5)_2\text{COH}}{\text{—}}} \xrightarrow{-H_2O} \text{XXXII}$$

treatment with benzophenone and dehydration of the carbinol to 1,9,9-triphenylfluorene (**XXXII**).[62] The coupling of chlorobenzene with phenyllithium to yield tri-*o*-phenylene is believed by the same investigators to involve a similar mechanism.

An interesting extension of this work is the study [62] of the production of phenyldiethylamine from the reaction of fluorobenzene and phenyllithium with triethylamine. It is suggested that the initially formed *o*-fluorophenyllithium combines with the amine to give the internal quaternary ammonium salt **XXXIII**, which then decomposes with the elimination of ethylene somewhat after the manner of the Hofmann degradation. A fair yield results when iodobenzene is used in place of fluorobenzene; other amines have also been used in the reaction.

---

[61] Wittig, Pieper, and Fuhrmann, *Ber.*, **73**, 1193 (1940).
[62] Wittig and Merkle, *Ber.*, **76**, 109 (1943).

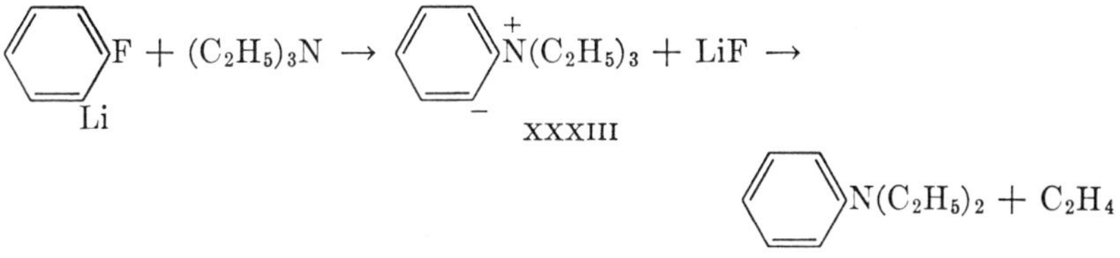

$$\underset{\text{Li}}{\bigcirc}\text{F} + (C_2H_5)_3N \rightarrow \underset{-}{\overset{+}{\bigcirc}}N(C_2H_5)_3 + \text{LiF} \rightarrow$$

XXXIII

$$\bigcirc N(C_2H_5)_2 + C_2H_4$$

The formation of acetylenic products from the reaction between vinyl halides and organolithium compounds seems to proceed through metalation. Vinyl bromide and n-butyllithium react to yield, on carbonation, acetylenedicarboxylic acid,[63] while β-chlorostyrene with phenyllithium gives a 70% yield of phenylacetylene.[64] The mechanism originally suggested for these and similar reactions involved replacement of a β-hydrogen atom by lithium, followed by the rapid elimination of lithium halide to yield the acetylenic product, which would then itself be metalated by excess organolithium compound.[64, 65] More recently, kinetic studies have indicated [66, 67] that the reaction between phenyllithium and β-chlorostyrene is third order (second order with respect to RLi). On the basis of this fact, Wittig [66] suggested a mechanism involving the intermediate dilithio compound XXXIV. However, it has been pointed

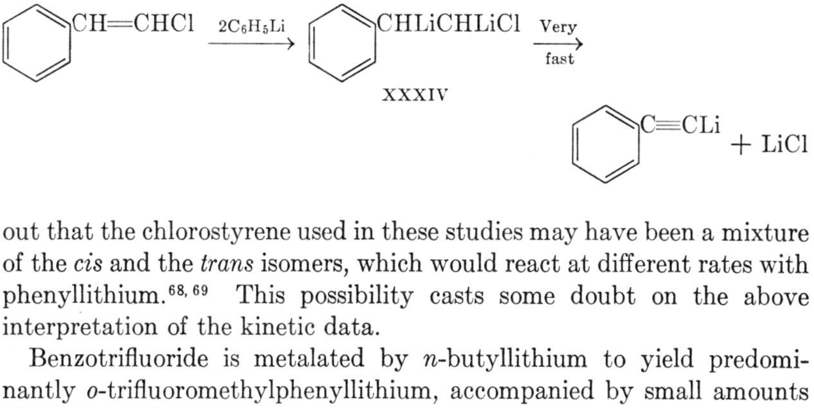

$$\bigcirc CH{=}CHCl \xrightarrow{2C_6H_5Li} \bigcirc CHLiCHLiCl \xrightarrow[\text{fast}]{\text{Very}}$$

XXXIV

$$\bigcirc C{\equiv}CLi + LiCl$$

out that the chlorostyrene used in these studies may have been a mixture of the *cis* and the *trans* isomers, which would react at different rates with phenyllithium.[68, 69] This possibility casts some doubt on the above interpretation of the kinetic data.

Benzotrifluoride is metalated by n-butyllithium to yield predominantly o-trifluoromethylphenyllithium, accompanied by small amounts of the m- and p-isomers.[37] This appears to be the only simple halide that yields a stable metalation product.

[63] Gilman and Haubein, *J. Am. Chem. Soc.*, **67**, 1420 (1945).
[64] Wittig and Witt, *Ber.*, **74**, 1474 (1941).
[65] Gilman, Langham, and Moore, *J. Am. Chem. Soc.*, **62**, 2327 (1940).
[66] Wittig and Harborth, *Ber.*, **77**, 315 (1944).
[67] Grummitt and Lucier, *Abstracts of Papers, 121st meeting American Chemical Society,* Mar. 31–April 2, 1952, p. 49K.
[68] Cristol, Ragsdale, and Meek, *J. Am. Chem. Soc.*, **73**, 810 (1951).
[69] J. J. Lucier, private communication.

Amines. The amino nitrogen atom is able to direct metalation *ortho* to itself in the absence of more strongly directing hetero atoms or groups. Primary, secondary, and tertiary amines have all been metalated by organolithium compounds. Aniline with *n*-butyllithium gives anthranilic acid after extended refluxing followed by carbonation, while diphenylamine and N-*n*-butylaniline are metalated by the same reagent to yield the analogous N-substituted anthranilic acids on carbonation.[70] In the metalation of primary and secondary amines, as with other compounds containing hydrogen attached to a hetero atom, it is necessary to use an excess of the metalating agent in order to effect metalation after the active hydrogens have been replaced by metal. The species actually metalated is, of course, the lithium salt of the compound in question. The metalation of benzylamine and of dibenzylamine by organolithium compounds results in the appearance of a bright red color, and the reaction has found use as a qualitative test for active organometallic compounds.[71] Although the color would suggest that the metalation is lateral, the carbonation of a mixture of dibenzylamine and *n*-butyllithium results in the formation of *o*-carboxydibenzylamine (**XXXV**) [71] and indicates that a rearrangement of the type common to some benzylmetallic compounds [72-76] may take place.

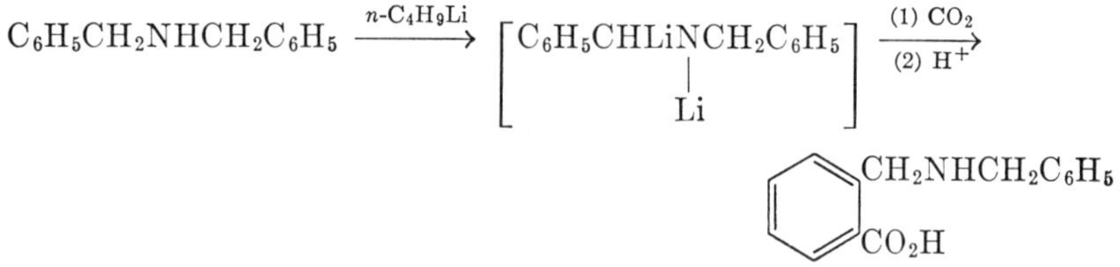

$$C_6H_5CH_2NHCH_2C_6H_5 \xrightarrow{n\text{-}C_4H_9Li} \left[\begin{array}{c} C_6H_5CHLiNCH_2C_6H_5 \\ | \\ Li \end{array} \right] \xrightarrow[(2)\ H^+]{(1)\ CO_2}$$

CH₂NHCH₂C₆H₅ / CO₂H

XXXV

With the previously mentioned exception of triphenylamine, which is metalated in the *meta* position, simple tertiary aromatic amines undergo *ortho* metalation. 9-Ethylcarbazole (**XXXVI**) undergoes monometala-

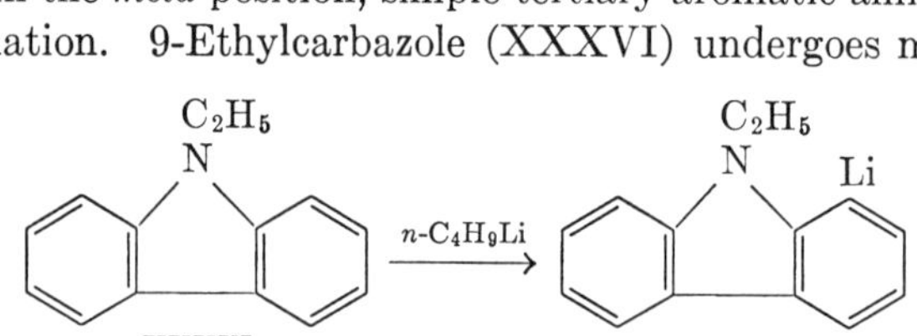

XXXVI

[70] Gilman, Brown, Webb, and Spatz, *J. Am. Chem. Soc.*, **62**, 977 (1940).
[71] Gilman and Woods, *J. Am. Chem. Soc.*, **65**, 33 (1943).
[72] Gilman and Breuer, *J. Am. Chem. Soc.*, **56**, 1127 (1934).
[73] Gilman and Nelson, *J. Am. Chem. Soc.*, **61**, 741 (1939).
[74] Gilman and Harris, *J. Am. Chem. Soc.*, **53**, 3541 (1931).
[75] Gaertner, *J. Am. Chem. Soc.*, **73**, 3934 (1951).
[76] Gaertner, *J. Am. Chem. Soc.*, **74**, 2185 (1952).

tion in the 1 position when treated with excess n-butyllithium.[77] 9-Methylcarbazole, however, is dimetalated by the same reagent under corresponding conditions. This difference in behavior has been ascribed to diminished steric hindrance in the methyl compound.[78] 9-Phenylcarbazole is metalated in the 9-phenyl ring by n-butyllithium.[50a, 50b]

Ammonium Salts. Tetramethylammonium bromide reacts with phenyllithium to yield a mixture of mono- and di-metalated products. When these are separated (on the basis of differing solubilities in diethyl ether) and treated with benzophenone, trimethyl(β-hydroxy-β,β-diphenylethyl)ammonium bromide (XXXVII) and dimethylbis(β-hydroxy-β,β-diphenylethyl)ammonium bromide (XXXVIII) are formed.[79]

$$(CH_3)_4\overset{+}{N}\ \overset{-}{Br} + C_6H_5Li \rightarrow (CH_3)_3\overset{+}{N}CH_2Li\ \overset{-}{Br} + (CH_3)_2\overset{+}{N}(CH_2Li)_2\ \overset{-}{Br}$$

$$\downarrow (C_6H_5)_2CO \qquad\qquad \downarrow (C_6H_5)_2CO$$

$$(CH_3)_3\overset{+}{N}CH_2C(C_6H_5)_2OH\ \overset{-}{Br} \qquad (CH_3)_2\overset{+}{N}[CH_2C(C_6H_5)_2OH]_2\ \overset{-}{Br}$$
$$\text{XXXVII} \qquad\qquad\qquad \text{XXXVIII}$$

The monometalation of tetramethylammonium chloride[80] and the di- and tetra-metalation of tetramethylphosphonium iodide[79] with phenyllithium have also been reported.

With certain quaternary ammonium salts, metalation with RLi is followed by a carbonium-ion migration similar to that observed in the alkali-induced Stevens rearrangement of ammonium[81] and sulfonium[82] salts. Bis-(α,α'-o-xylylene)ammonium bromide (XXXIX) reacts with phenyllithium to give, after rearrangement, the tertiary amine XL.

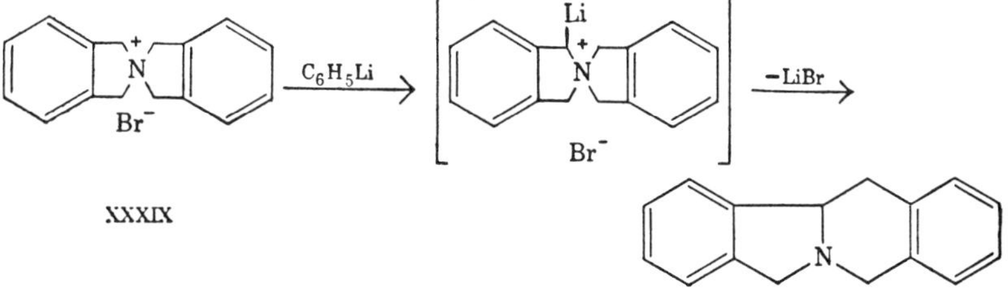

XXXIX

XL

[77] Gilman and Kirby, *J. Org. Chem.*, **1**, 146 (1936).
[78] Gilman and Spatz, *J. Org. Chem.*, **17**, 860 (1952).
[79] Wittig and Rieber, *Ann.*, **562**, 177 (1949).
[80] Wittig and Wetterling, *Ann.*, **557**, 193 (1947).
[81] Thomson and Stevens, *J. Chem. Soc.*, **1932**, 55.
[82] Thomson and Stevens, *J. Chem. Soc.*, **1932**, 69.

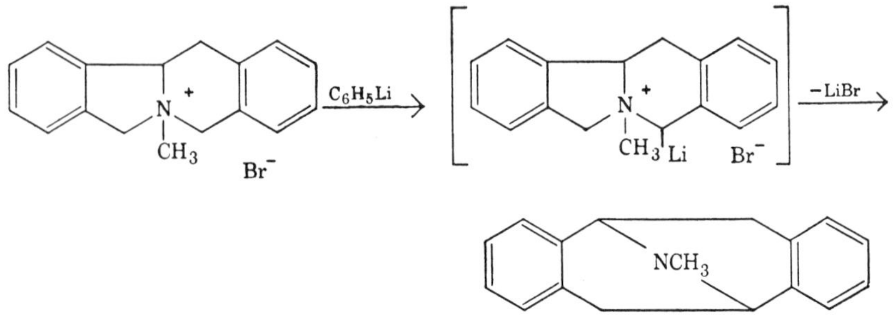

XLI

The methobromide of XL reacts in turn with phenyllithium to yield a second rearranged amine, XLI.[83]

Sulfur Compounds. The sulfide linkage apparently activates an *ortho* position toward metalation more strongly than a tertiary amino linkage does. When 9-ethylcarbazole and dibenzothiophene are allowed to compete for an insufficient quantity of *n*-butyllithium, only the dibenzothiophene is metalated; and, while 1-(9-ethylcarbazolyl)lithium (XLII)

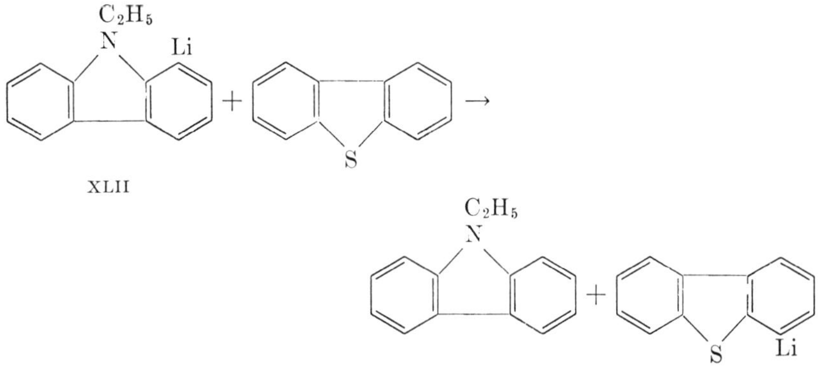

XLII

metalates dibenzothiophene in the 4 position, 4-dibenzothienyllithium has no effect upon 9-ethylcarbazole.[84] 10-Ethylphenothiazine (XLIII) and 10-phenylphenothiazine (XLIV) are both metalated by *n*-butyl-

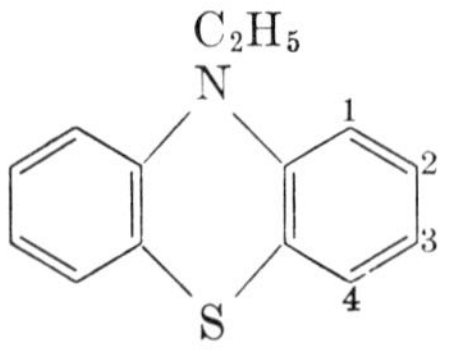

XLIII 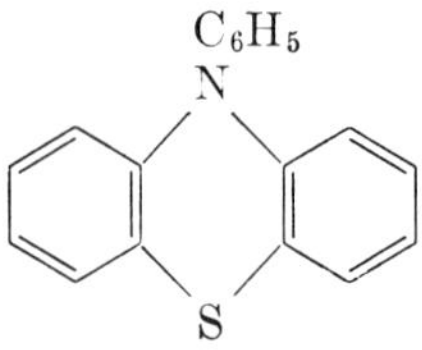   **XLIV**

[83] Wittig, Tenhaeff, Schoch, and Koenig, *Ann.*, **572**, 1 (1951).
[84] Gilman and Stuckwisch, *J. Am. Chem. Soc.*, **67**, 877 (1945).

lithium to yield 10-substituted phenothiazinemonocarboxylic acids on carbonation.[85] The rule of precedence given above indicates that the 4 position is probably attacked in each case. The acid obtained from 10-ethylphenothiazine is reductively cleaved by hydriodic acid to yield 3-carboxydiphenylamine, thus proving the original acid to have been either the 2- or the 4-substituted compound. 10-Ethylphenothiazine-2-carboxylic acid prepared by an independent synthesis is different from the acid obtained from the organolithium compound, which accordingly is presumed to be the 4-carboxylic acid.[86] Other 10-substituted phenothiazines have also been metalated with n-butyllithium, but the positions of substitution have not been rigorously determined.[87] The rule of precedence of sulfur over nitrogen in determining position of metalation apparently does not hold for secondary amines, for phenothiazine itself is metalated in the 1 position, and not in the 4 position, by n-butyllithium.[88]

Thiophene is metalated in the 2 position by n-butyllithium with unusual rapidity and in good yield.[6, 89] When the resulting 2-thienyllithium is added to quinoline and the adduct is oxidized, 2-(2'-thienyl)-quinoline (XLV) is obtained. The latter compound can in turn be

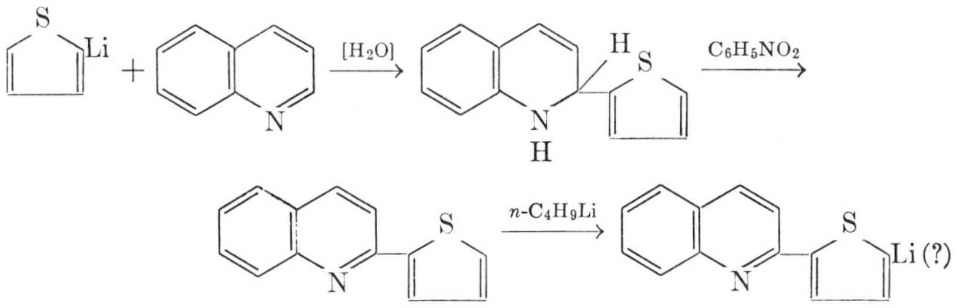

XLV

metalated rapidly, probably in the 5' position.[6] This reaction represents the comparatively rare case in which metalation proceeds with enough speed to compete successfully with addition to the azomethine linkage and recalls the metalation of 2-phenylquinoline by mesityllithium mentioned previously.

Benzothiazole, like thiophene, is metalated very rapidly and in good yield by n-butyllithium.[28] The metalation is carried out at low tem-

[85] Gilman, P. Van Ess, and Shirley, *J. Am. Chem. Soc.*, **66**, 1214 (1944).

[86] Baltzly, Harfenist, and Webb, *J. Am. Chem. Soc.*, **68**, 2673 (1946).

[87] R. D. Nelson, Doctoral Dissertion, Iowa State College, 1951.

[88] Gilman, Shirley, and P. Van Ess, *J. Am. Chem. Soc.*, **66**, 625 (1944).

[89] Gilman, Benkeser, and Dunn, *J. Am. Chem. Soc.*, **72**, 1690 (1950).

peratures and results in the product XLVI. Phenyllithium can also be

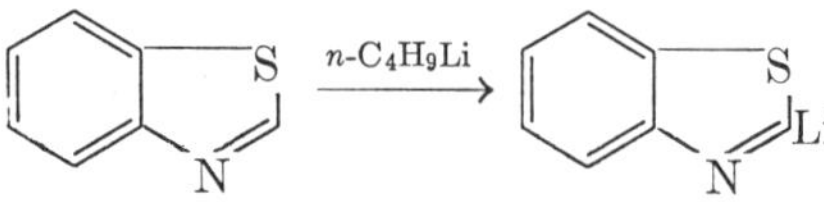

XLVI

used to effect this metalation.[90] It is interesting to note that benzoxa-zole, the oxygen analog of benzothiazole, apparently yields no metalation product when treated with n-butyllithium.[90]

Diphenyl sulfide is metalated in the *ortho* position by n-butyllithium;[7] methyl phenyl sulfide, however, undergoes lateral rather than nuclear metalation with the same reagent to yield phenylmercaptoacetic acid (XLVII) on carbonation.[8, 91] The less reactive metalating agent, n-butylmagnesium bromide, metalates methyl phenyl sulfide in the *ortho* position. This tendency toward lateral metalation by n-butyllithium persists in other methyl aryl sulfides but disappears in the higher alkyl phenyl sulfides; when the alkyl group is ethyl, n-propyl, isopropyl, n-butyl or cyclohexyl, metalation occurs in the *ortho* position of the aromatic nucleus.[91]

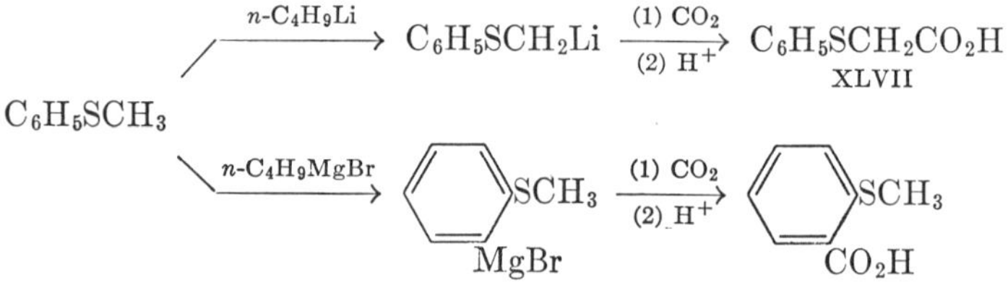

In the metalation of sulfides, cleavage may occur as a side reaction. When methyl phenyl sulfide is metalated by n-butyllithium, yields of thiophenol as high as 23% have been obtained under drastic conditions. In this respect, as in others, sulfur stands midway between oxygen and selenium, for anisole gives almost exclusively metalation with n-butyl-lithium while methyl phenyl selenide gives only cleavage products.[91]

The metalation of sulfur compounds other than sulfides has not been extensively studied. Dibenzothiophene-5-oxide (XLVIII) undergoes

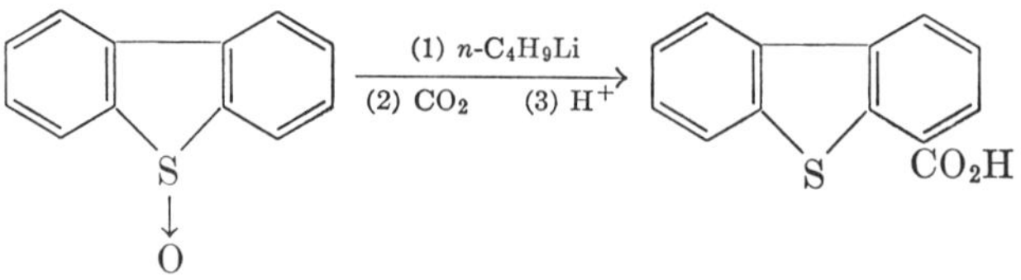

XLVIII

[90] J. A. Beel, Doctoral Dissertation, Iowa State College, 1949.
[91] Gilman and Webb, *J. Am. Chem. Soc.*, **71**, 4062 (1949).

reductive metalation with n-butyllithium at low temperatures to give a good yield of dibenzothiophene-4-carboxylic acid on carbonation.[92] The corresponding sulfone, dibenzothiophene-5-dioxide (XLIX), is

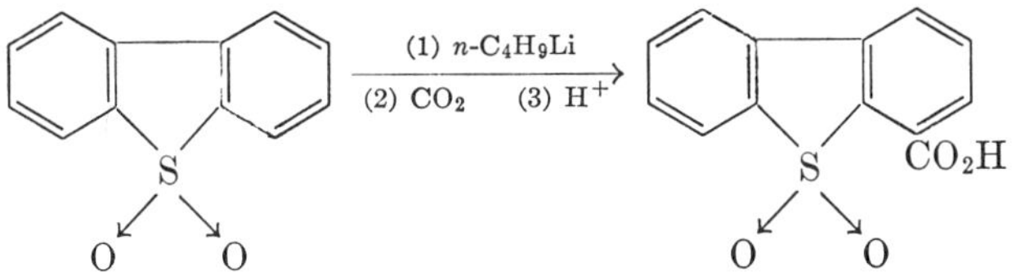

XLIX

metalated without reduction by the same reagent.[93]   Diphenyl sulfone can be either monometalated in the 2 position [94] or dimetalated in the 2 and 2' positions [93] by n-butyllithium, depending on the proportion of the reactants. m-Bromodiphenyl sulfone is metalated to yield, on carbonation, the acid L.   The p-bromo isomer yields 4-bromo-2-carboxy-

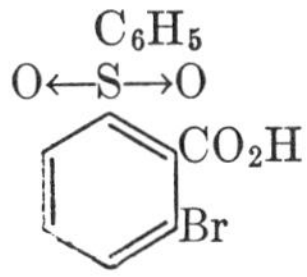

L

diphenyl sulfone, together with a little p-carboxydiphenyl sulfone resulting from halogen-metal interconversion, while the o-bromo isomer undergoes halogen-metal interconversion exclusively.   Phenyl 2-thienyl sulfone is metalated in the thienyl rather than in the phenyl nucleus, as might be expected from the ease of metalation of thiophene itself, to yield the acid LI after carbonation.[94]

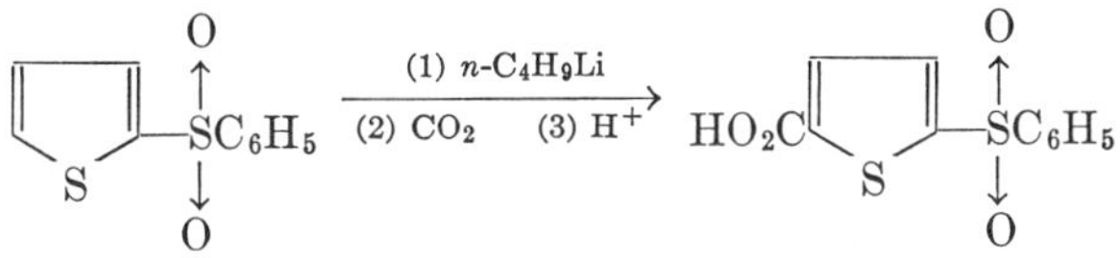

LI

Diphenyl disulfide is metalated in both nuclei by n-butyllithium; carbonation results in the formation of 2,2'-dicarboxydiphenyl disulfide

[92] Gilman and Esmay, *J. Am. Chem. Soc.*, **74**, 266 (1952).

[93] D. L. Esmay, Doctoral Dissertation, Iowa State College, 1951.

[94] Truce and Amos, *J. Am. Chem. Soc.*, **73**, 3013 (1951).

(LII).[91] The same product is formed in small amounts when a mixture

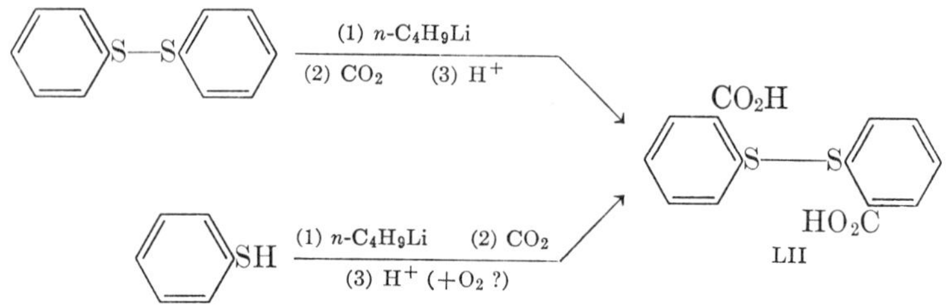

of thiophenol and n-butyllithium is carbonated.[95]

Ethers, Phenols, and Alcohols. The ether linkage has an even greater activating effect in metalation than does the sulfide linkage. Again, this order was established through competitive metalations. When a mixture of dibenzofuran and dibenzothiophene reacts with an insufficient quantity of n-butyllithium, only the dibenzofuran is metalated. 4-Dibenzothienyllithium (LIII) metalates dibenzofuran in the 4 position,

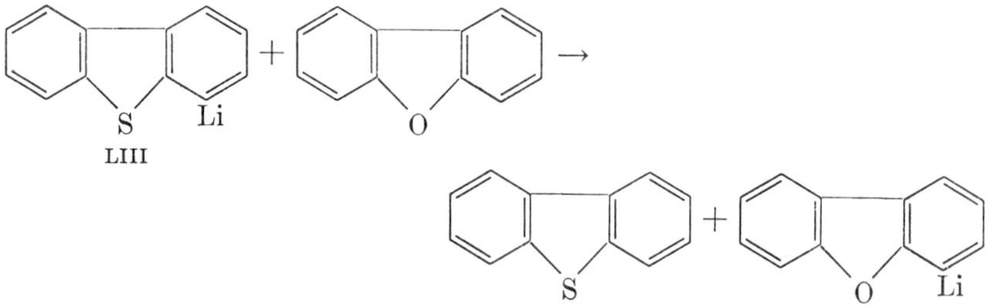

but the reverse reaction does not proceed. Similarly, the metalation of phenoxathiin (LIV) by n-butyllithium occurs *ortho* to the oxygen rather

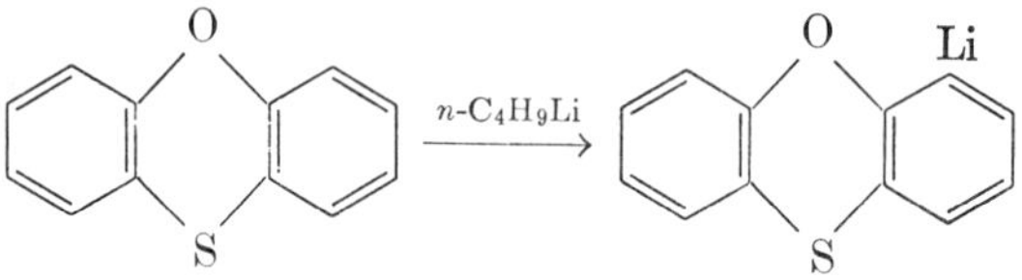

than to the sulfur atom.[96, 97] That the ether linkage also takes precedence over the trifluoromethyl group in governing the course of metalation is suggested by the competitive nuclear metalation of anisole and benzotrifluoride by n-butyllithium; in this reaction anisole alone is metalated.[37] Another reaction in which an ethereal oxygen atom com-

---

[95] Gilman, Arntzen, and Webb, *J. Org. Chem.*, **10**, 374 (1945).

[96] Gilman, M. Van Ess, Willis, and Stuckwisch, *J. Am. Chem. Soc.*, **62**, 2606 (1940).

[97] For similar competitive metalations involving organosodium compounds, see Gilman and Breuer, *J. Am. Chem. Soc.*, **56**, 1123 (1934).

petes with a less active hetero function is the metalation of 2-ethoxy-quinoline by n-butyllithium.[98] The 2-ethoxyquinoline is partially converted into 2-n-butylquinoline by displacement of the ethoxyl group and partially metalated in the 3 position to give the organolithium compound LV.

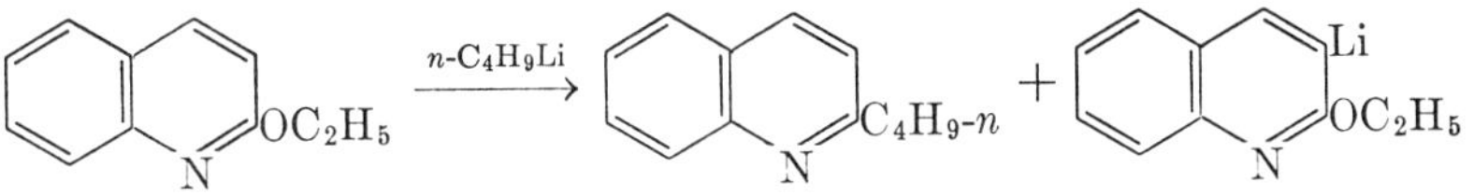

Most ethers, though not all, are more readily metalated than phenols. This difference may be due partly to electronic influences [38, 43] and partly to the insolubility of the lithium salts of phenols. 2-Methoxynaphthalene [38] gives a higher yield of metalation product than 2-naphthol,[95] while both 2-methoxyphenanthrene and its 3-methoxy isomer are metalated in substantially higher yields than the corresponding phenols.[47] In 4-hydroxydibenzofuran (LVI), where both groups are present,

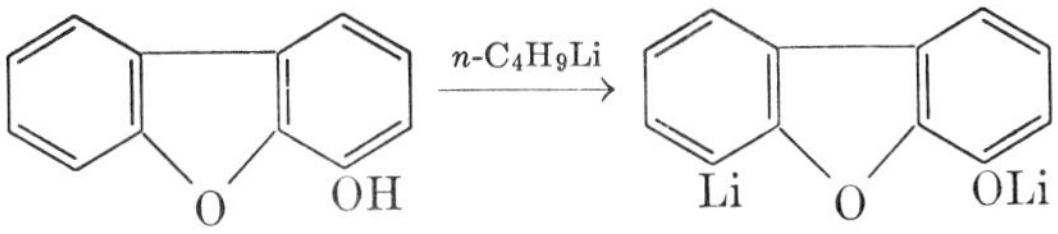

metalation occurs *ortho* to the ethereal rather than to the phenolic oxygen atom.[99] However, 2-hydroxydibenzofuran is metalated in the opposite way to give the derivative LVII,[99] and 9-hydroxyphenanthrene

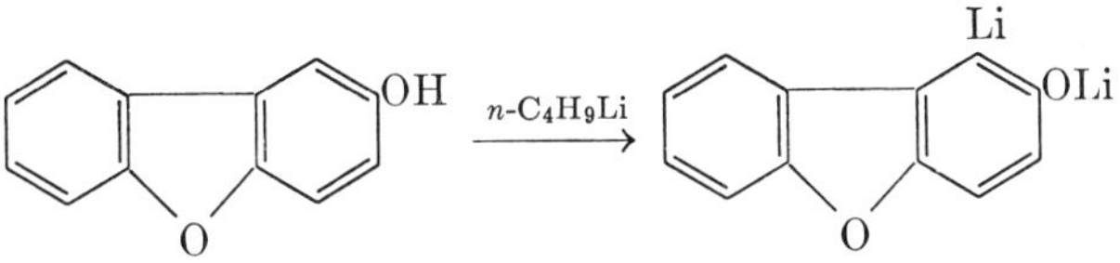

gives a higher yield of metalation product than does its methyl ether.[47] The available evidence indicates than an aryloxy group is less effective in directing metalation than an alkoxy group. 4-Methoxydiphenyl ether (LVIII) is metalated in the 3 position;[100] 2-methoxydibenzofuran

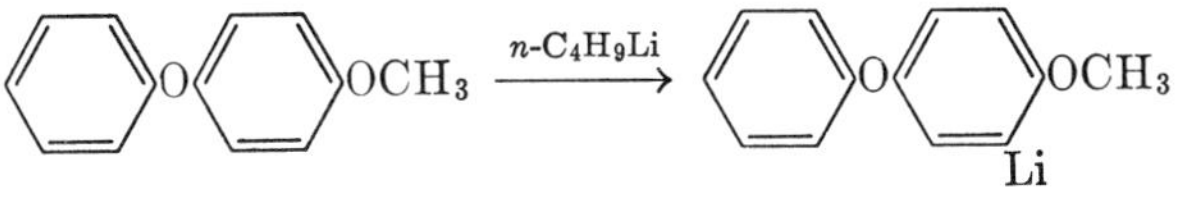

[98] Gilman and Beel, *J. Am. Chem. Soc.*, **73**, 32 (1951).
[99] Gilman, Willis, Cook, Webb, and Meals, *J. Am. Chem. Soc.*, **62**, 667 (1940).
[100] Langham, Brewster, and Gilman, *J. Am. Chem. Soc.*, **63**, 545 (1941).

gives a mixture of 1- and 3-metalated derivatives,[7] while 2,8-dimethoxy-dibenzofuran (LIX) is dimetalated [101] to yield a product which has been

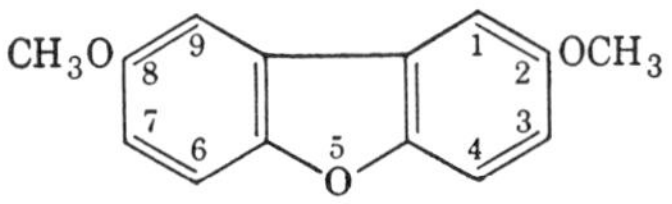

LIX

shown [102] to be either the 1,3- or the 1,7-dilithio compound. 4-Methoxy-dibenzofuran, however, is metalated *ortho* to each oxygen atom; car-bonation yields the isomeric acids LX and LXI.[99]

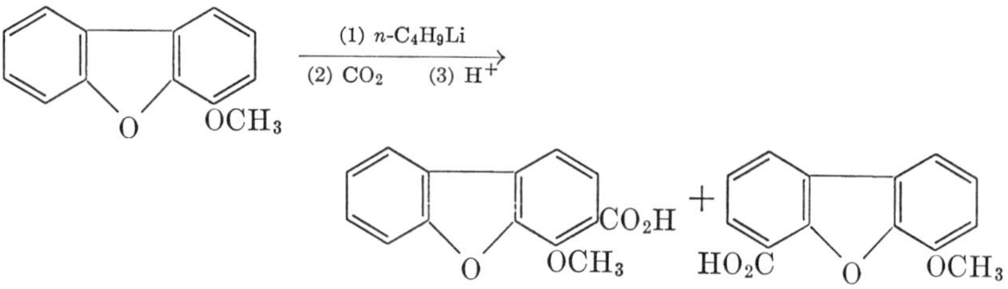

LX   LXI

Anisole is metalated in the ring only by *n*-butyllithium to yield *o*-anisyllithium; [7, 8] but *o*-methylanisole with *n*-butyllithium gives, on carbonation, not only the expected 2-methoxy-3-methylbenzoic acid (LXII) but also some *o*-methoxyphenylacetic acid (LXIII) resulting

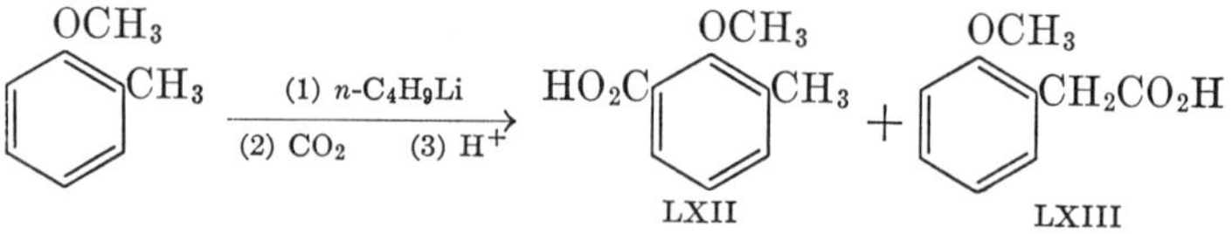

LXII   LXIII

from lateral metalation. The reaction of *o*-methylanisole with *n*-amyl-sodium in petroleum ether results in lateral metalation exclusively. The closely related 2-ethylanisole is metalated only in the nucleus by *n*-butyllithium, while *n*-amylsodium gives a mixture of lateral and nuclear metalation products.[103]

Certain ethers in which there is a particularly active α-hydrogen atom are metalated to yield products that rearrange to lithium alkoxides. Benzyl methyl ether (LXIV) rearranges upon treatment with phenyl-

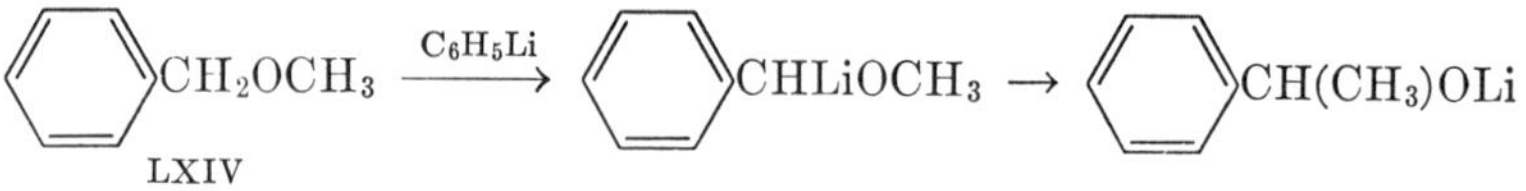

LXIV

[101] Swislowsky, *Iowa State Coll. J. Sci.*, **14**, 92 (1939) [*C. A.*, **34**, 6273 (1940)].
[102] Hogg, *Iowa State Coll. J. Sci.*, **20**, 15 (1945) [*C. A.*, **40**, 4716 (1946)].
[103] Letsinger and Schnizer, *J. Org. Chem.*, **16**, 869 (1951).

lithium to give the lithium salt of phenylmethylcarbinol.[104,*] Dibenzyl ether rearranges in a similar fashion to give the salt of phenylbenzylcarbinol, and a large number of 9-fluorenyl ethers of the type LXV give salts of the corresponding 9-substituted-9-fluorenols LXVI.[105] Reactions

LXV LXVI

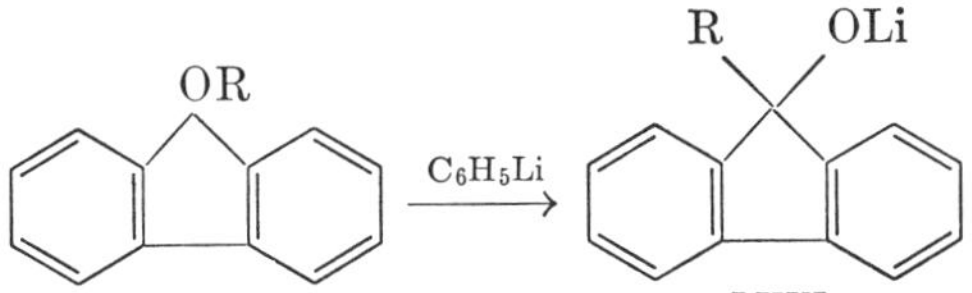

of this kind, which are similar to the metalation rearrangements of ammonium salts discussed earlier, also take place with metalating agents other than lithium compounds. A study of the dependence of the speed of rearrangement upon the type of metal has been made.[106]

Methyl trityl ether reacts with either phenyllithium or *n*-butyllithium to yield 9-phenyl-9-fluorenyllithium (LXVII). Carbonation of the reaction mixture produces either 9-phenylfluorene-9-carboxylic acid or 3,3-diphenylphthalide (LXVIII), depending on the conditions of

LXVII

LXVIII

* However, the same ether has been metalated by *n*-butyllithium to yield, after carbonation, a product tentatively identified as 2-methoxymethylbenzoic acid; see ref. 70.

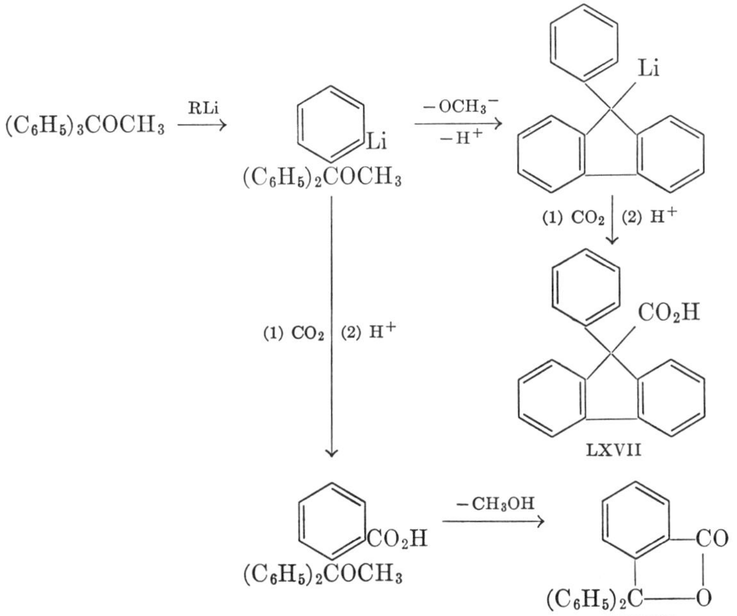

[104] Wittig and Löhmann, *Ann.*, **550**, 260 (1942).

[105] Wittig, Doser, and Lorenz, *Ann.*, **562**, 192 (1949).

[106] Wittig and Happe, *Ann.*, **557**, 205 (1947).

reaction.[107]   Although the mechanism has not yet been clarified, it seems probable that the first step is an *ortho* metalation, analogous to the metalation of triphenylcarbinol.[49]

The metalation of aryl ethers containing halogen substituents is sometimes complicated by the removal of the halogen atom by interconversion * or coupling reactions. No metalation of an ether containing a halogen atom *ortho* to the ether linkage has been recorded; instead, halogen-metal interconversion (of *o*-bromo and *o*-iodo ethers [100, 108]) and coupling (of *o*-chloro and *o*-fluoro ethers [62]) have been observed. The behavior of *m*-halogenated ethers toward RLi compounds is more complicated. For instance, 3-bromodibenzofuran reacts with *n*-butyllithium to give, on carbonation, a mixture of dibenzofuran-3-carboxylic acid and its 4 isomer.[109] It is thought that halogen-metal interconversion first takes place, yielding 3-dibenzofuryllithium (LXIX); that this com-

pound then metalates 3-bromodibenzofuran to give 3-bromo-4-dibenzofuryllithium (LXX) and dibenzofuran; and, finally, that the newly formed RLi compound metalates the dibenzofuran.

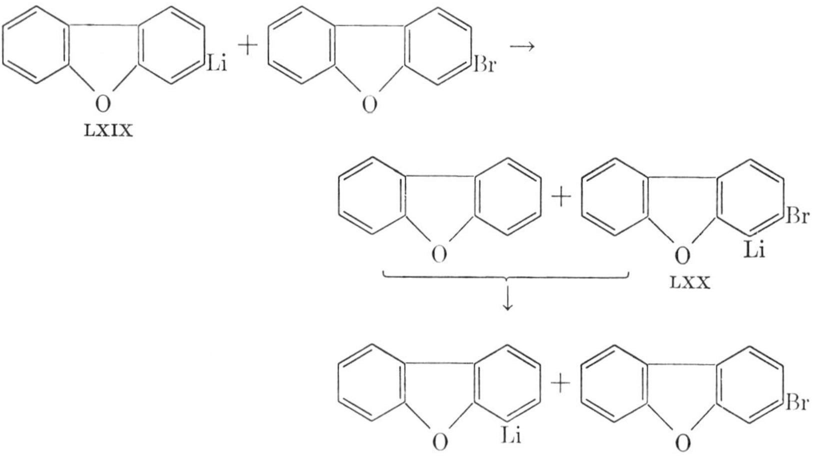

The reaction of *m*-iodoanisole with phenyllithium yields, after hydrolysis, a mixture of iodobenzene and *m*-phenylanisole. The latter product does not result simply from a one-step coupling process, for, if the reaction mixture is treated with benzophenone before hydrolysis,

---

* The occurrence of metalation as a side reaction in the halogen-metal interconversion of such ethers has been discussed in an earlier volume of this series (see ref. 39).

[107] Gilman, Meikle, and J. W. Morton, Jr., *J. Am. Chem. Soc.*, **74**, 6282 (1952).

[108] Wittig and Fuhrmann, *Ber.*, **73**, 1197 (1940).

[109] Gilman, Willis, and Swislowsky, *J. Am. Chem. Soc.*, **61**, 1371 (1939).

the carbinol LXXIII is obtained, showing that the intermediate RLi

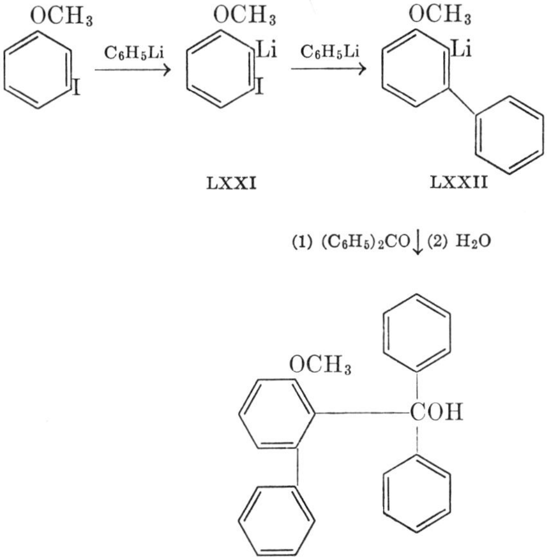

LXXI   LXXII

(1) $(C_6H_5)_2CO$↓ (2) H_2O

LXXIII

compound LXXII must have been present. This organolithium compound does not arise from the metalation of the coupling product, m-phenylanisole, by phenyllithium, for this metalation has been found to take place in the position *para* to the phenyl group. Consequently, the course of the reaction must be that shown in the accompanying formulation, in which m-iodoanisole is first metalated in the 2 position to give the halogen-containing RLi compound LXXI, which then undergoes coupling with phenyllithium to form LXXII. The other three m-halogenoanisoles behave in a similar manner toward phenyllithium.[108]

When a p-halogenophenyl ether is treated with an organolithium compound, either halogen-metal interconversion or metalation or both may occur, depending upon the halogen atom, the kind and amount of RLi used, and the time of reaction. All four p-halogenoanisoles are metalated *ortho* to the oxygen atom by phenyllithium [108] but when a mixture of n-butyllithium and p-bromo- or p-iodo-anisole is carbonated after a short period of reaction, only p-methoxybenzoic acid is obtained. If the same mixture is allowed to react for a longer time, carbonation then produces the corresponding 5-halogeno-2-methoxybenzoic acids. These facts suggest that interconversion takes place initially, and that, if sufficient time is allowed, the newly formed p-anisyllithium (LXXIV) metalates the unreacted halogenoether to give the final product LXXV.

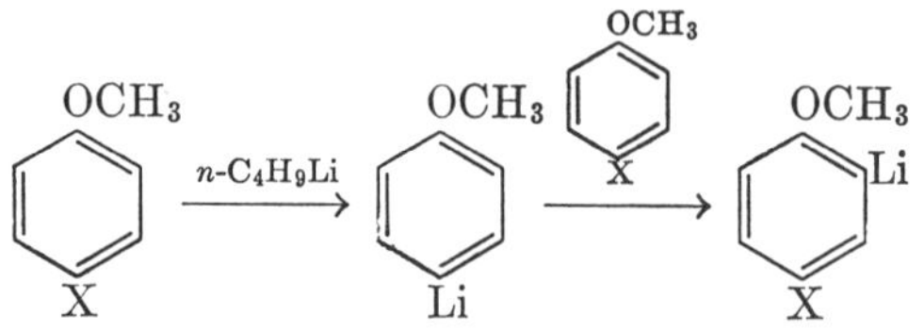

The fact that metalation products are isolated in higher yields when an excess of the halogenoether is used agrees with the suggested mechanism. Higher temperatures also favor the isolation of metalation rather than of interconversion product.[110]

Other metalations which seem to proceed by a two-stage process are those of 2-bromodibenzofuran [9,110] and of p-bromo- and p-iodo-diphenyl ether by n-butyllithium.[100] It is likely that the metalation of p-fluoro- and p-chloro-phenyl ethers is a simple one-stage process, since fluorine and chlorine do not undergo interconversion readily.[39] The p-halogeno-diphenyl ethers are metalated *ortho* to oxygen in the ring that contains the halogen substituent.[100]

Several arylcarbinols have been metalated by RLi compounds. Benzyl alcohol is metalated by n-butyllithium to yield o-carboxybenzyl alcohol (LXXVI) on carbonation,[70] while triphenylcarbinol undergoes

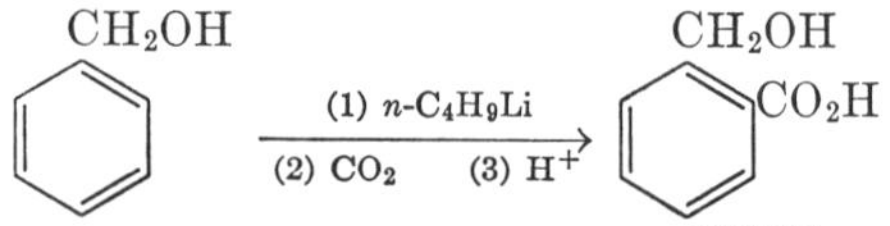

dimetalation with n-butyllithium to give the lithium salt of 2,2′-dilithio-triphenylcarbinol (LXXVII), the carbonation of which results in the formation of the lactonic acid LXXVIII.[49, 70]

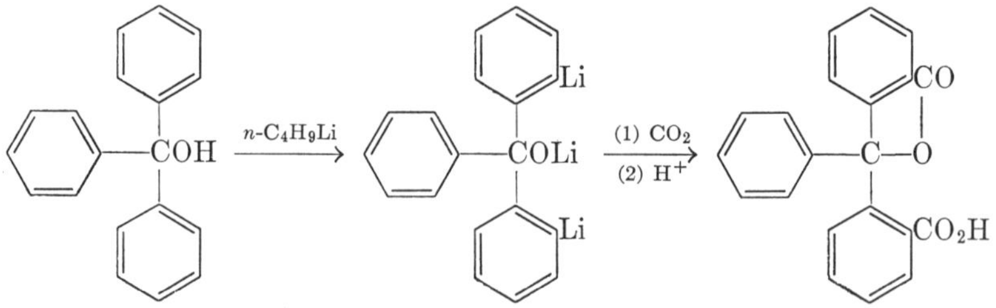

[110] Gilman, Langham, and Willis, *J. Am. Chem. Soc.*, **62**, 346 (1940).

OTHER TYPES OF METALATING AGENTS

The organometallic compounds of sodium [111-115] and of potassium [111, 116] have frequently been used to effect metalations; but only in a few instances [103, 117] have any systematic comparisons been drawn between these compounds and their lithium analogs with respect to their behavior in metalations. A series of metalations of dibenzofuran by ethyllithium, ethylsodium, and ethylpotassium shows that the three organometallic compounds give about the same yield of metalation product when the reaction is allowed to go to completion, but that, if the metalation is interrupted after two and one-half hours, the relative amounts of metalation products from the lithium, sodium, and potassium compounds are, respectively, 1, 46, and 139. Moreover, ethyllithium gives exclusively monometalation, while both ethylsodium and ethylpotassium react with dibenzofuran to yield a mixture of monometalated and 4,6-dimetalated products. The potassium compound gives a larger proportion of the dimetalated derivative.[117]

Lithium aluminum hydride, which resembles the organolithium compounds in containing an extremely basic anion, metalates fluorene when tetrahydrofuran is the solvent,[118] but not under milder conditions in diethyl ether.[54]

A few metalations employing the organometallic compounds of the alkaline-earth metals are known.[119, 120] Of particular interest is the metalation of dibenzothiophene by phenylcalcium iodide, in which substitution occurs anomalously *meta* to the sulfur atom.[121] The Grignard reagents usually do not effect metalation except under forcing conditions and the yields are generally poor.[91, 122-124]

The amides [125, 126] and hydroxides [127, 128] of alkali metals, and the free

[111] Gilman and Kirby, *J. Am. Chem. Soc.*, **58**, 2074 (1936).

[112] A. A. Morton and Hechenbleikner, *J. Am. Chem. Soc.*, **58**, 2599 (1936).

[113] A. A. Morton, Little, and Strong, *J. Am. Chem. Soc.*, **65**, 1339 (1943).

[114] A. A. Morton, Massengale, and Brown, *J. Am. Chem. Soc.*, **67**, 1620 (1945).

[115] A. A. Morton and Patterson, *J. Am. Chem. Soc.*, **65**, 1346 (1943).

[116] Gilman and Tolman, *J. Am. Chem. Soc.*, **68**, 522 (1946).

[117] Gilman and Young, *J. Org. Chem.*, **1**, 315 (1936).

[118] Trevoy and Brown, *J. Am. Chem. Soc.*, **71**, 1675 (1949).

[119] Gilman, Meals, O'Donnell, and Woods, *J. Am. Chem. Soc.*, **65**, 268 (1943).

[120] Gilman, O'Donnell, and Woods, *J. Am. Chem. Soc.*, **67**, 922 (1945).

[121] Gilman, Jacoby, and Pacevitz, *J. Org. Chem.*, **3**, 120 (1938).

[122] Challenger and Gibson, *J. Chem. Soc.*, **1940**, 305.

[123] Gilman and Haubein, *J. Am. Chem. Soc.*, **67**, 1033 (1945).

[124] Tucker and Whalley, *J. Chem. Soc.*, **1949**, 50.

[125] Werner and Grob, *Ber.*, **37**, 2898 (1904).

[126] Yost and Hauser, *J. Am. Chem. Soc.*, **69**, 2325 (1947).

[127] Weger and Döring, *Ber.*, **36**, 878 (1903).

[128] Weissgerber, *Ber.*, **34**, 1659 (1901).

metals themselves, [129-131] have been used in the metalation of hydrocarbons containing active hydrogen atoms.

Less closely related to the organolithium compounds are certain heavy-metal salts which have found use as metalating agents. The most familiar members of this group are the mercuric salts,[132] whose substitution reactions have been investigated from the earliest days of organic chemistry. The chlorides of gold,[133] tellurium,[134] thallium,[135] and germanium [136] have also been found to metalate certain aromatic nuclei. The presence, in these metalating agents, of a strong Lewis acid and the absence of a strongly basic anion suggest that their operation is mechanistically different from that of the organometallic compounds; but only in the case of mercuration [137] has the mechanism of heavy-metal substitution been explored in any detail.

EXPERIMENTAL CONDITIONS

The laboratory operations involved in organolithium metalations are analogous to those encountered in halogen-metal interconversions: [39] first, an organolithium compound, usually n-butyllithium, is prepared; next, the RLi compound is allowed to react with the substance to be metalated; and, finally, the newly formed organolithium compound is converted into a derivative. In all steps of the process, those precautions proper to the handling of reactive organometallic compounds are observed: moisture is rigidly excluded from the apparatus, and an inert atmosphere (usually dry nitrogen) is provided. The most generally followed procedure for metalation involves boiling under reflux a diethyl ether solution of the substance to be metalated together with an excess of n-butyllithium for a period of from four to twenty-four hours. However, successful metalations have been carried out in different solvents, at different temperatures, and with the use of different metalating agents from those mentioned above. A study [138] in which dibenzofuran was metalated with a number of different organolithium compounds and in a variety of solvents has shown that the normal alkyllithium compounds

[129] Saint-Pierre, *Bull. soc. chim. France*, [3], **5**, 292 (1891).

[130] Schick and Hartough, *J. Am. Chem. Soc.*, **70**, 286, 1646, 1647 (1948).

[131] Schlenk and Holtz, *Ber.*, **49**, 603 (1916).

[132] Whitmore, *Organic Compounds of Mercury*, Chemical Catalog Company, New York, 1921.

[133] Kharasch and Beck, *J. Am. Chem. Soc.*, **56**, 2057 (1934).

[134] Morgan and Burgess, *J. Chem. Soc.*, **1929**, 1103.

[135] Gilman and Abbott, *J. Am. Chem. Soc.*, **65**, 122 (1943).

[136] Schwartz and Reinhardt, *Ber.*, **65**, 1743 (1932).

[137] Klapproth and Westheimer, *J. Am. Chem. Soc.*, **72**, 4461 (1950).

[138] Gilman, Moore, and Baine, *J. Am. Chem. Soc.*, **63**, 2479 (1941).

are better metalating agents for dibenzofuran than are their secondary and tertiary isomers when diethyl ether is the solvent, but that this order is reversed in petroleum ether. Under comparable conditions in diethyl ether, the yield of metalation product from dibenzofuran decreases in the order n-butyllithium > ethyllithium > n-amyllithium > phenyllithium > methyllithium. n-Butyllithium metalates dibenzofuran in higher yield in di-n-butyl ether than in diethyl ether. The influence of the solvent on the metalation of dibenzothiophene by n-butyllithium has been studied. Of the solvents used, di-n-butyl ether at a temperature of 80° gave the highest yield (90%) of 4-dibenzothienyllithium. Under comparable conditions, no metalation at all was observed in benzene, dioxane, or petroleum ether.[139]

The effect of temperature, and of the type of RLi compound used, upon the yield of product from the metalation of benzothiazole has been investigated. This reaction is peculiar among metalations in its high speed and in the fact that a low temperature must be maintained to prevent decomposition of the product. It was found that methyllithium, phenyllithium, and n-butyllithium all effect metalation in yields exceeding 68%; the best yield (89.7%) was obtained with n-butyllithium at −75° by interrupting the reaction immediately after all the RLi had been added.[90] The studies just mentioned appear to be the only ones in which careful attempts have been made to find optimum conditions for the metalation of specific compounds by RLi. They indicate that whenever a high yield is of critical importance an investigation of the influence of solvent, temperature, and metalating agent may be worth while. In routine metalations, however, considerations of convenience and economy will generally dictate the use of n-butyllithium in boiling diethyl ether.

EXPERIMENTAL PROCEDURES

n-Butyllithium.[140] A 500-ml. three-necked flask is provided with a stirrer, a nitrogen inlet carrying a low-temperature thermometer, and, for convenience, a wide-throated solids funnel. After the apparatus has been swept with dry, oxygen-free nitrogen, 200 ml. of anhydrous ether is introduced, and, while nitrogen continues to pass through the flask, 8.6 g. (1.25 gram atoms) of lithium wire (or any other convenient form of lithium) is held over the funnel and cut into small pieces which fall directly into the flask. The solids funnel is replaced by a dropping funnel containing a solution of 68.5 g. (0.50 mole) of n-butyl bromide

[139] Bebb, Iowa State Coll. J. Sci., 13, 41 (1938) [C. A., 33, 9294 (1939)].

[140] Gilman, Beel, Brannen, Bullock, Dunn, and Miller, J. Am. Chem. Soc., 71, 1499 (1949).

in 100 ml. of anhydrous ether. The stirrer is started, and about 30 drops of the n-butyl bromide solution is run into the flask. The mixture is cooled to $-10°$ by immersing the flask in a solid carbon dioxide-acetone bath kept at about $-30°$ to $-40°$. When the solution becomes cloudy and bright spots appear on the lithium, indicating that reaction has begun, the remainder of the n-butyl bromide solution is added at an even rate over a period of thirty minutes while the internal temperature is kept at $-10°$. After addition is complete, the mixture is stirred for one to two hours while the temperature is allowed to rise to $0°$ to $10°$. The dropping funnel is replaced by a short L-shaped tube loosely plugged with glass wool, and the solution is decanted through this tube into a graduated dropping funnel that has been swept with nitrogen. The yield is 80–90%.

The resulting solution should be used at once or else stored at a temperature of $10°$ or lower until it is needed. n-Butyllithium cleaves ether fairly rapidly at room temperature; the concentration of n-butyllithium in an ether solution kept at $25°$ will drop to half its original value in about seven days.[141] Immediately before use, the strength of the solution is determined as follows:[142] An aliquot of the solution (2, 5, or 10 ml., depending on the approximate concentration) is withdrawn and hydrolyzed in 10 ml. of distilled water. The hydrolysate is titrated with standard acid, using phenolphthalein as indicator. A second aliquot of the same size is run into a solution of 1 ml. of benzyl chloride in 10 ml. of anhydrous ether. The benzyl chloride should be freshly distilled or taken from a freshly opened bottle. After one minute, the mixture is treated with 10 ml. of distilled water and titrated as before. The mixture should be shaken vigorously as the end point is approached. The first titration determines total alkali; the second determines total alkali due to compounds other than n-butyllithium. The difference between the two titration values represents the concentration of n-butyllithium.

Phenyllithium.[143] A 2-l. three-necked flask is equipped with a stirrer, a reflux condenser carrying a nitrogen inlet, and a solids funnel. The apparatus is swept with dry, oxygen-free nitrogen, and 500 ml. of anhydrous ether is introduced. While the flow of nitrogen continues, 29.4 g. (4.2 gram atoms) of lithium metal is cut into small pieces which are allowed to fall into the flask. The solids funnel is replaced by a dropping funnel containing a solution of 314 g. (2.0 moles) of bromobenzene in 1 l. of anhydrous ether. The stirrer is started, and about 40

---

[141] Haubein, *Iowa State Coll. J. Sci.*, **18**, 48 (1943) [*C. A.*, **38**, 716 (1944)].
[142] Gilman and Haubein, *J. Am. Chem. Soc.*, **66**, 1515 (1944).
[143] Gilman and Miller, unpublished studies.

drops of the solution is run into the flask. After the contents of the flask have become slightly cloudy, indicating that reaction has begun, more bromobenzene solution is added at a moderate rate until vigorous boiling begins. The flask is then cooled in an ice bath, and the addition of bromobenzene is continued at such a rate as to maintain constant refluxing. The bath should be temporarily removed if refluxing ceases, and should not be used at all in small-scale preparations. After most of the bromobenzene has been added, the bath is removed and stirring is continued until refluxing stops. The preparation requires about two hours. The solution is filtered by decantation in the same way as n-butyllithium (see the preceding preparation). The yield is determined by hydrolyzing a 2-ml. aliquot with distilled water and titrating the hydrolysate with standard acid, using phenolphthalein as indicator. The yield is 95–99%.

Phenyllithium cleaves ether less rapidly than n-butyllithium. An ether solution originally 0.4 M in phenyllithium requires about twelve days to fall to 0.2 M when kept at 35°.[141]

9-Phenylfluorene-9-carboxylic Acid.[54] A solution of 1.0 g. (0.0041 mole) of 9-phenylfluorene in 20 ml. of ether is treated with 0.01 mole of n-butyllithium in 10 ml. of ether. An orange color develops immediately, and heat is evolved. The solution is boiled under reflux for five hours and then poured over a slurry of solid carbon dioxide and ether. After the solid carbon dioxide has evaporated, the residue is extracted with cold water and the extract is acidified with hydrochloric acid. The mixture is allowed to stand at room temperature until the precipitated acid has coagulated sufficiently to permit filtration. This may require several hours. The mixture is then filtered, and the residue is washed with water and air-dried to give 0.94 g. (80%) of 9-phenyl-fluorene-9-carboxylic acid, m.p. 189–190.5° dec.

4-Aminodibenzofuran.[11, 144] To a solution of 42 g. (0.25 mole) of dibenzofuran in 150 ml. of anhydrous ether is added 0.4 mole of n-butyl-lithium in ether. The solution is stirred at room temperature for thirty-eight hours and then cooled in an ice-salt bath. Stirring is continued while a solution of 6.1 g. (0.13 mole) of methoxyamine in 40 ml. of anhydrous ether is added very slowly to the reaction mixture. The cooling bath is then removed; the mixture is stirred for two hours, then chilled and hydrolyzed by the addition of ice water. The ether layer is separated. The aqueous layer is extracted twice with ether, and the combined ethereal solutions are dried over sodium sulfate. Dry hydrogen chloride is then bubbled into the solution, and the precipitated 4-aminodibenzofuran hydrochloride is filtered and dissolved

[144] Gilman and Ingham, *J. Am. Chem. Soc.*, **75**, 4843 (1953).

in 1 l. of warm water. The solution is filtered to remove traces of dibenzofuran, and the filtrate is made alkaline by the addition of ammonium hydroxide. The mixture is filtered, and the residue is washed with water and dried to yield 12.9 g. (54%, based on the methoxyamine) of 4-aminodibenzofuran, m.p. 83–84°.

3-Methoxyphenanthrene-2-carboxylic Acid.[47] To a solution of 0.75 g. (0.0036 mole) of 3-methoxyphenanthrene in 20 ml. of anhydrous ether is added 0.0054 mole of an ethereal solution of n-butyllithium. The mixture is heated under reflux for fifteen hours and then poured in a rapid stream over a slurry of solid carbon dioxide in anhydrous ether. After the solid carbon dioxide has evaporated, water is added to the carbonation mixture to dissolve the precipitated salts, and the ether and water layers are separated. The aqueous solution is decolorized with charcoal, filtered, and acidified. The crude acidic material that precipitates is twice recrystallized from glacial acetic acid to yield 0.3 g. (33%) of 3-methoxyphenanthrene-2-carboxylic acid melting at 185°.

2,6-Dimethoxybenzaldehyde.[15] A mixture of 13.8 g. (0.1 mole) of resorcinol dimethyl ether and 0.1 mole of phenyllithium in ether is allowed to stand at room temperature for sixty hours. The 2-lithio derivative separates in large, colorless crystals. An ethereal solution of 13.5 g. of N-methylformanilide is added dropwise to the mixture. After the initial ebullition subsides, the mixture is allowed to stand for one-half hour and is then poured into an excess of dilute sulfuric acid. The ethereal layer is separated and dried, and the solvent is removed. The residue is distilled at a pressure of 13 mm. until the distillation temperature reaches 130°. The residue solidifies. After crystallization from cyclohexane or from a large quantity of water there is obtained 9.1 g. (55%) of the aldehyde as colorless needles melting at 98–99°.

2-(2′-Thienyl)quinoline.[6] A solution of 0.22 mole of n-butyllithium in 200 ml. of ether is added to a solution of 21 g. (0.25 mole) of thiophene in 100 ml. of ether, and the mixture is stirred at room temperature for fifteen minutes. To the resulting solution of 2-thienyllithium is added 28.1 g. (0.22 mole) of quinoline in 100 ml. of ether. This mixture is stirred at room temperature for two hours and then hydrolyzed by an excess of water, with the addition of a few milliliters of nitrobenzene for the oxidation of the intermediate 1,2-dihydro-2-(2′-thienyl)quinoline. The entire mixture is stirred for a few minutes; then the ethereal layer is separated and freed of solvent after being dried over anhydrous sodium sulfate. The residue is heated under a water-pump vacuum to remove nitrobenzene and quinoline, and the remaining solid material is recrystallized once from petroleum ether (b.p. 80–100°) and once from aqueous ethanol to give 17.5 g. (38%) of 2-

(2'-thienyl)quinoline melting at 130°. The picrate of this compound melts at 193.5–194°.

9-Benzyl-9-fluorenol.[105] To a solution of 1 g. (0.0036 mole) of 9-benzyloxyfluorene in 20 ml. of ether is added 0.05 mole of phenyllithium in ether. The mixture is maintained at −10° during the addition and is hydrolyzed with ice immediately after the phenyllithium has been added. The ether layer is separated, and the solvent is evaporated. The solid residue of 9-benzyl-9-fluorenol weighs 0.98 g. (98%) and melts at 142–143° after recrystallization from a mixture of benzene and petroleum ether.

2-Trimethylsilyl-1-methoxynaphthalene.[30] A solution of 0.075 mole of n-butyllithium in 90 ml. of ether is added to a solution of 11.8 g. (0.075 mole) of 1-methoxynaphthalene in 75 ml. of ether, and the mixture is heated under reflux with stirring for twenty-four hours. A copious precipitate separates after about ten hours, and the color of the solution changes from brown-red to pink. A solution of 8 g. (0.074 mole) of trimethylchlorosilane in 50 ml. of ether is added. The reaction mixture is heated under reflux for two hours and then hydrolyzed with water. The ethereal layer is separated, dried, and freed of solvent, and the residue is distilled at 99–100°/0.4 mm. to yield 3.1 g. (18%) of 2-trimethylsilyl-1-methoxynaphthalene.

4-Iododibenzothiophene.[14] A solution of 0.88 mole of n-butyllithium and 134 g. (0.73 mole) of dibenzothiophene in 1.5 l. of ether is heated under reflux for nineteen hours. The flask and contents are cooled in an ice bath, and 190 g. (0.75 mole) of powdered iodine is added slowly. The mixture is heated under reflux for one hour and hydrolyzed with an excess of water. The ether layer is separated, washed with sodium bisulfite, and dried over anhydrous sodium sulfate. The ether is then removed, and the residual oil is distilled at 160–170°/1 mm. to give 100 g. of crude product that melts over the range 90–100°. Recrystallization from petroleum ether (b.p. 63–78°) gives 50 g. (22%) of 4-iododibenzothiophene melting at 101–102°.

TABULAR SURVEY OF METALATIONS WITH ORGANOLITHIUM COMPOUNDS

The original literature was consulted wherever possible in the compilation of the following tables. The pertinent articles were located through a search of the abstract literature through the year 1952. Some reactions reported subsequent to 1952 are also tabulated. In each of the tables, formulas of compounds metalated are listed in an order that follows the Hill system used in *Chemical Abstracts* formula indices.

TABLE I

Metalations with n-Butyllithium Followed by Carbonation to Yield Carboxylic Acids

	Compound Metalated	Acid	Yield, %	Reference *
C_2H_3Br	Vinyl bromide	Acetylenedicarboxylic	26–34	63
C_4H_4S	Thiophene	2-Thenoic	87	6
C_5H_6O	2-Methylfuran	5-Methyl-2-furoic	17	7
C_6H_6	Benzene	Benzoic	5	57
C_6H_6O	Phenol	Salicylic	0.7	95
$C_6H_6O_2$	Resorcinol	2,6-Dihydroxybenzoic	25	99
		2,4-Dihydroxybenzoic	6	
C_6H_6S	Thiophenol	Diphenyl disulfide 2,2'-dicarboxylic	3	95
C_6H_7N	Aniline	Anthranilic	4	70
$C_7H_5F_3$	Benzotrifluoride	o-Trifluoromethylbenzoic	40	37
		m-Trifluoromethylbenzoic	8	
		p-Trifluoromethylbenzoic	0.5	
C_7H_5NS	Benzothiazole	Benzothiazole-2-carboxylic	90	28
C_7H_7ClO	p-Chloroanisole	5-Chloro-2-methoxybenzoic	49–70	65
C_7H_7ClS	Methyl p-chlorophenyl sulfide	p-Chlorophenylmercaptoacetic	6	91
C_7H_7FO	p-Fluoroanisole	5-Fluoro-2-methoxybenzoic	10–13	65
C_7H_8	Toluene	Phenylacetic	0.22	145
C_7H_8O	Anisole	o-Methoxybenzoic †	19–32	7, 8
	Benzyl alcohol	2-Hydroxymethylbenzoic	9	70
C_7H_8S	Methyl phenyl sulfide	Phenylmercaptoacetic	4–44	8, 91
C_8H_6O	Benzofuran	Benzofuran-2-carboxylic	47	146
C_8H_6S	Thianaphthene	Thianaphthene-2-carboxylic	55	36
C_8H_7Br	β-Bromostyrene	Phenylpropiolic	0–42	65
$C_8H_{10}O$	o-Methylanisole	o-Methoxyphenylacetic and 2-methoxy-3-methylbenzoic	3	103
	Methyl benzyl ether	2-Methoxymethylbenzoic ‡	—	70
	p-Methylanisole	2-Methoxy-5-methylbenzoic	11	103
$C_8H_{10}O_2$	Resorcinol dimethyl ether	2,6-Dimethoxybenzoic	55	99
	Veratrole	2,3-Dimethoxybenzoic	56	35
$C_8H_{10}S$	Methyl p-tolyl sulfide	p-Tolylmercaptoacetic	38	91
	Ethyl phenyl sulfide	o-Ethylmercaptobenzoic	5–8	91
C_9H_6ClN	2-Chloroquinoline	2-Chloroquinoline-x-carboxylic ‡	—	147
C_9H_8S	3-Methylthianaphthene	3-Methylthianaphthene-2-carboxylic	65	148
C_9H_9N	1-Methylindole	1-Methylindole-2-carboxylic	78	149a
$C_9H_{12}O$	o-Ethylanisole	3-Ethyl-2-methoxybenzoic	3	103
$C_9H_{12}O_2$	Orcinol dimethyl ether	2,6-Dimethoxy-4-methylbenzoic	27	149b
$C_9H_{12}O_3$	Phloroglucinol trimethyl ether	2,4,6-Trimethoxybenzoic	65	95
	1,2,4-Trimethoxybenzene	2,3,6-Trimethoxybenzoic	47	150
$C_9H_{12}S$	n-Propyl phenyl sulfide	o-n-Propylmercaptobenzoic	7	91
	Isopropyl phenyl sulfide	o-Isopropylmercaptobenzoic	9–11	91
$C_9H_{13}NS$	Methyl p-dimethylaminophenyl sulfide	p-Dimethylaminophenylmercaptoacetic	15–22	91
$C_{10}H_8$	Naphthalene	Mixture of 1- and 2-naphthoic	13–20	7
$C_{10}H_8O$	2-Naphthol	2-Hydroxy-3-naphthoic	7	95
$C_{10}H_8O_2S_2$	Phenyl 2-thienyl sulfone	5-Phenylsulfonyl-2-thenoic	4	94
$C_{10}H_{10}$	1,4-Dihydronaphthalene	1,2-Dihydro-2-naphthoic	26	60
$C_{10}H_{14}S$	n-Butyl phenyl sulfide	o-n-Butylmercaptobenzoic	5–6	91
$C_{10}H_{15}N$	N-n-Butylaniline	N-n-Butylanthranilic	2	70
$C_{11}H_{10}O$	1-Methoxynaphthalene	1-Methoxy-2-naphthoic	20–25	38
	2-Methoxynaphthalene	2-Methoxy-3-naphthoic	50	38
$C_{11}H_{10}S$	Methyl 1-naphthyl sulfide	1-Naphthylmercaptoacetic	35	91
	Methyl 2-naphthyl sulfide	2-Naphthylmercaptoacetic	12	91

* References 145–153 are on p. 292.
† A 5–40% yield of 2,2'-dimethoxybenzophenone, a by-product of carbonation, was also formed.
‡ This product was not definitely characterized.

TABLE I—*Continued*

METALATIONS WITH *n*-BUTYLLITHIUM FOLLOWED BY CARBONATION TO YIELD CARBOXYLIC ACIDS

Compound Metalated		Acid	Yield, %	Refer- ence *
$C_{11}H_{11}NO$	2-Ethoxyquinoline	2-Ethoxyquinoline-3-carboxylic	7	98
$C_{12}H_8O$	Dibenzofuran	Dibenzofuran-4-carboxylic §	1–76	4, 5, 11, 84, 138
$C_{12}H_8OS$	Dibenzothiophene-5-oxide	Dibenzothiophene-4-carboxylic	36	92
	Phenoxathiin	Phenoxathiin-4-carboxylic	53–61	96
$C_{12}H_8O_2$	Dibenzo-*p*-dioxin	*x,x'*-Dibenzo-*p*-dioxindicarboxylic (two isomers)	20	151
	2-Hydroxydibenzofuran	2-Hydroxydibenzofuran-1-carboxylic	21	99
	4-Hydroxydibenzofuran	6-Hydroxydibenzofuran-4-carboxylic	4	99
$C_{12}H_8O_2S$	Dibenzothiophene-5-dioxide	Dibenzothiophene-4-carboxylic-5-dioxide	21	93
$C_{12}H_8S$	Dibenzothiophene	Dibenzothiophene-4-carboxylic ‖	40–90	7, 84, 138
$C_{12}H_8S_2$	Thianthrene	Thianthrene-1-carboxylic	60	151
$C_{12}H_9BrO_2S$	*m*-Bromodiphenyl sulfone	2-Bromo-6-phenylsulfonylbenzoic	54	94
	p-Bromodiphenyl sulfone	5-Bromo-2-phenylsulfonylbenzoic	52	94
$C_{12}H_9ClO$	*p*-Chlorodiphenyl ether	5-Chloro-2-phenoxybenzoic	8–20	100
$C_{12}H_9N$	Carbazole	Carbazole-1-carboxylic	1	77
$C_{12}H_9NS$	Phenothiazine	Phenothiazine-1-carboxylic	52	88
$C_{12}H_{10}$	Acenaphthene	Mixture of mono- and di-basic acids	—	7
	Biphenyl	*p*-Phenylbenzoic	7–15	7
$C_{12}H_{10}O$	Diphenyl ether	*o*-Phenoxybenzoic	7–60	34
$C_{12}H_{10}O_2S$	Diphenyl sulfone	2-Phenylsulfonylbenzoic	61	94
$C_{12}H_{10}S$	Diphenyl sulfide	*o*-Phenylmercaptobenzoic	24–30	7
$C_{12}H_{10}S_2$	Diphenyl disulfide	Diphenyl disulfide 2,2'-dicarboxylic	4	91
$C_{12}H_{11}N$	Diphenylamine	N-Phenylanthranilic	11	70
$C_{12}H_{12}O$	2-Ethoxynaphthalene	2-Ethoxy-3-naphthoic	—	95
$C_{12}H_{12}O_2$	2,7-Dimethoxynaphthalene	2,7-Dimethoxy-3-naphthoic	43	38
	2,7-Dimethoxynaphthalene	2,7-Dimethoxynaphthalene-3,6-dicarboxylic	25	38
$C_{12}H_{12}S$	Ethyl 2-naphthyl sulfide	Unidentified, m.p. 157–158°	20	91
$C_{12}H_{16}S$	Cyclohexyl phenyl sulfide	*o*-Cyclohexylmercaptobenzoic	8–11	91
$C_{13}H_9NS$	2-(2'-Thienyl)quinoline	5-(2'-Quinolyl)-2(?)-thenoic	30	6
$C_{13}H_{10}$	Fluorene	Fluorene-9-carboxylic	75	152
$C_{13}H_{10}O$	4-Methyldibenzofuran	6-Methyldibenzofuran-4-carboxylic	46	153
$C_{13}H_{10}O_2$	2-Methoxydibenzofuran	2-Methoxydibenzofuran-1-carboxylic	48	7
		2-Methoxydibenzofuran-3-carboxylic	12	
	4-Methoxydibenzofuran	4-Methoxydibenzofuran-3-carboxylic	5	99
		6-Methoxydibenzofuran-4-carboxylic	9	
$C_{13}H_{11}N$	9-Methylcarbazole	9-Methylcarbazole-1-carboxylic	12	78
		9-Methylcarbazole-*x,x'*-dicarboxylic ¶	3	
$C_{13}H_{12}$	Diphenylmethane	Diphenylacetic	20	7
$C_{13}H_{12}O$	Benzhydrol	Lactone of *o*-phenylhydroxymethylbenzoic	19	70
	Phenyl *p*-methoxyphenyl ether	2-Methoxy-5-phenoxybenzoic	29	100
$C_{13}H_{13}N$	N-Methyldiphenylamine	N-Methyl-N-phenylanthranilic	4–8	78
$C_{13}H_{22}OSi$	Triethyl-*p*-anisylsilane	5-Triethylsilyl-2-methoxybenzoic	47	89
$C_{14}H_{10}O$	2-Hydroxyphenanthrene	2-Hydroxyphenanthrene-3-carboxylic	1	47
	3-Hydroxyphenanthrene	Unidentified product	Trace	47
	9-Hydroxyphenanthrene	9-Hydroxyphenanthrene-*x*-carboxylic	10	47
$C_{14}H_{11}N$	1-Phenylindole	1-Phenylindole-*x,x'*-dicarboxylic **	15	149*a*
$C_{14}H_{12}$	9, 10-Dihydroanthracene	9,10-Dihydroanthracene-9-carboxylic	65–80	7, 26
		9,10-Dihydroanthracene-9,10-dicarboxylic	4–16	

* References 145–153 are on p. 292.

§ In one experiment (ref. 11) a 20% yield of bis(4-dibenzofuryl) ketone was obtained as a by-product of carbonation.

‖ The formation of the by-product, *n*-butyl 4-dibenzothienyl ketone, in 5% yield has been reported (ref. 93).

¶ This product was thought to be the 1,8-dicarboxylic acid.

** This acid was thought to be the 2,2'-dicarboxy compound. A ketone, possibly the 2,2'-carbonyl compound, was obtained in 42% yield from the same reaction.

TABLE I—*Continued*

METALATIONS WITH *n*-BUTYLLITHIUM FOLLOWED BY CARBONATION TO YIELD CARBOXYLIC ACIDS

	Compound Metalated	Acid	Yield, %	Reference *
$C_{14}H_{12}O_3$	2,8-Dimethoxydibenzofuran	2,8-Dimethoxydibenzofuran-1,3- (or 1,7)-dicarboxylic	13	101
$C_{14}H_{13}N$	9-Ethylcarbazole	9-Ethylcarbazole-1-carboxylic	22	77
$C_{14}H_{13}NS$	10-Ethylphenothiazine	10-Ethylphenothiazine-4-carboxylic	6	85
$C_{14}H_{13}NSO$	10-Ethylphenothiazine-5-oxide	10-Ethylphenothiazine-4-carboxylic	25–53	87
$C_{14}H_{14}$	Bibenzyl	*m*- and *p*-Phenethylbenzoic	1	7
	Phenyl-*p*-tolylmethane	Phenyl-*p*-tolylacetic	50	7
$C_{14}H_{14}O$	Diphenylmethylcarbinol	Lactone of diphenylmethylcarbinol-2,2'-dicarboxylic	17	49
$C_{14}H_{14}O_2$	2,2'-Dimethoxybiphenyl	2,2'-Dimethoxybiphenyl-3,3'-dicarboxylic	50	35
		2,2'-Dimethoxybiphenyl-3-carboxylic	9	
$C_{14}H_{15}N$	Dibenzylamine	N-Benzyl-α-amino-*o*-toluic	27	71
$C_{15}H_{12}O$	2-Methoxyphenanthrene	2-Methoxyphenanthrene-3-carboxylic	39	47
	3-Methoxyphenanthrene	3-Methoxyphenanthrene-2-carboxylic	33	47
	9-Methoxyphenanthrene	9-Methoxyphenanthrene-10-carboxylic	0.5	47
		Unidentified acid	Trace	
$C_{16}H_{16}$	1,4-Diphenyl-2-butene	1,4-Diphenyl-2-butene-1,4-dicarboxylic	12	60
$C_{16}H_{18}Si$	Trimethyl-9-fluorenylsilane	9-Trimethylsilylfluorene-9-carboxylic ††	37–82	89
$C_{17}H_{14}$	Phenyl-2-naphthylmethane	Phenyl-2-naphthylacetic	80	7
$C_{18}H_{13}N$	9-Phenylcarbazole	9-Phenylcarbazole-2'-carboxylic	6	50*a*
		9-Phenylcarbazole-2',6'-dicarboxylic	25	50*b*
$C_{18}H_{13}NS$	10-Phenylphenothiazine	10-Phenylphenothiazine-4-carboxylic (?) ‡‡	9	85
$C_{18}H_{15}As$	Triphenylarsine	3-Diphenylarsinobenzoic	0.6	51
$C_{18}H_{15}N$	Triphenylamine	3-Diphenylaminobenzoic	7	49
$C_{18}H_{15}P$	Triphenylphosphine	3-Diphenylphosphinobenzoic	6	52
$C_{19}H_{14}$	9-Phenylfluorene	9-Phenylfluorene-9-carboxylic	80	107
$C_{19}H_{16}$	Triphenylmethane	Triphenylacetic	82	117
$C_{19}H_{16}O$	Triphenylcarbinol	Lactone of triphenylcarbinol-2,2'-dicarboxylic	5–57	49, 70
$C_{20}H_{18}O$	Trityl methyl ether	Lactone of triphenylcarbinol-2-carboxylic	17	107
$C_{22}H_{18}SSi$	Triphenyl-2-thienylsilane	5-Triphenylsilyl-2-thenoic (?) ‡‡	45	89

* References 145–153 are on p. 292.

†† This unstable acid was not isolated as such.   The product actually obtained was fluorene-9-carboxylic acid, presumably arising from hydrolysis of the silicon compound.

‡‡ The location of the carboxyl group was not proved.

REFERENCES FOR TABLE I

[145] Gilman, Pacevitz, and Baine, *J. Am. Chem. Soc.*, **62**, 1514 (1940).

[146] E. W. Smith, Doctoral Dissertation, Iowa State College, 1936.

[147] Gilman and Spatz, *J. Am. Chem. Soc.*, **63**, 1553 (1941).

[148] Shirley, Danzig, and Canter, *J. Am. Chem. Soc.*, **75**, 3278 (1953).

[149*a*] Shirley and Roussel, *J. Am. Chem. Soc.*, **75**, 375 (1953).

[149*b*] Adams, Wolff, Cain, and Clark, *J. Am. Chem. Soc.*, **62**, 1770 (1940).

[150] Gilman and Thirtle, *J. Am. Chem. Soc.*, **66**, 858 (1944).

[151] Gilman and Stuckwisch, *J. Am. Chem. Soc.*, **65**, 1461 (1943).

[152] Burtner and Cusic, *J. Am. Chem. Soc.*, **65**, 262 (1943).

[153] Gilman and Young, *J. Am. Chem. Soc.*, **57**, 1121 (1935).

TABLE II

MISCELLANEOUS METALATIONS WITH ORGANOLITHIUM COMPOUNDS

	Compound Metalated	RLi	Reactant	Final Product	Yield, %	Reference*
C_2H_3Br	Vinyl bromide	Phenyl	Benzophenone	1,4-Dihydroxy-1,1,4,4-tetraphenyl-2-butyne	28	154
C_4H_4O	Furan	n-Butyl	Triphenyltin chloride	Triphenyl-2-furyltin	44	31
		Ethyl	Germanium tetrabromide	Tetra-2-furylgermanium	—	32
		Methyl	Carbon dioxide	2-Furoic acid	7	7
		Phenyl	Carbon dioxide	2-Furoic acid	40	7
		n-Butyl	Quinoline	2-(2'-Thienyl)quinoline	38	6
C_4H_4S	Thiophene	n-Butyl	Triphenylchlorosilane	Triphenyl-2-thienylsilane	63	89
		2,4,6-Triphenylphenyl	Carbon dioxide	2-Thenoic acid	45	54
$C_4H_{12}BrN$	Tetramethylammonium bromide	Phenyl	Benzophenone	Dimethylbis(β-hydroxy-β,β-diphenylethyl)ammonium bromide	20	79
				Trimethyl-β-hydroxy-β,β-diphenylethylammonium bromide	18	
$C_4H_{12}ClN$	Tetramethylammonium chloride	Phenyl	Benzophenone	Trimethyl-β-hydroxy-β,β-diphenylethylammonium chloride	41	80
$C_4H_{12}IP$	Tetramethylphosphonium iodide	Phenyl	Benzophenone	Dimethylbis(β-hydroxy-β,β-diphenylethyl)phosphonium iodide	—	79
				Trimethyl-β-hydroxy-β,β-diphenylethylphosphonium iodide		
		Phenyl	Methyl iodide	Trimethylethylphosphonium iodide		
				Tetraethylphosphonium iodide		79
C_5H_6O	2-Methylfuran	Phenyl	Carbon dioxide	5-Methyl-2-furoic acid	29	7
$C_6H_4F_2$	m-Difluorobenzene	Phenyl	Benzophenone	1,9,9-Triphenylfluorene	—	155
C_6H_5Br	Bromobenzene	Phenyl	Benzophenone	9,9-Diphenylfluorene	1	155
C_6H_5Cl	Chlorobenzene	Phenyl	Benzophenone	9,9-Diphenylfluorene	2	155
C_6H_5F	Fluorobenzene	Phenyl	Benzophenone	o-Phenyltriphenylcarbinol	16	61
		Phenyl	1-Methylpiperidine	1-Phenylpiperidine	40-50	62
		Phenyl	Trimethylamine	Dimethylaniline	65	62
		Phenyl	Triethylamine	Diethylaniline	49-65	62

* References 154–170 are on p. 304.

TABLE II—Continued

MISCELLANEOUS METALATIONS WITH ORGANOLITHIUM COMPOUNDS

Compound Metalated	RLi	Reactant	Final Product	Yield, %	Reference*
C$_6$H$_5$I Iodobenzene	Phenyl	Benzophenone	9,9-Diphenylfluorene	5	155
	Phenyl	Triethylamine	Diethylaniline	23	62
	Phenyl	Triethylamine, then benzophenone	o-Diethylaminotriphenylcarbinol	2	62
C$_6$H$_7$N 2-Picoline	Methyl	Benzyl chloride	2-Phenethylpyridine	—	3
	Phenyl	Acetaldehyde	1-(2'-Pyridyl)-2-propanol	44–50	156
C$_7$H$_5$NS Benzothiazole	n-Butyl	Acetophenone	Methylphenyl-2-benzothiazolyl-carbinol	67	28
	n-Butyl	Benzaldehyde	Phenyl-2-benzothiazolylcarbinol	80	28
	n-Butyl	Benzonitrile	Phenyl 2-benzothiazolyl ketone	71	28
	n-Butyl	Benzophenone	Diphenyl-2-benzothiazolylcarbinol	95	28
	n-Butyl	Phenyl 2-benzothiazolyl ketone	Phenylbis(-2-benzothiazolyl)-carbinol	64	28
	n-Butyl	Benzoyl chloride	Phenyl 2-benzothiazolyl ketone	Poor	28
	n-Butyl	Butyraldehyde	n-Propyl-2-benzothiazolylcarbinol	56	28
	n-Butyl	p-Chloroacetophenone	Methyl-p-chlorophenyl-2-benzo-thiazolylcarbinol	72	28
	n-Butyl	p-Dimethylaminobenzaldehyde	p-Dimethylaminophenyl-2-benzo-thiazolylcarbinol	60	28
	n-Butyl	Methyl p-tolyl ketone	Methyl-p-tolyl-2-benzothiazolyl-carbinol	63	28
	n-Butyl	Bis-4,4'-dimethylamino-phenyl ketone	Bis(p-dimethylaminophenyl)-2-benzothiazolylcarbinol	64	28
	Methyl	Carbon dioxide	Benzothiazole-2-carboxylic acid	74–80	90
	Phenyl	Carbon dioxide	Benzothiazole-2-carboxylic acid	6–68	90
C$_7$H$_7$BrO m-Bromoanisole	Phenyl	Benzophenone	1-Methoxy-9,9-diphenylfluorene	16	108
p-Bromoanisole	Phenyl	Benzophenone	5-Bromo-2-methoxytriphenyl-carbinol	65	157
	p-Anisyl (?) †	Carbon dioxide	5-Bromo-2-methoxybenzoic acid	31	110
	Phenyl	Benzophenone	5-Bromo-2-methoxytriphenyl-carbinol	35–70	108, 157
	Phenyl	Cupric chloride	5,5'-Dibromo-2,2'-dimethoxybi-phenyl	19	35

Formula	Compound	Metalating agent	Reagent	Product	Yield %	Ref.
C7H7BrO	p-Bromoanisole(Cont.)	2,4,6-Triphenylphenyl	Carbon dioxide	5-Bromo-2-methoxybenzoic acid	25	54
C7H7ClO	m-Chloroanisole	Phenyl	Benzophenone	1-Methoxy-9,9-diphenylfluorene	17	108
	p-Chloroanisole	Phenyl	Benzophenone	5-Chloro-2-methoxytriphenyl-carbinol	75	108
C7H7FO	m-Fluoroanisole	Phenyl	Benzophenone	1-Methoxy-9,9-diphenylfluorene	17	108
	p-Fluoroanisole	Phenyl	Benzophenone	5-Fluoro-2-methoxytriphenyl-carbinol	—	108
C7H7IO	m-Iodoanisole	Phenyl	Benzophenone	1,5- (or 1,8)-Dimethoxy-9,9-di-phenylfluorene	—	
		Phenyl	Benzophenone	1-Methoxy-9,9-diphenylfluorene	—	108
	p-Iodoanisole	p-Anisyl (?) †	Carbon dioxide	5-Iodo-2-methoxybenzoic acid	0–24	110
		Phenyl	Benzophenone	5-Iodo-2-methoxytriphenylcarbi-nol	38	108
C7H7Li	Benzyllithium	Ethyl	—	Dilithiotoluene	Quant.	59b
C7H8	Toluene	Ethyl	—	Tetra- and penta-lithiotoluene	70–75	59b
C7H8O	Anisole	Phenyl	Benzophenone	2-Methoxytriphenylcarbinol	68	157
C7H8S	Methyl phenyl sulfide	Phenyl	Carbon dioxide	Phenylmercaptoacetic acid	9	91
		Methyl	Carbon dioxide	Phenylmercaptoacetic acid	0.1	91
C8H6	Phenylacetylene	Ethyl	—	Phenylethynyllithium	Quant.	59b
		Phenyl	Carbon dioxide	Phenylpropiolic acid	68	117
		Phenyl	Triphenylchlorosilane	Triphenylphenylethynylsilane	60	20
C8H6O	Benzofuran	3-Bromo-2-benzofuryl (?) †	Carbon dioxide	Benzofuran-2-carboxylic acid	10–23	158
C8H6S	Thianaphthene	n-Butyl	Acetaldehyde	Methyl-2-thianaphthenylcarbinol	72	159a
		n-Butyl	Benzaldehyde	Phenyl-2-thianaphthenylcarbinol	70	159a
		n-Butyl	Bromine	2-Bromothianaphthene	39	159a
		n-Butyl	p-Chlorobenzaldehyde	p-Chlorophenyl-2-thianaphthen-ylcarbinol	68	159a
		n-Butyl	p-Dimethylaminobenzalde-hyde	p-Dimethylaminophenyl-2-thia-naphthenylcarbinol	47	159a
		n-Butyl	Methyl p-toluenesulfonate	2-Methylthianaphthene	43	159a
		n-Butyl	Phenyl isocyanate	N-Phenylthianaphthene-2-car-boxamide	81	159a
		n-Butyl	Quinoline	2-(2'-Thianaphthenyl)quinoline	49	36
		n-Butyl	p-Tolualdehyde	p-Tolyl-2-thianaphthenylcarbinol	Low	159a
		n-Butyl	o-Tolyl isocyanate	N-o-Tolylthianaphthene-2-car-boxamide	41	159a

* References 154–170 are on p. 304.

† The identity of the metalating agent in this complex reaction was not established.

TABLE II—*Continued*

MISCELLANEOUS METALATIONS WITH ORGANOLITHIUM COMPOUNDS

Compound Metalated	RLi	Reactant	Final Product	Yield, %	Reference*
C$_8$H$_7$Br β-Bromostyrene	Phenyl	Benzophenone	Phenylethynyldiphenylcarbinol	95	64
C$_8$H$_7$Cl β-Chlorostyrene	n-Butyl	Benzophenone	Phenylethynyldiphenylcarbinol	93	66
	n-Butyl	Water	Phenylacetylene	82	66
	Phenyl	Water	Phenylacetylene	30–70	64
C$_8$H$_{10}$O Methyl benzyl ether	Phenyl	Water	Methylphenylcarbinol ‡	35	104
C$_8$H$_{10}$O$_2$ Hydroquinone dimethyl ether	Phenyl	Benzophenone	2,5-Dimethoxytriphenylcarbinol	65	157
Resorcinol dimethyl ether	n-Butyl	l-Menthone	2-(3'-Hydroxy-3'-menthyl)-1,3-dimethoxybenzene	24	149b
	Mesityl	Carbon dioxide	2,6-Dimethoxybenzoic acid	25	54
	Phenyl	Benzophenone	2,6-Dimethoxytriphenylcarbinol	37–72	157
	Phenyl	N-Methylformanilide	2,6-Dimethoxybenzaldehyde	55	15
	2,4,6-Triphenylphenyl	Carbon dioxide	2,6-Dimethoxybenzoic acid	Trace	54
Veratrole	n-Butyl	Cupric chloride	2,2',3,3'-Tetramethoxybiphenyl	2	35
	Phenyl	Benzophenone	2,3-Dimethoxytriphenylcarbinol	49–67	108
C$_8$H$_{11}$N Dimethylaniline	Phenyl	Benzophenone	o-Dimethylaminotriphenylcarbinol	84	155
C$_8$H$_8$ Indene	Ethyl	Diphenylbromomethane	1-Benzhydrylindene	8	24
	n-Propyl	Triphenylchlorosilane	Triphenyl-1-indenylsilane	—	29
			1,1-Bis(triphenylsilyl)indene (?)	8	
C$_9$H$_9$Cl 2-Chloro-1-phenyl-1-propene	Phenyl	Water	1-Phenyl-1-propyne	35	66
C$_9$H$_9$N 1-Methylindole	n-Butyl	p-Anisyl isocyanate	1-Methylindole-2-carboxaniside	40	149a
	n-Butyl	Benzophenone	α,α-Diphenyl-1-methyl-2-indolemethanol	53	149a
	n-Butyl	p-Chlorobenzaldehyde	α-(4'-Chlorophenyl)-1-methyl-2-indolemethanol	50	149a
	n-Butyl	Methyl p-toluensulfonate	1,2-Dimethylindole	45	149a
	n-Butyl	1-Naphthyl isocyanate	N-(1-Naphthyl)amide of 1-methylindole-2-carboxylic acid	52	149a
	n-Butyl	Phenyl isocyanate	1-Methylindole-2-carboxanilide	42	149a
	n-Butyl	Quinoline, then nitrobenzene	1-Methyl-2-(2'-quinolyl)indole	54	149a
	n-Butyl	o-Tolyl isocyanate	1-Methylindole-2-carboxy-4'-toluide	63	149a
C$_9$H$_{11}$NS 4,5-Dimethylthiazole	Phenyl	Formaldehyde	2-(Hydroxymethyl)-4,5-dimethylthiazole	55	159b

Formula	Compound	Organolithium	Reagent	Product	Yield (%)	Reference
$C_9H_{12}O_2$	Orcinol dimethyl ether	n-Butyl	N-Methylformanilide	2,6-Dimethoxy-4-methylbenzaldehyde	31–55	16, 17
		Phenyl	l-Menthone	2-(3'-Hydroxy-3'-menthyl)-1,3-dimethoxy-5-methylbenzene	—	149b
$C_9H_{12}O_3$	Phloroglucinol trimethyl ether	Phenyl	Benzophenone	2,4,6-Trimethoxytriphenylcarbinol	67–85	108
	Pyrogallol trimethyl ether	n-Dodecyl	Carbon dioxide	2,3,4-Trimethoxybenzoic acid	—	160
		Phenyl	Benzophenone	2,3,4-Trimethoxytriphenylcarbinol	7	108
$C_{10}H_9N$	Quinaldine	Phenyl	Allyl chloride	2-(3-Butenyl)quinoline	—	3
		Phenyl	Benzophenone	Diphenyl-α-quinaldylcarbinol	—	3
		Phenyl	Benzyl chloride	2-Phenethylquinoline	—	3
		Phenyl	n-Propyl bromide	2-n-Butylquinoline	Good	3
$C_{10}H_{10}$	1,4-Dihydronaphthalene	Phenyl	—	Naphthalene	85	60
$C_{10}H_{16}BrN$	Trimethylbenzylammonium bromide	Phenyl	—	Dimethyl-α-phenylethylamine ‡	—	161
$C_{11}H_{10}O$	1-Methoxynaphthalene	n-Butyl	Trimethylchlorosilane	2-Trimethylsilyl-1-methoxynaphthalene	18	30
		n-Butyl	Triphenylchlorosilane	2-Triphenylsilyl-1-methoxynaphthalene	10	30
	2-Methoxynaphthalene	n-Butyl	Trimethylchlorosilane	3-Trimethylsilyl-2-methoxynaphthalene	51	30
		n-Butyl	Triphenylchlorosilane	3-Triphenylsilyl-2-methoxynaphthalene	40	30
$C_{11}H_{14}O$	Acetomesitylene	n-Butyl	—	—	—	162
		Methyl	—	—	—	162
		Phenyl	—	—	—	162
$C_{11}H_{16}BrNO$	Trimethylphenacylammonium bromide	Phenyl	—	3-Dimethylamino-1,1-diphenyl-1-propanol ‡	10	161
				Vinyl phenyl ketone	34	9, 110
$C_{12}H_7BrO$	2-Bromodibenzofuran	2-Dibenzofuryl (?) †	Carbon dioxide	2-Bromodibenzofuran-4-carboxylic acid	24	12
$C_{12}H_8O$	Dibenzofuran	2-Dibenzofuryl (?) †	Oxygen	2-Bromo-4-hydroxydibenzofuran	21	138
		n-Amyl	Carbon dioxide	Dibenzofuran-4-carboxylic acid	45	109
		3-Bromo-4-dibenzofuryl (?) †	Carbon dioxide	Dibenzofuran-4-carboxylic acid	—	

* References 154–170 are on p. 304.

† The identity of the metalating agent in this complex reaction was not established.

‡ This product results from rearrangement following metalation.

TABLE II—*Continued*

MISCELLANEOUS METALATIONS WITH ORGANOLITHIUM COMPOUNDS

Compound Metalated	RLi	Reactant	Final Product	Yield, %	Reference *
$C_{12}H_8O$ Dibenzofuran (*Cont.*)	Isobutyl	Carbon dioxide	Dibenzofuran-4-carboxylic acid	1–57	138
	n-Butyl	Antimony trichloride	Tris(4-dibenzofuryl)antimony	80	33
	n-Butyl	N-Butoxymethylpiperidine	N-(4-Dibenzofurylmethyl)piperidine	25	163
	n-Butyl	Ethylene oxide	4-(β-Hydroxyethyl)dibenzofuran	45	25
	n-Butyl	Iodine	4-Iododibenzofuran	37–42	12, 13
	n-Butyl	Methoxyamine	4-Aminodibenzofuran	54	11, 144
	n-Butyl	Oxygen	4-Hydroxydibenzofuran	40–52	9
	n-Butyl	Triphenyllead chloride	4-Dibenzofuryltriphenyllead	—	34
	sec-Butyl	Carbon dioxide	Dibenzofuran-4-carboxylic acid	11–31	138
	t-Butyl	Carbon dioxide	Dibenzofuran-4-carboxylic acid	31–34	138
	4-Dibenzothienyl	Carbon dioxide	Dibenzofuran-4-carboxylic acid	20	96
	Ethyl	Carbon dioxide	Dibenzofuran-4-carboxylic acid	14–48	117, 138
	Methyl	Carbon dioxide	Dibenzofuran-4-carboxylic acid	3	1, 138
	Phenyl	Carbon dioxide	Dibenzofuran-4-carboxylic acid	31	138
	2,4,6-Triphenylphenyl	Carbon dioxide	Dibenzofuran-4-carboxylic acid	Trace	54
$C_{12}H_8OS$ Phenoxathiin	n-Butyl	Methoxyamine	4-Aminophenoxathiin	10	96
$C_{12}H_8O_2$ Dibenzo-p-dioxin	Methyl	Carbon dioxide	Dibenzo-p-dioxin-1-carboxylic acid	—	151
$C_{12}H_8S$ Dibenzothiophene	n-Butyl	Dimethyl sulfate	4-Methyldibenzothiophene	22	22
	n-Butyl	Iodine	4-Iododibenzothiophene	64	14
	n-Butyl	Methoxyamine	4-Aminodibenzothiophene	33	12
	n-Butyl	Oxygen	4-Hydroxydibenzothiophene	7	22
	n-Butyl	Triphenylethoxysilane	4-Triphenylsilyldibenzothiophene	50	164
	Ethyl	Carbon dioxide	Dibenzothiophene-4-carboxylic acid	20	84
	1-N-Ethylcarbazolyl	Carbon dioxide, then oxidation	Dibenzothiophene-4-carboxylic acid 5-dioxide	20	84
	2-Naphthyl	Carbon dioxide	Dibenzothiophene-4-carboxylic acid	8	53
	Phenyl	Carbon dioxide	Dibenzothiophene-4-carboxylic acid	12	53
	n-Propyl	Carbon dioxide	Dibenzothiophene-4-carboxylic acid	61	84
$C_{12}H_8S_2$ Thianthrene	n-Butyl	Iodine	1-Iodothianthrene	5	165
	n-Butyl	Methoxyamine	1-Aminothianthrene		151
$C_{12}H_9BrO$ Phenyl p-bromophenyl ether	p-Phenoxyphenyl (?) †	Carbon dioxide	5-Bromo-2-phenoxybenzoic acid	20–35	100, 166

Formula	Compound	Organolithium	Reagent	Product	Yield (%)	Reference
$C_{12}H_9ClO$	Phenyl p-chlorophenyl ether	Methyl	Carbon dioxide	5-Chloro-2-phenoxybenzoic acid	14	100
		Phenyl	Carbon dioxide	5-Chloro-2-phenoxybenzoic acid	36	100
$C_{12}H_9IO$	Phenyl p-iodophenyl ether	p-Phenoxyphenyl (?) †	Carbon dioxide	5-Iodo-2-phenoxybenzoic acid	24	100
$C_{12}H_{10}O$	1,4-Dihydrodibenzofuran	n-Butyl	—	Dibenzofuran	84	60
		Phenyl	Carbon dioxide	Dibenzofuran-4-carboxylic acid	66–86	60
$C_{12}H_{10}S$	1,4-Dihydrodibenzothiophene	Phenyl	—	Dibenzothiophene	5	22
$C_{12}H_{12}O$	1,2,3,4-Tetrahydrodibenzofuran	Phenyl	Carbon dioxide	1,2,3,4-Tetrahydrodibenzofuran-6-carboxylic acid	5	167
$C_{13}H_{10}$	Fluorene	n-Butyl or methyl	Acetyl chloride	9-Acetylfluorene	60	18
		n-Butyl or methyl	n-Butyl bromide	9-n-Butylfluorene	41	18
		n-Butyl	Trimethylchlorosilane	Trimethyl-9-fluorenylsilane	49	89
		Ethyl	—	9-Fluorenyllithium	Quant.	59b
		Ethyl	Benzophenone	9-Benzhydrylidenefluorene and 9-fluorenyldiphenylcarbinol	—	2
		Ethyl	Benzoyl chloride	Phenylbis-9-fluorenylcarbinol	—	19, 21, 168a
				9,9-Dibenzoylfluorene §	12	
		Ethyl	Carbon dioxide	Fluorene-9-carboxylic acid	—	2
		Ethyl	Dimethyl carbonate	9-Carbomethoxyfluorene	—	24
		Ethyl	Diphenylbromomethane	9-Benzhydrylfluorene	—	2
		Ethyl	Methyl iodide	9,9-Dimethylfluorene	53	24
		Mesityl	Carbon dioxide	Fluorene-9-carboxylic acid	78	54
		Phenyl	Carbon dioxide	Fluorene-9-carboxylic acid	70	54
		n-Propyl	Triphenylchlorosilane	Triphenyl-9-fluorenylsilane	84	29
		o-Tolyl	Carbon dioxide	Fluorene-9-carboxylic acid	65	54
		2,4,6-Triphenylphenyl	Carbon dioxide	Fluorene-9-carboxylic acid	—	54
$C_{13}H_{10}O$	Xanthene	n-Butyl	4-Chloro-1-methylpiperidine	9-(1-Methyl-4-piperidyl)xanthene	—	168b
			2-Di-n-butylaminoethyl chloride	9-(2-Di-n-butylaminoethyl)xanthene	—	168b
			2-Diethylaminoethyl chloride	9-(2-Diethylaminoethyl)xanthene	—	168b
$C_{13}H_{10}O_2$	4-Methoxydibenzofuran	n-Butyl	Bromine	4-Bromo-6-methoxydibenzofuran	7	9
		n-Butyl	Oxygen	3-Hydroxy-4-methoxydibenzofuran	20	9

* References 154–170 are on p. 304.

† The identity of the metalating agent in this complex reaction was not established.

§ This product was incorrectly characterized as 9-benzoylfluorene in ref. 21.

TABLE II—Continued

MISCELLANEOUS METALATIONS WITH ORGANOLITHIUM COMPOUNDS

Compound Metalated	RLi	Reactant	Final Product	Yield, %	Reference*
C$_{13}$H$_{10}$O$_2$ 4-Methoxydibenzofuran (Cont.)			Bi-(6-methoxy-4-dibenzofuryl)	3	
			4-Hydroxy-6-methoxydibenzofuran	20	
C$_{13}$H$_{10}$S Thiaxanthene	n-Butyl	2-Diethylaminoethyl chloride	9-(2-Diethylaminoethyl)thiaxanthene	—	168b
		3-Diethylaminopropyl chloride	9-(3-Diethylaminopropyl)thiaxanthene	—	168b
C$_{13}$H$_{12}$ Diphenylmethane	Ethyl	—	Tetralithiodiphenylmethane	—	59b
C$_{13}$H$_{12}$O m-Phenylanisole	Phenyl	Benzophenone	2-Methoxy-4-phenyltriphenyl-carbinol	13	108
C$_{13}$H$_{20}$O$_2$ Olivetol dimethyl ether	n-Butyl	N-Methylformanilide	2,6-Dimethoxy-4-n-amylbenzaldehyde	78	16
C$_{14}$H$_{10}$O 9-Hydroxyphenanthrene	n-Butyl	Bromine	Compound, m.p. 124–125.5°	—	47
C$_{14}$H$_{12}$ 9,10-Dihydroanthracene	n-Butyl	Ethylene oxide	9-(β-Hydroxyethyl)-9,10-dihydroanthracene	25	26
			9,10-Bis-(β-hydroxyethyl)-9,10-dihydroanthracene	2	
	Phenyl	Carbon dioxide	9,10-Dihydroanthracene-9-carboxylic acid	24–78	26
			9,10-Dihydroanthracene-9,10-dicarboxylic acid	7–8	26
C$_{14}$H$_{12}$O 9-Fluorenyl methyl ether	Phenyl	Benzophenone	9-(9-Methoxyfluorenyl)diphenyl-carbinol	46	106
C$_{14}$H$_{13}$NS 10-Ethylphenothiazine	Phenyl	Water	9-Fluorenylmethylcarbinol ‡	24	106
	n-Butyl	Benzophenone	4-Diphenylhydroxymethyl-10-ethylphenothiazine	50	87
C$_{14}$H$_{14}$O Benzhydryl methyl ether	Phenyl	Water	Diphenylmethylcarbinol ‡	12	106
Dibenzyl ether	Phenyl	Water	Benzylphenylcarbinol ‡	30	104
C$_{14}$H$_{14}$O$_2$ 2,2'-Dimethoxybiphenyl	n-Butyl	Oxygen	3-Hydroxy-2,2'-dimethoxybiphenyl	33	35
	n-Butyl	Dimethyl sulfate	2,2'-Dimethoxy-3,3'-dimethylbiphenyl	45	35

Formula	Compound metalated	RLi	Reagent	Product	Yield (%)	Reference
$C_{14}H_{14}O_2$	Ethylene glycol diphenyl ether	Phenyl	Benzophenone	Ethylene glycol bis-(o-diphenyl-hydroxymethylphenyl) ether	—	154
				Ethylene glycol o-(diphenylhy-droxymethyl)phenyl phenyl ether	—	
$C_{15}H_{11}N$	2-Phenylquinoline	Mesityl	Carbon dioxide	2-Phenylquinoline-8-carboxylic acid	23	56
$C_{15}H_{12}$	3-Phenylindene	Ethyl	Benzophenone	1-Benzhydrylidene-3-phenylindene	71	24
		Ethyl	Diphenylbromomethane	1-Benzhydryl-3-phenylindene	—	24
		Ethyl	Methyl chloroformate	3-Phenyl-9,9-dicarbomethoxyindene	—	24
$C_{15}H_{12}O$	2-Methoxyphenanthrene	n-Butyl	Oxygen	3-Hydroxy-2-methoxyphenanthrene	18	47
	3-Methoxyphenanthrene	n-Butyl	Oxygen	2-Hydroxy-3-methoxyphenanthrene	30	47
	9-Methoxyphenanthrene	n-Butyl	Oxygen	10-Hydroxy-9-methoxyphenanthrene (?) ||	—	47
$C_{15}H_{14}O$	9-Fluorenyl ethyl ether	Phenyl	Water	9-Ethyl-9-fluorenol ‡	13	104,105
$C_{16}H_{12}S$	3,4-Diphenylthiophene	n-Butyl	Formaldehyde	3,4-Diphenylthiophene-2-methanol	44	27
$C_{16}H_{14}O$	9-Fluorenyl allyl ether	Phenyl	Water	9-Allyl-9-fluorenol ‡	80	105
$C_{16}H_{16}BrN$	Di-o-xyleneammonium bromide	Phenyl	—	1,2-(o-Xylylene)-1,3-dihydroiso-indole ‡	41	83
				2-α-(o-Xylyl)isoindole	8	
$C_{16}H_{19}N$	2-(Dimethylaminomethyl)diphenylmethane	Phenyl	Diphenylbromomethane	Dimethyl(o-benzyl-α-benzhydryl-benzyl)amine (?) ¶	54	161
$C_{16}H_{20}BrN$	Dimethyldibenzylammonium bromide	Phenyl	—	Dimethyl(phenyl-o-tolylmethyl)-amine ‡	36	83
				α-Dimethylaminobibenzyl ‡	52	
	Trimethylbenzhydryl-ammonium bromide	Phenyl	—	Dimethyl-α,α-diphenylethyl-amine ‡		161
				Dimethyl(o-benzyl-α-benzhydryl-benzyl)amine (?) ¶	—	

* References 154–170 are on p. 304.
‡ This product results from rearrangement following metalation.
\| The location of the hydroxyl group was not proved.
¶ The structure of this product was not established.

TABLE II—*Continued*

MISCELLANEOUS METALATIONS WITH ORGANOLITHIUM COMPOUNDS

Compound Metalated	RLi	Reactant	Final Product	Yield, %	Reference*
$C_{17}H_{17}NO_2$ Dibenzofuran-2-carboxylic acid diethylamide	Phenyl	Carbon dioxide	2-Benzoyldibenzofuran-x-carboxylic acid	38	11
$C_{17}H_{18}BrN$ (structure)	Phenyl	—	(structure) ‡	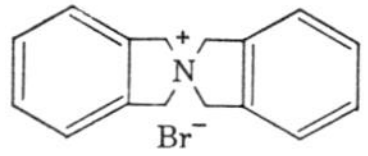 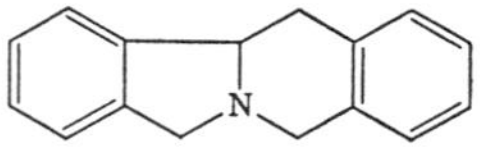 37	83
$C_{17}H_{24}BrNO$ Dimethylbenzylphenacyl-ammonium bromide	Phenyl	—	1,3-Diphenyl-2-dimethylamino-1-propanone ‡ Benzalacetophenone ‡	— —	161
$C_{18}H_{14}$ 9,10-Dihydro-1,2-benzanthracene	n-Butyl	Methyl chloride	cis- (or trans-)9,10-Dimethyl-9,10-dihydro-1,2-benzanthracene	—	26
$C_{18}H_{16}N_2S$ 10-[β-(1-Pyrrolidyl)ethyl]-phenothiazine	n-Butyl	Benzophenone	4-Diphenylhydroxymethyl-10-[β-(1-pyrrolidyl)ethyl]phenothiazine (?) ¶ 4,6-Bis(diphenylhydroxymethyl)-10-[β-(1-pyrrolidyl)ethyl]phenothiazine (?) ¶	2–3 15	87
$C_{18}H_{20}BrN$ (structure)	Phenyl	—	(structure) ‡	—	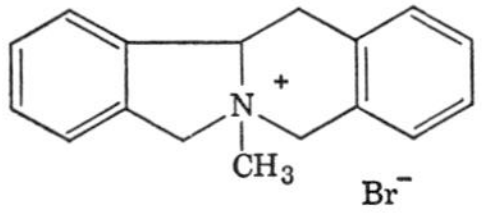 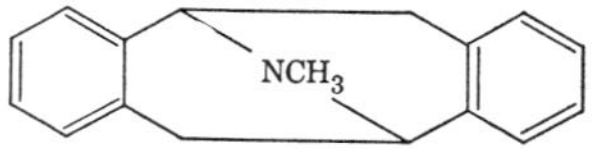 83
$C_{19}H_{14}O$ Phenyl 9-fluorenyl ether	Phenyl	Water	Bis-9-fluorenylidene	67	105
$C_{19}H_{16}$ Triphenylmethane	Phenyl	Carbon dioxide	Triphenylacetic acid	11	54
	n-Propyl	Carbon dioxide	Triphenylacetic acid	70	29
	n-Propyl	Trimethylchlorosilane	Trimethyltritylsilane	—	29
	o-Tolyl	Carbon dioxide	Triphenylacetic acid	12	54

Formula	Compound	RLi	Reagent	Product	Yield %	Ref.
$C_{19}H_{24}N_2S$	10-(γ-Diethylaminopropyl)-phenothiazine	n-Butyl	Benzonitrile	10-(γ-Diethylaminopropyl)-4-benzoylphenothiazine (?) ¶	—	31
		n-Butyl	Benzophenone	4-Diphenylhydroxymethyl-10-(γ-diethylaminopropyl)phenothiazine (?) ¶	Poor	87
$C_{20}H_{16}O$	Benzyl 9-fluorenyl ether	Phenyl	Water	9-Benzyl-9-fluorenol ‡	98	105
$C_{20}H_{18}O$	Methyl trityl ether	n-Butyl	Water	9-Phenylfluorene	17	107
		Phenyl	Carbon dioxide	9-Phenylfluorene-9-carboxylic acid	10	107
		Phenyl	Water	9-Phenylfluorene	21-34	107
$C_{21}H_{16}$	2,3-Diphenylindene	Ethyl	Benzyl chloride	1-Benzyl-2,3-diphenylindene	45	23
$C_{22}H_{22}BrN$	Dimethylbenzyl-9-fluorenylammonium bromide	Phenyl	—	9-Benzyl-9-dimethylaminofluorene ‡	94	169
$C_{26}H_{18}O$	9,9'-Difluorenyl ether	Phenyl	Water	9-(9'-Fluorenyl)-9-fluorenol ‡	80	105
$C_{28}H_{24}BrN$	Dimethylbis(9-fluorenyl)-ammonium bromide	Phenyl	—	9-Dimethylamino-9-(9'-fluorenyl)-fluorene ‡	60	83
H_2	Hydrogen **	n-Butyl	—	Lithium hydride	90	170
		n-Heptyl	—	Lithium hydride	90	170
		n-Lauryl	—	Lithium hydride	90	170
		Methyl	—	Lithium hydride	90	170
		1-Naphthyl	—	Lithium hydride	90	170
		p-Tolyl	—	Lithium hydride	90	170

* References 154-170 are on p. 304.

‡ This product results from rearrangement following metalation.

¶ The structure of this product was not established.

** The so-called "metalations of hydrogen" are included in this table because of their formal resemblance to the usual organolithium metalations.

REFERENCES FOR TABLE II

[154] Wittig and Harborth, *Ber.*, **77**, 306 (1944).

[155] Wittig and Merkle, *Ber.*, **75**, 1491 (1942).

[156] Walter, *Org. Syntheses*, **23**, 83 (1943).

[157] Wittig, Pockels, and Dröge, *Ber.*, **71**, 1903 (1938).

[158] Gilman and Melstrom, *J. Am. Chem. Soc.*, **70**, 1655 (1948).

[159a] Shirley and Cameron, *J. Am. Chem. Soc.*, **74**, 664 (1952).

[159b] Erne and Erlenmeyer, *Helv. Chim. Acta*, **31**, 652 (1948).

[160] Meals, *J. Org. Chem.*, **9**, 211 (1944).

[161] Wittig, Mangold, and Felletschin, *Ann.*, **560**, 116 (1948).

[162] Gilman and Jones, *J. Am. Chem. Soc.*, **63**, 1162 (1941).

[163] F. A. Yeoman, Doctoral Dissertation, Iowa State College, 1944.

[164] Gilman and Nobis, *J. Am. Chem. Soc.*, **72**, 2629 (1950).

[165] Martin, *Iowa State Coll. J. Sci.*, **21**, 38 (1946) [*C. A.*, **41**, 952 (1947)].

[166] Gilman, Langham, and Jacoby, *J. Am. Chem. Soc.*, **61**, 106 (1939).

[167] Gilman, Smith, and Cheney, *J. Am. Chem. Soc.*, **57**, 2095 (1935).

[168a] Pfeiffer and Lübbe, *Ber.*, **63**, 762 (1930).

[168b] Cusic, U. S. pat. 2,368,006 [*C. A.*, **39**, 3630 (1945)].

[169] Wittig and Felletschin, *Ann.*, **555**, 133 (1944).

[170] Gilman, Jacoby, and Ludeman, *J. Am. Chem. Soc.*, **60**, 2336 (1938).

CHAPTER 7

β-LACTONES

HAROLD E. ZAUGG

Abbott Laboratories

CONTENTS

INTRODUCTION

β-Lactones contain a strained four-membered heterocyclic ring. Consequently, they differ from the γ- and δ-lactones both in the general methods available for their preparation and in their chemical reactivity. Because of their high order of reactivity, only those β-lactones with favorable physical properties can be isolated readily in pure form.

In 1883 Einhorn [1] first succeeded in isolating a β-lactone by treatment of β-bromo-o-nitrohydrocinnamic acid with sodium carbonate.

$$o\text{-}O_2NC_6H_4CHBrCH_2CO_2H \rightarrow o\text{-}O_2NC_6H_4CHCH_2$$
$$\underset{O\text{---}CO}{\qquad\qquad\qquad\qquad\qquad\quad|\quad\;|}$$

Three years before, Erlenmeyer [2] had failed to prepare the corresponding β-lactone lacking the nitro group and concluded that this compound was too unstable to isolate. A later unsuccessful attempt [3] to prepare the same β-lactone in essentially the same way from the β-bromo acid seemed to support Erlenmeyer's conclusion that the compound was unstable. However, a transitory existence of the β-lactone was assumed from the two products actually isolated.

$$C_6H_5CHBrCH_2CO_2H \xrightarrow{\;NH_4OH\;}$$

$$\begin{bmatrix} C_6H_5CH\text{---}CH_2 \\ \;\;|\qquad\quad| \\ O\text{-----}CO \end{bmatrix} \begin{array}{l} \rightarrow C_6H_5CH{=}CH_2 \\ \\ \rightarrow C_6H_5CH(OH)CH_2CONH_2 \end{array}$$

[1] Einhorn, Ber., **16**, 2208 (1883).
[2] Erlenmeyer, Ber., **13**, 303 (1880).
[3] Senter and Ward, J. Chem. Soc., **1925**, 1847.

A similar course was proposed [4] for the corresponding reaction with hydrazine which produced the hydroxy acid hydrazide. More recently,[5-7] the catalyzed reaction of ketene with benzaldehyde has led to a product which, although not purified, must have contained β-phenyl-β-propiolactone since pyrolysis gave styrene,[6] and catalytic reduction gave β-cyclohexylpropionic acid,[7] both in good yield.

$$C_6H_5CHO + CH_2{=}C{=}O \xrightarrow[CH_3CO_2Na]{Anhydrous}$$

$$\begin{bmatrix} C_6H_5CH{-}CH_2 \\ | \qquad | \\ O{-}CO \end{bmatrix} \xrightarrow[\text{H}_2,\ \text{Ni}]{\text{Heat}} \begin{array}{l} C_6H_5CH{=}CH_2 \\ C_6H_{11}CH_2CH_2CO_2H \end{array}$$

Apparently β-phenyl-β-propiolactone, though not necessarily any less stable than its isolable o-nitro derivative, does not possess a high enough melting point or a low enough boiling point to permit ready isolation. The many other β-lactones that have been assumed to be reaction intermediates but have not been characterized are surveyed in Table IV.

Unlike γ- and δ-lactones, β-lactones cannot be prepared from their corresponding hydroxy acids or esters. Instead, water is lost to give the α,β-unsaturated acid or ester. If both α-hydrogen atoms are substituted by alkyl groups, drastic treatment results either in polyester formation [8] or in cleavage between the α and β carbon atoms.[9, 10]

$$CH_3CH(OH)C(R)_2CO_2H \xrightarrow{170°} CH_3CHO + R_2CHCO_2H$$

Consequently, interpretations [11] of reactions of β-hydroxy acids that involve hypothetical β-lactone intermediates should be viewed with reserve.[12]

Since the highly reactive β-lactones are customarily prepared in order to transform them into other products, this chapter will consider, first, the preparation of β-lactones and, second, their reactions of synthetic value. The synthesis and reactions of several types of compounds structurally similar to β-lactones will not be considered in this survey.

[4] Darapsky, *J. prakt. Chem.*, [2], **96**, 271 (1917).

[5] Hagemeyer, *Ind. Eng. Chem.*, **41**, 765 (1949).

[6] Hagemeyer, U. S. pat. 2,466,420 [*C. A.*, **43**, 5037 (1949)].

[7] Hagemeyer, U. S. pats. 2,484,497 and 2,484,499 [*C. A.*, **44**, 6426 (1950)].

[8] Blaise and Marcilly, *Bull. soc. chim. France*, [3], **31**, 308 (1904).

[9] Schnapp, *Ann.*, **201**, 70 (1880).

[10] Jones, *Ann.*, **226**, 291 (1884).

[11] Tsatsas, *Ann. chim.*, [12], **1**, 342 (1946).

[12] Salkowski, *J. prakt. Chem.*, [2], **106**, 253 (1923).

The generally accepted [13-17] structure for ketene dimer is that of an enolic β-lactone. The chemistry of this substance and of higher ketene dimers, which apparently do not necessarily have analogous structures,[18] has been reviewed elsewhere in this series.[19] Consideration of the other enolic β-lactones which have been reported [20-22] likewise will be omitted. Ott [23] included the dialkyl malonic anhydrides in a short review of β-lactones. Chemically, these compounds appear to have little in common with β-lactones, and therefore they will not be discussed in this chapter.

SYNTHESIS OF β-LACTONES

Only two general methods for the preparation of β-lactones are known: the treatment of β-halogen acids with basic reagents and the reaction of ketenes with carbonyl compounds. The latter method requires the presence of a catalyst except when diphenylketene is used.

From β-Halogen Acids

$$
-\overset{|}{\underset{\underset{X}{|}}{C}}-\overset{|}{\underset{|}{C}}-CO_2H \xrightarrow[\text{(base)}]{MA} \left[-\overset{|}{\underset{\underset{X}{|}}{C}}-\overset{|}{\underset{|}{C}}-CO_2M \right] \rightleftarrows -\overset{|}{\underset{\underset{O-CO}{}}{C}}-\overset{|}{\underset{}{C}}- + MX
$$

$$
\downarrow
$$

$$
\overset{|}{\underset{|}{C}}=\overset{|}{\underset{|}{C}} + CO_2 + MX
$$

β-Halogen acids have been converted to β-lactones by reagents varying in basicity from potassium acetate to sodium hydroxide. The agents most commonly used are sodium hydroxide and sodium carbonate in aqueous solution, and moist silver oxide suspended in ether. Temperatures of the reactions are always moderate, never over 50°, and usually at or near room temperature. Since β-lactones are easily hydrolyzed by excess alkali to β-hydroxy acids, only enough reagent is

[13] Johnson and Shiner, J. Am. Chem. Soc., **75**, 1350 (1953).
[14] Blomquist and Baldwin, J. Am. Chem. Soc., **70**, 29 (1948).
[15] Hurd and Blanchard, J. Am. Chem. Soc., **72**, 1461 (1950).
[16] Wassermann, J. Chem. Soc., **1948**, 1323.
[17] Whiffen and Thompson, J. Chem. Soc., **1946**, 1005.
[18] Woodward and Small, J. Am. Chem. Soc., **72**, 1297 (1950).
[19] Hanford and Sauer, Org. Reactions, **3**, 108-140, 1946.
[20] Minunni and D'Urso, Gazz. chim. ital., **58**, 485 (1928).
[21] Minunni and D'Urso, Gazz. chim. ital., **59**, 32 (1929).
[22] Minunni, Gazz. chim. ital., **59**, 116 (1929).
[23] Ott, Houben's Die Methoden der organischen Chemie, 3rd ed., **3**, p. 646, G. Thieme, Leipzig, 1930.

used to convert the acid to its salt. An excess of alkaline reagent also tends to increase the quantity of α,β-unsaturated acid formed both by dehydration of the β-hydroxy acid and possibly by direct dehydrohalogenation of the β-bromo acid.

The most troublesome side reaction, however, results from the tendency for salts of β-halogen acids to split out both metal halide and carbon dioxide to give ethylenes. At first [1] it was believed that these ethylenes were formed spontaneously from the β-lactones, since it had been found that pyrolysis of the β-lactones did indeed yield these ethylenes. Later, however, kinetic studies [24-26] showed ethylene formation to be independent of β-lactone formation, both being first order with respect to the salt of the halogen acid. A dual mechanism has been proposed [27,28] for this "decarboxylative elimination" reaction of salts of β-halogen acids. In highly polar solvents a non-stereospecific mechanism involving initial ionization of the β-halogen seems to be important, whereas, in less polar media a stereospecific concerted elimination reaction predominates. The former mechanism resembles the unimolecular elimination (E_1), and the latter the bimolecular elimination (E_2) reaction of alkyl halides. The effect of α- and β-substituents on the yield of olefin relative to β-lactone qualitatively parallels the effect of similar substituents on the yield of elimination product (olefin) relative to substitution product in reactions of alkyl halides.[28] Thus, an alkyl group in either the α or β position increases both the rate and extent of olefin relative to β-lactone formation; a β-phenyl is equivalent to two β-methyl groups; and a bromine atom in the α position also favors olefin formation. Increase in reaction temperature likewise seems to promote olefin production at the expense of β-lactone.

Unfortunately, as β-lactones can react with soluble inorganic salts of halogen acids, the reaction leading to β-lactones is reversible. As the reaction leading to the formation of ethylenes is not reversible, it is important to provide some means for the rapid removal of β-lactone from the metal halide formed with it. For the preparation of water-insoluble β-lactones this presents no problem. For water-soluble β-lactones separation is accomplished in two ways: the reaction is carried out in aqueous medium in the presence of a second phase, usually ether or chloroform, which removes the product from the aqueous layer; or the β-lactone is prepared through the silver salt of the halogen acid.

[24] Johansson, *Ber.*, **48**, 1262 (1915).

[25] Johansson and Hagman, *Ber.*, **55**, 647 (1922).

[26] S. M. Hagman, Dissertation, Lund, 1924 [*C. A.*, **18**, 2497 (1924)].

[27] Cristol and Norris, *J. Am. Chem. Soc.*, **75**, 632, 2645 (1953).

[28] Grovenstein and Lee, *J. Am. Chem. Soc.*, **75**, 2639 (1953).

β-Propiolactone was first prepared by Johansson [29] in 9% yield by the action of silver oxide (prepared *in situ*) on an aqueous solution of β-iodopropionic acid. However, a later attempt [12] to prepare β-butyrolactone, α-ethyl-β-butyrolactone, and α,α-dimethyl-β-butyrolactone using moist silver oxide or by dry distillation of the silver salts failed, whereas preparation with aqueous sodium carbonate and ether as a second phase succeeded. Conversely, the β-lactone I and a series of analogous β-lactonic acids were successfully prepared [30] by the action of moist silver oxide on the bromo acids in ether solution, but aqueous sodium carbonate failed completely.

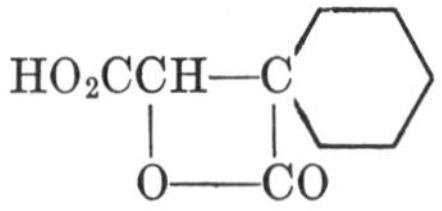

$$HO_2CCH-C \begin{array}{c} \\ \end{array}$$

$$O\text{——}CO$$

I

When the β-halogen atom is activated by an adjacent carbonyl group a weaker base can be used for effecting lactone formation. Treatment of the higher-melting (208°) racemic modification of the bromo keto acid II with 1% aqueous sodium bicarbonate gives a 90% yield of β-lactone in only three hours.[31] However, steric factors are of impor-

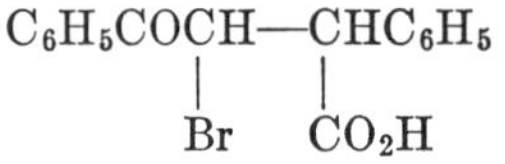

$$C_6H_5COCH-CHC_6H_5$$
$$\qquad | \qquad\quad |$$
$$\qquad Br \qquad CO_2H$$

II

tance, for the lower-melting (185°) racemic modification of II reacts more slowly under the same conditions and gives only a poor yield of β-lactone together with large quantities of the corresponding β-hydroxy acid.[32] When there are two carbonyl groups adjacent to the halogen atom as in the acid III, aqueous potassium acetate suffices to convert it to the β-lactone.[33] The methyl ester of III is reported to eliminate

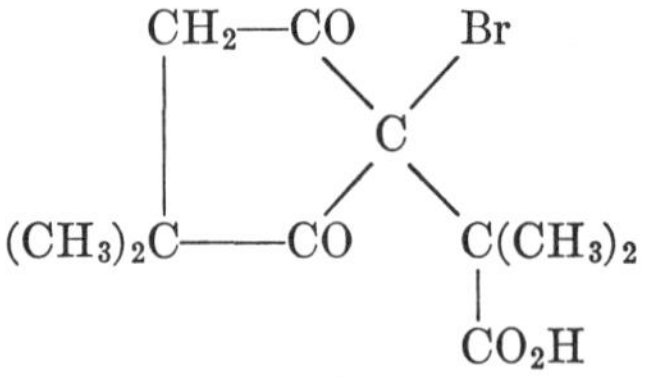

$$CH_2\text{——}CO \qquad Br$$
$$\quad | \qquad\qquad \diagdown \diagup$$
$$\qquad\qquad\qquad C$$
$$\quad | \qquad\qquad \diagup \diagdown$$
$$(CH_3)_2C\text{———}CO \qquad C(CH_3)_2$$
$$\qquad\qquad\qquad\qquad |$$
$$\qquad\qquad\qquad\qquad CO_2H$$

III

methyl bromide to give the β-lactone simply on heating.[33]

[29] Johansson, *C. A.*, **11**, 2576 (1917) [*Chem. Zentr.*, **87**, II, 557 (1916)].
[30] Kandiah, *J. Chem. Soc.*, **1932**, 1215.
[31] Kohler and Kimball, *J. Am. Chem. Soc.*, **56**, 729 (1934).
[32] Kohler, Peterson, and Bickel, *J. Am. Chem. Soc.*, **56**, 2000 (1934).
[33] Toivonen, *Chem. Zentr.*, **1928**, II, 39.

The majority of β-lactones obtained by the above method have been prepared from β-bromo acids; four have been made from the iodo acids and only one from the chloro acid (Table I).

Simpson [34] studied the relative stabilities in aqueous solution at 70° of the sodium salts of β-chloro-, β-bromo-, and β-iodo-propionic acid. Although β-propiolactone was not isolated, but only its hydrolysis product, hydracrylic acid, the β-chloro acid proved to be appreciably less reactive than the bromo and iodo acids, which were nearly equal in this respect.

More recently,[35] α,α-diphenyl-β-propiolactone (IV) has been prepared from all three β-halogen acids. Although it reacts more slowly, the chloro acid gives a 95% yield of IV with aqueous sodium hydroxide,

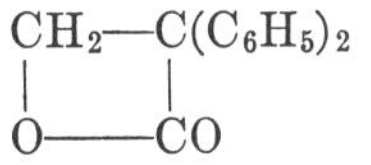

$$CH_2—C(C_6H_5)_2$$
$$O———CO$$
$$IV$$

whereas the more reactive bromo and iodo acids give IV in 64% and 25% yields, respectively. The yield of by-product 1,1-diphenylethylene varies in the inverse manner. Similarly, when the β-lactone IV is treated with sodium chloride, bromide, or iodide under comparable conditions, the yield of 1,1-diphenylethylene increases in that order.[35]

Mechanism. The course of the formation of β-lactones from salts of β-halogen acids is stereospecific. The β-bromo acid obtained by the addition of hydrogen bromide to tiglic acid leads to one racemic modification of α-methyl-β-butyrolactone while the corresponding bromo acid derived from angelic acid gives the other modification.[26] (−)Iodosuccinic acid gives the optically active β-lactone V of malic acid.[36]

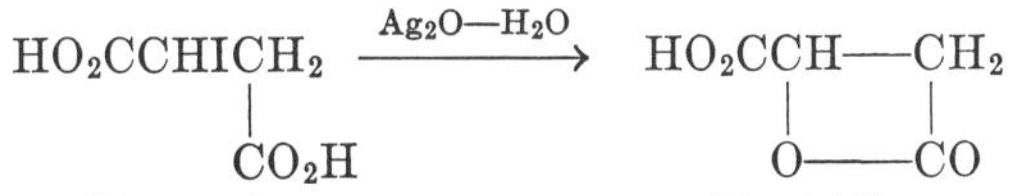

$$HO_2CCHICH_2 \xrightarrow{Ag_2O—H_2O} HO_2CCH—CH_2$$
$$CO_2H \qquad\qquad O———CO$$
$$[\alpha]_D -55° \qquad\qquad [\alpha]_D +41°$$
$$V$$

It has been noted above that the two racemic modifications of the bromo keto acid II give two stereoisomeric β-lactones.[31, 32] Likewise, the four optically active isomers of these two racemic modifications have been prepared from the four resolved bromo keto acids II.[37, 38]

Kohler and Jansen [39] prepared both the *cis* and the *trans* modifica-

[34] Simpson, *J. Am. Chem. Soc.*, **40**, 674 (1918).
[35] Zaugg, *J. Am. Chem. Soc.*, **72**, 2998 (1950).
[36] Holmberg, *Svensk Kem. Tidskrift*, **30**, 190, 215 (1918) [*C. A.*, **13**, 1582 (1919)].
[37] Bickel, *J. Am. Chem. Soc.*, **68**, 941 (1946).
[38] Kohler and Bickel, *J. Am. Chem. Soc.*, **63**, 1531 (1941).
[39] Kohler and Jansen, *J. Am. Chem. Soc.*, **60**, 2142 (1938).

tions of the bromo keto acid VI and found that, whereas one form gave a 97% yield of β-lactone in two hours with 1% sodium bicarbonate, the other form was completely inert. On the basis of chemical studies, these workers assigned the *cis* configuration to the reactive isomer. However, Bartlett and Rylander,[40] using infrared spectra, have shown this assignment to be erroneous and that it is the *trans*-bromo acid that gives the β-lactone VII. These results, therefore, are consistent with the commonly accepted mechanism for the formation of small ring compounds, which involves inverse nucleophilic replacement by the entering group.[41, 42]

Many reactions of salts of β-halogen acids must take place through intermediate β-lactones. Although the β-lactones were not isolated, a number of workers [3, 4, 34, 36, 43-55a] have recognized their presence as intermediates from the products that were isolated. Certainly the possibility of β-lactone formation should always be taken into account whenever conditions are such that β-halogen acids may be converted into their corresponding salts.

[40] Bartlett and Rylander, *J. Am. Chem. Soc.*, **73**, 4275 (1951).

[41] Winstein and Grunwald, *J. Am. Chem. Soc.*, **70**, 828 (1948).

[42] Grunwald and Winstein, *J. Am. Chem. Soc.*, **70**, 841 (1948).

[43] McKenzie and Strathern, *J. Chem. Soc.*, **1925**, 82.

[44] Woodward and Loftfield, *J. Am. Chem. Soc.*, **63**, 3169 (1941).

[45] Walden, *Ber.*, **29**, 133 (1896).

[46] Johansson, *Z. physik. Chem.*, **81**, 573 (1913).

[47] Holmberg, *Ber.*, **45**, 1713 (1912).

[48] Holmberg, *J. prakt. Chem.*, [2], **87**, 456 (1913).

[49] Holmberg, *J. prakt. Chem.*, [2], **88**, 553 (1913).

[50] Holmberg, *Arkiv Kemi, Min. Geol.*, **6**, No. 8 (1916) (*Chem. Zentr.*, **1917**, I, 1079).

[51] Holmberg, *Arkiv Kemi, Min. Geol.*, **6**, No. 23 (*Chem. Zentr.*, **1918**, I, 1147).

[52] Holmberg and Lenander, *Arkiv Kemi, Min. Geol.*, **6**, No. 17 (1917) (*Chem. Zentr.*, **1918**, I, 1145).

[53] Rørdam, *J. Chem. Soc.*, **1932**, 2931.

[54] Holmberg, *Finska Kemistsamfundets Medd.*, **54**, 116 (1945) [*C. A.*, **44**, 9380 (1950)].

[55] Lane and Heine, *J. Am. Chem. Soc.*, **73**, 1348 (1951).

[55a] O. Lutz, Dissertation, Rostock, 1899 [*Chem. Zentr.*, **1900**, II, 1009].

From Ketenes and Carbonyl Compounds

Ketenes react with carbonyl compounds to give β-lactones.

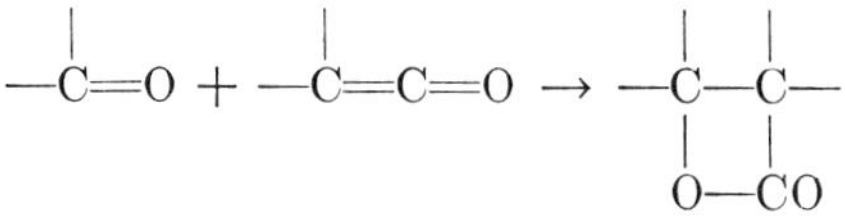

$$-\overset{|}{C}=O + -\overset{|}{C}=C=O \rightarrow -\overset{|}{\underset{|}{C}}-\overset{|}{\underset{|}{C}}- \\ \quad\quad O-CO$$

For the most general application of this reaction a catalyst is required. However, with diphenylketene no catalyst is needed.

From Diphenylketene. Diphenylketene reacts with benzoquinone in ethereal solution at room temperature to give the mono-β-lactone VIII in 72% yield.[56] However, an excess of diphenylketene must be avoided,

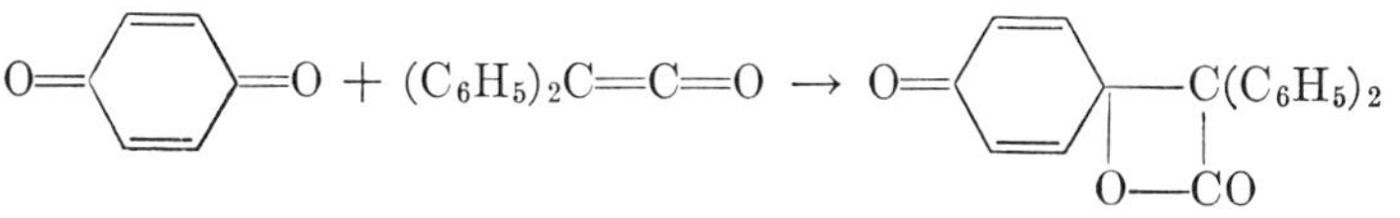

VIII

or the di-β-lactone is formed and spontaneously loses two moles of carbon dioxide to give the quinodimethane IX. When 2.5 moles of diphenylketene per mole of benzoquinone are used, the quinodimethane IX is formed in 37% yield even at room temperature.[57, 58]

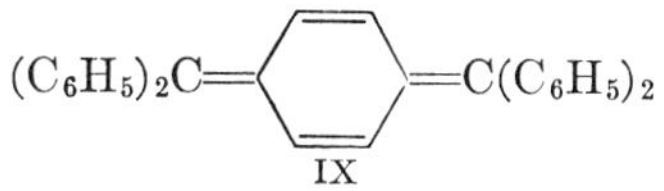

IX

Staudinger [56] found that a number of methylated and halogenated benzoquinones and even 1,4-naphthoquinone react with diphenylketene to give monolactones (Table II). However, the reaction is subject to steric hindrance. Whereas m-xyloquinone, trichloroquinone, and 1,4-naphthoquinone add diphenylketene at room temperature, p-xyloquinone, chloranil, and 9,10-anthraquinone do not.[56] When one quinone carbonyl group is highly hindered as in m-xyloquinone, excess diphenylketene can be used at room temperature without risk of diquinomethane formation. It is advisable to conduct these reactions in the absence of

[56] Staudinger and Bereza, *Ann.*, **380**, 243 (1911).
[57] Staudinger, *Ann.*, **356**, 63 (1907).
[58] Staudinger, *Ber.*, **41**, 1355 (1908).

light since irradiation of the β-lactone VIII results in a rearrangement to the benzofuranone X.[56]

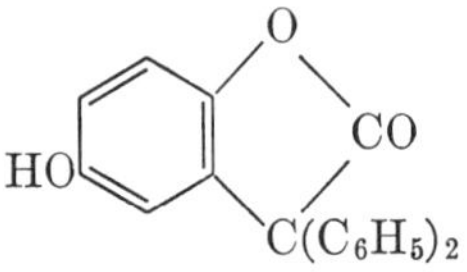

$$\underset{\text{X}}{\text{HO}}\overset{O}{\diagdown}\text{CO}\diagup C(C_6H_5)_2$$

When the reaction with diphenylketene is carried out at elevated temperatures, addition even to the hindered quinones takes place but the only isolable products are the quinodimethanes (Table IVA). Even benzoquinone reacts with one molar equivalent of diphenylketene under these conditions to give only the quinodimethane IX. This is explained by the fact that on heating the monolactone VIII in toluene or xylene under reflux disproportionation takes place to give benzoquinone and the quinodimethane IX. However, it is possible to prepare the quinomethane XI by heating the monolactone VIII to 100–110° under vacuum.[58]

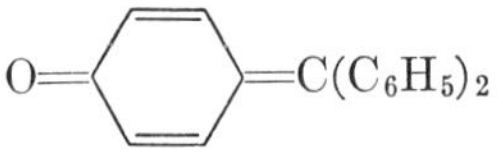

$$O = \underset{\text{XI}}{\text{⟨⟩}} = C(C_6H_5)_2$$

From Ketene. Ketene reacts with enolizable ketones in the presence of catalysts such as sulfuric acid,[59-61] sulfoacetic acid,[62] acetylsulfoacetic acid,[5, 63] and other sulfuric acid derivatives [64] to give enol acetates. In the presence of basic catalysts such as tertiary amines [65] or alkali or alkaline-earth metals,[66] β-keto esters and β-diketones react with ketene to give C-acetylation products. Aromatic aldehydes with potassium acetate as catalyst undergo a Perkin-type reaction with ketene.[67, 68] Aliphatic aldehydes with ketene or ketene dimer in the absence of catalyst give α,β-unsaturated ketones.[5, 69]

With the proper catalyst, the reaction of ketene with carbonyl compounds can be controlled to give good yields of β-lactones in a reaction

[59] Gwynn and Degering, *J. Am. Chem. Soc.*, **64**, 2216 (1942); U. S. pat. 2,383,965 [*C. A.*, **40**, 346 (1946)].

[60] Spence and Degering, *J. Am. Chem. Soc.*, **66**, 1624 (1944).

[61] Hurd, Edwards, and Roach, *J. Am. Chem. Soc.*, **66**, 2013 (1944).

[62] Young, U. S. pats. 2,461,016 and 2,461,017 [*C. A.*, **43**, 3838 (1949)].

[63] Hagemeyer and Hull, *Ind. Eng. Chem.*, **41**, 2920 (1949).

[64] Degering, U. S. pat. 2,466,655 [*C. A.*, **43**, 7505 (1949)].

[65] Spence and Degering, U. S. pat. 2,472,628 [*C. A.*, **43**, 6654 (1949)].

[66] Boese, U. S. pat. 2,432,499 [*C. A.*, **42**, 2615 (1948)].

[67] Hurd and Thomas, *J. Am. Chem. Soc.*, **55**, 275 (1933).

[68] Hurd and Williams, *J. Am. Chem. Soc.*, **58**, 962 (1936).

[69] Boese, U. S. pat. 2,108,427 [*C. A.*, **32**, 2956 (1938)].

analogous to the addition of diphenylketene to quinones. The many catalysts which have been used for this purpose are listed in Table III. The better catalysts of this group include boric acid, boron triacetate, mercuric chloride, zinc chloride, zinc thiocyanate, magnesium perchlorate, and boron trifluoride etherate.[5] These compounds are capable of forming complexes with hydroxyl groups and exhibit notable catalytic activity with the carbonyl derivatives. However, peroxide catalysis has been reported with one reaction.[70]

To condense the lower aliphatic aldehydes with ketene, the most active catalysts are not required; the preferred ones are boric acid, boron triacetate, zinc thiocyanate, and zinc chloride. For less reactive ketones, more active catalysts such as boron trifluoride etherate, zinc fluoborate, zinc fluophosphate, and mercuric chloride are required for the best yields.[5] Although possessing lower catalytic efficiency, the alkyl borates and alkyl ortho- and meta-phosphates offer some advantages over the anhydrous metal salts. They do not require anhydrous conditions for their action, and, since they do not catalyze the polymerization of β-lactones, they need not be destroyed at the end of the reaction.

Experimental details for the preparation of only seven pure β-lactones by the catalyzed ketene condensation have been published. These are the β-lactones from formaldehyde, acetaldehyde, acetone, methyl ethyl ketone, n-butyraldehyde, isobutyraldehyde, and α-methylacrolein. The experimental details are summarized in Table III. The reaction is customarily carried out at temperatures in the range 0–20°, and ketene is usually added to an excess of the carbonyl compound containing the catalyst. An inert solvent such as ether or dioxane can also be used. With the highly reactive formaldehyde and acetaldehyde, acetone or methyl ethyl ketone can serve as solvent; there is no danger that the ketone will react with the ketene as long as aldehyde is present. In continuous commercial processes, the β-lactone containing the catalyst is used as solvent, while ketene and carbonyl compound are added simultaneously with periodic addition of fresh catalyst as the product is withdrawn.[71, 72]

When higher aldehydes, ketones, and keto esters are employed in the condensation with ketene, the resulting β-lactones become more difficult to isolate in pure form because the higher distillation temperatures result in pyrolysis and polymerization. Therefore, it is customary to use the crude condensation product, freed of excess starting materials, in subsequent reactions.

[70] Barnett, U. S. pat. 2,513,615 [C. A., **44**, 9475 (1950)].
[71] Stone, U. S. pat. 2,469,704 [C. A., **43**, 5795 (1949)].
[72] Hagemeyer and Cooper, U. S. pat. 2,469,690 [C. A., **43**, 5794 (1949)].

Other Reported Syntheses of β-Lactones

One β-lactone synthesis [73] has been reported which is not of general applicability. Two others [74, 75] have also been described, but the products obtained from them are not β-lactones as originally believed.

The Reaction of Chlorine and Bromine with the Sodium Salts of Dimethylmaleic and Dimethylfumaric Acids. Tarbell and Bartlett [73] have carried out these reactions in aqueous solution. Instead of simple halogenation of the double bond, β-lactone formation occurred in poor yields. It was shown that the expected dihalogen addition products

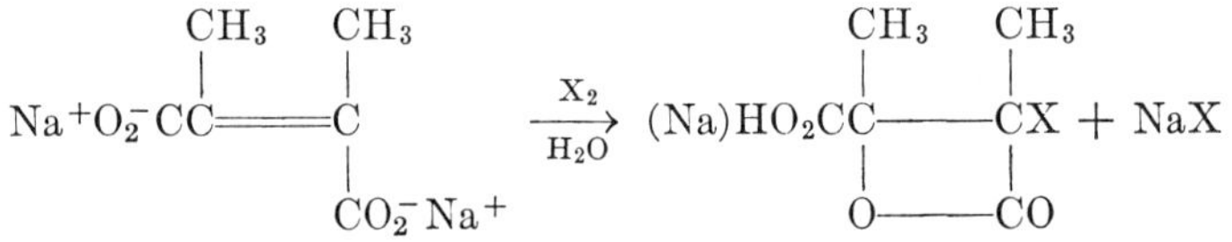

$$Na^+O_2^-CC{=\!=\!=}C \quad \xrightarrow[H_2O]{X_2} \quad (Na)HO_2CC{-\!-\!-}CX + NaX$$

with CH_3 CH_3 and $CO_2^-Na^+$ groups on the left, and CH_3 CH_3 with $O{-\!-\!-}CO$ on the right.

XII

are not intermediate to β-lactone formation as might be assumed. Also it was found that, with both halogens, sodium dimethylmaleate gives one pure racemic modification of the β-lactone while sodium dimethylfumarate leads to the other. Sodium maleate and fumarate do not react in this manner. Apparently, steric interaction between the methyl groups promotes the closure of the strained four-membered ring.[73] A suggested [76] mechanism for this reaction involving the hypothetical halonium ion intermediate XIII explains the observed retention of configuration. The four β-lactones of type XII are included in Table I D with other β-lactonic acids.

$$CH_3$$
$$|$$
$$CCO_2^-Na^+$$
$$\overset{+}{X}\diagup|$$
$$\diagdown|$$
$$CCO_2^-Na^+$$
$$|$$
$$CH_3$$

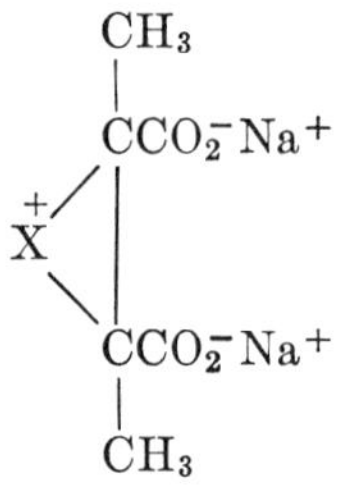

XIII

ble I D with other β-lactonic acids.

Meldrum's "β-Lactonic Acids." In 1908 Meldrum [74] treated acetone with malonic acid in the presence of acetic anhydride and sulfuric acid.

[73] Tarbell and Bartlett, *J. Am. Chem. Soc.*, **59**, 407 (1937).
[74] Meldrum, *J. Chem. Soc.*, **1908**, 598.
[75] Bains and Thorpe, *J. Chem. Soc.*, **1923**, 2742.
[76] Winstein and Lucas, *J. Am. Chem. Soc.*, **61**, 1579 (1939).

To the product he assigned the β-lactonic acid structure XIV. This

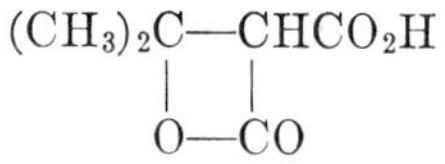

$$(CH_3)_2C\text{—}CHCO_2H$$
$$\underset{\text{O—CO}}{|\qquad|}$$

XIV

structure was not questioned by a number of later workers [23, 30, 77-84] until Davidson and Bernhard [85] pointed out certain inconsistencies in previous work and proved that Meldrum's compound is actually the cyclic isopropylidene malonate XV. Since several analogs were shown

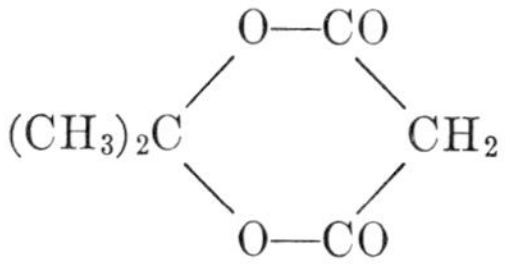

$$(CH_3)_2C\underset{\diagdown}{\overset{\diagup}{}}\overset{\text{O—CO}}{\underset{\text{O—CO}}{}}\underset{\diagup}{\overset{\diagdown}{}}CH_2$$

XV

to possess similar structures, all published work concerned with this reaction should be revised in the light of these findings.

The β-Lactonic Acid of Bains and Thorpe. These workers [75] reported the preparation of a β-lactonic acid by the following reaction.

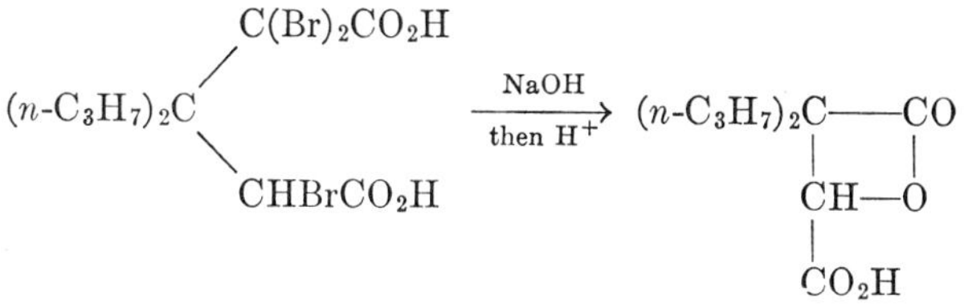

$$(n\text{-}C_3H_7)_2C\underset{\diagdown}{\overset{\diagup}{}}\overset{\text{C(Br)}_2CO_2H}{\underset{\text{CHBrCO}_2H}{}}\xrightarrow[\text{then H}^+]{\text{NaOH}}(n\text{-}C_3H_7)_2C\underset{\substack{|\\ CH\text{—}O\\ |\\ CO_2H}}{\overset{\text{—}CO}{|}}$$

They assumed that under the conditions of the reaction the dibromomethylene group was hydrolyzed to a carbonyl group which then was lost to give the monobromosuccinic acid and finally the β-lactone. This "β-lactone" possessed the peculiar property of being regenerated spon-

---

[77] Ott, *Ann.*, **401**, 159 (1913).

[78] Michael and Ross, *J. Am. Chem. Soc.*, **55**, 3684 (1933).

[79] Michael and Weiner, *J. Am. Chem. Soc.*, **58**, 680, 999 (1936).

[80] Vul'fson, *J. Gen. Chem. U.S.S.R.*, **20**, 425, 435, 595, 600, 603 (1950) [*C. A.*, **45**, 556, 557 (1951)].

[81] Vul'fson and Shemyakin, *Compt. rend. acad. sci. U.R.S.S.*, **29**, 206 (1940) [*C. A.*, **35** 3968 (1941)].

[82] Vul'fson and Shemyakin, *J. Gen. Chem. U.S.S.R.*, **13**, 436, 448 (1943) [*C. A.*, **38**, 3254 (1944)].

[83] Shemyakin and Vul'fson, *Compt. rend. acad. sci. U.R.S.S.*, **30**, 812 (1941) [*C. A.*, **37**, 610 (1943)].

[84] Hanford and Sauer, *Org. Reactions*, **3**, 124, 1946.

[85] Davidson and Bernhard, *J. Am. Chem. Soc.*, **70**, 3426 (1948).

taneously on acidification of the disodium salt of the corresponding hydroxy acid. This unique behavior was explained by the presence of the two bulky propyl groups whose mutual interaction supposedly promoted ring closure. However, since then a number of β-lactones closely related to this one have been prepared,[30] and none of them could be regenerated from the corresponding hydroxy acids even under dehydrating conditions. This, combined with the roundabout method used by Bains and Thorpe in preparing the compound, makes it extremely doubtful whether the β-lactone structure is correct.

REACTIONS OF β-LACTONES

It is convenient to divide the reactions of β-lactones that are of synthetic interest into three groups: those in which β-lactones are probable reaction intermediates; those in which the β-lactones have not been isolated in a pure state; and those in which relatively pure preparations of β-lactones were used as starting materials.

With β-Lactones as Probable Intermediates

β-Lactones are probable intermediates in the synthesis of substituted 1,1-diphenylethylenes from diphenylketene and in the synthesis of β,γ-unsaturated δ-lactones, ethylenic ketones, dienes, and quinodimethanes from ketene.

Reactions of Diphenylketene. At elevated temperatures diphenylketene reacts with aldehydes and ketones to give the corresponding diphenylethylenes.[86-89]

$$-\overset{|}{C}{=}O + (C_6H_5)_2C{=}C{=}O \rightarrow -\overset{|}{C}{=}C(C_6H_5)_2 + CO_2$$

Diphenylketene is usually employed in the form of its quinoline complex, which contains two moles of ketene per mole of quinoline and which reverts to its components on heating above its melting point (121°). The carbonyl compound is usually heated without solvent with this complex at a temperature between 120° and 160° until evolution of carbon dioxide ceases. An inert high-boiling solvent such as xylene can also be used. Carbonyl groups activated by conjugated double bonds react readily with diphenylketene, but a concurrent reaction

[86] Staudinger, *Ber.*, **41**, 1493 (1908).
[87] Staudinger, *Ber.*, **42**, 4249 (1909).
[88] Staudinger and Endle, *Ann.*, **401**, 263 (1913).
[89] Staudinger and Kon, *Ann.*, **384**, 38 (1911).

leads to δ-lactones (XVI). In many reactions δ-lactones are the main products.[88]

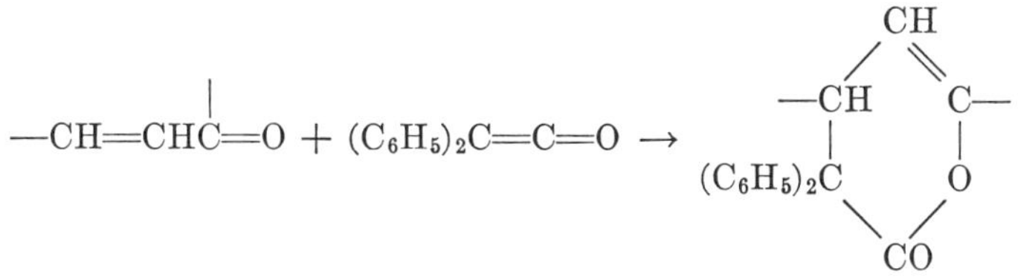

$$-CH{=}CHC({-}O) + (C_6H_5)_2C{=}C{=}O \rightarrow$$

XVI

Reactions between carbonyl compounds and diphenylketene from which diphenylethylenes have been isolated are summarized in Table IVA. Many other carbonyl compounds have also been treated with diphenylketene under similar conditions, but the only evidence of reaction has been the evolution of carbon dioxide.[89]

Reactions of Ketene. Besides the normal 1,2 addition to the carbonyl group to form the β-lactone, ketene can add 1,4 to α,β-unsaturated aldehydes and ketones to give δ-lactones. This is similar to the uncatalyzed reaction of diphenylketene with unsaturated carbonyl compounds,[88] and, indeed, it has been found that the reaction of ketene with methyl vinyl ketone in the absence of catalyst yields the δ-lactone XVII exclusively.[90] However, the catalyzed reaction gives mainly the

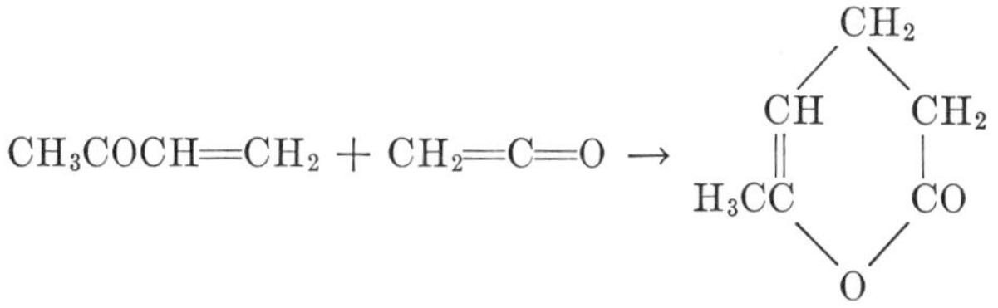

$$CH_3COCH{=}CH_2 + CH_2{=}C{=}O \rightarrow$$

XVII

β-lactone, usually in the ratio of 10 to 1 of the δ-lactone.[5] Both lactones lose carbon dioxide on pyrolysis, the δ-lactone at slightly higher temperature, to give isomeric dienes.

Methyl β-alkylvinyl ketones react differently with ketene. Unlike methyl vinyl ketone itself they do not react in the absence of catalyst. When boron trifluoride is present a γ,δ-unsaturated lactone of type XVII is not formed, but rather a β,γ-unsaturated lactone. It is believed that this product is formed through an intermediate unstable β-lactone.[91] Thus, with ethylideneacetone, ketene gives the δ-lactone XVIII in a

[90] Hopff and Rapp, U. S. pat. 2,265,165 [C. A., **36**, 1614 (1942)].
[91] Young, J. Am. Chem. Soc., **71**, 1346 (1949).

95% yield.[91] In a similar manner, butylideneacetone and mesityl oxide

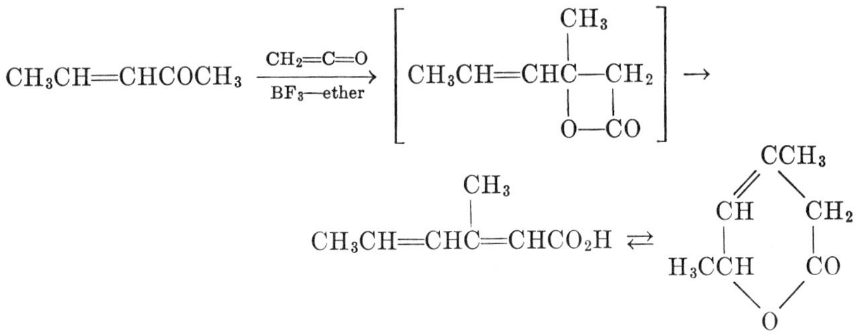

$$CH_3CH{=}CHCOCH_3 \xrightarrow[\text{BF}_3\text{—ether}]{CH_2{=}C{=}O} \left[\begin{array}{c} CH_3 \\ | \\ CH_3CH{=}CHC{-}CH_2 \\ |\quad\quad | \\ O{-}CO \end{array} \right] \rightarrow$$

$$\begin{array}{c} CH_3 \\ | \\ CH_3CH{=}CHC{=}CHCO_2H \end{array} \rightleftarrows$$

XVIII

give the corresponding β,γ-unsaturated δ-lactones in 80% and 99% yields, respectively.[91]

In the absence of excess ketene, diketones react to give mixtures of mono- and di-β-lactones. Their presence is indicated by distillation, which splits off carbon dioxide to give ethylenic ketones (from the mono-lactones) and dienes (from the dilactones). Yields are generally poor. Examples are summarized in Table IV C.

In the presence of a catalyst, ketene will add to quinones.[92] The corresponding quinodimethanes are the only products isolated, indicating the addition of two moles of ketene. Methylketene and diphenylketene have likewise been added to quinones in the presence of a catalyst. These reactions are listed in Table IV D.

Employing Crude β-Lactones

The three principal reactions that have been employed in obtaining useful products from crude β-lactones are summarized in Table IVB. They consist of catalytic hydrogenation with Raney nickel to give saturated carboxylic acids, pyrolysis to give ethylenes, and acidic or alkaline hydrolysis followed by dehydration of the resulting hydroxy acids to give α,β-unsaturated carboxylic acids.

In the catalytic hydrogenations of β-lactones containing aromatic nuclei, reduction is usually carried through to the perhydroaromatic stage. Particular care need not be taken to prevent polymerization of the β-lactone before hydrogenation, since hydrogenolysis of the polyester leads to the monomeric saturated carboxylic acid. The crude β-lactone from benzaldehyde has been polymerized and then hydrogenated

[92] Hagemeyer, U. S. pat. 2,481,742 [C. A., **44**, 4504 (1950)].

to give a 36% yield (based on benzaldehyde) of β-phenylpropionic acid.[7]

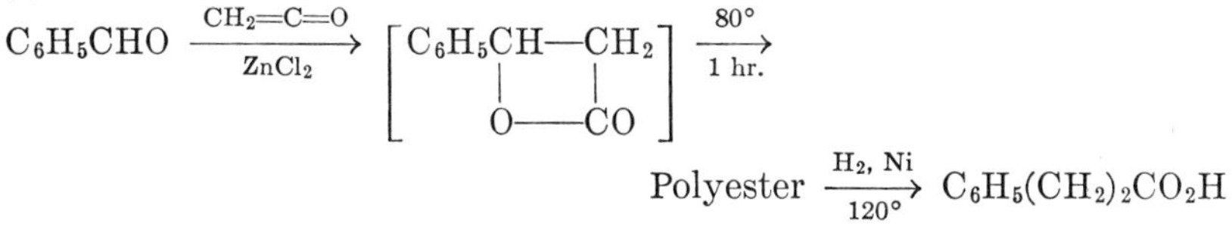

$$C_6H_5CHO \xrightarrow[ZnCl_2]{CH_2=C=O} \left[\begin{array}{c} C_6H_5CH-CH_2 \\ | \quad\quad | \\ O-\!\!-\!\!CO \end{array} \right] \xrightarrow[1\ hr.]{80°}$$

$$Polyester \xrightarrow[120°]{H_2,\ Ni} C_6H_5(CH_2)_2CO_2H$$

Incidentally, the dimer of ketene can be hydrogenated to β-butyrolactone, which on further reduction gives butyric acid in 83% yield.[5, 93]

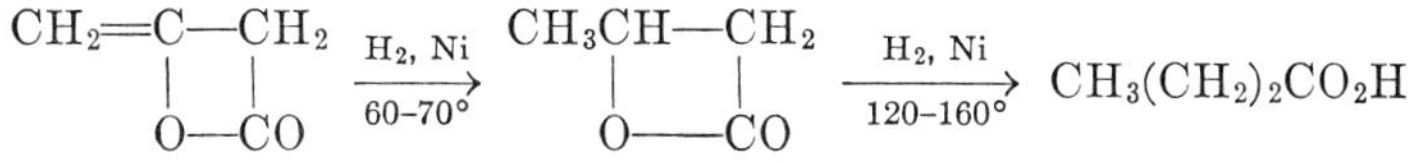

$$\begin{array}{c} CH_2=C-CH_2 \\ | \quad\quad | \\ O-\!\!-\!\!CO \end{array} \xrightarrow[60-70°]{H_2,\ Ni} \begin{array}{c} CH_3CH-CH_2 \\ | \quad\quad | \\ O-\!\!-\!\!CO \end{array} \xrightarrow[120-160°]{H_2,\ Ni} CH_3(CH_2)_2CO_2H$$

When pyrolysis to eliminate carbon dioxide from the crude β-lactone is the desired reaction preliminary polymerization must be avoided, for destructive distillation of the polymer yields the same α,β-unsaturated acid that is obtained by hydrolysis and dehydration of the monomeric β-lactone. Thus, the crude β-lactone from methyl amyl * ketone when allowed to polymerize before pyrolysis gives an 81% yield of β-methyl-β-amylacrylic acid.[94] Similar reactions have been reported starting with

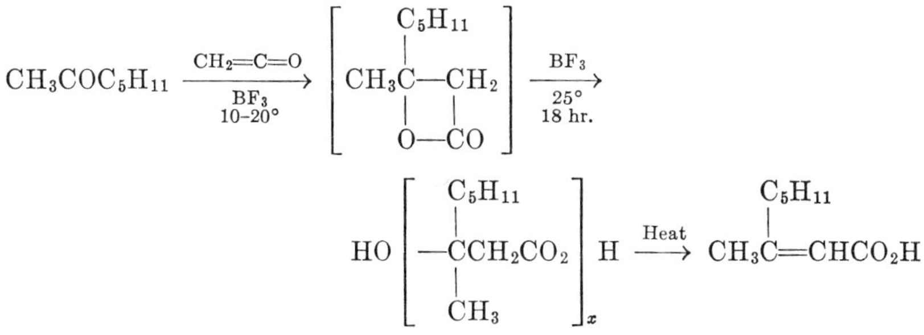

$$CH_3COC_5H_{11} \xrightarrow[BF_3 \atop 10-20°]{CH_2=C=O} \left[\begin{array}{c} C_5H_{11} \\ | \\ CH_3C-CH_2 \\ | \quad\quad | \\ O-\!\!-\!\!CO \end{array} \right] \xrightarrow[25° \atop 18\ hr.]{BF_3}$$

$$HO \left[\begin{array}{c} C_5H_{11} \\ | \\ -CCH_2CO_2 \\ | \\ CH_3 \end{array} \right]_x H \xrightarrow{Heat} \begin{array}{c} C_5H_{11} \\ | \\ CH_3C=CHCO_2H \end{array}$$

2-ethyl-3-hepten-5-one,[94] with α-ethylcrotonaldehyde to yield γ-ethylsorbic acid,[95] and with a "heptadecenone" to give a "nonadecadienoic" acid.[94] In general it can be stated that, whereas β-lactones of high molecular weight can be pyrolyzed to carbon dioxide and ethylenes in good yields, β-lactones of low molecular weight polymerize so rapidly under the influence of heat or catalysts that both ethylenes and α,β-unsaturated acids will be formed on pyrolysis.

When the crude β-lactones are first hydrolyzed and then dehydrated by distillation of the intermediate β-hydroxy acids, prevention of poly-

---

* The structure of the amyl group was not stated.

[93] Hagemeyer, U. S. pat. 2,484,498 [C. A., 44, 6427 (1950)].

[94] Boese, U. S. pat. 2,382,464 [C. A., 40, 1867 (1946)].

[95] Boese, U. S. pat. 2,484,067 [C. A., 44, 1529 (1950)].

merization is not necessary. Hydrolysis of the polyester obviously leads to monomeric β-hydroxy acid and the same end product. Likewise, the monomeric β-lactone can be esterified and dehydrated to give the α,β-unsaturated ester as final product. Thus, the condensation product derived from ketene and crotonaldehyde, treated with anhydrous ethanol in the presence of a strongly acidic catalyst and then distilled, gives a good yield of ethyl sorbate.[95]

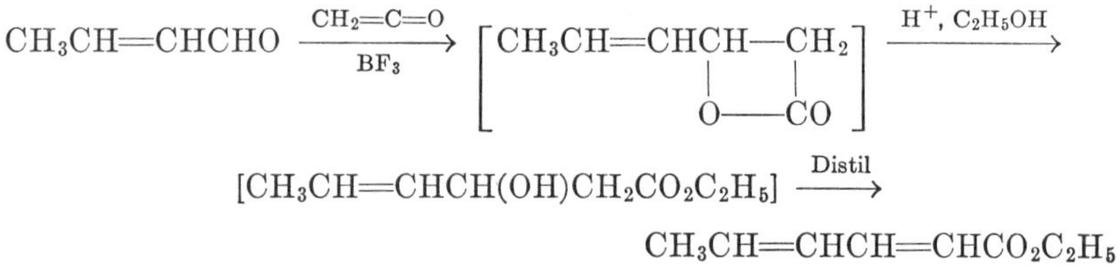

$$CH_3CH{=}CHCHO \xrightarrow[BF_3]{CH_2=C=O} \left[\begin{array}{c} CH_3CH{=}CHCH{-}CH_2 \\ | \quad\quad | \\ O{-}{-}CO \end{array} \right] \xrightarrow{H^+,\ C_2H_5OH}$$

$$[CH_3CH{=}CHCH(OH)CH_2CO_2C_2H_5] \xrightarrow{Distil}$$

$$CH_3CH{=}CHCH{=}CHCO_2C_2H_5$$

With some β-lactones, particularly those obtained from keto esters, hydrolysis or alcoholysis leads to isolable intermediates. Alkaline hydrolysis of the β-lactone XIX, prepared from ketene and methyl pyruvate, leads to the hydroxydicarboxylic acid XX, while reaction with methanol in the absence of catalyst gives the methoxy acid ester XXI.[96]

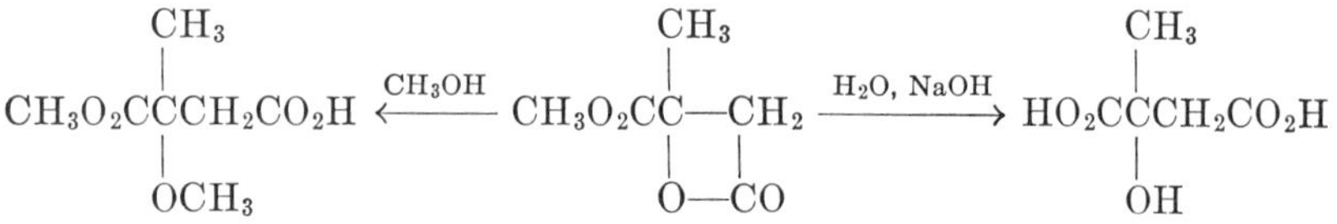

$$\begin{array}{ccccc} CH_3 & & CH_3 & & CH_3 \\ | & & | & & | \\ CH_3O_2CCCH_2CO_2H & \xleftarrow{CH_3OH} & CH_3O_2CC{-}CH_2 & \xrightarrow{H_2O,\ NaOH} & HO_2CCCH_2CO_2H \\ | & & | \quad | & & | \\ OCH_3 & & O{-}CO & & OH \\ XXI & & XIX & & XX \end{array}$$

Employing Purified β-Lactones

Many reactions have already been discussed in connection with transformation of those β-lactones that have been obtained only in the crude state, or of those that serve as transient intermediates. Until about 1945 the reactions applied to β-lactones had been limited essentially to polymerization, pyrolysis, hydrolysis, and reactions with a few anions. With the commercial availability [97] of β-propiolactone has come an acceleration in the study of its chemical properties, largely through the efforts of Gresham and co-workers. Nearly all the known reactions of β-propiolactone, together with those of other β-lactones that have so far been isolated in the pure state, are summarized in Table V. Usually, the β-lactone is added slowly to an equivalent or excess of the reactant dissolved in a suitable solvent held at a moderate temperature. In this way polymerization of the β-lactone is mini-

[96] Hagemeyer, U. S. pats. 2,456,503 and 2,496,791 [C. A., **44**, 4026 (1950)].
[97] Küng, U. S. pat. 2,356,459 [C. A., **39**, 88 (1945)].

mized. In general, since most simple aliphatic β-lactones containing less than six carbon atoms are soluble in water,[98] this solvent can be used for their reactions. Many of the chemical properties of β-propiolactone are common to its higher homologs. However, as molecular weights increase, as solubility characteristics change, and as steric effects become important, increasing care must be exercised in extrapolating the chemical reactivity of β-propiolactone to its higher homologs.

β-Propiolactone can react with a reagent MX in either or both of two ways.

1. $CH_2CH_2 + MX \rightarrow MOCH_2CH_2COX.$
$$\begin{array}{c|c|c} & | & \vdots & | \\ & O{-}\!\!\vdots{-}CO & \end{array}$$

2. $CH_2CH_2 + MX \rightarrow XCH_2CH_2CO_2M.$
$$\begin{array}{c} \text{------}|\text{------} \ | \\ O{-\!-}CO \end{array}$$

In 1, cleavage occurs at the carbonyl-oxygen bond, and in 2 at the alkyl-oxygen bond. In general, whenever MX reacts in the ionized form, M^+X^-, type 2 cleavage takes place and the anion, X^-, becomes attached to the β-carbon atom. This is true not only for strong mineral acids and salts of inorganic and organic acids but also for salts of phenols, thiophenols, mercaptans, and compounds capable of tautomerization to mercapto derivatives. Compounds containing active methylene groups likewise react by type 2 cleavage. On the other hand, carboxylic acid chlorides and anhydrides, thionyl chloride, and phosphorus pentachloride seem to react according to type 1. Other reactions such as hydrolysis, alcoholysis, aminolysis, and polymerization are more complex and will be discussed separately. In all these reactions varying amounts of polymers are usually formed concurrently.

Hydrolysis. The nature of the products of addition of the elements of water to β-lactones permits no choice between type 1 and type 2 mechanisms. On the basis of kinetic [99,100] and isotopic [101] studies, Olson and co-workers concluded that the hydrolysis of β-butyrolactone takes place by any one of three mechanisms, depending on whether it is carried out in an acid, neutral, or basic medium. Only neutral hydrolysis involves cleavage of the alkyl-oxygen bond (type 2 cleavage). Similar results have been obtained in a study of the hydrolysis of β-propiolactone [102,102a]

[98] Gresham and Shaver, U. S. pat. 2,525,794 [*C. A.*, **45**, 2971 (1951)].
[99] Olson and Miller, *J. Am. Chem. Soc.*, **60**, 2687 (1938).
[100] Olson and Youle, *J. Am. Chem. Soc.*, **73**, 2468 (1951).
[101] Olson and Hyde, *J. Am. Chem. Soc.*, **63**, 2459 (1941).
[102] Long and Purchase, *J. Am. Chem. Soc.*, **72**, 3267 (1950).
[102a] Bartlett and Small, *J. Am. Chem. Soc.*, **72**, 4867 (1950).

with the additional reservation that the acid-catalyzed reaction does not become predominant until high hydrogen-ion concentrations are reached.

Alcoholysis. The above hydrolytic mechanisms are consistent with results obtained from the alcoholysis of β-propiolactone where the end products do indicate which of the two oxygen bonds is broken. Thus, in neutral alcoholic solution β-alkoxypropionic acids are formed in good yields (type 2 reaction), but in the presence of an alkaline catalyst β-hydroxypropionic esters are formed in good yields (type 1 reaction).

$$\begin{array}{c} CH_2CH_2 \\ | \quad | \\ O\!-\!CO \end{array} \xrightarrow{\text{ROH(OR}^-)} HOCH_2CH_2CO_2R \qquad (1)$$

$$\xrightarrow{\text{ROH}} ROCH_2CH_2CO_2H \qquad (2)$$

In weakly acid solution, mixed reactions occur with formation of hydroxy esters, alkoxy acids, and alkoxy esters in varying amounts. In strongly acid solution, the reaction again becomes more unidirectional with the production of good yields of acrylic esters.

$$\begin{array}{c} CH_2CH_2 \\ | \quad | \\ O\!-\!CO \end{array} \xrightarrow[\text{Strong acid}]{\text{ROH}} [HOCH_2CH_2CO_2R] \xrightarrow[H^+]{-H_2O} CH_2\!=\!CHCO_2R$$

Alcoholysis in alkaline solution by carbonyl-oxygen cleavage (type 1) is exemplified by the reaction of α,α-diphenyl-β-propiolactone with methanolic sodium methoxide.[103] Here, the intermediate β-hydroxy es-

$$\begin{array}{c} CH_2\!-\!C(C_6H_5)_2 \\ | \qquad | \\ O\!-\!\!-\!\!-\!CO \end{array} \xrightarrow[\text{CH}_3\text{ONa}]{\text{CH}_3\text{OH}} \begin{bmatrix} \overset{+}{Na} \ \overset{-}{O}CH_2C(C_6H_5)_2 \\ | \\ CO_2CH_3 \end{bmatrix} \rightarrow (C_6H_5)_2CHCO_2CH_3$$

ter undergoes a reverse aldol reaction to give methyl diphenylacetate in good yield.

Phenols behave much like alcohols in their reactions with β-propiolactone, except that the acid-catalyzed reactions give β-hydroxy aryl esters rather than the expected β-aryloxy acids.

Aminolysis. The reactions of β-propiolactone with ammonia and amines are even more complex.[104] Either amino acids (type 2 reaction) or hydroxy amides (type 1 reaction) are formed, depending on three principal factors: the amine used, the solvent employed, and the order in which the reactants are combined. For example, dimethylamine

[103] Zaugg, *J. Am. Chem. Soc.*, **72**, 3001 (1950).
[104] Gresham, Jansen, Shaver, Bankert, and Fiedorek, *J. Am. Chem. Soc.*, **73**, 3168 (1951).

$$CH_2CH_2 \xrightarrow[R_2NH]{Type\ 1} HOCH_2CH_2CONR_2$$

$$O\!\!-\!\!CO \xrightarrow[R_2NH]{Type\ 2} R_2NCH_2CH_2CO_2H$$

(The two lines share the CH₂CH₂ / O—CO bracketed structure)

added to an ethereal solution of β-propiolactone gives mostly the amino acid, while diethylamine under the same conditions leads to the hydroxy amide as the main product. Likewise, in acetonitrile solution, ammonia, dimethylamine, ethylamine, and dodecylamine give the corresponding amino acids, while methylamine, diethylamine, and n-propylamine produce the hydroxy amides.

Water is, with few exceptions, the best solvent for hydroxy amide formation and acetonitrile for amino acid production. For example, in aqueous solution, ammonia and β-propiolactone give mainly hydracrylamide but in acetonitrile solution β-alanine is formed in good yield. However, the order of addition of the reactants can also be important. When dimethylamine is added to an ethereal solution of β-propiolactone, N,N-dimethyl-β-alanine is the main product; but when the lactone is added to the amine, the dimethylamide of hydracrylic acid is formed.

In general, aromatic and hydroaromatic amines with β-propiolactone lead to amino acids more consistently than to hydroxy amides. A

$$CH_2CH_2 \atop O\!\!-\!\!CO + AC_6H_4NH_2 \rightarrow AC_6H_4NHCH_2CH_2CO_2H$$

XXII   XXIII

1952 study [105] has shown that a number of substituted anilines XXII (A = o-, m-, and p-CO₂H, o-, m-, and p-CO₂C₂H₅, m- and p-NO₂, p-SO₂NH₂, p-Cl, and p-Br) react with β-propiolactone to give the amino acids XXIII in high yields, whether the reactions are conducted in acetone, acetonitrile, or water. Only p-toluidine gives significant amounts (40%) of the β-hydroxy amide. The amino acids XXIII in which A = m-CO₂C₂H₅, p-Cl, or p-Br could be made to react with a second mole of β-propiolactone to give the corresponding iminodipropionic acids, $AC_6H_4N(CH_2CH_2CO_2H)_2$, in yields ranging from 60 to 90%. No catalytic effect of sodium ethoxide or of sulfuric acid was noted in these reactions, although increase in basicity of the amines seemed to increase their reactivity towards the lactone.

In another study [106] of the reaction of the β-substituted lactone, β-

[105] Hurd and Hayao, J. Am. Chem. Soc., **74**, 5889 (1952).
[106] Dornow and Schumacher, Arch. Pharm., **286**, 205 (1953).

(p-nitrophenyl)-β-propiolactone, with ammonia and amines it was found that, with most amines, β-hydroxy amide formation predominates regardless of reaction conditions. Only with benzylamine and cyclohexylamine could appreciable yields (30–60%) of the corresponding amino acids be obtained, and then only if a dilute solution of the amine was added slowly to a well-stirred solution of the β-lactone in acetonitrile or nitromethane.

In contrast to this β-substituted lactone, the α-disubstituted lactone, α,α-diphenyl-β-propiolactone (IV), reacts with several heterocyclic secondary amines to give almost exclusively the corresponding β-amino acids [107] (Table V C).

Polymerization. β-Propiolactone has been polymerized under the influence of heat alone [108, 109] or in the presence of sulfuric acid,[108–110] ferric chloride,[108, 109] sodium acetate,[108, 111, 112] potassium carbonate,[113, 114] or a potassium carbonate-copper acetate mixture.[115] The products are semisolid or solid polyester acids which can be hydrolyzed to monomeric β-hydroxypropionic acid (hydracrylic acid), alcoholyzed to hydracrylic esters,[108] aminolyzed to hydracrylamides,[110] or pyrolyzed in good yield to acrylic acid.[113–115]

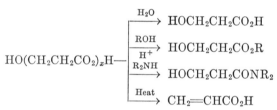

β-Propiolactone has been copolymerized with a number of polyhydroxy compounds to give stable resinous materials.[116] Ultraviolet irradiation of β-propiolactone produces, in addition to carbon monoxide, carbon dioxide, ethylene, and acetaldehyde, a yellow polymer differing in properties from the usual polyester acid.[117]

β-Butyrolactone has also been polymerized in the presence of potassium carbonate [113] and a potassium carbonate-copper acetate mixture.[115]

[107] H. E. Zaugg, L. R. Swett, and R. J. Michaels, unpublished results.
[108] Gresham and Jansen, U. S. pat. 2,526,554 [C. A., **45**, 2500 (1951)].
[109] Gresham, Jansen, and Shaver, J. Am. Chem. Soc., **70**, 998 (1948).
[110] Jansen, U. S. pat. 2,623,070 [C. A., **47**, 3039 (1953)].
[111] Gresham and Jansen, U. S. pat., 2,449,990 [C. A., **43**, 1053 (1949)].
[112] Gresham, Jansen, and Shaver, J. Am. Chem. Soc., **70**, 1003 (1948).
[113] Küng, U. S. pat. 2,361,036 [C. A., **39**, 2080 (1945)].
[114] Japs, U. S. pat. 2,568,636 [C. A., **46**, 3557 (1952)].
[115] Jansen and Beears, U. S. pat. 2,568,635 [C. A., **46**, 3557 (1952)].
[116] Caldwell, U. S. pat. 2,455,731 [C. A., **43**, 2032 (1949)].
[117] Linnell and Noyes, J. Am. Chem. Soc., **72**, 3863 (1950).

Pyrolysis of this polymer gives crotonic acid. Heating β-isovalerolactone at 50° for three hours gives predominantly the trimeric polyester acid.[108]

Other Reactions of β-Lactones. The reaction of β-propiolactone with Grignard reagents is complex.[118] Methylmagnesium iodide gives a mixture of β-iodopropionic acid, methyl vinyl ketone, and polymer. Benzylmagnesium chloride gives γ-phenylbutyric acid in only 32% yield as the main product. On the other hand, the more hindered α,α-diphenyl-β-propiolactone does not react with methylmagnesium iodide,[119] although lithium aluminum hydride reduces it to 2,2-diphenylpropane-1,3-diol in an 84% yield.[107]

Of interest is the reaction of β-propiolactone with dimethyl sulfide [120] and with tertiary amines.[104, 121] With the former, dimethyl-β-propiothetin (XXIV), and with the latter, betaines (XXV), are formed in good yields. However, the yields with sulfides decrease with the higher homologs.

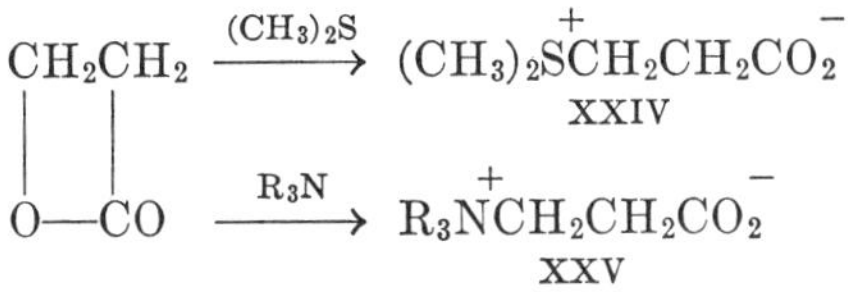

$$\begin{array}{c} CH_2CH_2 \\ | \quad\quad | \\ O\text{---}CO \end{array} \begin{array}{c} \xrightarrow{(CH_3)_2S} (CH_3)_2\overset{+}{S}CH_2CH_2CO_2^- \\ \text{XXIV} \\ \xrightarrow{R_3N} R_3\overset{+}{N}CH_2CH_2CO_2^- \\ \text{XXV} \end{array}$$

Indoles, whether substituted or not on the nitrogen atom, react with β-propiolactone under fairly drastic conditions to give products substituted at the 3 position.[122, 123] Yields are low.

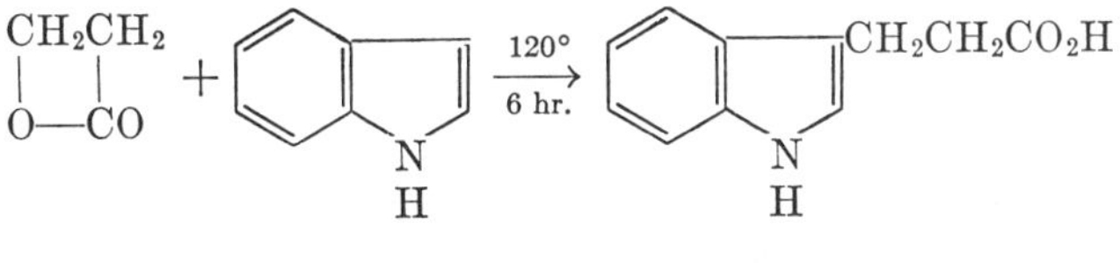

Pyrrole reacts analogously, with substitution presumably taking place at the 2 position.[123]

A general reaction of certain β-lactonic acids should be mentioned. When β-carboxy-β-lactones are pyrolyzed, the expected elimination of carbon dioxide does not occur. Instead rearrangement to an isomeric hydroxysuccinic anhydride takes place.[30, 124, 125]

[118] Gresham, Jansen, Shaver, and Bankert, *J. Am. Chem. Soc.*, **71**, 2807 (1949).
[119] Zaugg and Horrom, *Anal. Chem.*, **20**, 1026 (1948).
[120] Blau and Stuckwisch, *J. Am. Chem. Soc.*, **73**, 2355 (1951).
[121] Fiedorek, U. S. pat. 2,548,428 [*C. A.*, **45**, 8033 (1951)].
[122] Harley-Mason, *Chemistry & Industry*, **1951**, 886.
[123] Harley-Mason, *J. Chem. Soc.*, **1952**, 2433.
[124] Baeyer and Villiger, *Ber.*, **30**, 1954 (1897).
[125] Fichter and Hirsch, *Ber.*, **33**, 3270 (1900).

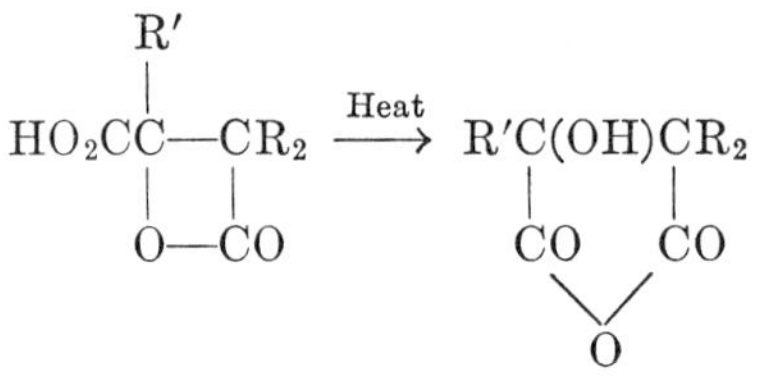

$$\underset{\substack{\text{O---CO}}}{\overset{\substack{\text{R'}}}{HO_2C\overset{|}{C}\text{---}CR_2}} \xrightarrow{\text{Heat}} \underset{\substack{\text{CO}\quad\text{CO}\\\diagdown\diagup\\\text{O}}}{R'C(OH)CR_2}$$

Another rearrangement of suitably constituted β-lactones takes place under the influence of an acid catalyst.[126] When a β-lactone containing at least one β-alkyl substituent and at least one α-hydrogen atom is treated with concentrated sulfuric acid under anhydrous conditions, an exothermic reaction leads to the corresponding substituted acrylic acid. In this way an 89% yield of β,β-dimethylacrylic acid can be obtained

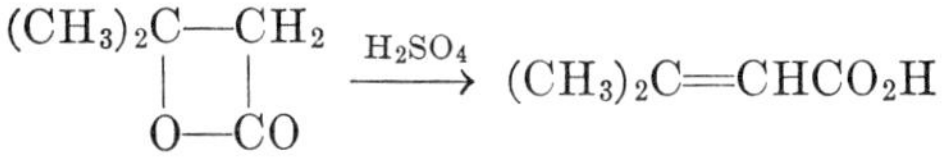

$$\underset{\substack{\text{O---CO}}}{(CH_3)_2C\text{---}CH_2} \xrightarrow{\text{H}_2\text{SO}_4} (CH_3)_2C{=}CHCO_2H$$

from β-methyl-β-butyrolactone.[126]

EXPERIMENTAL PROCEDURES

α-Ethyl-β-butyrolactone.[25] A suspension of 32.1 g. (0.165 mole) of α-ethyl-β-bromobutyric acid in 15 ml. of water is allowed to react with vigorous stirring with a suspension of 23.5 g. (0.19 mole) of sodium carbonate monohydrate in 30 ml. of water. After the acid is dissolved, 40 ml. of chloroform is added and stirring at room temperature is continued for six hours, while the reaction mixture is kept neutral by the periodic addition of further quantities (a total of about 3 g.) of sodium carbonate. After eighty minutes of stirring, and again after two hours, the chloroform is removed and replaced by a fresh portion. The combined chloroform extracts are filtered and dried over anhydrous calcium chloride. After filtration and removal of the chloroform by distillation, the residue is distilled under reduced pressure. The product (6.0 g.; 32%) distils at 77–85°/17 mm. It may be purified by dissolving it in chloroform, shaking with a small volume of sodium carbonate solution, drying, and redistilling. Pure α-ethyl-β-butyrolactone boils at 79–81°/18 mm.

α,α-Diphenyl-β-propiolactone (IV).[35] To 86.2 ml. (0.04 mole) of 0.464 N sodium hydroxide solution is added 10.4 g. (0.04 mole) of finely powdered α,α-diphenyl-β-chloropropionic acid. The mixture is shaken mechanically for two hours and then filtered. There is obtained 3.55 g.

[126] Beears and Jansen, U. S. pat. 2,623,067 [C. A., **47**, 12420 (1953)].

of product, m.p. 88–90°. In the course of three days at room temperature, the filtrate deposits more product of the same melting point, bringing the total to 8.51 g. (95%). Crystallization of the crude product from 35 ml. of petroleum ether (Skellysolve C) gives 7.8 g. (86%) of α,α-diphenyl-β-propiolactone, m.p. 90–92°.

β-Lactone (VII) of 2-(p-Bromobenzoyl)-2-hydroxycyclohexanecarboxylic Acid.[39] A solution of 5 g. (0.013 mole) of trans-2-bromo-2-(p-bromobenzoyl)cyclohexanecarboxylic acid (VI), m.p. 147°, in 250 ml. of ethanol-free ether is shaken for two hours with 250 ml. of 1% sodium bicarbonate solution (0.03 mole). The ethereal layer is washed thoroughly with water, dried over sodium sulfate, concentrated, and diluted with low-boiling petroleum ether. A solid is deposited which, after crystallization from methanol, melts at 83°. The yield of the β-lactone VII is 3.84 g. (97%).

β-Lactone (I) of α-Hydroxy-1-carboxycyclohexane-1-acetic Acid.[30] Moist silver oxide freshly prepared from 51 g. (0.3 mole) of silver nitrate is added in portions and with stirring to a solution of 25 g. (0.095 mole) of α-bromo-1-carboxycyclohexane-1-acetic acid in 250 ml. of ether. Silver bromide separates at once, and the solvent boils spontaneously under reflux. After six hours, any ether lost is replaced and the mixture is cooled in ice. Concentrated hydrochloric acid is added dropwise, with stirring, and with continued cooling until the exothermic neutralization reaction ceases (25 to 30 ml. is required). The ethereal solution is then filtered, separated from any aqueous phase, and dried over anhydrous sodium sulfate. Filtration and removal of the ether by distillation gives 14 g. (70%) of crude product. The pure β-lactone I, obtained by crystallization from a mixture of benzene and petroleum ether (b.p. 60–80°), melts at 129°. Treatment with aniline in benzene solution gives the anilinium salt, m.p. 116°.

β-Lactone (VIII) of 4-Carboxydiphenylmethylquinol (Reaction of Benzoquinone with Diphenylketene.[56] A suspension of 30 g. (0.28 mole) of finely ground benzoquinone in 300 ml. of dry ether is treated with a solution of 38.8 g. (0.20 mole) of diphenylketene in 300 ml. of petroleum ether. The mixture is shaken mechanically for thirty-six hours and then filtered. The crude product is heated under reflux with a number of 100-ml. portions of carbon disulfide until the yellow color of unreacted quinone is almost completely removed. The insoluble product consists of the colorless β-lactone VIII, m.p. 143°, and weighs 43 g. (72% yield based on diphenylketene). It can be crystallized from acetone.

1,1-Diphenyl-2-diphenylenethylene (Reaction of Fluorenone with Diphenylketene).[89] A mixture of 1 g. of fluorenone and 5 g. of diphenylketene-quinoline complex is heated for three hours at 150°. The cooled melt is dissolved in ether and washed successively with dilute sodium carbonate, with dilute hydrochloric acid, and with water. After drying and removing the ether by distillation, the colorless crystalline residue is washed with cold ether and crystallized from benzene to give 1 g. (54% based on fluorenone) of the pure hydrocarbon, m.p. 228°.

β-Butyrolactone.[97] To a solution of 2 ml. of boron trifluoride-ethyl ether complex in 50 ml. of dry ether are added simultaneously, over a period of about one hour, 22 g. (0.5 mole) of acetaldehyde dissolved in ether, and 0.45 mole of gaseous ketene.[19] The ketene is passed into the solution through a hollow-shaft high-speed stirrer. The temperature is maintained between 10° and 15°. A solution of 2 g. of sodium hydroxide in 4 ml. of water is added to decompose the catalyst. The reaction mixture is distilled, first at atmospheric pressure to remove the excess solvent and then at reduced pressure. Redistillation of the product at reduced pressure yields 26.5 g. (70%) of purified β-butyrolactone, b.p. 54–56°/10 mm.

β-Isovalerolactone.[127] Two hundred and fifty milliliters of dry acetone containing 0.5 g. of zinc thiocyanate is stirred at 25–30°, and one mole of gaseous ketene [19] is passed into the solution through a hollow-shaft high-speed stirrer. The catalyst is neutralized by adding 1.5 g. of sodium carbonate dissolved in 5 ml. of water, and most of the acetone is removed under vacuum at 25°. The residue is distilled to give 70–75 g. (70–75%) of β-isovalerolactone, b.p. 54–55°/10 mm., n_D^{20} 1.4126.

2,4,6-Octatrienoic Acid (Hydrolysis and Dehydration of a β-Lactone).[95] To a solution of 0.5 g. of boron trifluoride in 280 g. of dry ether maintained at 0° are added simultaneously, over a period of about one hour, 44 g. (0.46 mole) of 2,4-hexadienal and 19 g. (0.45 mole) of gaseous ketene.[19] The ketene is introduced as described above. To the mixture is added 150 ml. of glacial acetic acid, and the ether is removed under vacuum. Upon the addition of 75 ml. of 6 N hydrochloric acid to the acetic acid solution, a slight temperature rise occurs and the product separates. The reaction mixture is left overnight and then filtered to give 33.5 g. (54%) of the octatrienoic acid as pale yellow crystals, m.p. 201–203°.

Ethyl Isopropenylacetate and Monoethyl β-Methylglutarate (Pyrolysis and Hydrogenation of a β-Lactone).[96] Four milliliters of boron trifluoride etherate is dissolved in 500 g. (3.85 moles) of ethyl acetoacetate kept at 0°. Gaseous ketene (4.0 moles) is passed into the solution through a high-speed hollow-shaft stirrer at the rate of 21 g. per hour for eight hours. The catalyst is neutralized by addition of 40% sodium

---

[127] Caldwell, U. S. pat. 2,450,117 [C. A., **43**, 1055 (1949)].

hydroxide, the precipitate is removed, and the filtrate is heated to 90–110° until evolution of carbon dioxide ceases. Fractional distillation gives 350 g. (71%) of ethyl isopropenylacetate, b.p. 54°/20 mm., n_D 1.440.

If the crude β-lactone is hydrogenated with 5 g. of Raney nickel at 150° and 100 atm., 382 g. (57%) of the monoethyl ester of β-methylglutaric acid, b.p. 154°/10 mm., is obtained.[128]

α-Phenyltropic Acid (Hydrolysis of α,α-Diphenyl-β-propiolactone).[103] A solution of 11.95 g. of α,α-diphenyl-β-propiolactone in a mixture of 195 ml. of glacial acetic acid, 43 ml. of concentrated sulfuric acid, and 85 ml. of water is heated on the steam bath for seven hours. The reaction mixture is diluted with water to a volume of 1.5 l., and the oil that separates is taken up in ether. The ethereal layer is washed with water and then extracted with 150 ml. of 2 N sodium hydroxide; the aqueous extract is separated and acidified with concentrated hydrochloric acid. The precipitated oil is again dissolved in ether, washed with water, and dried over anhydrous magnesium sulfate. Filtration followed by removal of the ether by distillation gives 12.7 g. of acid, m.p. 150–156°. This material is purified by dissolving it in 60 ml. of hot 95% ethanol, adding 50 ml. of hot water, boiling with charcoal for a few minutes, filtering, and adding hot water (180–200 ml.) to the hot filtrate until a faint cloudiness develops. Seeding and cooling gives 10.8 g. (83%) of α-phenyltropic acid, m.p. 156–158°.

β-Phenylmercaptopropionic Acid (Reaction of β-Propiolactone with Sodium Thiophenoxide).[129] One mole (72 g.) of β-propiolactone is added slowly to a stirred solution of 41.7 g. (1 mole) of 97% sodium hydroxide and 110 g. (1 mole) of thiophenol in 200 ml. of water. The temperature is held at 10° during the addition and at room temperature for an additional hour. The crystals that separate after acidification with 100 ml. of concentrated hydrochloric acid are collected, washed with water, dried, and recrystallized from an ether-petroleum ether mixture. The β-phenylmercaptopropionic acid weighs 166 g. (91%) and melts at 57–58°.

N,N-Dimethylhydracrylamide (Reaction of β-Propiolactone with Dimethylamine).[104] Dimethylamine is bubbled into 300 ml. of ether at 0° until the ether is saturated. One mole (72 g.) of β-propiolactone is added to the stirred solution over a period of two hours. During the addition of the lactone, dimethylamine is passed into the solution to ensure an excess of the amine throughout the reaction. After the solu-

[128] Hagemeyer, U. S. pat. 2,444,735 [C. A., **42**, 7326 (1948)].
[129] Gresham, Jansen, Shaver, Bankert, Beears, and Prendergast, J. Am. Chem. Soc., **71** 661 (1949).

tion warms to room temperature the ether is removed and the product
is distilled. The N,N-dimethylhydracrylamide distils at 71–74°/0.17
mm. and weighs 111 g. (95%). The residue consists of 3.8 g. (3%) of
N,N-dimethyl-β-alanine, m.p. 141–142°.

N,N-Dimethyl-β-alanine (Reaction of β-Propiolactone with Dimethylamine).[104] Gaseous dimethylamine (50 g., 1.1 moles) is bubbled
into a stirred solution of 72 g. (1 mole) of β-propiolactone in 300 ml. of
ether over a period of two hours, the temperature being maintained at
0°. The solid (104 g., m.p. 136–140°) that forms is recovered, dried,
and recrystallized from methanol. The N,N-dimethyl-β-alanine weighs
98 g. (84%) and melts at 142–143°.

Methyl-β-dimethylaminopropionate Betaine (Reaction of β-Propiolactone with Trimethylamine).[104] Gaseous trimethylamine (0.7 mole) is
bubbled into a stirred solution of 36 g. (0.5 mole) of β-propiolactone in
300 ml. of acetonitrile at a temperature of 10–15°. The precipitated
betaine is collected and dried. The hygroscopic material weighs 64 g.
(98%) and melts at 120.5–121°. A sample, dissolved in ethanol, treated
with concentrated hydrochloric acid, collected, and crystallized from
aqueous ethanol gives N-(2-carboxyethyl)trimethylammonium chloride, m.p. 200–200.5°.

4-Acetyl-5-oxohexanoic Acid (Reaction of β-Propiolactone with Acetylacetone).[130] Acetylacetone (300 g., 3 moles) is added with stirring
and cooling at 25° to a solution of 100 g. (2.5 moles) of sodium hydroxide
in 800 ml. of water. β-Propiolactone (144 g., 2 moles) is added to this
solution at 25° with stirring and cooling over a period of one hour.
After an additional hour the solution is acidified with 215 ml. of concentrated hydrochloric acid and the organic layer is extracted with
three 300-ml. portions of ether. The ether is removed from the combined extracts at reduced pressure, and the residue is distilled; 98 g. of
unreacted acetylacetone, b.p. 40–90°/10 mm., is collected first, and the
crude 4-acetyl-5-oxohexanoic acid is collected as the main fraction at
124–142°/1 mm. The acid, which weighs 142 g. (41.5%), slowly crystallizes. After recrystallization from benzene-hexane it melts at 73–76°.

TABULAR SURVEY OF β-LACTONES

In Tables I, II, and III are listed those β-lactones that have been
isolated and characterized and for which preparative procedures have
been reported. Table IV summarizes reactions in which β-lactones
either served as transient intermediates for other reactions or in which
β-lactones were obtained only in crude form prior to further reaction.

---

[130] Gresham, Jansen, Shaver, Frederick, and Beears, *J. Am. Chem. Soc.*, **73**, 2345 (1951).

Table V lists all the reactions of the β-lactones included in the first three tables. The reactions of β-propiolactone (Table V A) are treated in somewhat more detail than those of its higher derivatives.

Arrangement of compounds within the tables is in the order of increasing complexity of substituents on the β-lactone ring. Substituents generally follow the order: aliphatic, aromatic, ketonic, carboxylic, and quinoid. In Table IV, the carbonyl reactants are also arranged in order of increasing complexity, starting with aldehydes and progressing through ketones, α,β-unsaturated carbonyl compounds, keto esters, and diketones to quinones. In Table V A (reactions of β-propiolactone) the reactants are arranged in the following arbitrary order: water, alcohols, phenols, thiophenols, mercaptans and other organic sulfur compounds, ammonia and amines, tertiary amines, salts of inorganic and organic acids, inorganic and organic acids and derivatives, Grignard reagents, active methylene compounds, and miscellaneous reactants.

The literature has been reviewed through 1952, but several later references are included. In the patent literature, which was consulted in the original, reference is often made to β-lactonic structures for which no example of a preparative procedure or reaction is given. These compounds have not been included in the tables.

TABLE I

β-Lactones from β-Halogen Acids

$$\underset{|}{X}\underset{|}{C}-\underset{|}{C}-CO_2^- \rightarrow -\overset{\beta}{\underset{|}{C}}-\overset{\alpha}{\underset{|}{C}}- + X^-$$
$$\underset{O-CO}{}$$

Substituents in β-Lactone	X	Experimental Conditions	Yield, %	Reference
A. Aliphatic				
None	I	Aq. AgNO₃, NaOH	9	29
α-Methyl	I	Aq. AgNO₃, NaOH	55	29
β-Methyl	Br	Aq. Na₂CO₃, CHCl₃	70	29
	Br	Aq. Na₂CO₃; 45°	—	24
	Br	2N Na₂CO₃; 40–50°	40	12
α,β-Dimethyl *	Br	Aq. NaOH or Ba(OH)₂	—	26
	Br	Aq. Na₂CO₃, CHCl₃; 30–40°	29	25
α,β-Dimethyl †	Br	Aq. NaOH or Ba(OH)₂	—	26
α,α-Dimethyl	Br	Aq. NaOH or Ba(OH)₂	—	26
β,β-Dimethyl	Br	Aq. NaOH or Ba(OH)₂	—	26
α,α,β-Trimethyl	Br	2N Na₂CO₃; 40–50°	16	12
α-Ethyl	Br	Aq. NaOH or Ba(OH)₂	—	26
α-Ethyl-β-methyl	Br	Aq. Na₂CO₃; CHCl₃; 30–40°	32	25
	Br	2N Na₂CO₃; 40–50°	14	12
B. Aromatic and Heterocyclic				
β-o-Nitrophenyl	Br	Excess aq. Na₂CO₃	40	1
β-m-Nitrophenyl	Br	Equiv. aq. Na₂CO₃	—	131
β-p-Nitrophenyl	Br	Excess aq. Na₂CO₃	90	132
β-(2-Nitro-5-chlorophenyl)	Br	Aq. Na₂CO₃ or conc. NH₄OH	—	133
β-(2-Nitro-5-methoxyphenyl)	Br	Equiv. NH₄OH in C₂H₅OH	—	134
β-(2-Nitro-4-isopropylphenyl)	Br	Equiv. aq. Na₂CO₃	—	135
α,α-Diphenyl	Cl	Equiv. aq. NaOH	95	35
	Br	Equiv. aq. NaOH	64	35
	I	Equiv. aq. NaOH	25	35
α-Bromo-β-(2-N-methylpiperidyl)	Br	Aq. K₂CO₃, NaOH, or NH₄OH; 0°	—	136
β-(2-Quinolyl)	Br	Equiv. aq. Na₂CO₃	—	137
C. Ketonic β-Lactones				
α-Phenyl-β-benzoyl ‡	Br	1% Aq. NaHCO₃; 3 hr.	90	31, 32
α-Phenyl-β-benzoyl §	Br	1% Aq. NaHCO₃; 3 hr.	—	37, 38
α-Phenyl-β-benzoyl ‖	Br	1% Aq. NaHCO₃; 5 d.	Poor	32
α-Phenyl-β-benzoyl ¶	Br	1% Aq. NaHCO₃; 5 d.	—	37, 38

COC₆H₄Br-*p* **
|
H

〈O—CO〉

| | Br | 1% Aq. NaHCO₃, ether; 2 hr. | 97 | 39, 40 |

Note: References 131–214 are on pp. 362–363.
* Racemic modification, b.p. 67°/21 mm., derived from tiglic acid.
† Racemic modification, b.p. 63°/12 mm., derived from angelic acid.
‡ Racemic modification, m.p. 95°, derived from the racemic bromo acid, m.p. 208°.
§ Optical isomers, m.p. 75°, $[\alpha]_D^{25}$ + or −155°, derived from liquid bromo acids, $[\alpha]_D^{25}$ + or −157°.
‖ Racemic modification, m.p. 148°, derived from the racemic bromo acid, m.p. 185°.
¶ Optical isomers, m.p. 130°, $[\alpha]_D^{25}$ + or −92°, derived from bromo acids, m.p. 148°, $[\alpha]_D^{25}$ + or −90°.
** Derived from the *trans* bromo acid, m.p. 147°.

TABLE I—*Continued*

β-LACTONES FROM β-HALOGEN ACIDS

Substituents in β-Lactone	X	Experimental Conditions	Yield, %	Reference
CH₂CO (CH₃)₂C⟍ ⟋C—C(CH₃)₂ ⟍CÓ⟋ Ó—CO	Br	Aq. CH_3CO_2K	—	33

D. β-Lactonic Acids

Substituents in β-Lactone	X	Experimental Conditions	Yield, %	Reference
β-Carboxy ††	I	Ag_2O, H_2O	Poor	36, 51
β-Carboxy ‡‡	I	Ag_2O, H_2O	—	36
α,α-Dimethyl-β-carboxy	Br	Ag_2O, H_2O; 0°	—	124, 125
	Br	Moist Ag_2O, ether	—	30
α,α-Dimethyl-β-carbomethoxy	—	Silver salt + CH_3I	60	138
α-Methyl-α-ethyl-β-carboxy §§	Br	Moist Ag_2O, ether	—	30
α,α-Dimethyl-β-methyl-β-carboxy	Br	Ag_2O, H_2O; 0°	—	139
	Br	Moist Ag_2O, ether	—	30
α,α-(1,4-Butano)-β-carboxy	Br	Moist Ag_2O, ether	74	30
α,α-(1,5-Pentano)-β-carboxy	Br	Moist Ag_2O, ether	80	30
α,α-(1,5-Pentano)-β-methyl-β-carboxy	Br	Moist Ag_2O, ether	100	30
HO_2CCH—C⟨ ⟩CH₃ Ó—CO	Br	"Hexane"; 25°	—	140
HO_2CCH—C⟨ ⟩ Ó—CO *Cis* isomer, m.p. 125°	Br	Moist Ag_2O, ether	—	30
HO_2CCH—C⟨ ⟩ Ó—CO *Trans* isomer, m.p. 116°	Br	Moist Ag_2O, ether	—	30
α-Methyl-α-chloro-β-methyl-β-carboxy ‖ ‖	Cl	Sodium dimethylmaleate + aq. Cl_2	7	73
α-Methyl-α-chloro-β-methyl-β-carboxy ¶¶	Cl	Sodium dimethylfumarate + aq. Cl_2	28	73
α-Methyl-α-bromo-β-methyl-β-carboxy ***	Br	Sodium dimethylmaleate + aq. Br_2	33	73
α-Methyl-α-bromo-β-methyl-β-carboxy †††	Br	Sodium dimethylfumarate + aq. Br_2	37	73

Note: References 131–214 are on pp. 362–363.

†† Racemic modification, m.p. 64–65°, from the racemic iodo acid, m.p. 135–140°.

‡‡ Isomer, $[\alpha]_D + 41°$, from the iodo acid, m.p. 150–152°, $[\alpha]_D^{20} -55°$.

§§ Isolated as the anilinium salt.

‖ ‖ Racemic modification, m.p. 92–94°.

¶¶ Racemic modification, m.p. 141–142°.

*** Racemic modification, m.p. 95–96°.

††† Racemic modification, m.p. 148–150°.

TABLE II

β-Lactones from Quinones and Diphenylketene

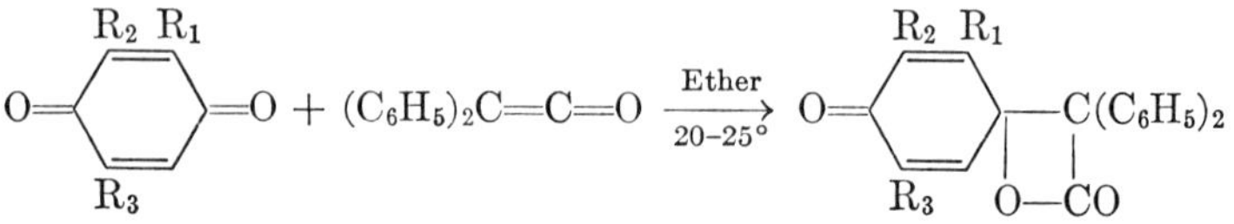

$$O = \text{(ring, } R_2, R_1, R_3\text{)} = O + (C_6H_5)_2C=C=O \xrightarrow[20-25°]{\text{Ether}} O = \text{(ring, } R_2, R_1, R_3\text{)} - C(C_6H_5)_2$$

R_1	R_2	R_3	Yield, %	Reference
H	H	H	—	141
			57	58
			72	56
H	H	CH_3	28	56
H	CH_3	CH_3	36	56
H	H	Cl	74	56
Cl	H	Cl	56	56
H	Cl	Cl	70	56
Cl	Cl	Cl	61	56
H	Br	Br	78	56
		H	43	56

Note: References 131–214 are on pp. 362–363.
* The quinone reactant was 1,4-naphthoquinone.

TABLE III

β-Lactones from the Catalyzed Reaction of Ketene with Simple Carbonyl Compounds

$$-\overset{|}{C}=O + CH_2=C=O \xrightarrow{\text{Catalyst}} -\overset{\overset{\beta}{|}}{C}-\overset{\overset{\alpha}{|}}{C}- \\ \underset{O-CO}{}$$

Substituents in β-Lactone	Solvent	Temperature	Catalyst	Yield, %	Reference
None *	β-Propiolactone	5–10°	ZnCl₂	88	5, 71
	β-Propiolactone	5–10°	None	7	5
	Acetone	7–10°	ZnCl₂	85, 90	72, 97
	Acetone	−60°	BF₃ etherate	64	97
	β-Propiolactone	5–20°	AlCl₃-ZnCl₂	Excellent	142,143
	β-Propiolactone	0–15°	Zn(ClO₄)₂	70–80	144
	β-Propiolactone	0–15°	Zn(SCN)₂	70–80	127
	β-Propiolactone	0–15°	Zn(NO₃)₂	70–80	145
	β-Propiolactone	0°	(C₂H₅)₃PO₄	55	146
	Methyl ethyl ketone	0°	Zn(BF₄)₂	70	147
	Acetone	0–10°	HgCl₂	95	148
	Ether	0–20°	Al₂O₃-SiO₂	70–80	149
	Acetone	0–10°	Activated Al₂O₃	37	149
	Acetone	10°	H₃BO₃	72	72, 150
	Acetone	10°	(C₂H₅)₃BO₃	34	150
	Ether	0–10°	Zn(PF₂O₂)₂	80	151
	Ether	0–10°	UO₂(NO₃)₂·6H₂O	70–80	152
	Ether	10°	Activated clay	53–64	153
	Mineral oil	50°	Activated clay	26	153
β-Methyl	β-Butyrolactone	5–10°	ZnCl₂	74, 85	5, 71
	Ether	10–15°	BF₃ etherate	70	97
	β-Butyrolactone	0–15°	Zn(ClO₄)₂	Excellent	144
	Dioxane	0–10°	Zn(SCN)₂	70–80	127
	β-Butyrolactone	−5–20°	Zn(NO₃)₂	Excellent	145
	Acetone	0–10°	C₂H₅PO₃	19	146
	Acetone	0°	Fe(BF₄)₂	64	147
	Acetone	—	HgCl₂	30	148
	Ether	0–5°	Al₂O₃-SiO₂-ZrO₂	75–80	149
	Acetone	10°	H₃BO₃	64	150
	Acetone	10°	(C₂H₅)₃BO₃	49	150
	Acetone	10°	B(O₂CCH₃)₃	62	72
	Acetaldehyde	20–25°	Zn(PF₂O₂)₂	—	151
	Ether	0°	Activated clay	63	153
	Ether	0°	Untreated clay	37	153
	Dioxane	100°	Activated clay	17	153
β,β-Dimethyl	Acetone	20–30°	Zn(ClO₄)₂	45–50	144
	Acetone	25–30°	Zn(SCN)₂	70–75	127
	Acetone	5–30°	Zn(NO₃)₂	Good	145
	Acetone	20°	C₂H₅PO₃	26	146
	Acetone	0–10°	Pb(BF₄)₂	43	147
	Acetone	0°	HgCl₂	68	148
	Acetone	20–30°	Al₂O₃-SiO₂-ZrO₂	Excellent	149
	Acetone	10°	(C₂H₅)₃BO₃	22	150
	Acetone	20–25°	Zn(PF₂O₂)₂	70	151
	Acetone	−40°	BF₃ etherate	90	155
β-Methyl-β-ethyl	Methyl ethyl ketone	5–10°	ZnCl₂	—	5
	Methyl ethyl ketone	−25°	BF₃	93	156
	Methyl ethyl ketone	25–30°	Al₂O₃-SiO₂	70	149
	Methyl ethyl ketone	20–30°	Mg(ClO₄)₂	50	144
	Methyl ethyl ketone	20–30°	Zn(SCN)₂	50	127
	Methyl ethyl ketone	20–30°	Zn(NO₃)₂	50	145
β-n-Propyl	Ether	0°	Activated clay	58	153
	Ether	0°	Dry fuller's earth	25	153
β-Isopropyl	Diisopropyl ether	0°	UO₂Cl₂	85–90	152
β-Isopropenyl	Diisopropyl ether	0–10°	BF₃ etherate	36	157

Note: References 131–214 are on pp. 362–363.
* For a method of rigorous purification of β-propiolactone, see ref. 154.

TABLE IV

REACTIONS OF KETENES WITH CARBONYL COMPOUNDS INVOLVING UNISOLATED β-LACTONE INTERMEDIATES

A. Uncatalyzed Reactions of Diphenylketene

$$-\overset{|}{\underset{|}{C}}{=}O + (C_6H_5)_2C{=}C{=}O \xrightarrow[\text{2-6 hr.}]{120\text{-}160^\circ} \left[-\overset{|}{\underset{\underset{O-CO}{|}}{C}}-C(C_6H_5)_2 \right] \xrightarrow{-CO_2} -\overset{|}{\underset{|}{C}}{=}C(C_6H_5)_2$$

Carbonyl Compound	Product	Yield, %	Reference
1. Aldehydes			
C_6H_5CHO	$C_6H_5CH{=}C(C_6H_5)_2$	20	89
$p\text{-}CH_3OC_6H_4CHO$	$p\text{-}CH_3OC_6H_4CH{=}C(C_6H_5)_2$	—	89
$p\text{-}(CH_3)_2NC_6H_4CHO$	$p\text{-}(CH_3)_2NC_6H_4CH{=}C(C_6H_5)_2$	—	89
CCl_3CHO	$(C_6H_5)_2C{=}CHCO_2H$ *	—	89
2. Aromatic Ketones			
$(C_6H_5)_2CO$	$(C_6H_5)_2C{=}C(C_6H_5)_2$	—	89
$(p\text{-}CH_3OC_6H_4)_2CO$	$(p\text{-}CH_3OC_6H_4)_2C{=}C(C_6H_5)_2$	51	89
$[p\text{-}(CH_3)_2NC_6H_4]_2CO$	$[p\text{-}(CH_3)_2NC_6H_4]_2C{=}C(C_6H_5)_2$	77	89
$p\text{-}CH_3C_6H_4COC_6H_5$	$p\text{-}CH_3C_6H_4C(C_6H_5){=}C(C_6H_5)_2$	36	89
$p\text{-}(CH_3)_2NC_6H_4COC_6H_5$	$p\text{-}(CH_3)_2NC_6H_4C(C_6H_5){=}C(C_6H_5)_2$	—	89
C_6H_5COCN	$C_6H_5C(CN){=}C(C_6H_5)_2$	—	89
Fluorenone	$={}C(C_6H_5)_2$	54	89
3. α,β-Unsaturated Carbonyl Compounds			
$C_6H_5CH{=}CHCHO$	$C_6H_5CH{=}CHCH{=}C(C_6H_5)_2$	—	87
$C_6H_5CH{=}CHCOC_6H_5$	$C_6H_5CH{=}CHC(C_6H_5){=}C(C_6H_5)_2$	—	87, 88
$p\text{-}CH_3OC_6H_4CH{=}CHCOC_6H_5$	$p\text{-}CH_3OC_6H_4CH{=}CHC(C_6H_5){=}C(C_6H_5)_2$	32	88
$p\text{-}(CH_3)_2NC_6H_4CH{=}CHCOC_6H_5$	$p\text{-}(CH_3)_2NC_6H_4CH{=}CHC(C_6H_5){=}C(C_6H_5)_2$	—	88
$C_6H_5(CH{=}CH)_2COC_6H_5$	$C_6H_5(CH{=}CH)_2C(C_6H_5){=}C(C_6H_5)_2$	—	87
$C_6H_5CH{=}CHCOCN$	$C_6H_5CH{=}CHC(CN){=}C(C_6H_5)_2$	—	87
4. bis-α,β-Unsaturated Ketones:			
$(-\overset{|}{C}{=}\overset{|}{C})_2CO$			
$(C_6H_5CH{=}CH)_2CO$	$(C_6H_5CH{=}CH)_2C{=}C(C_6H_5)_2$	95	86
$(p\text{-}ClC_6H_4CH{=}CH)_2CO$	$(p\text{-}ClC_6H_4CH{=}CH)_2C{=}C(C_6H_5)_2$	—	86
$(p\text{-}CH_3OC_6H_4CH{=}CH)_2CO$	$(p\text{-}CH_3OC_6H_4CH{=}CH)_2C{=}C(C_6H_5)_2$	—	86
$[p\text{-}(CH_3)_2NC_6H_4CH{=}CH]_2CO$	$[p\text{-}(CH_3)_2NC_6H_4CH{=}CH]_2C{=}C(C_6H_5)_2$	—	89
$(C_6H_5CH{=}CHCH{=}CH)_2CO$	$(C_6H_5CH{=}CHCH{=}CH)_2C{=}C(C_6H_5)_2$	—	86
$={}O$	$={}C(C_6H_5)_2$	—	89
$={}O$	$={}C(C_6H_5)_2$	—	89

* Obtained by alkaline hydrolysis of the unisolated condensation product, $(C_6H_5)_2C{=}CHCCl_3$.

TABLE IV—*Continued*

REACTIONS OF KETENES WITH CARBONYL COMPOUNDS INVOLVING UNISOLATED
β-LACTONE INTERMEDIATES

Carbonyl Compound	Product	Yield, %	Reference
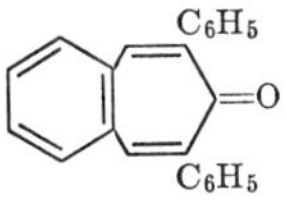 C$_6$H$_5$ / C$_6$H$_5$ =O	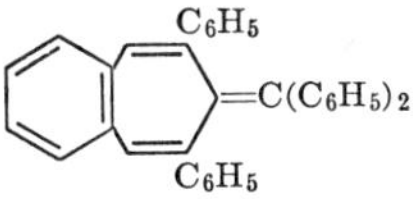 C$_6$H$_5$ / C$_6$H$_5$ =C(C$_6$H$_5$)$_2$	—	89
γ-Pyrone	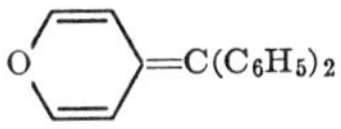 O =C(C$_6$H$_5$)$_2$	28	89
5. Quinones			
Benzoquinone	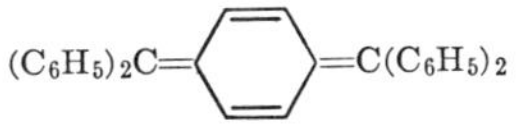 (C$_6$H$_5$)$_2$C=⟨⟩=C(C$_6$H$_5$)$_2$	37 † / 100	57 / 58
Toluquinone	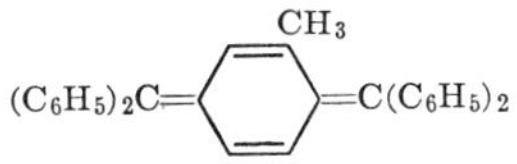 (C$_6$H$_5$)$_2$C=⟨CH$_3$⟩=C(C$_6$H$_5$)$_2$	—	56
p-Xyloquinone	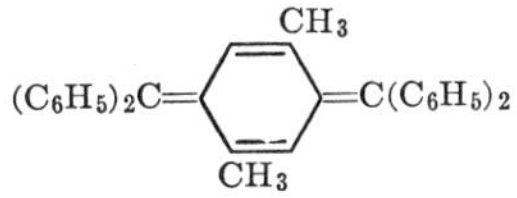 (C$_6$H$_5$)$_2$C=⟨CH$_3$/CH$_3$⟩=C(C$_6$H$_5$)$_2$	—	58
Chloroquinone	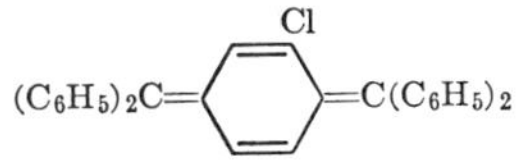 (C$_6$H$_5$)$_2$C=⟨Cl⟩=C(C$_6$H$_5$)$_2$	—	56
m-Dichloroquinone	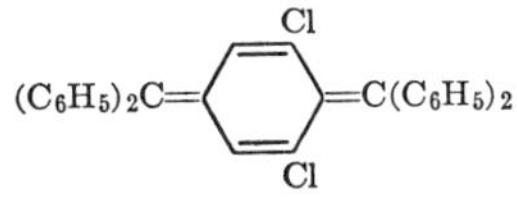 (C$_6$H$_5$)$_2$C=⟨Cl/Cl⟩=C(C$_6$H$_5$)$_2$	—	56
1,4-Naphthoquinone	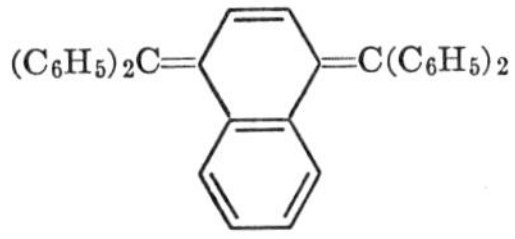 (C$_6$H$_5$)$_2$C=⟨⟩=C(C$_6$H$_5$)$_2$	60	58
Anthraquinone	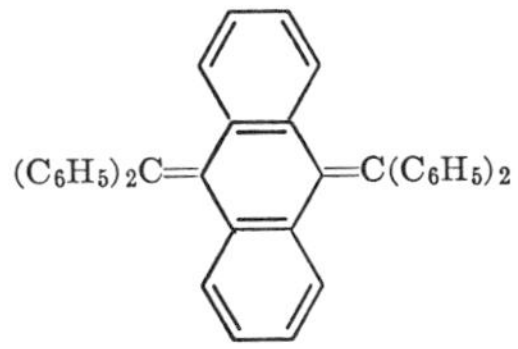 (C$_6$H$_5$)$_2$C=⟨⟩=C(C$_6$H$_5$)$_2$	—	58

† This reaction was carried out at 25° instead of at 120–160°.

TABLE IV—*Continued*

REACTIONS OF KETENES WITH CARBONYL COMPOUNDS INVOLVING UNISOLATED
β-LACTONE INTERMEDIATES

B. Catalyzed Reactions of Ketene with Aldehydes, Ketones, and Keto Esters

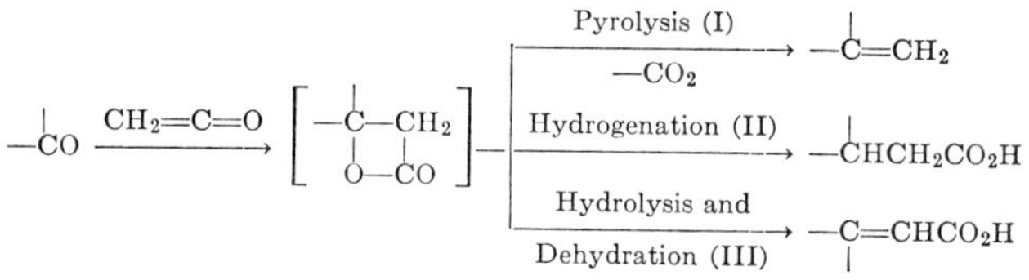

$$-CO \xrightarrow{\ CH_2=C=O\ } \left[\ -\overset{|}{\underset{O-CO}{C}}-CH_2\ \right]$$

Pyrolysis (I) $\xrightarrow{-CO_2} -\overset{|}{C}=CH_2$

Hydrogenation (II) $\longrightarrow -\overset{|}{C}HCH_2CO_2H$

Hydrolysis and Dehydration (III) $\longrightarrow -\overset{|}{C}=CHCO_2H$

Secondary Reactions, Yields, and References

Carbonyl Compound	Catalyst	Pyrolysis (I)	Hydrogenation (II)	Hydrolysis and Dehydration (III)
1. *Aldehydes*				
$CH_3(CH_2)_5CHO$	Peroxide			(60%) 70
$CH_3CH=CHCHO$	BF_3 or $ZnCl_2$	(31%) 157		
	H_3BO_3	(4%) 150		
	$Zn(BF_4)_2$	(31%) 147		
	BF_3			(73%) 95
	$AlCl_3$			(40%) 95
$CH_3CH=C(C_2H_5)CHO$	BF_3			(—) 95
$CH_3(CH=CH)_2CHO$	BF_3			(54%) 95
C_6H_5CHO	$HgCl_2$	(21%) 6		
	BF_3			(42%) 95
	CH_3CO_2Na		(38%) 7 *	
	CH_3CO_2K	(—) 67		
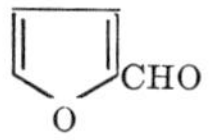 (furfural structure) CHO	H_3BO_3	(33%) 150		
	$(CH_3CH_2CH_2CO_2)_2Ni$	(16%) 6		
	$(CH_3CO_2)_2Ba$	(18%) 6		
	$[(CH_3)_2CHCO_2]_2Co$	(18%) 6		
	$(CH_3CH_2CH_2CO_2)_2Zn$	(15%) 6		
	None	(6%) 6		
	CH_3CO_2K	(—) 67	(38%) 7 *	
$C_6H_5CH=CHCHO$	BF_3			(85%) 95
2. *Ketones*				
$(CH_3)_2CO$	BF_3			(60%) 158
	UO_2Cl_2			(85–90%) 152
$CH_3COC_5H_{11}$ †	BF_3			(—) 94
$[(CH_3)_2CHCH_2]_2CO$	BF_3			(—) 94
$CH_3COC(CH_3)=CH_2$	BF_3	(28%) 157		
Cyclohexanone	BF_3			(—) 94
3,3,5-Trimethylcyclo-hexanone	BF_3			(—) 94
$C_6H_5COCH_3$	BF_3			(—) 94
	$ZnCl_2$		(15%) 7 *	
3. *Keto Esters*				
$CH_3COCO_2CH_3$	BF_3	(41%) 96	(34%) 128	
$CH_3COCH_2CO_2C_2H_5$	BF_3	(71%) 96	(57%) 128	
	$Cd(PF_2O_2)_2$	(50%) 151		
	$HgBr_2$	(61%) 148		
	$C_2H_5PO_3 + (C_2H_5)_3PO_4$	(67%) 146		

Note: References 131–214 on pp. 362–363.
* The aromatic ring was also hydrogenated.
† The structure of the amyl group was not specified.

TABLE IV—*Continued*

REACTIONS OF KETENES WITH CARBONYL COMPOUNDS INVOLVING UNISOLATED
β-LACTONE INTERMEDIATES

		Secondary Reactions, Yields, and References		
Carbonyl Compound	Catalyst	Pyrolysis (I)	Hydrogenation (II)	Hydrolysis and Dehydration (III)
$CH_3COCH_2CO_2C_2H_5$	H_3BO_3	(63%) 150		
(*Contd.*)	$Zn(BF_4)_2$	(62%) 147		
	Al_2O_3-SiO_2-ZrO_2	(40-50%) 149		
	$Co(ClO_4)_2$	(—) 144		
	$Zn(SCN)_2$	(35-40%) 127		
	$Zn(NO_3)_2$	(25-30%) 145		
$CH_3COCH_2CH_2CO_2CH_3$	BF_3	(31%) 96		
	$UO_2(NO_3)_2$	(50-60%) 152		
$CH_3COCH_2CH_2CO_2C_2H_5$	BF_3		(59%) 128	

C. Catalyzed Reactions of Ketene with Diketones

$$-CO(CH_2)_xCO- \xrightarrow{CH_2=C=O}$$

$$\left[-CO(CH_2)_x\overset{|}{\underset{O—CO}{C}}—CH_2\right] \xrightarrow[-CO_2]{Pyrolysis} -CO(CH_2)_x\overset{|}{C}=CH_2 \quad (I)$$

$$\left[CH_2—\overset{|}{\underset{CO—O}{C}}(CH_2)_x\overset{|}{\underset{O—CO}{C}}—CH_2\right] \xrightarrow[-2CO_2]{Pyrolysis} CH_2=\overset{|}{C}(CH_2)_x\overset{|}{C}=CH_2 \quad (II)$$

		Pyrolysis Products, Yields, and References	
Diketone	Catalyst	Ethylenic Ketone (I)	Diene (II)
$CH_3COCOCH_3$	BF_3	(14%) 159	(5%) 159
	$Co(PF_2O_2)_2$	(—) 151	(—) 151
$CH_3COCH_2COCH_3$	BF_3	(16%) 159	(8%) 159
	$HgBr_2$	(—) 148	(—) 148
	$C_2H_5PO_3 + (C_2H_5)_3PO_4$	(21%) 146	(7%) 146
	$B(OCOCH_3)_3$	(9%) 150	
	$Zn(BF_4)_2$	(15%) 147	(3%) 147
	Al_2O_3-SiO_2	(30%) 149	(15%) 149
	$Mg(ClO_4)_2$	(35%) 144	(—) 144
	$Zn(SCN)_2$	(—) 127	(—) 127
	$Zn(NO_3)_2$	(—) 145	(—) 145
	UO_2Cl_2	(30-40%) 152	(15-20%) 152
$CH_3COCH_2CH_2COCH_3$	BF_3	(—) 159	(—) 159
$C_6H_5COCH_2COC_6H_5$	BF_3	(—) 159	(—) 159

D. Catalyzed Reactions of Ketenes with Quinones

$$O=\langle\!\!\!\bigcirc\!\!\!\rangle=O + R_2C=C=O \xrightarrow[15-25°]{Dioxane} [Di-β-lactone] \xrightarrow[-2CO_2]{Pyrolysis} R_2C=\langle\!\!\!\bigcirc\!\!\!\rangle=CR_2$$

(I)

Quinone	Ketene	Catalyst	Yield of I	Reference
Benzoquinone	$CH_2=C=O$	H_3BO_3	15%	92
	$(C_6H_5)_2C=C=O$	$ZnCl_2$	74%	92
Chlorobenzoquinone	$CH_2=C=O$	$B(OCOCH_3)_3$	Excellent	92
Toluquinone	$CH_3CH=C=O$	$(C_2H_5)_3BO_3$	Good	92
p-Xyloquinone	$CH_2=C=O$	H_3BO_3	Good	92
1,4-Naphthoquinone	$CH_2=C=O$	$(C_2H_5)_3BO_3$	Excellent	92

Note: References 131–214 on pp. 362–363.

TABLE V

REACTIONS OF PURE β-LACTONES

A. β-Propiolactone

$$CH_2CH_2\ MX \longrightarrow \begin{array}{l} MOCH_2CH_2COX\ \ (1) \\ XCH_2CH_2CO_2M\ \ (2) \end{array}$$
(with O—CO ring and —CO)

Second Reactant M—X	Solvent	Experimental Conditions	Yields of Products Type 1, %	Type 2, %	Reference
1. Water					
H—OH	H₂O	Neutral solution	—	—	29, 102
H—OH	H₂O	Alkaline solution			29
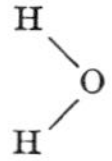 H—O—H (ether)	None	0.5 equiv. of H_2O; 90–100°; 12 hr.		51 ^{a}	160
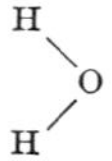 H—O—H (ether)	CH₃COC₂H₅	0.5 equiv. of H_2O; reflux 2 hr.		58 ^{a}	160
2. Alcohols					
H—OCH₃	CH₃OH	NaOH catalyst; 0°; 15 min.	85		161, 162
		Reflux; 16 hr.	23	72	162, 163
		H₂SO₄ catalyst; 0°; 72 hr.	43	33 ^{b}	162
		H₂SO₄ catalyst; 65°; 2 hr.	89	34 ^{b}	162
		NaOCH₃ catalyst	79 ^{c}		164
		Activated C; 175°; 3 hr.	82–95 ^{c}		165
		FeSO₄ catalyst; H₂SO₄; 125–135°	80		166
H—OC₂H₅	C₂H₅OH	NaOH catalyst; 0°; 15 min.		73	161, 162
		Reflux; 5 hr.	0		162, 163
		H₂SO₄ catalyst; 46°; 6 hr.	25	54 ^{b}	162
		H₂SO₄ catalyst; 80°; 2 hr.	49 ^{c}	54 ^{b}	162
		Excess H₂SO₄; reflux; 2 hr.	94 ^{c}		167
		FeSO₄ catalyst; H₂SO₄; 135–145°	48 ^{c}		166
		Activated C; 250°; 3 hr.	65		165
H—OC₃H₇-n	n-C₃H₇OH	NaOH catalyst; 0°; 15 min. 65°; 15 hr.		73	162

Reactant	Reagent	Conditions	Yield	Yield	Ref.
H—OC3H7-i	i-C3H7OH	H2SO4 catalyst; 46°, 6 hr.	0	45ᵇ	162
		H2SO4 catalyst; 80°, 2 hr.	0	53ᵇ	162
		65°, 16 hr.		45	162
H—OC4H9-n	n-C4H9OH	H2SO4 catalyst; 80°, 2 hr.	77	38ᵇ	162
		NaOH catalyst; 0°, 15 min.	0		162
		65°, 16 hr.		65	162
H—OC8H17-n	n-C8H17OH	H2SO4 catalyst; 46°, 6 hr.		28ᵇ	162
H—OCH2CH(C2H5)(C4H9-n)	n-C4H9CH(C2H5)CH2OH	NaOH catalyst; 0°, 15 min.	64		161
H—OCH2CH=CH2	CH2=CHCH2OH	NaOH catalyst; −20-5°	30		161
		NaOH catalyst; −40°	70		161

3. Phenols, Thiophenols and Their Salts

Reactant	Reagent	Conditions	Yield	Yield	Ref.
H—OC6H5	C6H5OH	100°, 18 hr.		24	129
	None	Reflux; 10 hr.		39	168
	C6H5OH	Reflux; 8 hr.		15	168
	C6H5OH	H2SO4 catalyst; 50°, 30 min.	40		129
	C6H5OH	H2SO4 catalyst; 46°, 1 hr.	50		169
Na—OC6H5	H2O	100°, 15 min.		18	129
H—OC6H4CH3-o	o-CH3C6H4OH	100°, 6 hr.		3	129
	o-CH3C6H4OH	H2SO4 catalyst; 50°, 30 min.	38		129,169
Na—OC6H4CH3-o	H2O	100°, 15 min.		13	129
H—OC6H4CH3-m	m-CH3C6H4OH	100°, 6 hr.		4	129
	m-CH3C6H4OH	H2SO4 catalyst; 50°, 30 min.	41		129,169
Na—OC6H4CH3-m	H2O	100°, 15 min.		17	129
	H2O	20-40°; 2-4 hr.		Good	168
H—OC6H4CH3-p	p-CH3C6H4OH	100°, 6 hr.		14	129
	p-CH3C6H4OH	H2SO4 catalyst; 50°, 30 min.	47		129,169
Na—OC6H4CH3-p	H2O	100°, 15 min.		15	129
Na—OC6H3(CH3)2-3,5	H2O	100°, 15 min.		16	129
Na—OC6H4C4H9-t-p	H2O	100°, 15 min.		13	129
Na—OC6H3(C3H7-i)-2-CH3-5	H2O	100°, 15 min.		4	129
Na—OC6H4C6H11-o	H2O	100°, 15 min.		3	129
Na—OC6H4C6H11-p	H2O	100°, 15 min.		12	129
Na—OC6H4CH2C6H5-p	H2O	100°, 15 min.		14	129
Na—OC6H4C6H5-o	H2O	100°, 15 min.		13	129

Note: References 131–214 are on pp. 362–363.

ᵃ The product is O(CH2CH2CO2H)2.

ᵇ This was the combined yield of alkoxy acid and alkoxy ester.

ᶜ The product isolated was the acrylic ester produced by dehydration of the β-hydroxy ester.

TABLE V—*Continued*

REACTIONS OF PURE β-LACTONES

A. *β-Propiolactone (Cont.)*

Second Reactant M—X	Solvent	Experimental Conditions	Yields of Products Type 1, %	Type 2, %	Reference
Na—OC6H4C6H5-m	H2O	100°; 15 min.		19	129
Na—OC6H4C6H5-p	H2O	100°; 15 min.		3	129
H—OC6H4Cl-o	o-ClC6H4OH	100°; 6 hr.		0.4	129
Na—OC6H4Cl-o	o-ClC6H4OH	H2SO4 catalyst; 50°; 30 min.	22		129, 170
	H2O	100°; 15 min.		50	129
	H2O	25–30°; 2 hr.		80	168
H—OC6H4Cl-m	m-ClC6H4OH	100°; 6 hr.		1.5	129
Na—OC6H4Cl-m	H2O	100°; 15 min.		36	129
H—OC6H4Cl-p	p-ClC6H4OH	100°; 6 hr.		5	129
Na—OC6H4Cl-p	p-ClC6H4OH	H2SO4 catalyst; 50°; 30 min.	33		129, 170
	H2O	100°; 15 min.		29	129, 168
Na—OC6H3Cl2-2,4	H2O	100°; 15 min.		51	129
	H2O	25–30°; 2 hr.		78	168
Na—OC6H4Br-o	H2O	100°; 15 min.		52	129
Na—OC6H4Br-p	H2O	100°; 15 min.		30	129
H—OC6H4NO2-o	o-NO2C6H4OH	100°; 6 hr.		0.2	129
Na—OC6H4NO2-o	H2O	100°; 15 min.		32	129
	H2O	20–40°; 2–4 hr.		48	168
H—OC6H4NO2-m	m-NO2C6H4OH	100°; 6 hr.		4	129
Na—OC6H4NO2-m	H2O	100°; 15 min.		45	129, 168
H—OC6H4NO2-p	p-NO2C6H4OH	100°; 6 hr.		0.2	129
Na—OC6H4NO2-p	H2O	100°; 15 min.		51	129, 168
H—OC6H4OCH3-o	o-CH3OC6H4OH	100°; 6 hr.		0.8	129
Na—OC6H4OCH3-o	o-CH3OC6H4OH	H2SO4 catalyst; 50°; 30 min.	19		129
	H2O	100°; 15 min.		20	129
	H2O	20–40°; 2–4 hr.		Good	168
H—OC6H4OCH3-m	m-CH3OC6H4OH	100°; 6 hr.		4	129
Na—OC6H4OCH3-m	H2O	100°; 15 min.		24	129
H—OC6H4OCH3-p	p-CH3OC6H4OH	100°; 6 hr.		12	129
Na—OC6H4OCH3-p	p-CH3OC6H4OH	H2SO4 catalyst; 50°; 30 min.	35		129
	H2O	100°; 15 min.		12	129

	Solvent	Conditions	Yield %	Reference
Na—OC$_6$H$_3$OCH$_3$-2-CH$_3$-4	H$_2$O	100°; 15 min.	21	129
Na—OC$_6$H$_4$OCH$_2$C$_6$H$_5$-p	H$_2$O	100°; 15 min.	13	129
Na—OC$_6$H$_4$CHO-o	H$_2$O	100°; 15 min.	32	129
Na—OC$_6$H$_4$CHO-p	H$_2$O	100°; 15 min.	55	129
Na—OC$_{10}$H$_7$-β	H$_2$O	20–40°; 2–4 hr.	Good	168
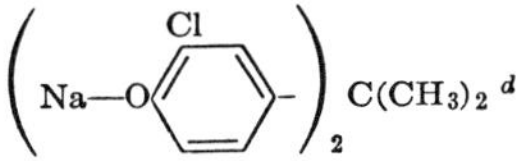	H$_2$O	2 equiv. of β-lactone; 80°; 2 hr.	—	168
H—SC$_6$H$_5$	None	100°; 2 hr.	49	129, 171
Na—SC$_6$H$_5$	H$_2$O	20–30°; 2 hr.	91	129, 171
(Na—S)$_2$C$_6$H$_4$-m ^{d}	H$_2$O	2 equiv. of β-lactone; 20–30°; 2 hr.	High	171
4. Mercaptans and Other Organic Sulfur Compounds				
Na—SC(CH$_3$)$_3$	H$_2$O	30°; 2 hr.	81	171
Na—SC$_6$H$_{13}$-n	H$_2$O	30°; 2 hr.	60	171
Na—SCH$_2$CH$_2$CO$_2$C$_2$H$_5$	H$_2$O	3–10°; 3 hr.	54	171
H—SCH$_2$CH$_2$CO$_2$Na	H$_2$O	0–25°; 16 hr.	50	172
Na—SCH$_2$CO$_2$C$_2$H$_5$	H$_2$O	3–10°; 3 hr.	40	171
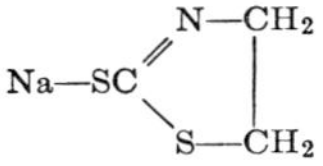	H$_2$O	27–34°; 20 min.	92	173
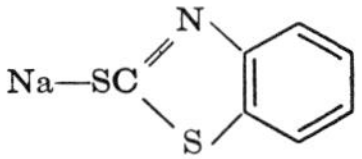	H$_2$O	30°; 20 min.	92	173
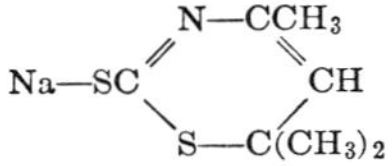	H$_2$O	25–30°; 25 min.	—	173
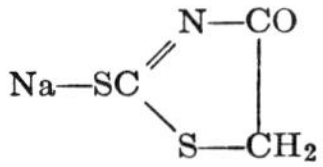	H$_2$O	20–30°	60	174

Note: References 131–214 are on pp. 362–363.
^{d} Both functional groups reacted with the lactone.

TABLE V—Continued

REACTIONS OF PURE β-LACTONES

A. β-Propiolactone (Cont.)

Second Reactant M—X	Solvent	Experimental Conditions	Yields of Products		Reference
			Type 1, %	Type 2, %	
S(CH₃)₂	CH₃NO₂	25°, 16 hr.		75[e]	120
	CH₃CN	25°; 22 hr.		84[e]	175
S(C₂H₅)CH₃	CH₃CN	25°; 24 hr.		44[e]	175
H—SC(=NH)NH₂	H₂O	10°; 2 hr.		90	176, 177
	H₂O	MgBr₂ + HCl		70	118
H—SC(=NH)NHCH₂CH=CH₂	H₂O	30°		59	178
H—SC(=NH)NHC₆H₅	H₂O	28°		72	178
H—SC(=NH)NHNH₂	H₂O	10–15°		67	178
(H—SC(=NH)₂NH[d]	H₂O	2 equiv. of β-lactone; 20–30°		86	178
NH₄—SCONH₂	H₂O	10°; 30 min.		85	179
NH₄—SCONHC₄H₉-n	H₂O	10°; 30 min.		Excellent	179
NH₄—SCSNH₂	H₂O	20–30°; 30 min.		92	176, 180
NH₄—SCSNHC₂H₅	H₂O	20°; 20 min.		20	176
NH₄—SCSN(CH₃)₂	H₂O	20°; 20 min.		97	176
NH₄—SCSN(C₂H₅)₂	H₂O	20–30°; 45 min.		80	176, 180
NH₄—SCSNHNH₂	H₂O	10–15°		53	181
K—SCSNHNHC₆H₅	H₂O	10°; 15 min.		87	181
CH₃O—SO₃CH₃	None	0–5°; 4 hr.		86[f]	182
C₂H₅O—SO₃C₂H₅	None	0–5°; 4 hr.		72[f]	182
Na—SO₂C₆H₅	H₂O	30°; 3 hr.		18	183
H—SO₂C₆H₄CH₃-p	H₂O	100°; 7 hr.		26	183
Na—SO₂C₆H₄CH₃-p	H₂O	30°; 3 hr.		58	183
H—SO₂C₆H₄Cl-p	H₂O	100°; 7 hr.		17	183
Na—SO₂C₆H₄Cl-p	H₂O	30°; 3 hr.		3	183
H—SO₂C₆H₃Cl₂-2,5	H₂O	100°; 7 hr.		21	183
Na—SO₂C₆H₃Cl₂-2,5	H₂O	30°; 3 hr.		29	183

5. *Ammonia and Amines* (The β-lactone was added to ammonia or the amine unless otherwise indicated.)

Second Reactant M—X	Solvent	Experimental Conditions	Type 1, %	Type 2, %	Reference
H—NH₂[g]	NH₃	100°; 16 hr.; autoclave	50		184
H—NH₂	H₂O	0–30°; 2 hr.	90		104

Reactant	Solvent	Conditions	Yield (%)	Yield (%)	References
H—NH₂ [h]	(CH₃)₃COH	0–16°; 2 hr.		79	98, 104
	CH₃CN	30°; 2 hr.		82	98
	H₂O	3–7°; 3 hr.		97	98, 104
H—NHCH₃	(C₂H₅)₂O	30–35°; 1 hr.	91		104, 185
H—NHCH₃ [h]	(C₂H₅)₂O	0–30°; 2 hr.	78		104
	CH₃CN	0–30°; 2 hr.	74		104
H—N(CH₃)₂	H₂O	0–30°; 2 hr.	90		104
	(C₂H₅)₂O	20°; 1 hr.	80	13	104, 185
H—N(CH₃)₂ [h]	CH₃CN	0–30°; 2 hr.	95	3	104, 186
	(C₂H₅)₂O	0–30°; 2 hr.		87	104
	H₂O	0–30°; 2 hr.		84	104, 187
H—N(CH₃)₂ [g]	None	20°; 3 hr.	70		185
	(C₂H₅)₂O	15–20°; 40 min.		65	187
H—NHC₂H₅	H₂O	20°; 1 hr.		47	186
H—NHC₂H₅ [h]	(C₂H₅)₂O	20–25°; 1 hr.	44		104, 185
	CH₃CN	0–30°; 2 hr.	97		104
H—N(C₂H₅)₂	H₂O	20°; 2 hr.	76		104, 187
	(C₂H₅)₂O	10–20°; 2 hr.	80	84–87	104, 185
	CH₃CN	35°; 4 hr.	75		186
H—N(C₂H₅)₂ [h]	(C₂H₅)₂O	20°; 1–2 hr.	71	4	104, 186
	CH₃CN	30–35°; 1–2 hr.	70	6	104, 186
H—NHC₃H₇-n	H₂O	0–30°; 2 hr.	86		104
	(C₂H₅)₂O	0–30°; 2 hr.	76		104
	CH₃CN	0–30°; 2 hr.	72		104
H—N(C₃H₇-n)₂	H₂O	0–30°; 2 hr.	68	24	104
H—N(C₃H₇-n)₂ [h]	CH₃CN	25–30°; 2 hr.	62	25	104, 186
H—NHC₄H₉-n [h]	H₂O	0–30°; 2 hr.	98		104
H—NHC₁₂H₂₅-n [h]	CH₃CN	0–30°; 2 hr.		61	104
H—NHC₆H₁₁	CH₃CN	20–30°; 2 hr.		98	104, 188
	(C₂H₅)₂O	25°; 2 hr.		41	188
H—NHC₆H₁₁ [h]	CH₃CN	20–30°; 2 hr.	16	95	104, 188
	(C₂H₅)₂O	25°; 2 hr.		40	104, 188

Note: References 131–214 are on pp. 362–363.

d Both functional groups reacted with the lactone.

e The product was isolated as the thetin hydrochloride, $(R_2\overset{+}{S}CH_2CH_2CO_2H)Cl^-$.

f The product was isolated as the acrylic ester by distillation of the intermediate sulfate ester, $ROSO_2CH_2CH_2CO_2R$.

g The reactants were combined all at once or added simultaneously to a common solvent.

h The ammonia or amine was added to the β-lactone.

TABLE V—*Continued*

Reactions of Pure β-Lactones

A. β-Propiolactone (Cont.)

Second Reactant M—X	Solvent	Experimental Conditions	Yields of Products Type 1, %	Yields of Products Type 2, %	Reference
H—N$(C_6H_{11})_2$	None	145–150°; 2 hr.		74	104, 188
H—N$(C_2H_5)C_6H_{11}$	CH_3CN	20–30°; 2 hr.		Good	188
H—NC_5H_{10} (piperidine)	H_2O	30–50°	85		185
H—NC_5H_{10} [h]	CH_3CN	0–30°; 2 hr.		79	104
H—N$(CH_2CH_2)_2O$ (morpholine)	None	50°		79	189
H—N$(CH_2CH_2)_2O$ [h]	CH_3CN	15–20°; 30 min.		92	104, 189
H—$NHCH_2CH_2OH$ [h]	CH_3CN	20°; 2 hr.		51–66	104, 190
H—N$(CH_2CH_2OH)_2$	C_2H_5OH	0–5°; 2 hr.		65	104, 190
H—N$(CH_2CH_2OH)_2$ [h]	CH_3CN	20–30°; 12 hr.		56	104, 190
H—$NHCH_2CO_2H$	H_2O	20–50°; 2–3 hr.	—		191
H—$NHCH_2C_6H_5$	H_2O	30°; 2 hr.	51	36	104
	$(C_2H_5)_2O$	30°; 2 hr.	44	11	104
H—$NHCH_2C_6H_5$ [h]	CH_3CN	0–30°; 2 hr.		94	104
H—N$(CH_2C_6H_5)_2$	CH_3CN	83°; 2 hr.	7	78	104
H—N$(CH_2C_6H_5)_2$ [h]	CH_3CN	0–30°; 2 hr.		67	104
H—NHC_6H_5	H_2O	20–50°; 2–3 hr.		93	104, 192
H—NHC_6H_5 [h]	$(C_2H_5)_2O$	25–30°	65		193
H—NHC_6H_5 [g]	$(C_2H_5)_2O$	30°; 2 hr.	52	17	104
	CH_3CN	30°; 2 hr.	27	35	104
H—N$(CH_3)C_6H_5$	CH_3CN	83°; 2 hr.	6	76	104
H—$NHC_6H_4CH_3$-*o*	H_2O	20–50°; 2–3 hr.		Good	192
H—$NHC_6H_4CH_3$-*p*	CH_3COCH_3	8–60°; 2 hr.	50		191
H—$NHC_6H_4CH_3$-*p* [g]	$(C_2H_5)_2O$	25–30°; 16 hr.	39	59	105
H—NHC_6H_4Cl-*o*	CH_3CN	83°; 2 hr.		95	104
H—NHC_6H_4Cl-*p*	CH_3COCH_3	60°; 2–4 hr.		92	105
H—NHC_6H_4Cl-*p* [g]	CH_3COCH_3	2 equiv. of β-lactone; 60°; 4 hr.		90 [i]	105
H—NHC_6H_4Br-*p*	CH_3COCH_3	60°; 2–4 hr.		50	105
H—NHC_6H_4Br-*p* [g]	CH_3COCH_3	2 equiv. of β-lactone; 60°; 4 hr.		90 [i]	105
H—$NHC_6H_4NO_2$-*o* [h]	CH_3CN	83°; 2 hr.		92	104
H—$NHC_6H_4NO_2$-*m*	CH_3COCH_3	60°; 2–4 hr.		68	105
H—$NHC_6H_4NO_2$-*m* [g]	CH_3COCH_3	2 equiv. of β-lactone; 60°; 4 hr.		Trace [i]	105

Reactant	Solvent	Conditions	Yield (%)	Refs.
H–NHC$_6$H$_4$NO$_2$-*p*	CH_3COCH_3	60°; 2–4 hr.	100	105
H–NHC$_6$H$_4$CO$_2$H-*o* [g]	CH_3COCH_3	60°; 2–4 hr.	82	105
H–NHC$_6$H$_4$CO$_2$H-*m*	CH_3CN	25–30°; 16 hr.	64	105
H–NHC$_6$H$_4$CO$_2$H-*p* [g]	CH_3COCH_3	60°; 4 hr.	82	105
H–N(CH$_3$)C$_6$H$_4$CO$_2$H-*p* [g]	CH_3COCH_3	60°; 2–4 hr.	87	105
H–NHC$_6$H$_4$CO$_2$C$_2$H$_5$-*o*	CH_3CN	25–30°; 16 hr.	78	105
H–NHC$_6$H$_4$CO$_2$C$_2$H$_5$-*m*	CH_3CN	25–30°; 16 hr.	72	105
H–NHC$_6$H$_4$CO$_2$C$_2$H$_5$-*p*	CH_3CN	2 equiv. of β-lactone; 20–25°, 2 days; reflux, 4 hr.	60 [i]	105
H–NHC$_6$H$_4$CO$_2$C$_2$H$_5$-*p*	CH_3CN	25–30°; 16 hr.	84	105
H–NHC$_6$H$_4$SO$_3$H-*p*	H_2O	100°; 2 hr.	88 [j]	105
H–NHC$_6$H$_4$SO$_2$NH$_2$-*p* [g]	CH_3COCH_3	Reflux, 2 hr.; 25°, 16 hr.	78	105
H–N(CH$_2$CH$_2$CO$_2$C$_2$H$_5$)(C$_6$H$_4$CO$_2$C$_2$H$_5$-*p*) [g]	CH_3CN	Reflux; 19 hr.	84	105
H–N(C$_6$H$_5$)$_2$	None	2 equiv. of amine; 140–160°; 2 hr.	70, 17	104, 194
H–NHC$_{10}$H$_7$-α	$(C_2H_5)_2O$	30°; 2 hr.	61, 40	104
H–NHC$_{10}$H$_7$-β	$(C_2H_5)_2O$	30°; 2 hr.	55	104
H–NH–C$_6$H$_4$–NH–H (o) [d]	H_2O	2 equiv. of β-lactone; 10–30°; 2 hr.	—	191
H–NHNH$_2$, H$_2$O [h]	CH_3CN	0–30°; 2 hr.	36	104
H–NHNHC$_6$H$_5$	$(C_2H_5)_2O$	30°; 1–2 hr.	63–70	104, 191
H–NHNHC$_6$H$_5$	None	100°; 0.5–1 hr.	— [k]	195

Note: References 131–214 are on pp. 362–363.

[d] Both functional groups reacted with the lactone.

[g] The reactants were combined all at once or added simultaneously to a common solvent.

[h] The ammonia or amine was added to the β-lactone.

[i] Two equivalents of the β-lactone reacted with the primary aromatic amine to give ArN(CH$_2$CH$_2$CO$_2$H)$_2$.

[j] The product was isolated as the methyl ester.

[k] The product was the pyrazolone formed by elimination of water from the intermediate hydrazide, HOCH$_2$CH$_2$CONHNHC$_6$H$_5$.

TABLE V—*Continued*

REACTIONS OF PURE β-LACTONES

A. *β-Propiolactone (Cont.)*

Second Reactant M—X	Solvent	Experimental Conditions	Yields of Products Type 1, %	Type 2, %	Reference
6. Tertiary Amines [l]					
—N(CH₃)₃ [h]	CH₃CN	10–15°		98	104, 121
	H₂O	10–15°		80	104, 121
—N(CH₃)₂CH₂CH₂OH [h]	CH₃CN	10–15°		93	104
—N(CH₂CH₂OH)₂CH₃ [h]	CH₃CN	10–15°		76	104, 121
—N(CH₂CH₂OH)₃ [h]	CH₃CN	10–15°		14	104, 121
—N₄(CH₂)₆ (hexamethylenetetramine) [h]	CH₃CN	10–15°		100	104, 121
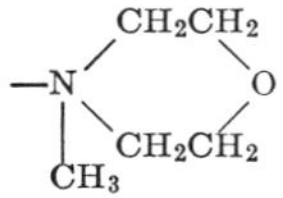 $\begin{array}{c} CH_2CH_2 \\ -N \quad \quad O^{\,h} \\ CH_2CH_2 \\ CH_3 \end{array}$	H₂O	10–15°		52	104
—N(CH₃)₂C₁₂H₂₅-n	(C₂H₅)₂O, CH₃CN	25–30°; 16 hr.		76	104
—N(CH₃)₂C₁₄H₂₉-n	(C₂H₅)₂O, CH₃CN	25–30°; 16 hr.		80	104
—N(CH₃)₂C₁₆H₃₃-n	(C₂H₅)₂O, CH₃CN	25–30°; 16 hr.		82	104
—N(CH₃)₂C₁₈H₃₇-n	(C₂H₅)₂O, CH₃CN	25–30°; 16 hr.		83	104
—NC₅H₅ (pyridine)	H₂O	25–30°; 16 hr.		91	104
—NC₆H₇ (α-picoline)	H₂O	25–30°; 16 hr.		85	104
—NC₉H₇ (quinoline)	H₂O	25–30°; 16 hr.		76	104
—NC₉H₇ (isoquinoline)	H₂O	25–30°; 16 hr.		94	104
7. Salts of Inorganic and Organic Acids					
Na—Cl	H₂O	0–25°; 1 hr.		34	196
	H₂O	25–45°; 1 hr.		74	196, 197
Li—Cl	H₂O	30–45°; 1 hr.		90	197
NH₄—Cl	H₂O	30–45°; 1 hr.		80	197
Na—Br	H₂O	0–25°; 1 hr.		58	196
Na—I	H₂O	0–25°; 1 hr.		61	196
Mg—Br₂	(C₂H₅)₂O	25°		83	118
Na—SH	H₂O	5°; 1 hr.		81	196, 197
	H₂O	−25° to −10°; 1.5 hr.		87	198

Na₂—S	C₂H₅OH	5°; 1 hr.	90 [m]	196
Na₂—S₂ [d]	H₂O	15°; 3–4 hr.	28 [n]	196, 198
NH₄—OSO₂NH₄	H₂O	2 equiv. of β-lactone; 0°, 1.5 hr.	94	196
Na₂—S₂O₃	H₂O	0°	—	197
Na₂—S₂O₄	H₂O	30°; then 100°, 3 hr.	75 [o]	196, 197
	H₂O—CH₃COCH₃	18–25°, 2 hr.; then add HCl, 100°; 30 min.	44 [p]	183, 199
Na—SCN	H₂O	21–28°; 1 hr.	81	183, 197
Na—NO₂	H₂O	15–25°; 2 hr.	35–47	183, 200
Na—CN	H₂O—C₂H₅OH	50°; 25 min.	68–73	183, 197, 201
Na—N(COCH₂)(COCH₂)	H₂O	25°; 1.25 hr.	61	183
Na—O₂CCH₃	H₂O	1 equiv. of acetate; 20°; 1 hr.	32	111, 112
	H₂O	2 equiv. of acetate; 20°; 1 hr.	57	111, 112
	H₂O	4 equiv. of acetate; 20°; 1 hr.	73	111, 112
Na—O₂CCH₂CH₂Cl	H₂O	30°; 45 min.	High	111
Na—O₂CCH₂CH₂CN	H₂O	30°; 45 min.	—	111

8. Inorganic and Organic Acids, Acid Chlorides, and Anhydrides

H—Cl	H₂O	0°; 3 hr.	58	202, 203
	CH₃OH	2–10°; then reflux 6 hr.	Good [q]	204
	C₂H₅OH	2–10°; then reflux 6 hr.	63 [q]	204
	n-C₃H₇OH	2–10°; then reflux 6 hr.	Good [q]	204
	n-C₄H₉OH	25–30°; then reflux 6 hr.	79 [q]	204
	CH₃(CH₂)₃CH(C₂H₅)CH₂OH	2–10°; then reflux 6 hr.	Good [q]	204
	ClCH₂CH₂OH	0–10°; 8 hr.	50 [q]	204

Note: References 131–214 are on pp. 362–363.

[d] Both functional groups reacted with the lactone.

[h] The ammonia or amine was added to the β-lactone.

[l] Products were isolated either as the betaines, R₃NCH₂CH₂CO₂⁻, or as the quaternary salts, R₃N(Cl)CH₂CH₂CO₂H.

[m] This was the combined yield of acid (55%) and ester (35%).

[n] This was the combined yield of HSCH₂CH₂CO₂H (10%) and S(CH₂CH₂CO₂H)₂ (18%).

[o] This was the combined yield of HSCH₂CH₂CO₂H (70%) and (SCH₂CH₂CO₂H)₂ (5%).

[p] The product was SO₂(CH₂CH₂CO₂H)₂.

[q] The product was the β-halopropionic ester, XCH₂CH₂CO₂R.

TABLE V—*Continued*

REACTIONS OF PURE β-LACTONES

A. *β-Propiolactone (Cont.)*

Second Reactant M—X	Solvent	Experimental Conditions	Yields of Products Type 1, %	Type 2, %	Reference
H—Br	H₂O	0°; 3 hr.		77–85	202, 203
H—I	C₂H₅OH	2–5°; 5 hr.		69 [q]	204
SOCl—Cl	H₂O	0°; 3 hr.		98	202, 203
PCl₄—Cl	None	25–30°; then 80–100°, 2 hr.	87 [r]		202, 205, 206
	CCl₄	20°; 1 hr.	70–93 [r]		202, 205
H—OCOCH₃	CH₃CO₂H	H₂SO₄ catalyst; 80°; 2 hr.		78	202, 207
H—OCOCH₂CH₃	CH₃CH₂CO₂H	H₂SO₄ catalyst; 60–100°		48	207
CH₃CO—Cl	CH₃COCl	H₂SO₄ catalyst; 30–50°; 3 hr.	67		202, 208
CH₃CO—CO₂CH₃	(CH₃CO)₂O	H₂SO₄ catalyst; 125°; 30 min.	85 [s]		202, 207
9. Grignard Reagents					
IMg—CH₃	(C₂H₅)₂O	−10–13°; 30 min.	18 [t]	43 [u]	118, 209
ClMg—CH₂C₆H₅	(C₂H₅)₂O	−12–0°		32 [v]	118
BrMg—C₆H₅	(C₂H₅)₂O	−6–0°; 1.25 hr.	21 [t]	43 [u]	118, 209
C₆H₅Mg—C₆H₅	(C₂H₅)₂O	−32–25°; 30 min.	Poor [t]		118
10. Active Methylene Compounds					
H—CH(COCH₃)CO₂C₂H₅	H₂O	Equiv. NaOH; 15–30°; 1.25 hr.		34	130, 210
H—CH(COCH₃)₂	H₂O	4 equiv. of NaOH and ester; 0–27°		55	210
H—CH(COCH₃)COC₆H₅	H₂O	NaOH; 23–26°; 1–2 hr.		41	130, 210
H—CH(CN)CONH₂	H₂O	NaOH; 25–35°		29 [w]	130, 210
H—CH(CN)CONH₂	C₂H₅OH	NaOH; 5–72°; 30 min.		16 [x]	130
H—CH(CO₂C₂H₅)₂	C₂H₅OH	NaOC₂H₅; 35–50°; 2.5 hr.		12 [y]	130
	C₂H₅OH	NaOC₂H₅; 30–35°; 2.5 hr.		21	130
11. Miscellaneous Reactants					
H₂—Raney Ni	None	Cu⁺⁺ catalyst; 100–160°; 300–600 p.s.i.		92 [v]	156, 211
H—C₆H₅	C₆H₆	AlCl₃; 6–9°, 4 hr.; 60–70°, 4 hr.	15 [t]	62 [z]	212
H—C₆H₄OCH₃	C₆H₅OCH₃	AlCl₃; 0°; 4 hr.	25 [t]	23 [z]	212
H—C₆H₄Cl	CHCl₂CHCl₂	AlCl₃; 34–35°; 4 hr.	21 [t]		212
H—C₆H₄CH₃	C₆H₅CH₃	AlCl₃; 17–21°, 4 hr.	11 [t]	31 [z]	212
H—C₁₀H₇	None	AlCl₃; 5–9°, 4 hr.; 60–70°, 4 hr.	— [t]	— [z]	212

	None	100°; 2 hr	— [aa]	123
	None	120°; 6 hr	40–50 [bb]	122
	None	110°; 3 hr	— [bb]	123
	None	110°; 3 hr	— [bb]	123
	None	120°; 6 hr.	— [bb]	123

Note: References 131–214 are on pp. 362–363.

[q] The product was the β-halopropionic ester, $XCH_2CH_2CO_2R$.

[r] The product was $ClCH_2CH_2COCl$.

[s] The product was $(CH_3CO_2CH_2CH_2CO)_2O$.

[t] The product was isolated as the vinyl ketone, $XCOCH=CH_2$.

[u] The product was the β-halopropionic acid.

[v] The product was $C_6H_5(CH_2)_3CO_2H$.

[w] The product was isolated as the deacetylated product, $C_6H_5CO(CH_2)_3CO_2H$.

[x] The product was isolated as the cyclized glutarimide,
$$\begin{array}{c} CH_2{-}CO \\ CH_2 \qquad NH \\ CH(CN)CO \end{array}$$

[y] The product was propionic acid.

[z] The product was the hydrocinnamic acid, $XCH_2CH_2CO_2H$.

[aa] The product was probably 2-pyrrolepropionic acid.

[bb] The product was the corresponding 3-indolepropionic acid.

TABLE V—*Continued*

REACTIONS OF PURE β-LACTONES

B. Aliphatic β-Lactones Other Than β-Propiolactone

β-Lactone structure:

$$\underset{\begin{array}{c}\\ \text{O}\!-\!\text{C}\!-\!\text{O}\end{array}}{\overset{\begin{array}{c}\beta\quad\alpha\\ \text{C}\!-\!\text{C}\!-\!\text{CO}\end{array}}{}}$$

β-Lactone	Reactant	Product	Yield, %	Reference
α-Methyl	SOCl$_2$	ClCH$_2$CH(CH$_3$)COCl	Appreciable	206
	H$_2$; Raney Ni	(CH$_3$)$_2$CHCO$_2$H	95	211
β-Methyl	H$_2$O (0.5 equivalent)	O[CH(CH$_3$)CH$_2$CO$_2$H]$_2$	57	160
	NaOH; H$_2$O	CH$_3$CHOHCH$_2$CO$_2$H	—	29
	C$_6$H$_5$OH; H$_2$SO$_4$	CH$_3$CHOHCH$_2$CO$_2$C$_6$H$_5$ + dimer	—	169
	p-ClC$_6$H$_4$OH; H$_2$SO$_4$	CH$_3$CHOHCH$_2$CO$_2$C$_6$H$_4$Cl-p + dimer	—	170
	CH$_3$CH(SH)CH$_2$CO$_2$H	S[CH(CH$_3$)CH$_2$CO$_2$H]$_2$	—	29
	C$_2$H$_5$OCSSK	CH$_3$CH(SSCOC$_2$H$_5$)CH$_2$CO$_2$K	—	29
		+		
	(CH$_3$)$_2$S	(CH$_3$)$_2$SCH(CH$_3$)CH$_2$CO$_2^-$	—	175
	NH$_4$OH	CH$_3$CHOHCH$_2$CONH$_2$	—	29, 153
	C$_6$H$_5$NH$_2$; H$_2$O	CH$_3$CH(NHC$_6$H$_5$)CH$_2$CO$_2$H	Good	192
	C$_6$H$_5$NH$_2$; (C$_2$H$_5$)$_2$O	CH$_3$CHOHCH$_2$CONHC$_6$H$_5$	—	193
	CH$_3$COCH$_2$CO$_2$C$_2$H$_5$; NaOH	CH$_3$CH[CH(COCH$_3$)CO$_2$C$_2$H$_5$]CH$_2$CO$_2$H	31	210
	H$_2$; Raney Ni	CH$_3$CH$_2$CH$_2$CO$_2$H	80-90	156
	C$_6$H$_6$; SbCl$_3$	CH$_3$CH(C$_6$H$_5$)CH$_2$CO$_2$H + CH$_3$CH=CHCOC$_6$H$_5$	—	212
	Heat	CH$_3$CH=CH$_2$ + CO$_2$	—	12
β,β-Dimethyl	HCl; H$_2$O	(CH$_3$)$_2$C=CHCO$_2$H	40-60	127, 144, 145, 149
	H$_2$; Raney Ni	(CH$_3$)$_2$CHCH$_2$CO$_2$H	90-95	156
	H$_2$SO$_4$ (conc.)	(CH$_3$)$_2$C=CHCO$_2$H	89	126
α,α,β-Trimethyl	Heat	(CH$_3$)$_2$C=CHCH$_3$ + CO$_2$	—	12
α-Ethyl	H$_2$; Raney Ni	CH$_3$CH$_2$CH(CH$_3$)CO$_2$H	93	212
α-Ethyl-β-methyl	Heat	C$_2$H$_5$CH=CHCH$_3$ + CO$_2$	—	12
β-Methyl-β-ethyl	HCl; H$_2$O	C$_2$H$_5$C(CH$_3$)=CHCO$_2$H	50-60	127, 144, 145, 149
β-n-Propyl	H$_2$—Raney Ni	CH$_3$CH$_2$CH(CH$_3$)CH$_2$CO$_2$H	90-95	149, 156
β-Isopropyl	H$_2$—Raney Ni	CH$_3$(CH$_2$)$_4$CO$_2$H	85-90	156
β-Isopropenyl	H$_2$—Raney Ni	CH$_3$CH(CH$_3$)CH$_2$CH$_2$CO$_2$H	85-90	156
	Heat	CH$_2$=C(CH$_3$)C(CH$_3$)=CH$_2$ + CO$_2$	—	157

C. Aromatic and Heterocyclic β-Lactones

β-Lactone general structure (β, α carbons, –O–CO– ring)

β-Lactone	Reactant	Product	Yield, %	Reference
β-(o-Nitrophenyl)	Ba(OH)$_2$; H$_2$O	o-O$_2$NC$_6$H$_4$CHOHCH$_2$CO$_2$H	—	1
	NH$_4$OH	o-O$_2$NC$_6$H$_4$CHOHCH$_2$CONH$_2$	—	135, 213
	Zn; HCl; CH$_3$CO$_2$H	(fused bicyclic lactam: benzene ring fused to ring with CH$_2$, CO, NH)	—	1
β-(m-Nitrophenyl)	NaOH; H$_2$O	m-O$_2$NC$_6$H$_4$CHOHCH$_2$CO$_2$H	—	131
β-(p-Nitrophenyl)	H$_2$O	p-O$_2$NC$_6$H$_4$CHOHCH$_2$CO$_2$H	—	132
	NH$_4$OH	p-O$_2$NC$_6$H$_4$CHOHCH$_2$CONH$_2$	—	135, 214
	NH$_3$; CH$_3$CN ^{cc}	p-O$_2$NC$_6$H$_4$CHOHCH$_2$CONH$_2$	63	106
	(CH$_3$)$_2$NH; CH$_3$CN ^{cc}	p-O$_2$NC$_6$H$_4$CHOHCH$_2$CON(CH$_3$)$_2$	52	106
	C$_2$H$_5$NH$_2$; CH$_3$CN ^{cc}	p-O$_2$NC$_6$H$_4$CHOHCH$_2$CONHC$_2$H$_5$	58	106
	HOCH$_2$CH$_2$NH$_2$; CH$_3$NO$_2$ ^{cc}	p-O$_2$NC$_6$H$_4$CHOHCH$_2$CONHCH$_2$CH$_2$OH and p-O$_2$NC$_6$H$_4$CH(NHCH$_2$CH$_2$OH)CH$_2$CO$_2$H	24 / 5	106
	C$_6$H$_{11}$NH$_2$; CH$_3$CN ^{cc}	p-O$_2$NC$_6$H$_4$CHOHCH$_2$CONHC$_6$H$_{11}$ and p-O$_2$NC$_6$H$_4$CH(NHC$_6$H$_{11}$)CH$_2$CO$_2$H	10 / 56	106
	C$_5$H$_{10}$NH (piperidine); CH$_3$CN ^{cc}	p-O$_2$NC$_6$H$_4$CHOHCH$_2$CONC$_5$H$_{10}$ and p-O$_2$NC$_6$H$_4$CH(NC$_5$H$_{10}$)CH$_2$CO$_2$H	32 / 4	106
	C$_6$H$_5$CH$_2$NH$_2$; CH$_3$CN ^{cc}	p-O$_2$NC$_6$H$_4$CHOHCH$_2$CONHCH$_2$C$_6$H$_5$ and p-O$_2$NC$_6$H$_4$CH(NHCH$_2$C$_6$H$_5$)CH$_2$CO$_2$H	37 / 27	106
	C$_6$H$_5$CH$_2$NH$_2$; CH$_3$CN ^{dd}	p-O$_2$NC$_6$H$_4$CHOHCH$_2$CONHCH$_2$C$_6$H$_5$	49	106
	C$_6$H$_5$NH$_2$; CH$_3$CN ^{cc}	p-O$_2$NC$_6$H$_4$CHOHCH$_2$CONHC$_6$H$_5$ and p-O$_2$NC$_6$H$_4$CH(NHC$_6$H$_5$)CH$_2$CO$_2$H	27 / 5	106, 214
	HBr; CH$_3$CO$_2$H	p-O$_2$NC$_6$H$_4$CHBrCH$_2$CO$_2$H	95	132
	Heat; 100°	p-O$_2$NC$_6$H$_4$CH=CH$_2$ and CO$_2$	—	132
β-(2-Nitro-5-chlorophenyl)	NaOH; H$_2$O	2-O$_2$N-5-ClC$_6$H$_3$CHOHCH$_2$CO$_2$H	—	133
	NH$_4$OH	2-O$_2$N-5-ClC$_6$H$_3$CHOHCH$_2$CONH$_2$	—	133

Note: References 131–214 are on pp. 362–363.

^{cc} The ammonia or amine was added to the β-lactone.

^{dd} Concentrated solutions of the reactants were combined all at once.

TABLE V—Continued

REACTIONS OF PURE β-LACTONES

C. Aromatic and Heterocyclic β-Lactones (Cont.)

β-Lactone	Reactant	Product	Yield, %	Reference
β-(2-Nitro-5-methoxyphenyl) $\begin{array}{c}\beta\quad\alpha\\ \text{C—C}\\ \text{C—C}\\ \text{O—CO}\end{array}$	KOH; H_2O	2-O_2N-5-CH_3OC_6H_3CHOHCH$_2$CO$_2$H	—	134
	NH_4OH	2-O_2N-5-CH_3OC_6H_3CHOHCH$_2$CONH$_2$	—	134
β-(2-Nitro-4-isopropylphenyl)	NaOH; H_2O	2-O_2N-4-(i-C_3H_7)C_6H_3CHOHCH$_2$CO$_2$H	—	135
	NH_4OH	2-O_2N-4-(i-C_3H_7)C_6H_3CHOHCH$_2$CONH$_2$	—	135
	HBr; CH_3CO_2H	2-O_2N-4-(i-C_3H_7)C_6H_3CHBrCH$_2$CO$_2$H	—	135
	Heat	2-O_2N-4-(i-C_3H_7)C_6H_3CH=CH$_2$ + CO$_2$	—	135
α,α-Diphenyl	H_2SO_4; H_2O; CH_3CO_2H	$(C_6H_5)_2$C(CH$_2$OH)CO$_2$H	83	103
	$NaOCH_3$	$(C_6H_5)_2$CHCO$_2$CH$_3$ + $(C_6H_5)_2$CHCO$_2$H	—	103
	n-$C_4H_9NH_2$	$(C_6H_5)_2$C(CH$_2$OH)CONH(C$_4$H$_9$-n)	45	107
	C_4H_8NH (pyrrolidine)	$(C_6H_5)_2$C(CH$_2$OH)CONC$_4$H$_8$	83	107
	C_5H_{10}NH (piperidine)	$(C_6H_5)_2$C(CH$_2$OH)CONC$_5$H$_{10}$	87	107
	O(CH$_2$CH$_2$)$_2$NH (morpholine)	$(C_6H_5)_2$C[CH$_2$N(CH$_2$CH$_2$)$_2$O]CO$_2$H	95	107
	CH$_3$N(CH$_2$CH$_2$)$_2$NH (N-methylpiperazine)	$(C_6H_5)_2$C[CH$_2$N(CH$_2$CH$_2$)$_2$NCH$_3$]CO$_2$H	36	107
	O(CH$_2$CH$_2$)$_2$N(CH$_2$)$_3$NH$_2$ (γ-aminopropylmorpholine)	$(C_6H_5)_2$C[CH$_2$NH(CH$_2$)$_3$N(CH$_2$CH$_2$)$_2$O]CO$_2$H + $(C_6H_5)_2$C(CH$_2$OH)CONH(CH$_2$)$_3$N(CH$_2$CH$_2$)$_2$O	53 12	107
	NaCl; H_2O	$(C_6H_5)_2$C=CH$_2$ + CO$_2$	6	35
	NaBr; H_2O	$(C_6H_5)_2$C=CH$_2$ + CO$_2$	54	35
	NaI; H_2O	$(C_6H_5)_2$C=CH$_2$ + CO$_2$	86	35
	HCl; CH_3CO_2H; H_2O	$(C_6H_5)_2$C(CH$_2$Cl)CO$_2$H	84	35
	HBr; CH_3CO_2H	$(C_6H_5)_2$C(CH$_2$Br)CO$_2$H	93	35
	HI; CH_3CO_2H; H_2O	$(C_6H_5)_2$C(CH$_2$I)CO$_2$H	99	35
	LiAlH$_4$	$(C_6H_5)_2$C(CH$_2$OH)$_2$	84	107, 119
α-Bromo-β-(2-N-methylpiperidyl)	Heat; 170°	$\begin{array}{c}\text{N(CH}_3\text{)-piperidyl}\end{array}$CH=CHBr + CO$_2$	—	136
β-(2-Quinolyl)	H_2O	(2-C$_9$H$_6$N)CHOHCH$_2$CO$_2$H	—	137
	NH_4OH	(2-C$_9$H$_6$N)CHOHCH$_2$CONH$_2$	—	137
	Heat	(2-C$_9$H$_6$N)CH=CH$_2$	Poor	137

D. Ketonic β-Lactones

β-Lactone

	Reactant	Product	Yield, %	Reference
α-Phenyl-β-benzoyl [ee]	NaOH; H_2O	$C_6H_5COCHOHCH(C_6H_5)CO_2H + C_6H_5CH_2COCHOHC_6H_5 +$ $C_6H_5CH_2CHOHCOC_6H_5 + C_6H_5CH_2C(OH)(C_6H_5)CO_2H$	—	31, 32
			—	31, 32
	H_2SO_4; H_2O	$C_6H_5COCHOHCH(C_6H_5)CO_2H$	100	31
	H_2SO_4; CH_3OH	$C_6H_5COCHOHCH(C_6H_5)CO_2CH_3$	—	31
	HBr; H_2O	$C_6H_5COCHBrCH(C_6H_5)CO_2H$	100	31
	HBr; CH_3OH	$C_6H_5COCHBrCH(C_6H_5)CO_2CH_3$	—	31
	C_5H_5N; heat	cis-$C_6H_5COCH{=}C(C_6H_5)CO_2H$	—	31, 32
α-Phenyl-β-benzoyl [ff]	H_2SO_4; H_2O	$C_6H_5COCHOHCH(C_6H_5)CO_2H$	—	37
	H_2SO_4; CH_3OH	$C_6H_5COCHOHCH(C_6H_5)CO_2CH_3$	—	37
	CH_3OH; 25°	$C_6H_5COCH(OCH_3)CH(C_6H_5)CO_2H$	—	37, 38
	HBr; H_2O	$C_6H_5COCHBrCH(C_6H_5)CO_2H$	—	37
	HI; H_2O	$C_6H_5COCH_2CH(C_6H_5)CO_2H$	—	37
	CH_3I; Ag_2O	$C_6H_5COCH(OCH_3)CH(C_6H_5)CO_2CH_3$	—	37
	H_2SO_4; CH_3OH	$C_6H_5COCHOHCH(C_6H_5)CO_2CH_3$	—	37
α-Phenyl-β-benzoyl [gg]	CH_3OH; 25°	No reaction	—	37, 38
	NaOH; H_2O or $NaHCO_3$; H_2O		—	39, 40
	$NaOCH_3$; CH_3OH		—	39, 40
	H_2SO_4; CH_3OH		—	39, 40

Note: References 131–214 are on pp. 362–363.

[ee] Both racemic modifications, m.p. 95° and m.p. 148°, were employed.

[ff] The optically active isomers, m.p. 75°, $[\alpha]_D^{25}$ + and −155°, related to the racemic modification of m.p. 95°, were employed.

[gg] The optically active isomers, m.p. 130°, $[\alpha]_D^{25}$ + and −92°, related to the racemic modification of m.p. 148°, were employed.

TABLE V—*Continued*
REACTIONS OF PURE β-LACTONES

D. *Ketonic β-Lactones (Cont.)*

β-Lactone 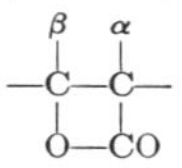	Reactant	Product	Yield, %	Reference
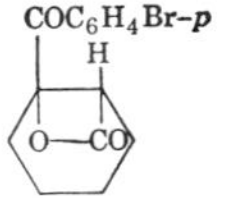 COC_6H_4Br-p structure	HBr; $(CH_3)_2CO$	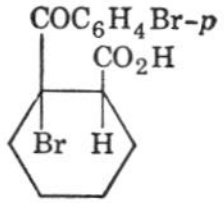 COC_6H_4Br-p, CO_2H structure	—	39, 40
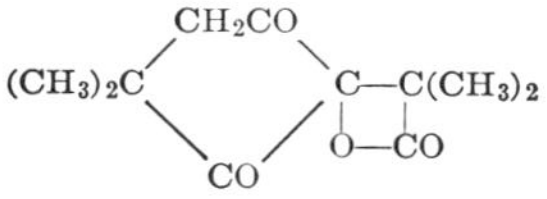 $(CH_3)_2C$ ... CH_2CO structure	NaOH; H_2O	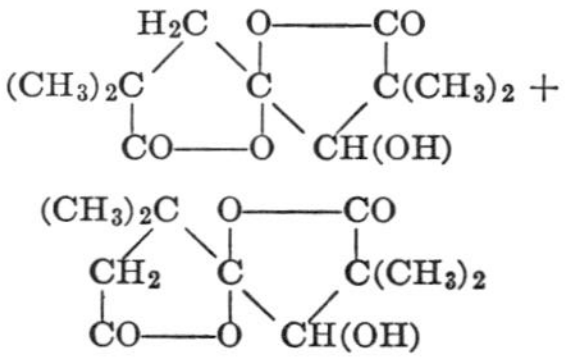 structures	—	**33**

E. *β-Lactonic Acids*

β-Lactone 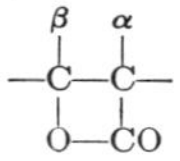	Reactant	Product	Yield, %	Reference
β-Carboxy (structure)	H_2SO_4 or NaOH; H_2O	$HO_2CCHOHCH_2CO_2H$	—	36, 45, 46, 47, 48, 49, 51, 53, 54
	KSH; H_2O	$HO_2CCH(SH)CH_2CO_2H$	—	50, 52
	$KSSCOC_2H_5$; H_2O	$HO_2CCH(SSCOC_2H_5)CH_2CO_2H$	—	50, 52
	KI; H_2O	$HO_2CCHICH_2CO_2H$	—	50
α,α-Dimethyl-β-carboxy (structure)	H_2SO_4 or NaOH; H_2O	$HO_2CCHOHC(CH_3)_2CO_2H$	—	124

Name	Conditions	Products		Yield (%)	References
	Heat; 150°	(CH₃)₂C—CO / CH(OH)CO		—	124, 125
α,α-Dimethyl-β-carbomethoxy	NaOH; H₂O Heat; Pt	HO₂CCHOHC(CH₃)₂CO₂H (CH₃)₂C=CHCO₂CH₃ + CO₂		— 44	138 138
α-Methyl-α-ethyl-β-carboxy	Heat	CH₃(C₂H₅)C—CO / CH(OH)CO		—	30
α,α-Dimethyl-β-methyl-β-carboxy	NaOH; H₂O Heat	HO₂CC(OH)(CH₃)C(CH₃)₂CO₂H (CH₃)₂C—CO / CH₃C(OH)CO		— —	139 30, 139
α,α-(1,4-Butano)-β-carboxy	Heat			—	30
α,α-(1,5-Pentano)-β-carboxy	Heat			—	30
α,α-(1,5-Pentano)-β-methyl-β-carboxy	Heat			—	30
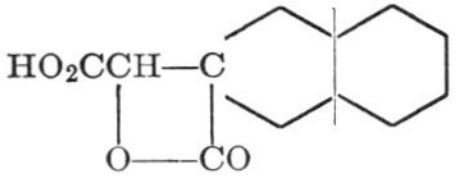 HO₂CCH—C / CO (cis)	Heat			—	30

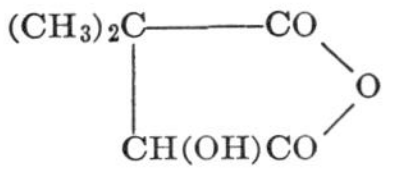

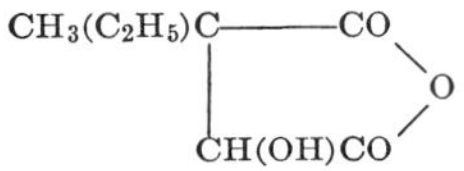

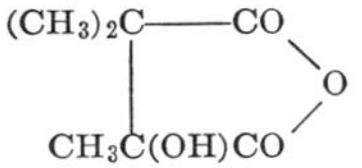

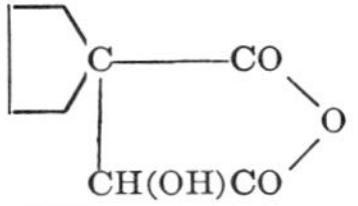

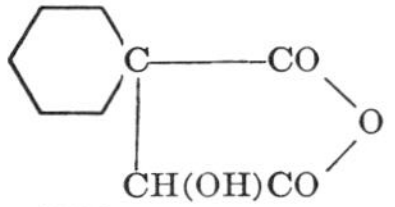

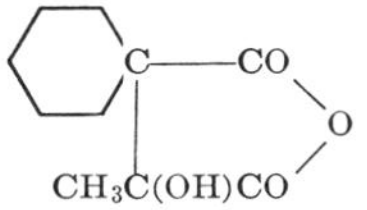

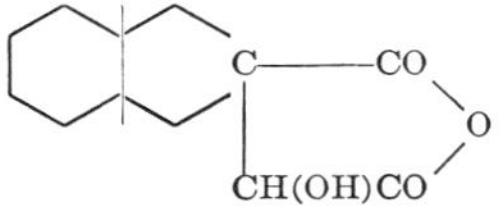

Note: References 131–214 are on pp. 362–363.

TABLE V—*Continued*
REACTIONS OF PURE β-LACTONES
E. *β-Lactonic Acids (Cont.)*

β-Lactone 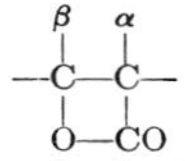	Reactant	Product	Yield, %	Reference
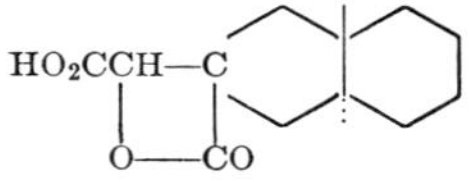 (β-Lactone structure)	Heat	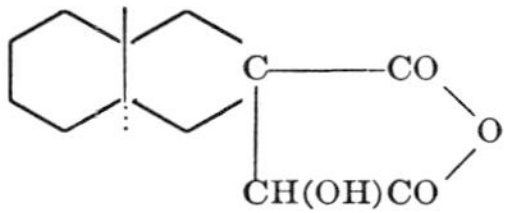 (lactone structure)	—	30
α-Methyl-α-chloro-β-methyl-β-carboxy	H_2SO_4; H_2O	$HO_2CC(OH)(CH_3)CCl(CH_3)CO_2H$ [hh]	—	73
α-Methyl-α-bromo-β-methyl-β-carboxy	H_2SO_4 or HBr; H_2O	$HO_2CC(OH)(CH_3)CBr(CH_3)CO_2H$ [hh]	—	73

F. *Quinoid β-Lactones*

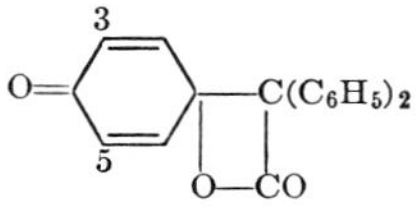

β-Lactone	Reactant	Product	Yield, %	Reference
Unsubstituted (3-H, 5-H)	$NaOH$; CH_3OH	Acid, m.p. 203° [ii]	Good	56
	$Ba(OH)_2$; H_2O	Acid, m.p. 208° [ii]	—	56
	$NaOC_2H_5$; C_6H_6	$C_{19}H_{14}O_2$ (red), m.p. 270° [ii]	—	56
	$C_6H_5NHNH_2$; $ClCH_2CH_2Cl$	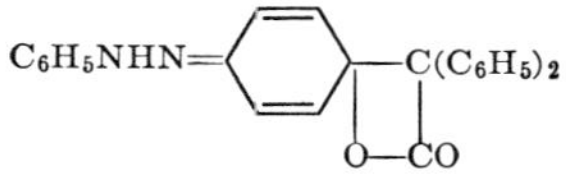 $C_6H_5NHN=$ (structure)	46	56
	Sunlight; C_6H_6	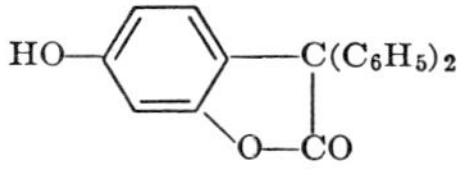 (structure)	25	56
	CH_3CO_2H	$C_{22}H_{18}O_5$, m.p. 165° [ii]	55	56
	CH_3OH; H_2SO_4	$C_{21}H_{18}O_4$, m.p. 123° [ii]	100	56

Substituent	Conditions	Products	Yield	Ref.
	Heat; vacuum	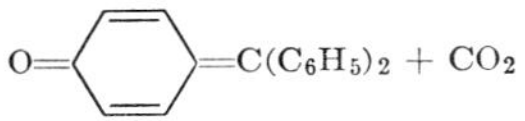 (quinone)=$C(C_6H_5)_2$ + CO_2	—	56, 58
	Heat; xylene	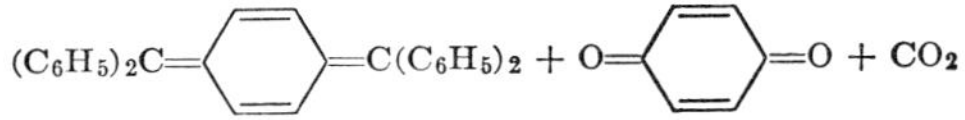 $(C_6H_5)_2C$=(quinone)=$C(C_6H_5)_2$ + CO_2	—	56, 58
3-Methyl	Heat; vacuum	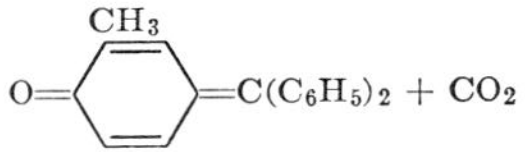 (CH₃-quinone)=$C(C_6H_5)_2$ + CO_2	35	56
3-Chloro	Heat; vacuum	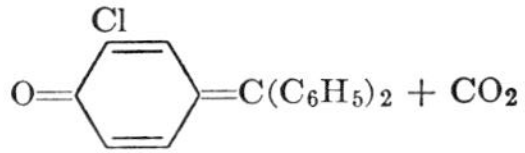 (Cl-quinone)=$C(C_6H_5)_2$ + CO_2	34	56
3,5-Dichloro	Heat; xylene	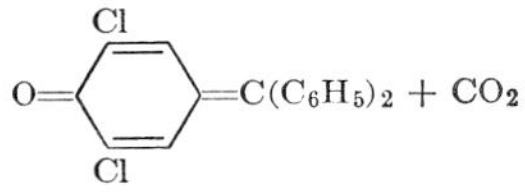 (Cl,Cl-quinone)=$C(C_6H_5)_2$ + CO_2	40	56
3,5-Dibromo	Heat; xylene	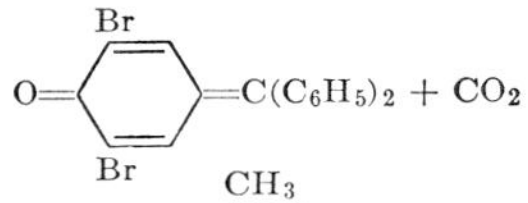 (Br,Br-quinone)=$C(C_6H_5)_2$ + CO_2	33	56
3,5-Dimethyl	Heat to m.p.	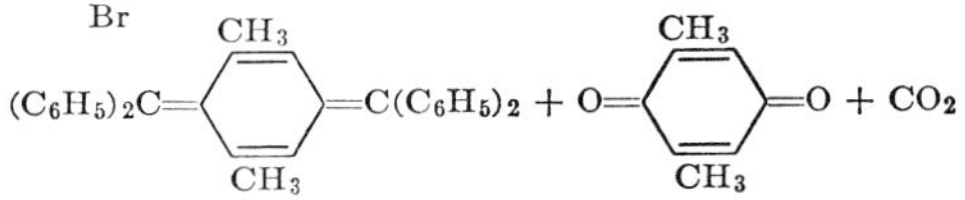 $(C_6H_5)_2C$=(CH₃,CH₃-quinone)=$C(C_6H_5)_2$ + CO_2	—	56
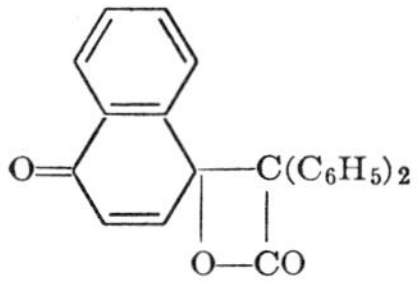	Heat to m.p.	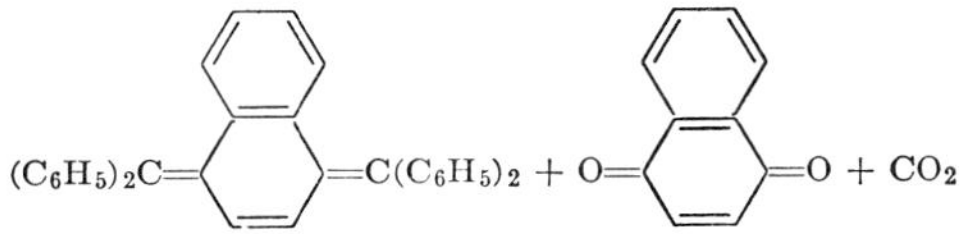 $(C_6H_5)_2C$=(naphthoquinone)=$C(C_6H_5)_2$ + CO_2	—	56

hh The same hydroxy acid was obtained from both racemic modifications of the β-lactone
ii The product was not completely characterized.

REFERENCES TO TABLES

[131] Prausnitz, *Ber.*, **17**, 595 (1884).
[132] Basler, *Ber.*, **16**, 3001 (1883).
[133] Eichengrün and Einhorn, *Ann.*, **262**, 157 (1891).
[134] Eichengrün and Einhorn, *Ann.*, **262**, 175 (1891).
[135] Einhorn and Hess, *Ber.*, **17**, 2015 (1884).
[136] Eichengrün and Einhorn, *Ber.*, **23**, 2876 (1890).
[137] Einhorn and Lehnkering, *Ann.*, **246**, 160 (1888).
[138] Ott, *Ber.*, **48**, 1350 (1915).
[139] Komppa, *Ber.*, **35**, 534 (1902).
[140] Desai, Hunter, and Sahariya, *Proc. Indian Acad. Sci.*, **15A**, 168 (1942) [*C. A.*, **36**, 6143 (1942)].
[141] Staudinger, *Ber.*, **40**, 1145 (1907).
[142] Steadman, U. S. pat. 2,424,589 [*C. A.*, **41**, 7413 (1947)].
[143] Steadman and Breyfogle, U. S. pat. 2,424,590 [*C. A.*, **41**, 7413 (1947)].
[144] Caldwell, U. S. pat. 2,450,116 [*C. A.*, **43**, 1055 (1949)].
[145] Caldwell, U. S. pat. 2,450,118 [*C. A.*, **43**, 1055 (1949)].
[146] Hagemeyer, U. S. pat. 2,450,131 [*C. A.*, **43**, 1056 (1949)].
[147] Hagemeyer, U. S. pat. 2,450,133 [*C. A.*, **43**, 1056 (1949)].
[148] Hagemeyer, U. S. pat. 2,450,134 [*C. A.*, **43**, 1056 (1949)].
[149] Caldwell and Hagemeyer, U. S. pat. 2,462,357 [*C. A.*, **43**, 3840 (1949)].
[150] Hagemeyer, U. S. pat. 2,469,110 [*C. A.*, **43**, 5414 (1949)].
[151] Caldwell, U. S. pat. 2,518,662 [*C. A.*, **44**, 10732 (1950)].
[152] Caldwell, U. S. pat. 2,585,223 [*C. A.*, **46**, 8672 (1952)].
[153] Young and Fitzpatrick, U. S. pat. 2,580,714 [*C. A.*, **46**, 8147 (1952)].
[154] Gresham and Jansen, U. S. pat. 2,602,802 [*C. A.*, **47**, 3872 (1953)].
[155] T. L. Gresham, private communication.
[156] Caldwell, U. S. pat. 2,484,486 [*C. A.*, **44**, 5379 (1950)].
[157] Hagemeyer, U. S. pat. 2,478,388 [*C. A.*, **44**, 1133 (1950)].
[158] Hart, *Bull. soc. chim. Belges*, **58**, 255 (1949) [*C. A.*, **45**, 6155 (1951)].
[159] Hagemeyer, U. S. pat. 2,450,132 [*C. A.*, **43**, 1056 (1949)].
[160] Hagemeyer, U. S. pat. 2,466,419 [*C. A.*, **43**, 5037 (1949)].
[161] Gregory, U. S. pat. 2,568,619 [*C. A.*, **46**, 3559 (1952)].
[162] Gresham, Jansen, Shaver, Gregory, and Beears, *J. Am. Chem. Soc.*, **70**, 1004 (1948).
[163] Küng, U. S. pat. 2,352,641 [*C. A.*, **38**, 5507 (1944)].
[164] Bartlett and Rylander, *J. Am. Chem. Soc.*, **73**, 4273 (1951).
[165] Steadman and Feazel, U. S. pat. 2,466,501 [*C. A.*, **43**, 5035 (1949)].
[166] Shaver, U. S. pat. 2,510,423 [*C. A.*, **44**, 8364 (1950)].
[167] Küng, U. S. pat. 2,376,704 [*C. A.*, **40**, 1868 (1946)].
[168] Gresham and Shaver, U. S. pat. 2,449,991 [*C. A.*, **43**, 1053 (1949)].
[169] Beears, U. S. pat. 2,526,533 [*C. A.*, **45**, 2500 (1951)].
[170] Beears, U. S. pat. 2,535,832 [*C. A.*, **45**, 3420 (1951)].
[171] Gresham and Shaver, U. S. pat. 2,449,992 [*C. A.*, **43**, 1054 (1949)].
[172] Gresham and Shaver, U. S. pat. 2,449,996 [*C. A.*, **43**, 1054 (1949)].
[173] Jansen and Mathes, U. S. pat. 2,483,416 [*C. A.*, **44**, 1544 (1950)].
[174] Gresham and Shaver, U. S. pat. 2,563,034 [*C. A.*, **46**, 1594 (1952)].
[175] Roha, U. S. pat. 2,602,801 [*C. A.*, **47**, 3882 (1953)].
[176] Gresham, Jansen, and Shaver, *J. Am. Chem. Soc.*, **70**, 1001 (1948).
[177] Gresham and Shaver, U. S. pat. 2,474,838 [*C. A.*, **43**, 7506 (1949)].
[178] Gresham and Shaver, U. S. pat. 2,563,035 [*C. A.*, **46**, 1594 (1952)].
[179] Jansen, U. S. pat. 2,602,813 [*C. A.*, **47**, 7536 (1953)].
[180] Gresham and Jansen, U. S. pat. 2,474,839 [*C. A.*, **43**, 7506 (1949)].
[181] Mathes, U. S. pat. 2,623,059 [*C. A.*, **47**, 9532 (1953)].
[182] Gresham and Shaver, U. S. pat. 2,449,995 [*C. A.*, **43**, 1055 (1949)].

β-LACTONES

[183] Gresham, Jansen, Shaver, Frederick, Fiedorek, Bankert, Gregory, and Beears, *J. Am. Chem. Soc.*, **74**, 1323 (1952).
[184] Küng, U. S. pat. 2,375,005 [*C. A.*, **39**, 4085 (1945)].
[185] Gresham and Shaver, U. S. pat. 2,548,155 [*C. A.*, **46**, 2568 (1952)].
[186] Gresham and Shaver, U. S. pat. 2,548,156 [*C. A.*, **45**, 8551 (1951)].
[187] Gresham and Shaver, U. S. pat. 2,526,556 [*C. A.*, **45**, 2501 (1951)].
[188] Gresham and Shaver, U. S. pat. 2,526,555 [*C. A.*, **45**, 2502 (1951)].
[189] Gresham and Shaver, U. S. pat. 2,526,558 [*C. A.*, **45**, 1291 (1951)].
[190] Gresham and Shaver, U. S. pat. 2,526,557 [*C. A.*, **45**, 2502 (1951)].
[191] B. F. Goodrich Co., Brit. pat. 648,886 [*C. A.*, **45**, 8031 (1951)].
[192] Gresham and Shaver, U. S. pat. 2,568,621 [*C. A.*, **46**, 3567 (1952)].
[193] Iwakura, Nagakubo, Kawasumi, and Kigawa, *J. Chem. Soc. Japan*, **72**, 406 (1951) [*C. A.*, **46**, 3013 (1952)].
[194] Gresham and Bankert, U. S. pat. 2,502,453 [*C. A.*, **44**, 8046 (1950)].
[195] Kendall, Brit. pat. 650,911 [*C. A.*, **46**, 144 (1952)].
[196] Gresham, Jansen, Shaver, and Gregory, *J. Am. Chem. Soc.*, **70**, 999 (1948).
[197] Gresham, U. S. pat. 2,449,987 [*C. A.*, **43**, 1056 (1949)].
[198] Gresham, U. S. pat. 2,449,989 [*C. A.*, **43**, 1054 (1949)].
[199] Frederick, U. S. pat. 2,485,271 [*C. A.*, **44**, 2544 (1950)].
[200] Hass, Feuer, and Pier, *J. Am. Chem. Soc.*, **73**, 1858 (1951).
[201] Gresham, U. S. pat. 2,449,988 [*C. A.*, **43**, 1053 (1949)].
[202] Gresham, Jansen, and Shaver, *J. Am. Chem. Soc.*, **72**, 72 (1950).
[203] Gresham and Shaver, U. S. pat. 2,449,993 [*C. A.*, **43**, 1054 (1949)].
[204] Gresham and Shaver, U. S. pat. 2,422,728 [*C. A.*, **42**, 209 (1948)].
[205] Gresham and Shaver, U. S. pat. 2,411,875 [*C. A.*, **41**, 2431 (1947)].
[206] Jansen and Beears, U. S. pat. 2,548,161 [*C. A.*, **45**, 8551 (1951)].
[207] Jansen, U. S. pat. 2,568,634 [*C. A.*, **46**, 3559 (1952)].
[208] Gresham and Shaver, U. S. pat. 2,449,994 [*C. A.*, **43**, 1056 (1949)].
[209] Bankert, U. S. pat. 2,510,364 [*C. A.*, **44**, 8373 (1950)].
[210] Beears, U. S. pat. 2,600,387 [*C. A.*, **47**, 3340 (1953)].
[211] Hagemeyer, U. S. pat. 2,484,500 [*C. A.*, **44**, 6427 (1950)].
[212] Shaver, U. S. pat. 2,587,540 [*C. A.*, **46**, 9603 (1952)].
[213] Einhorn, *Ber.*, **16**, 2645 (1883).
[214] Basler, *Ber.*, **17**, 1494 (1884).

CHAPTER 8

THE REACTION OF DIAZOMETHANE AND ITS DERIVATIVES WITH ALDEHYDES AND KETONES

C. David Gutsche

Washington University

CONTENTS

INTRODUCTION

Diazomethane and its derivatives react with aldehydes and ketones, usually under very mild conditions, to yield a variety of interesting and often useful products. With most aldehydes and ketones the reaction follows scheme A; with α,β-unsaturated aldehydes and ketones and with 1,4-quinones the reaction follows scheme B; with α-dicarbonyl compounds, including 1,2-quinones, the reaction follows either scheme C or scheme A.

Scheme A

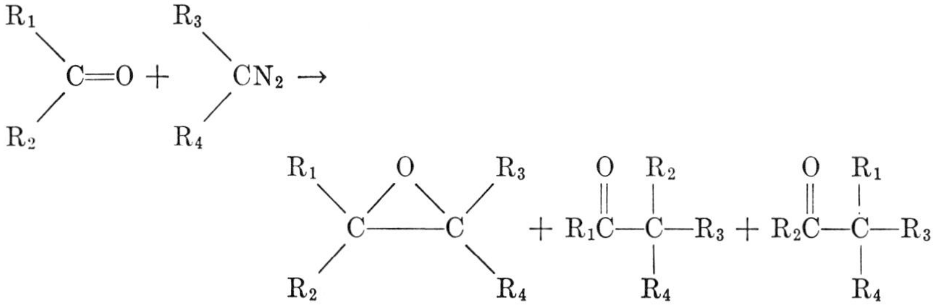

$$
\begin{array}{c}
R_1 \\ \diagdown \\ C=O \\ \diagup \\ R_2
\end{array}
+
\begin{array}{c}
R_3 \\ \diagdown \\ CN_2 \\ \diagup \\ R_4
\end{array}
\rightarrow
$$

$$
\begin{array}{c}
R_1 \quad O \quad R_3 \\ \diagdown \diagup \diagdown \diagup \\ C \text{——} C \\ \diagup \qquad \diagdown \\ R_2 \qquad R_4
\end{array}
+ R_1\overset{O}{\overset{\|}{C}}\text{—}C\text{—}R_3 + R_2\overset{O}{\overset{\|}{C}}\text{—}C\text{—}R_3
$$

with R_2, R_4 and R_1, R_4 substituents respectively.

Scheme B

$$
\begin{array}{c}
\diagup \\ \text{—}C=C \\ \diagdown \\ C=O \\ \diagup \\ R_2
\end{array}
+
\begin{array}{c}
R_3 \\ \diagdown \\ CN_2 \\ \diagup \\ R_4
\end{array}
\rightarrow
\begin{array}{c}
R_3 \quad N \\ \diagdown \diagup \diagdown \\ C \qquad N \\ \diagup \qquad | \\ R_4 \qquad \\ \text{—}C\text{——}C \\ | \qquad \diagdown \\ \qquad C=O \\ \qquad \diagup \\ \qquad R_2
\end{array}
$$

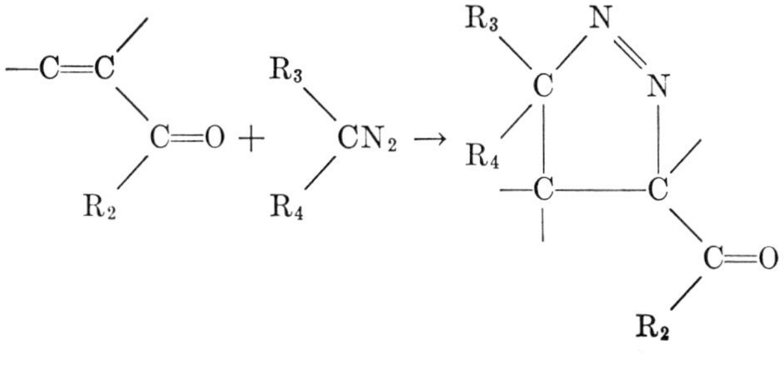

Scheme C

$$
\begin{array}{c}
\underset{R_2}{\overset{\displaystyle \overset{\textstyle O}{\underset{\displaystyle \parallel}{}}}{\underset{}{\overset{-C}{\diagdown}}}} \\
\end{array}
C\!\!=\!\!O \;+\; \overset{R_3}{\underset{R_4}{\diagdown \!\! CN_2}} \;\rightarrow\;
$$

In 1907 Schlotterbeck [1] carried out reactions of diazomethane with
benzaldehyde, isovaleraldehyde, and *n*-heptaldehyde and obtained
acetophenone, methyl isobutyl ketone, and methyl *n*-hexyl ketone. He
is sometimes considered to be the discoverer of this type of reaction
but, in fact, was anticipated by Buchner and Curtius [2] in 1885, by
v. Pechmann [3] in 1895, and by Meyer [4] in 1905, who had shown that
ethyl diazoacetate and diazomethane react with compounds such as
benzaldehyde, biacetyl, benzil, nitrobenzaldehyde, and chlorobenzalde-
hyde. Not until 1927–1930, as a result of the careful work of Arndt,
Mosettig, Meerwein and their respective co-workers, however, was the
reaction, particularly those examples following scheme A, put on a firm
basis. These and subsequent investigations have shown that the reaction is fairly general.

The reaction is most often carried out either by allowing the carbonyl
compound to react with an ethereal solution of the diazomethane derivative with or without the addition of a catalyst, or by treating a
methanol solution of the carbonyl compound with a nitrosoalkylurethan in the presence of a base.

Only the reactions of diazomethane and its alkyl and aryl derivatives
are discussed in detail in this chapter, although reference is made to
similar reactions involving ethyl diazoacetate. Several reviews cover-
ing the aliphatic diazo compounds and their reactions are available.[5-10]

[1] Schlotterbeck, *Ber.*, **40**, 479 (1907).

[2] Buchner and Curtius, *Ber.*, **18**, 2371 (1885).

[3] v. Pechmann, *Ber.*, **28**, 855 (1895).

[4] Meyer, *Monatsh.*, **26**, 1295 (1905).

[5] Arndt, *Angew. Chem.*, **40**, 1099 (1927).

[6] Smith, *Chem. Revs.*, **23**, 193 (1938).

[7] Hurd, in Gilman, *Organic Chemistry*, Vol. I, 1st ed., pp. 645–656, Wiley, New York,
1938.

[8] Grevenstuk, *Chem. Weekblad*, **37**, 632 (1940) [*C. A.*, **36**, 4801 (1942)].

[9] Eistert, *Angew. Chem.*, **54**, 99, 124 (1941); translated and revised by Spangler in *Newer
Methods of Preparative Organic Chemistry*, 1st ed., pp. 513–570, Interscience, New York,
1948.

[10] Hancox, *Roy. Australian Chem. Inst. J. & Proc.*, **16**, 282 (1949) [*C. A.*, **44**, 1014
(1950)].

MECHANISM AND FACTORS INFLUENCING THE COURSE OF THE REACTION

The aliphatic diazo compound (I) is one of the few organic molecules that cannot be even approximately expressed by a single structure but must be represented as a resonance hybrid of several charge-separated forms (Ia, b, c).[11] That the diazo group is linear has been established

(a)   (b)   (c)

I

by electron diffraction [12] and infrared [13] studies and from other considerations.[14]

The reaction according to scheme A has been interpreted as a nucleophilic attack of I (the contribution of c being the most important) on the carbonyl group to yield an addition compound, currently expressed as a diazonium betaine (II).[15] The betaine is the charge-separated form of a dihydrofuradiazole (Δ^3-1,3,4-oxadiazoline) and has also been postulated as an intermediate in the reaction of nitrous oxide with olefins [16] and in the reaction of β-amino alcohols with nitrous acid.[17] Usually this intermediate is too unstable to be isolated. Chloral, for example, reacts with ethereal diazomethane to form an addition product (in solution) that is not decomposed by benzoic acid but which evolves nitrogen upon evaporation of the ether.[18-20] In a few instances, however, nitrogen-containing products have been obtained. Diphenylketene reacts with diphenyldiazomethane [21] to form 2,2-diphenyl-5-diphenylmethylidene-Δ^3-1,3,4-oxadiazoline as an isolable compound which loses nitrogen only upon prolonged heating at 150°. Similarly, 2,3,5,6-tetramethyl-1,4-benzoquinone reacts with diazomethane [22] to form sev-

[11] Sidgwick, *The Organic Chemistry of Nitrogen*, new edition, revised and rewritten by Taylor and Baker, pp. 347–363, Oxford University Press, 1942.

[12] Boersch, *Monatsh.*, **65**, 331 (1935).

[13] Ramsay, *J. Chem. Phys.*, **17**, 666 (1949); Crawford, Fletcher, and Ramsay, *ibid.*, **19**, 406 (1951).

[14] Murty, *Current Sci.*, **5**, 424 (1937) [*C. A.*, **31**, 4644 (1937)].

[15] Arndt and Eistert, *Ber.*, **68**, 193 (1935).

[16] Bridson-Jones, Buckley, Cross, and Driver, *J. Chem. Soc.*, **1951**, 2999.

[17] McKenzie and Richardson, *J. Chem. Soc.*, **123**, 79 (1923).

[18] Schlotterbeck, *Ber.*, **42**, 2559 (1909).

[19] Arndt, Eistert, and Ender, *Ber.*, **62**, 44 (1929).

[20] Meerwein, Bersin, and Burneleit, *Ber.*, **62**, 999 (1929).

[21] Staudinger and Reber, *Helv. Chim. Acta*, **4**, 3 (1921).

[22] Smith and Pings, *J. Org. Chem.*, **2**, 95 (1937).

eral stable, nitrogen-containing compounds (cf. p. 424, structures D–G). The decomposition of II may be pictured as proceeding through a labile intermediate (III) which becomes stabilized by any or all of three paths to yield IV, V, and/or VI. Probably, however, the process is a concerted one.[23]

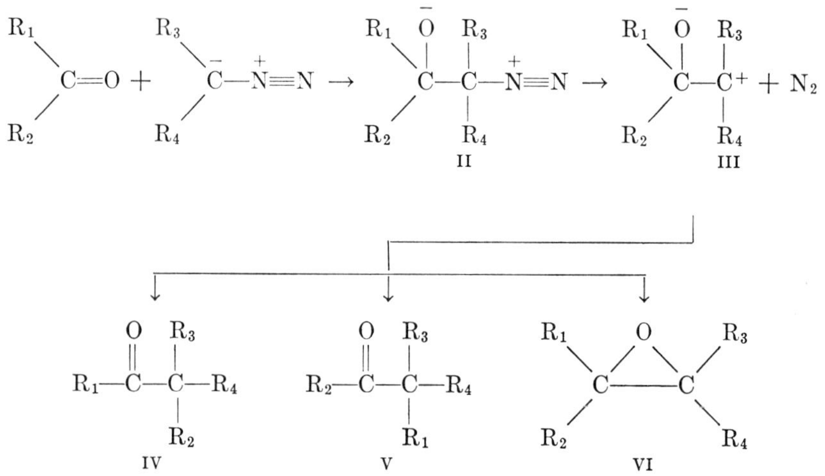

This mechanism is supported by several observations. Rate studies of reactions between diazomethane and various ketones indicate that the overall reaction is second order.[24] The reactivity of two series of ketones studied under controlled conditions is in the order $Cl_3CCOCH_3 >$ $CH_3COCH_3 > C_6H_5COCH_3$ and cyclohexanone > cyclopentanone > cycloheptanone > cyclooctanone; [24, 25] this is the same order of reactivity observed for reactions that are well established as involving nucleophilic attack on the carbonyl group. The reaction is catalyzed by semipolar substances,[20, 26] probably through coordination of the catalyst with the carbonyl group. The suggestion that ions, particularly hydrogen ions, exert a catalytic action by promoting the decomposition of diazomethane to the methylene radical, $H_2C:$, [27, 28] is unlikely because the reaction proceeds at identical rates in pure water and in 0.1 N sodium hydroxide.[24, 26]

[23] Robinson and Smith, *J. Chem. Soc.*, **1937**, 371.
[24] P. Pöhls, Inaug. diss. University of Marburg, Marburg, 1934.
[25] O. Pauli, Inaug. diss. University of Marburg, Marburg, 1935.
[26] Meerwein and Burneleit, *Ber.*, **61**, 1840 (1928).
[27] Bergmann, Magat, and Wagenberg, *Ber.*, **63**, 2576 (1930).
[28] Bergmann and Bergmann, *J. Org. Chem.*, **3**, 125 (1938).

The path followed in the stabilization of the reactive intermediate III is dependent upon structural features, which may be interpreted in terms of steric effects and electronic effects, and upon catalytic factors. Table I shows the amount of ketone and oxide formed from several methyl alkyl ketones. The increase in the amount of oxide formed and the decrease in the rate of reaction as the alkyl group becomes larger seem best interpreted as a steric effect.

TABLE I

Starting Ketone	Ketone, %	Oxide, %	Relative Rate [24]
CH_3COCH_3	38	33.5	1.0
$CH_3COCH_2CH_3$	32	40	0.4
$CH_3COCH_2CH_2CH_3$	18	55	0.15
$CH_3COCH(CH_3)_2$			0.095
$CH_3CO(CH_2)_8CH_3$	0	100	

(The "Ketone, %" and "Oxide, %" columns are under the spanning header "Product [24]".)

Electronic factors have been studied in more detail than steric factors and can be shown to have an effect on the rate of the reaction, the ratio of carbonyl products to oxide, and the ratio of one carbonyl product to the other. Although no quantitative rate measurements are available, a considerable amount of qualitative evidence indicates that aldehydes and ketones bearing electron-withdrawing groups (negative substituents) react more readily than those bearing electron-donating groups (positive substituents). Thus, acetone is unreactive toward ethereal diazomethane, but negatively substituted acetones such as chloroacetone, trichloroacetone, and methoxyacetone react under these conditions; acetophenone reacts with diazomethane in ether-methanol solution, but 3,4-methylenedioxyacetophenone (positive substituents) under the same conditions fails to react.

Negative substituents in the carbonyl compound, in addition to accelerating the reaction, usually increase the amount of oxide formed as illustrated in Table II. The ratio of oxide to carbonyl product may be influenced by the reaction medium, however, and in the reactions of o-nitrobenzaldehyde,[29] p-nitrobenzaldehyde,[19] and phenylacetaldehyde [24] this ratio is increased by addition of methanol to the reaction mixture. Piperonal behaves in the opposite manner [30] and gives more carbonyl product when methanol is present.

The effect of substituents in the diazomethane derivative is, as would be anticipated, in the opposite direction; negative groups hinder the reaction, and positive groups facilitate it. Carbethoxydiazomethane (ethyl diazoacetate) is considerably less reactive than diazomethane,

TABLE II

Starting Compound	Product Carbonyl, %	Oxide, %	Reference
Benzaldehyde	97	—	1
o-Nitrobenzaldehyde	16.5	65	29
p-Nitrobenzaldehyde	29	46	29
Piperonal	31–46	18	30
Acetone	20–38	33–40	9, 31
Chloroacetone	Some	65	9, 29
Trichloroacetone	Trace	90	9, 29
Methoxyacetone	—	39	25
Cyclohexanone	65	15	32
2-Chlorocyclohexanone	11	50	33
2-Hydroxycyclohexanone	—	90	34

which, in turn, appears to be somewhat less reactive than its higher homologs.[35–40]

The ratio of the carbonyl compounds formed, IV to V, is dependent on the relative migratory aptitudes of R_1 and R_2. In general, with the exception of hydrogen, the group migrating preferentially is the group more able to contribute electrons, but the migratory preferences may be strongly influenced by the solvent and by the diazoalkane employed. For instance, piperonal reacts with diazomethane in the presence of methanol mainly with aryl migration to form the homologous aldehyde X (which cannot be isolated because it reacts further to form the oxide IX and the ketone VIII) and in the absence of methanol mainly with hydrogen migration to form the ketone VII. Thus, methanol appears to promote aryl migration.[29,30] The effect of the diazoalkane employed is illustrated by two reactions of o-nitropiperonal; with diazomethane

[29] Arndt, Amende, and Ender, Monatsh., 59, 202 (1932).

[30] Mosettig, Ber., 61, 1391 (1928).

[31] Meerwein, Ger. pat., 579,309 [C. A., 27, 4546 (1933)].

[32] Kohler, Tishler, Potter, and Thompson, J. Am. Chem. Soc., 61, 1057 (1939).

[33] Gutsche, J. Am. Chem. Soc., 71, 3513 (1949).

[34] Mousseron and Manon, Bull. soc. chim. France, 1949, 392.

[35] Mosettig and Burger, J. Am. Chem. Soc., 53, 2295 (1931).

[36] Giraitis and Bullock, J. Am. Chem. Soc., 59, 951 (1937).

[37] Adamson and Kenner, J. Chem. Soc., 1937, 1551.

[38] Adamson and Kenner, J. Chem. Soc., 1939, 181.

[39] Wilds and Meader, J. Org. Chem., 13, 763 (1948).

[40] Ramonczai and Vargha, J. Am. Chem. Soc., 72, 2737 (1950).

the products are the oxide XII (90%) and the ketone XIII (10%) (aryl migration), whereas with diazoethane the only isolable product (74%) is the ketone XI (hydrogen migration).[41] Similarly, piperonal yields only the propiophenone derivative (84%) upon treatment with diazoethane.[41]

[41] Mosettig and Czadek, *Monatsh.*, **57**, 291 (1931).

SCOPE AND LIMITATIONS

The following section deals with the scope and limitations of the reactions of various diazoalkanes with the several types of aldehydes and ketones listed previously. No attempt has been made to survey completely certain types of carbonyl compounds such as β-ketoaldehydes (hydroxymethylene ketones), β-keto esters, β-diketones, etc., so far as they react to give O-alkylated derivatives. The formation of enol ethers is simply an example of the well-known and very general reaction involving the displacement by diazoalkanes of hydrogen attached to hetero atoms. The examples of O-alkylation that are included are cited either to illustrate the general behavior of a type of compound or to point out differential behavior of similarly constituted compounds. Numerous articles have appeared in the literature describing the use of diazomethane in the study of enolization phenomena.[42-49]

Aldehydes

Simple aliphatic aldehydes react with diazomethane to yield the homologous ketones along with, in most cases, the oxides. The yield of ketone varies from 25 to 75% and appears to increase as the aliphatic chain increases in length, in contrast to the situation with methyl ketones as shown in Table I. n-Heptaldehyde, for instance, forms methyl n-hexyl ketone in 73% yield.[1] Arylacetaldehydes similarly yield mixtures containing arylacetones and oxides in ratios depending to some extent on the substitution in the aromatic ring but to a greater extent on the solvent. For example, phenylacetaldehyde forms phenylacetone in 52% yield in the absence of methanol [24] but gives only 10% of a mixture of ketones along with 35% of a non-ketonic fraction in the presence of methanol.[24]

More complex aliphatic aldehydes such as aldehydo sugars and steroids also react with diazomethane. D- and L-Arabinose tetraacetate (XIV) give D- and L-1-deoxyfructose tetraacetate (XV) in 62% yield.[50]   17-Formyl-4-androsten-17-ol-3-one (XVI) yields the ketone

[42] Arndt, Z. angew. Chem., **44**, 723 (1931).

[43] Arndt and Martius, Ann., **499**, 228 (1932).

[44] Arndt, Rev. fac. sci. univ. Istanbul, **1**, No. 4, 1 (1936) [C. A., **31**, 1006 (1937)].

[45] Arndt, Loewe, Özsöy, Ögüt, Arslan, and Bagevi, Ber., **71**, 1631 (1938).

[46] Arndt, Loewe, and Ginkök, Rev. fac. sci. univ. Istanbul, Ser. A, **11**, No. 4, 147 (1946) [C. A., **41**, 3760 (1949)].

[47] Eistert, Arndt, Loewe, and Ayça, Chem. Ber., **84**, 156 (1951).

[48] Arndt, Loewe, Ün, and Ayça, Chem. Ber., **84**, 319 (1951); Arndt, Loewe, and Ayça, ibid., **84**, 329 (1951); Arndt and Avan, ibid., **84**, 343 (1951).

[49] Eistert, Weygand, and Csendes, Chem. Ber., **84**, 745 (1951).

[50] Wolfrom, Weisblat, Zophy, and Waisbrot, J. Am. Chem. Soc., **63**, 201 (1941).

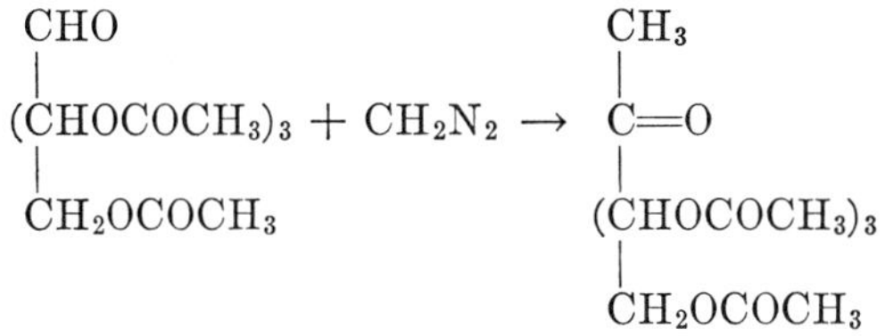

$$\begin{matrix} \text{CHO} \\ | \\ (\overset{|}{\text{CHOCOCH}_3})_3 \\ | \\ \text{CH}_2\text{OCOCH}_3 \end{matrix} + \text{CH}_2\text{N}_2 \rightarrow \begin{matrix} \text{CH}_3 \\ | \\ \text{C}{=}\text{O} \\ | \\ (\overset{|}{\text{CHOCOCH}_3})_3 \\ | \\ \text{CH}_2\text{OCOCH}_3 \end{matrix}$$

$$\text{XIV} \qquad\qquad \text{XV}$$

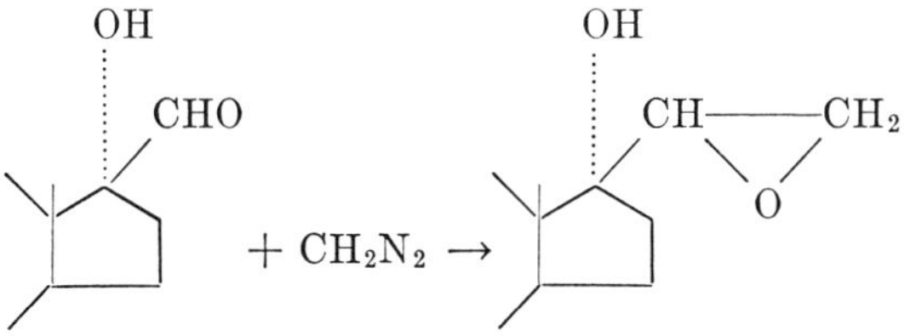

XVII (30%) from the α-isomer and the oxide XVIII (33%) from the β-isomer.[51]

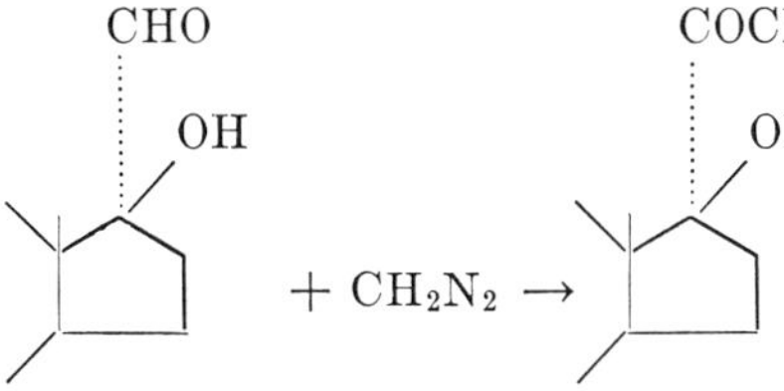

αXVI + CH₂N₂ → XVII

βXVI + CH₂N₂ → XVIII

Aliphatic aldehydes carrying electron-withdrawing substituents on the α-carbon usually form either the oxide or the enol ether. The first reaction is observed with compounds such as chloral, which yields trichloropropylene oxide (XIX) almost exclusively.[18, 52] The second reaction takes place with β-ketoaldehydes and with compounds such as the diphenylaminosulfonyl derivative of acetaldehyde (XX).[43] The forma-

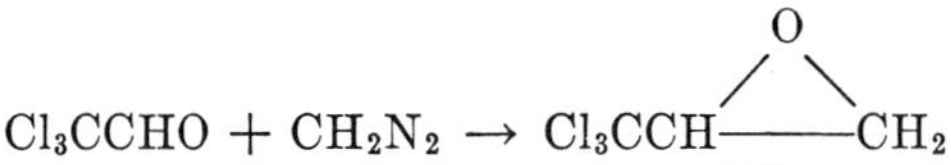

$$\text{Cl}_3\text{CCHO} + \text{CH}_2\text{N}_2 \rightarrow \text{Cl}_3\text{CCH}\overset{\displaystyle O}{\overbrace{\qquad}}\text{CH}_2$$
$$\text{XIX}$$

$$[(\text{C}_6\text{H}_5)_2\text{NSO}_2]_2\text{CHCHO} + \text{CH}_2\text{N}_2 \rightarrow [(\text{C}_6\text{H}_5)_2\text{NSO}_2]_2\text{C}{=}\text{CHOCH}_3$$
$$\text{XX} \qquad\qquad\qquad\qquad \text{XXI}$$

tion of the enol ether XXI has been interpreted by Arndt[29] as an attack by diazomethane (the contribution of Ia being most important) at the carbonyl oxygen atom of XX. The intermediate so formed is

[51] Prins and Reichstein, Helv. Chim. Acta, 24, 945 (1941).
[52] Arndt and Eistert, Ber., 61, 1118 (1928).

postulated to decompose with migration of a methylene hydrogen and expulsion of nitrogen as shown below.

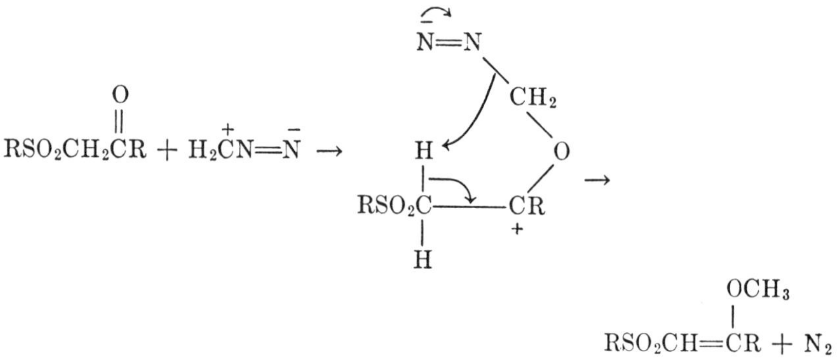

$$RSO_2CH = CR + N_2$$
with OCH_3 above the second carbon.

The products from aromatic aldehydes depend on the solvent and on the substituents in the ring. For example, benzaldehyde forms acetophenone in 97% yield in the absence of methanol [1] but in only 40–50% yield when methanol is present.[41] When electron-withdrawing groups are present, particularly in the *ortho* or *para* positions, the product is predominately the oxide. Thus, *o*-nitrobenzaldehyde yields 65% of the oxide XXII, 16% of *o*-nitroacetophenone, and only a small amount of *o*-nitrophenylacetone.[29] Electron-donating substituents, on the other hand, promote the formation of homologous carbonyl compounds in preference to the oxide as illustrated by the previously cited example of piperonal.

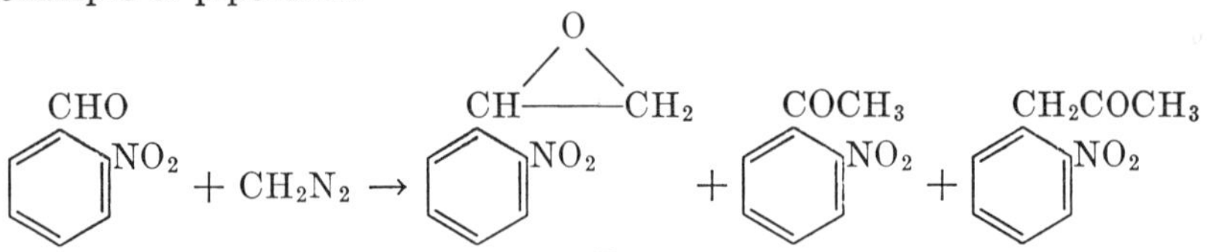

XXII

Glyoxal, the only dialdehyde that has been investigated, is reported to form biacetyl in 85% yield.[53]

Higher diazoalkanes and aldehydes furnish ketones in excellent yields. Benzaldehyde reacts with diazoethane to give 94% of propiophenone, with 1-diazopropane to give 89% of butyrophenone, and with 1-diazobutane to give 100% of valerophenone.[38] Piperonal, *o*-nitropiperonal,[41] 2-furaldehyde, and 5-methyl-2-furaldehyde [40] give the corresponding ethyl ketones in excellent yield with diazoethane. These reactions appear to warrant further study, for they may provide useful routes to otherwise difficultly obtainable aliphatic aromatic ketones

---

[53] Biltz and Paetzold, *Ann.*, **433**, 64 (1923).

(e.g., where the desired orientations preclude Friedel-Crafts acylations or where methods such as the reaction of acid chlorides with dialkylcadmium reagents fail).

Several halogenated aldehydes such as chloral yield, upon treatment with ethyl diazoacetate, products originally formulated as β-keto esters [54, 55] but more likely possessing the oxide type of structure.[29, 56] Although benzaldehyde and p-nitrobenzaldehyde may react with ethyl diazoacetate to yield β-keto esters,[2, 55] possibly by a rearrangement of an initially formed oxide,[56] a later investigation resulted in the isolation only of the dioxolane XXIII (R = C_6H_5).[57] n-Heptaldehyde also yields a dioxolane derivative XXIII (R = n-C_6H_{13}).[57]

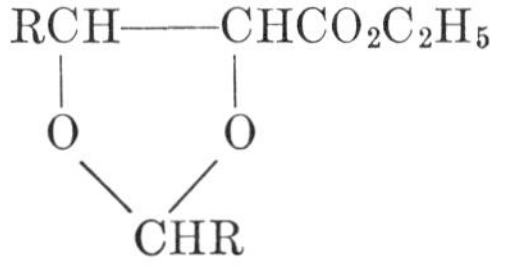

$$RCH\!\!-\!\!-\!\!-\!\!CHCO_2C_2H_5$$

$$\begin{array}{cc} | & | \\ O & O \\ \diagdown & \diagup \\ & CHR \end{array}$$

XXIII

Acyclic Ketones

Acyclic ketones react more slowly than the corresponding aldehydes and have a much greater tendency to form oxides. A solvent such as methanol is often necessary to promote the reaction.[20, 26] Only the simplest ketones yield appreciable amounts of the homolog, and the yield drops as the chain length increases (cf. Table I). However, the reaction is quite satisfactory as a method for preparing many oxides, particularly when negative substituents are attached to the α-position. Thus, compounds such as chloroacetone, ω-chloroacetophenone, methoxyacetone, ω-methoxyacetophenone, and diethyl oxomalonate react with diazomethane to form the corresponding oxides in high yield. Methyl pyruvate and D-fructose pentaacetate furnish the oxides XXIV and XXV in 87% [58] and 75% [59] yield, respectively.

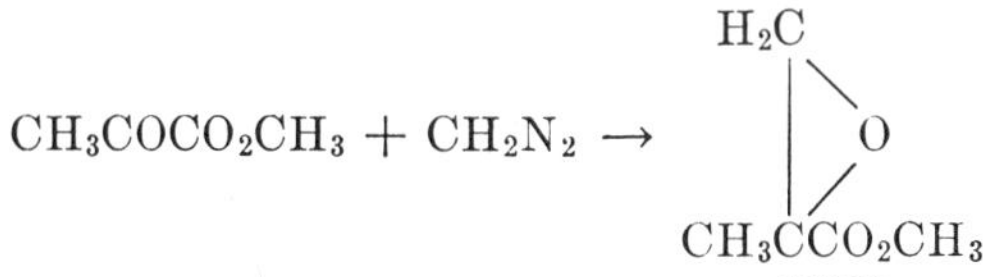

$$CH_3COCO_2CH_3 + CH_2N_2 \rightarrow$$

$$\begin{array}{c} H_2C \\ \diagdown \\ |\quad O \\ \diagup \\ CH_3CCO_2CH_3 \\ XXIV \end{array}$$

[54] Schlotterbeck, *Ber.*, **40**, 3000 (1907).

[55] Schlotterbeck, *Ber.*, **42**, 2565 (1909).

[56] Staudinger and Siegwart, *Helv. Chim. Acta*, **3**, 833 (1920).

[57] Dieckmann, *Ber.*, **43**, 1024 (1910).

[58] Arndt, Ozansoy, and Üstünyar, *Rev. fac. sci. univ. Istanbul*, [N.S.] **4**, No. 1–2, 83 (1939) [*C. A.*, **33**, 6246 (1939)].

[59] Wolfrom, Weisblat, and Waisbrot, *J. Am. Chem. Soc.*, **63**, 632 (1941).

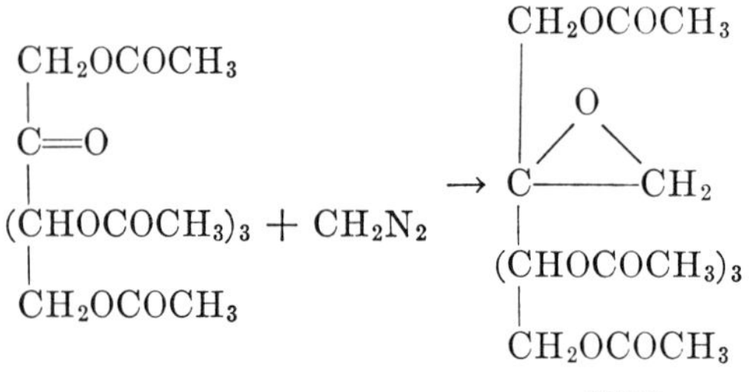

$$
\begin{array}{c}
CH_2OCOCH_3 \\
| \\
C{=}O \\
| \\
(CHOCOCH_3)_3 \ + \ CH_2N_2 \\
| \\
CH_2OCOCH_3
\end{array}
\longrightarrow
\begin{array}{c}
CH_2OCOCH_3 \\
| \\
\overset{O}{\overset{\diagup\diagdown}{C{-}{-}CH_2}} \\
| \\
(CHOCOCH_3)_3 \\
| \\
CH_2OCOCH_3
\end{array}
$$

XXV

Ketones with active methylene groups may yield O-alkylated products, C-alkylated products, oxides, or mixtures of these. Thus, ethyl acetoacetate,[60] p-toluenesulfonylacetone,[43] ω-(p-toluenesulfonyl)acetophenone,[43] and di-(p-toluenesulfonyl)acetone [43] form enol ethers with diazomethane. Ethyl acetoacetate yields some of the oxide XXVII (R = H) in addition to the enol ether XXVI (R = H), and ethyl methylacetoacetate yields the oxide XXVII (R = CH_3) as the major product. The substituted pyruvic ester XXVIII yields only 14% of the enol ether XXIX and 54% of the C-methylated compound XXX.[43] Another interesting example of C-alkylation is seen in the reaction of 3,4-dihydroxy-2,5-diphenylthiophene-1,1-dioxide with diazomethane; in addition to 76% of the expected dimethyl ether, 1.8% of a C-methyl compound is obtained.[61]

$$ CH_3COCH(R)CO_2C_2H_5 \ + \ CH_2N_2 \ \longrightarrow $$

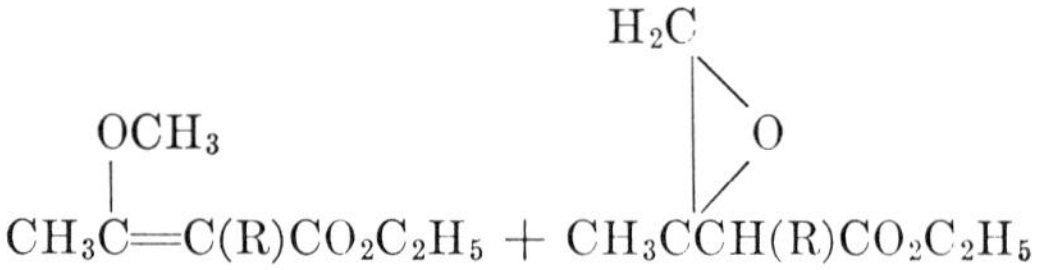

$$
\begin{array}{cc}
OCH_3 & H_2C \\
| & \diagdown \\
CH_3C{=}C(R)CO_2C_2H_5 & \quad\diagup O \\
\text{XXVI} & \diagup \\
& CH_3CCH(R)CO_2C_2H_5 \\
& \text{XXVII}
\end{array}
$$

$$
\underset{\text{XXVIII}}{[(C_6H_5)_2NSO_2]_2CHCOCO_2C_2H_5} \ + \ CH_2N_2 \ \longrightarrow
$$

$$
\begin{array}{cc}
OCH_3 & CH_3 \\
| & | \\
[(C_6H_5)_2NSO_2]_2C{=}CCO_2C_2H_5 & + \ [(C_6H_5)_2NSO_2]_2CCOCO_2C_2H_5 \\
\text{XXIX} & \text{XXX}
\end{array}
$$

Compounds such as benzil,[53] p,p'-dibromobenzil,[53] furil,[53] and diphenylpropanetrione [62] that contain a 1,2-diketo grouping react with diazomethane to form methylenedioxy derivatives similar to XXXI. Bi-

---

[60] Arndt, Loewe, Severge, and Türegün, *Ber.*, **71**, 1640 (1938).
[61] Overberger and Hoyt, *J. Am. Chem. Soc.*, **73**, 3305 (1951).
[62] Schönberg, Moubasher, and Mostafa, *J. Chem. Soc.*, **1941**, 348.

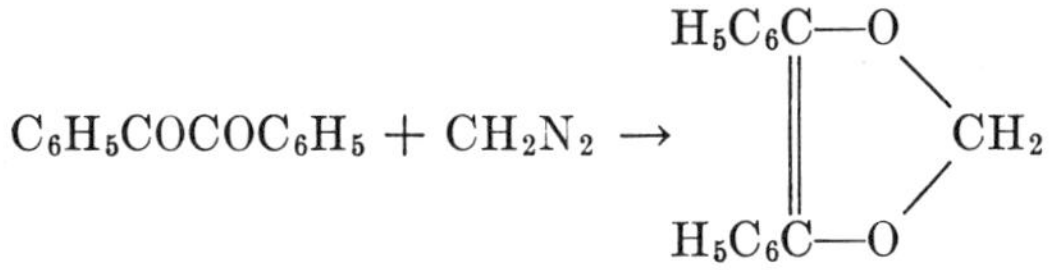

$$C_6H_5COCOC_6H_5 + CH_2N_2 \rightarrow \begin{array}{c} H_5C_6C-O \\ \parallel \qquad \diagdown \\ \qquad \qquad CH_2 \\ \parallel \qquad \diagup \\ H_5C_6C-O \end{array}$$

$$XXXI$$

acetyl [53] and acetonylacetone [53] are reported to be unreactive toward diazomethane, although it is possible that in the presence of catalysts a reaction might be induced.

In the only reported experiment involving an acyclic ketone and a higher diazoalkane,[38] acetone and diazoethane yield 9% of the oxide XXXII and 44% of methyl isopropyl ketone. This striking contrast to the reaction of acetone with diazomethane, from which the oxide

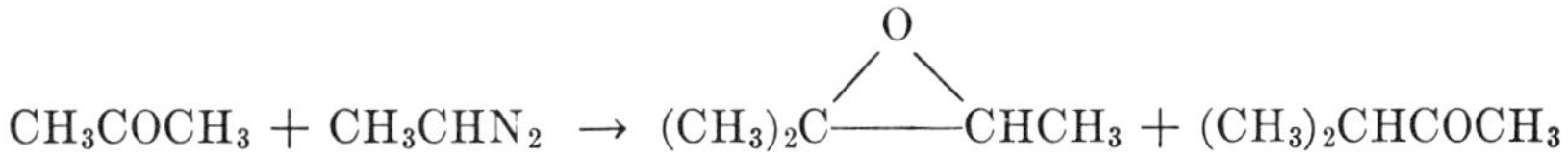

$$CH_3COCH_3 + CH_3CHN_2 \rightarrow (CH_3)_2C\overset{\displaystyle O}{\overbrace{\diagup \qquad \diagdown}}CHCH_3 + (CH_3)_2CHCOCH_3$$

$$XXXII$$

and homologous ketone are obtained in equal amounts, suggests a possibly fruitful field for further investigation. Ethyl diazoacetate has been used with one acyclic ketone; ω,ω-di(phenoxysulfonyl)acetophenone yields an enol derivative.[43]

Carbocyclic Ketones

Ketene and carbocyclic ketones with ring sizes as large as cyclopentadecanone react with diazomethane to give the ring-enlarged ketone and, in most cases, the oxide. The relative reaction rates for several members of the series are as follows: [24, 25] cyclopentanone (1.00), cyclohexanone (1.80–2.65), cycloheptanone (1.25), cyclooctanone (0.62), cyclopentadecanone (1.70), cycloheptadecanone (2.42). Qualitative observations [63] indicate that the large-ring ketones (C_{15} to C_{19}) with an even number of carbon atoms react more readily than those with an odd number of carbon atoms.

The reaction is best suited to the preparation of cycloheptanones and cyclooctanones. Cyclopentanone, as would be anticipated on the basis of relative reactivities of the five-, six-, and seven-membered ketones, yields principally cycloheptanone instead of cyclohexanone when treated with diazomethane.[36] Cyclic ketones of intermediate ring size react too sluggishly for practical usefulness, and large ring ketones form mixtures of higher homologs. Cyclohexanone reacts smoothly with one mole of di-

[63] H. Schroeder, Ph.D. Thesis, Harvard, 1938.

azomethane to form 63% of cycloheptanone, 15% of the oxide XXXIII,

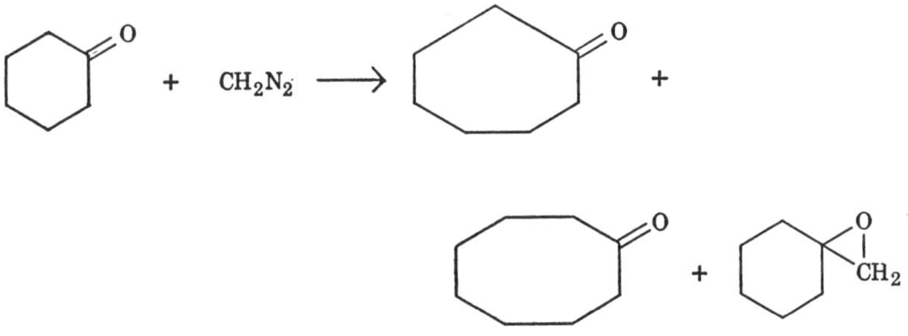

XXXIII

and small amounts of higher ketones.[32] Cyclohexanone with two moles of diazomethane [24] or cycloheptanone with one mole of diazomethane [32] yields about 60% of cyclooctanone.

Substituents on the cyclohexanone or cycloheptanone ring may change the ketone to oxide ratio, change the speed of the reaction, give rise to a mixture of isomeric homologous ketones, and/or give rise to various side products. Electron-withdrawing groups attached to the α-positions promote oxide formation. Thus, 2-hydroxycyclohexanone yields 10% of 2-methoxycyclohexanone and 90% of an oxide; [34] 2-chlorocyclohexanone yields 11% of 2-chlorocycloheptanone, 14% of the oxide, and 40% of another compound that is probably an oxide.[33]

Alkyl or aryl groups in the α-positions may reduce the yield and, unless the substitution is symmetrical, may give rise to a mixture of isomeric ring-enlarged ketones. An extreme example of the first effect is the reaction of 2-cyclohexylcyclohexanone to yield only 4–5% of a cyclohexylcycloheptanone.[34] A typical example of the second effect is the ring enlargement of 2-phenylcyclohexanone, which proceeds smoothly to give 37% of 2-phenylcycloheptanone, 12% of 3-phenylcycloheptanone, and 21% of the oxide XXXIV.[33] It is interesting to compare these

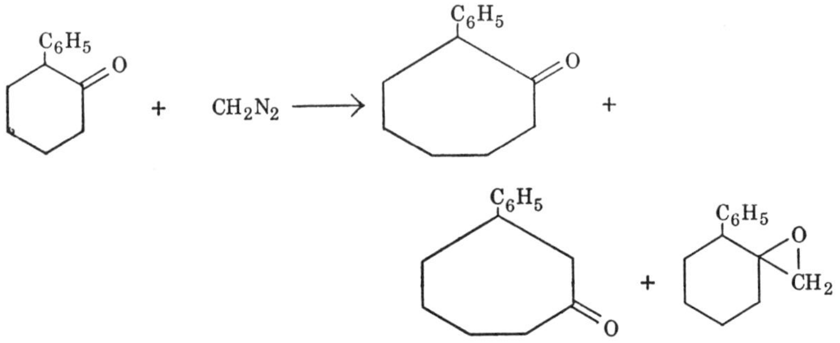

XXXIV

two reactions; the steric effect of the cyclohexyl group and the phenyl group should be approximately the same, and other factors, not thoroughly understood, must be responsible for this marked difference in reactivity. Substituents further removed from the carbonyl group usually do not interfere with the reaction but, unless they are symmetrically situated, may give rise to mixtures containing isomeric ring-enlarged ketones. Thus, 3,5,5-trimethylcyclohexanone yields a mixture of 3,3,5-trimethylcycloheptanone and 3,5,5-trimethylcycloheptanone,[64, 65] but 4-isopropylcyclohexanone and 4-methoxycyclohexanone give 4-isopropylcycloheptanone [66] and 4-methoxycycloheptanone [38] in 70% and 42% yield, respectively.

Ketene, considered here as the two-membered carbocyclic ketone, reacts with diazomethane to yield cyclopropanone hydrate XXXV (R = H) if water is present,[67] or the hemiacetal XXXV (R = alkyl) if an alcohol is present.[67] In the absence of water or alcohol and with excess diazomethane, cyclobutanone can be obtained in yields as high as 75%.[67-69] Dimethylketene has been similarly treated to provide 3,3-

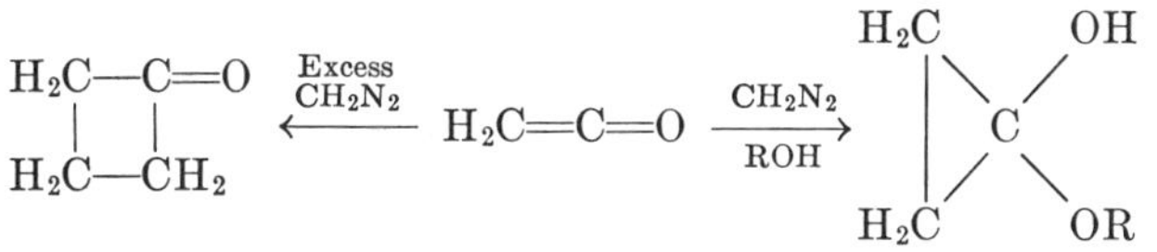

dimethylcyclobutanone in 18% yield.[70] Cyclopropanone (known only as the hydrate) and cyclobutanone have not been studied in the diazomethane ring-enlargement reaction.

An interesting phenomenon is observed with aromatic ketones. Although α-tetralone reacts very slowly and incompletely to yield oxides, and benzophenone is unreactive toward diazomethane, fluorenone [71] and 2,3,4,7-tetramethoxyfluorenone [72] react fairly readily to give the 9 (or 10)-methoxyphenanthrene derivative in 30% and 44% yield, respectively. Similarly, chrysofluorenone [73] is converted to 6-methoxychrysene.

[64] Stoll and Scherrer, *Helv. Chim. Acta*, **23**, 941 (1940).
[65] Tchoubar, *Bull. soc. chim. France*, **1949**, 164.
[66] Cook, Raphael, and Scott, *J. Chem. Soc.*, **1951**, 695.
[67] Lipp, Buchkremer, and Seeles, *Ann.*, **499**, 1 (1932).
[68] Lipp and Köster, *Ber.*, **64**, 2823 (1931).
[69] Kaarsemeker and Coops, *Rec. trav. chim.*, **70**, 1033 (1951).
[70] Owen, Ramage, and Simonsen, *J. Chem. Soc.*, **1938**, 1211.
[71] Schultz, Schultz, and Cochran, *J. Am. Chem. Soc.*, **62**, 2902 (1940).
[72] Barton, Cook, Loudon, and MacMillan, *J. Chem. Soc.*, **1949**, 1079.
[73] Cook and Schoental, *J. Chem. Soc.*, **1945**, 288.

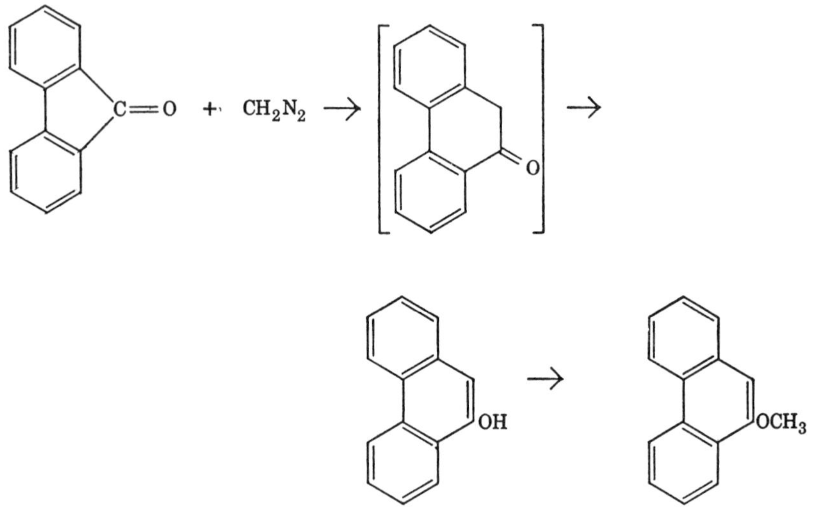

Some cyclic dicarbonyl compounds react by ring enlargement. 2-Carbethoxyindan-1,3-dione yields the naphthalene derivative XXXVI,[74, 75] and camphorquinone (XXXVII) yields 90% of a mixture containing the isomeric keto enol ethers XXXVIII and XXXIX.[76-78] Other cyclic

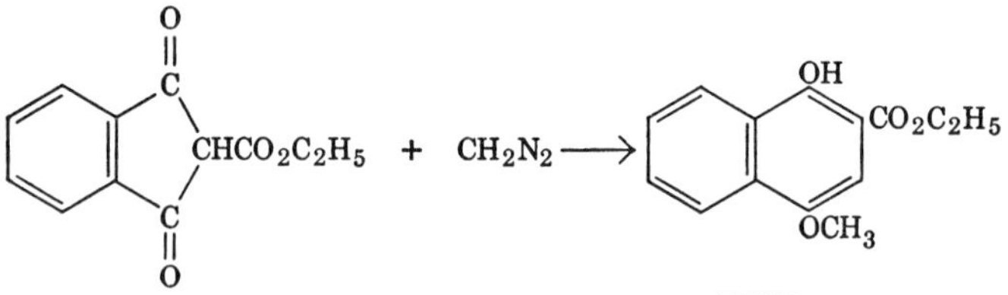

XXXVI

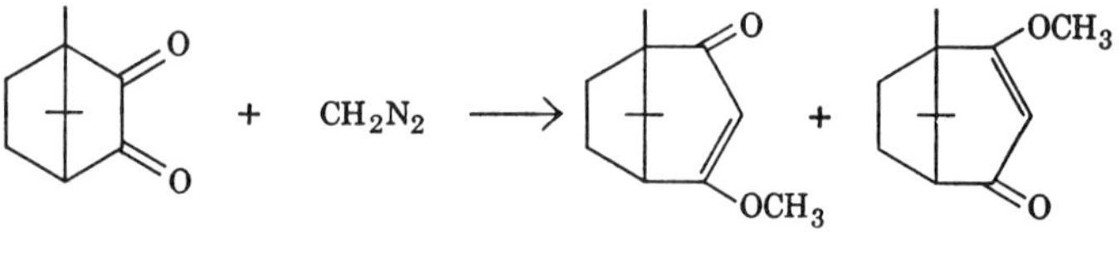

XXXVII   XXXVIII   XXXIX

dicarbonyl compounds show different modes of reaction. Cyclohexane-1,4-dione yields the oxides XL and XLI along with two unidentified

[74] Hantzsch and Czapp, *Ber.*, **63**, 566 (1930).
[75] Arndt, *Ber.*, **63**, 1180 (1930).
[76] Rupe and Häfliger, *Helv. Chim. Acta*, **23**, 139 (1940).
[77] Rupe and Frey, *Helv. Chim. Acta*, **27**, 627 (1944).
[78] Isshiki, *J. Pharm. Soc. Japan*, **65**, No. 2A, 10 (1945) [*C. A.*, **45**, 5663 (1951)].

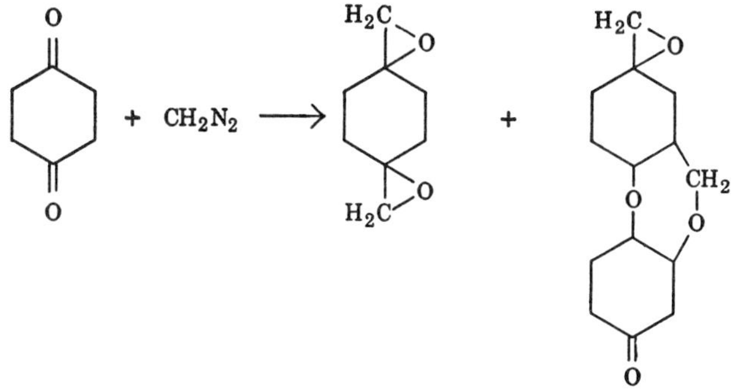

XL   XLI

oils.[79] The diketone XLII gives 35–39% of a compound for which several structures, including XLIII, have been suggested.[80] The cyclo-

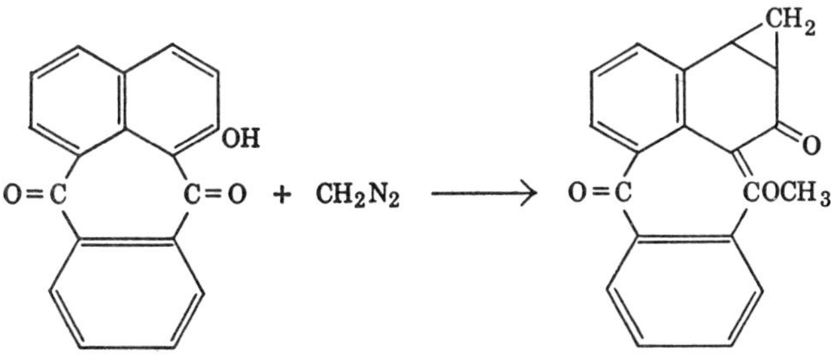

XLII   XLIII

pentanedione derivative XLIV reacts in a fashion similar to benzil to yield the methylenedioxy derivative XLV.[81] Oximino derivatives of

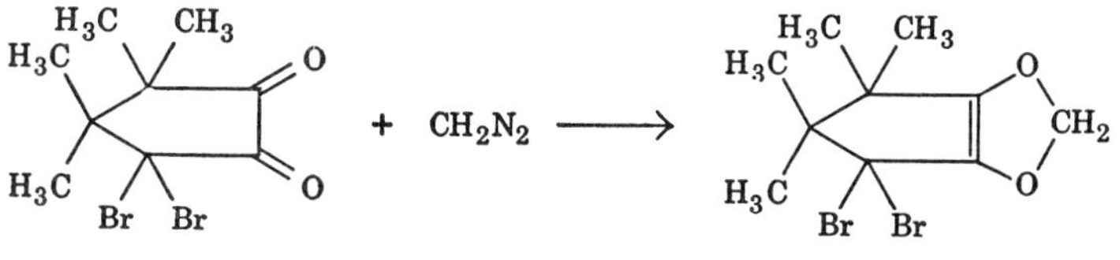

XLIV   XLV

the type XLVI are reported to yield heterocyclic compounds XLVII,[82] while isonitrosocamphor [83] and 3-isonitroso-4-ketohomocamphor [84] furnish O-methyl derivatives.

[79] Vincent, Thompson, and Smith, J. Org. Chem., 3, 603 (1939).

[80] Fieser, J. Am. Chem. Soc., 55, 4963 (1933).

[81] Francis and Willson, J. Chem. Soc., 103, 2238 (1913).

[82] Schönberg and Awad, J. Chem. Soc., 1950, 72.

[83] Forster and Holmes, J. Chem. Soc., 93, 242 (1908).

[84] Takeda, Nagata, and Kikkawa, J. Pharm. Soc. Japan, 72, 1482 (1952) [C. A., 47, 8046 (1953)].

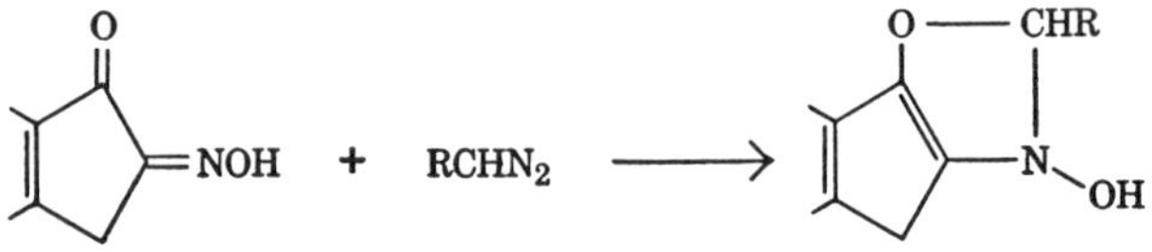

XLVI   XLVII

The reaction between cyclohexanone and higher diazoalkanes provides an excellent method for obtaining many 2-substituted cycloheptanones (XLVIII). 2-Alkylcycloheptanones such as 2-methyl-,[36, 38, 43] 2-isopropyl-,[66, 85] and 2-n-heptyl-cycloheptanone [38] have been prepared in 30–50% yield; phenylcycloheptanone [33, 86, 87] and several methoxyphenyl- and methylphenyl-cycloheptanones [87] have been synthesized in 7–45% yield. Particularly interesting is the reaction between cyclohexanone and ethyl ω-diazocaproate which yields 55% of the keto ester XLIX.[38] Also of interest is the ring enlargement with cyclohexanone and 4-(3′, 4′, 5′-trimethoxyphenyl)-1-diazobutane to yield 61% of the cycloheptanone derivative L.[87]

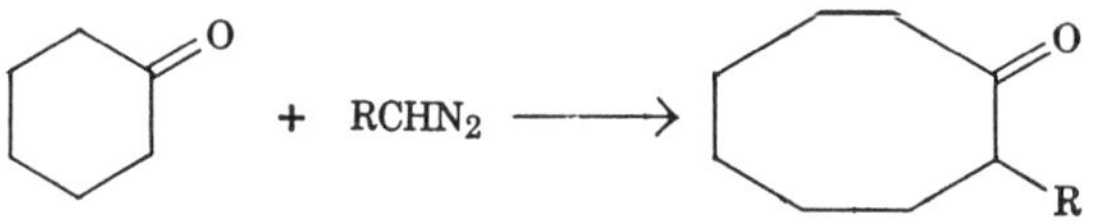

XLVIII

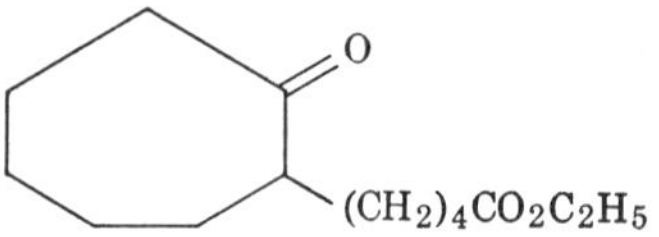

XLIX 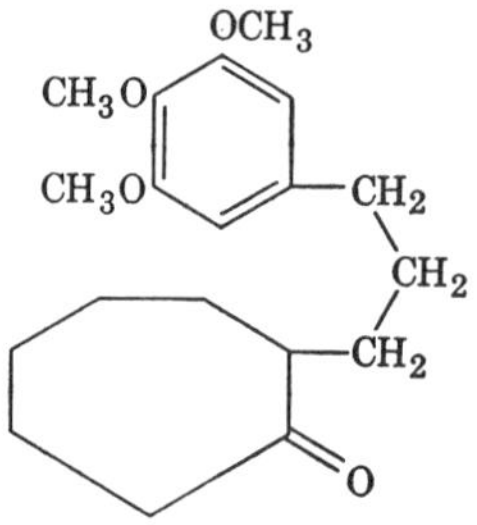   L

The method is less favorable for the preparation of 2-substituted cyclohexanones; cyclopentanone reacts with diazoethane to give 8% of 2-methylcyclohexanone,[38] with 1-diazobutane to give 26% of 2-n-propylcyclohexanone,[88] and with phenyldiazomethane to give 5% of 2-phenylcyclohexanone.[88]

[85] Nozoe, Kitahara, and Ito, *Proc. Japan Acad.*, 26, No. 7, 47 (1950) [*C. A.*, 45, 7099 (1951)].

[86] Burger, Walter, Bennet, and Turnbull, *Science*, 112, 306 (1950).

[87] C. D. Gutsche and H. E. Johnson, unpublished observations.

[88] C. D. Gutsche and E. F. Jason, unpublished observations.

Diphenylketene reacts with diphenyldiazomethane to form a stable, nitrogen-containing product [21, 89] and with ethyl diazoacetate to form a mixture containing the oxide and a cyclopropane derivative.[21] The nitrogen-containing product loses nitrogen on vigorous heating but yields an ill-defined material. Benzosuberone and ethyl diazoacetate give an enol derivative.[90]

   bis-Diazoalkanes have been prepared,[90a, b] but only one reaction with a carbonyl compound has been reported: bis-1,4-diazobutane reacts with cyclohexanone to yield products for which analyses only have been reported.[90b]

Heterocyclic Ketones

Heterocyclic compounds of the general structure LI react with diazomethane to form ring-enlarged products LII (or LIII) and oxides LV when A is nitrogen,[19, 91, 92] or methylenedioxy derivatives LIV when A is sulfur or oxygen.[62] Isatin substituted in the 5 or 5 and 7 positions with halogen or on the nitrogen by any group other than hydrogen forms the type LIII product, whereas alkylated isatins with hydrogen attached to the nitrogen usually yield the type LII product.[92] The few yields reported range from 50 to 90%. Isatin itself reacts with diazomethane to give, depending on the particular conditions employed, 18–27% of 2,3-dihydroxyquinoline, 13–52% of 2-hydroxy-3-methoxyquinoline, and 14–17% of the oxide LV.[19]

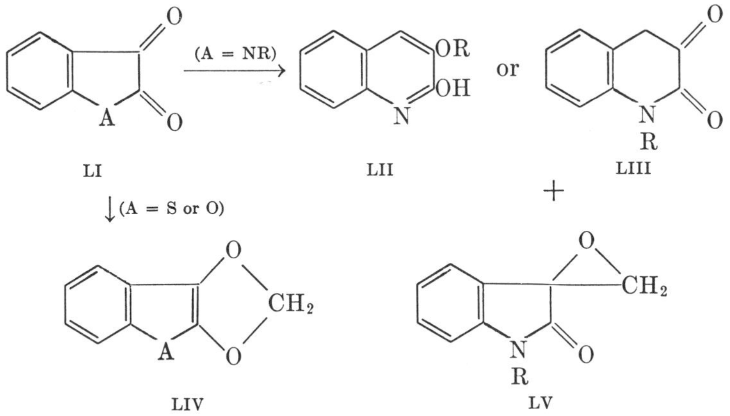

[89] Staudinger, Anthes, and Pfenninger, Ber., **49**, 1928 (1916).

[90] C. D. Gutsche and M. Hillman, unpublished observations.

[90a] Lettré and Brose, Naturwissenschaften, **36**, 57 (1949); Lieser and Beck, Ber., **83**, 137 (1950).

[90b] Petersen, ORTS Report No. 694 (1941).

[91] Heller, Ber., **52**, 741 (1919).

[92] Heller, Ber., **59**, 704 (1926).

Alloxan reacts with diazomethane to form in almost quantitative yield a product that was originally formulated [53] as a methylenedioxy derivative but is more likely the oxide LVI.[19] Ethyl diazoacetate reacts in a somewhat different manner to yield a nitrogen-containing product for which the structure LVII has been written.[93]

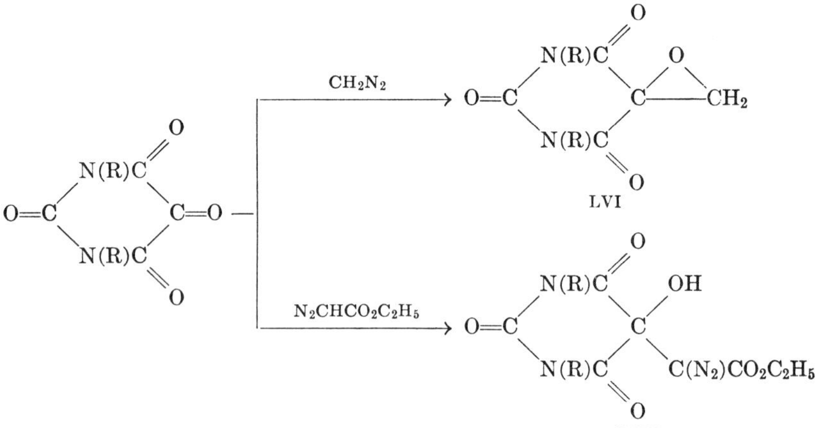

The keto groups in LI and alloxan cannot exist in the enol form. When an enol form of the heterocyclic ketone is possible the reaction with diazomethane results in O-methylation, a typical example being the formation of the enol ether LIX from the dihydrothianaphthene derivative LVIII.[43]

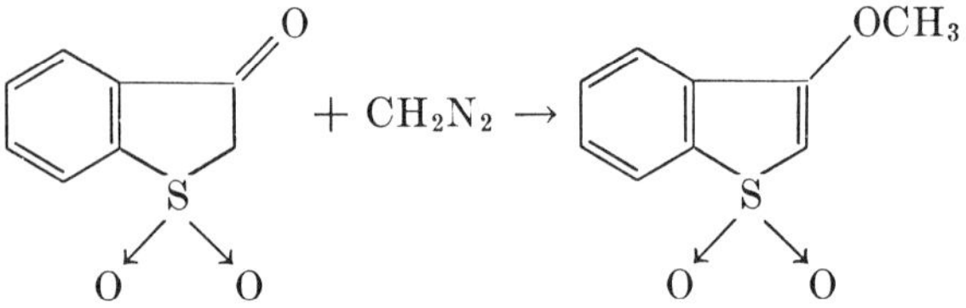

α,β-Unsaturated Aldehydes and Ketones

There are no reported instances of a true α,β-unsaturated aldehyde or ketone reacting with an aliphatic diazo compound at the carbonyl group. The reaction instead involves the carbon-to-carbon unsaturation with the formation of pyrazoline derivatives. For instance, benzalacetone,[94] *trans*-dibenzoylethylene,[95] and 5,16-pregnadiene-3β-ol-20-

[93] Biltz and Kramer, *Ann.*, **436**, 154 (1924).
[94] Smith and Howard, *J. Am. Chem. Soc.*, **65**, 165 (1943).
[95] Smith and Howard, *J. Am. Chem. Soc.*, **65**, 159 (1943).

one [96] add diazomethane to yield the pyrazolines LX, LXI, and LXII,

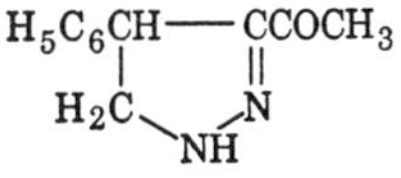

LX 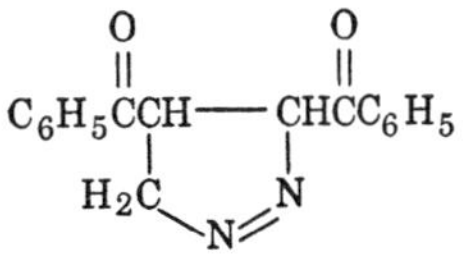   LXI

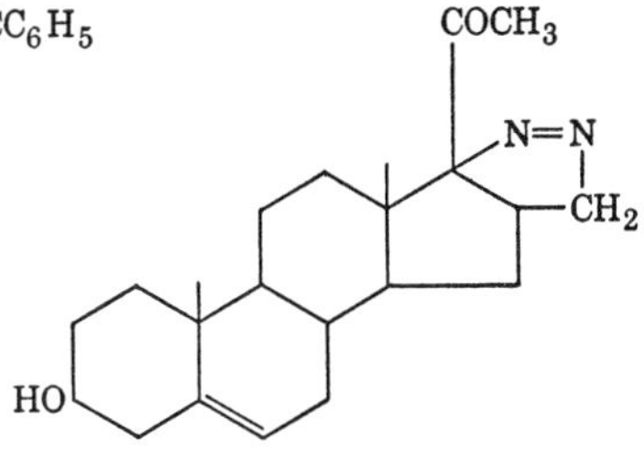

LXII

respectively. Pyrazole derivatives arise from the reactions of diazoalkanes with chlorovinyl ketones [97, 98] and acyl acetones (reacting in dilute sodium hydroxide solution as α,β-unsaturated ketones) [99] through
the intermediate formation of the chloro- and hydroxy-pyrazolines, respectively.

Pyrazolines, which may be formed not only from α,β-unsaturated aldehydes and ketones but also from other types of compounds carrying
activating groups attached to a double bond, are useful synthetic intermediates. Upon pyrolysis they often undergo decomposition, with loss
of nitrogen, to form olefins and/or cyclopropanes. For instance, decomposition of LXII yields 71% of the olefin LXIII and 5% of the
cyclopropane derivative LXIV.[100]

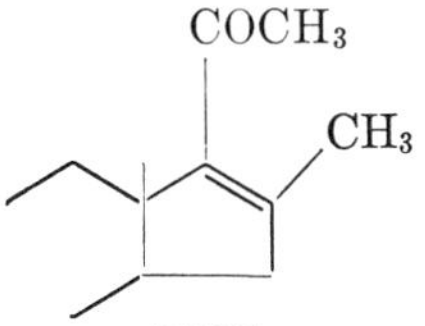

LXIII 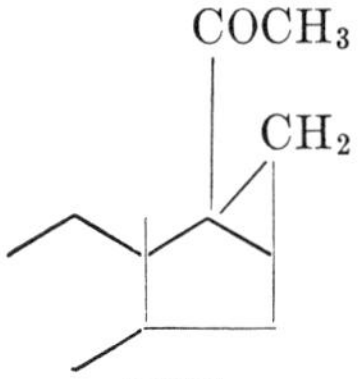   LXIV

Quinones

1,4-Quinones of the benzoquinone and naphthoquinone type react
with diazomethane to yield pyrazoline derivatives (LXV, LXVI,
LXVII).[3, 101] Substituents in the 5, 6, 7, or 8 positions of the naphtho-

[96] Wettstein, *Helv. Chim. Acta*, **27**, 1803 (1944).

[97] Nesmeyanov and Kochetkov, *Doklady Akad. Nauk S.S.S.R.*, **77**, 65 (1951) [*C. A.*, **46**, 497 (1952)].

[98] Nesmeyanov and Kochetkov, *Izvest. Akad. Nauk S.S.S.R., Otdel Khim. Nauk*, **1951**, 686 [*C. A.*, **46**, 7565 (1952)].

[99] Klages, *J. prakt. Chem.*, [2], **65**, 387 (1902).

[100] Sandoval, Rosenkranz, and Djerassi, *J. Am. Chem. Soc.*, **73**, 2383 (1951).

[101] Fieser and Peters, *J. Am. Chem. Soc.*, **53**, 4080 (1931).

quinone do not interfere with pyrazoline formation, but substituents in the 2 position may cause the formation of 3-methylated products and/or

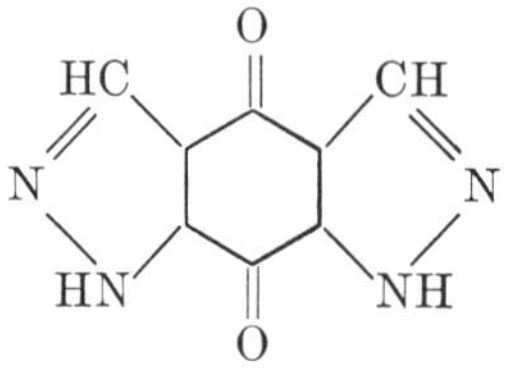

LXV 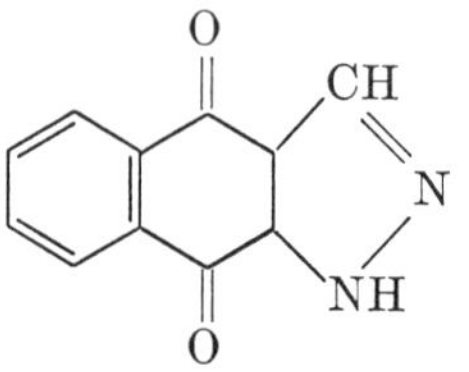   LXVI 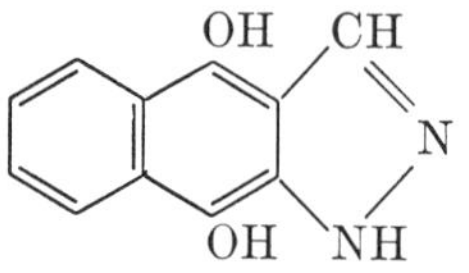   LXVII

diquinonylmethane products in addition to, or to the exclusion of, the pyrazoline. 2-Methylnaphthoquinone, for instance, yields the pyrazoline LXVIII, the dimethylnaphthoquinone LXIX, and the diquinonyl derivative LXX.[28] In unexpected contrast to this, 2-diphenylmethyl-1,4-naphthoquinone forms the pyrazoline derivative in 89% yield.[102] Diphenyldiazomethane and ethyl diazoacetate react with benzoquinone and naphthoquinone to form the corresponding substituted pyrazolines.

Hydroxyl groups attached to the aromatic nuclei are ordinarily attacked in preference to unsaturated centers by diazomethane. In the 1,4-naphthoquinone series, however, if the 2 and 3 positions are unsubstituted, pyrazoline formation proceeds faster than methylation of hydroxyl groups in the 5, 6, 7, or 8 positions.[103–105]

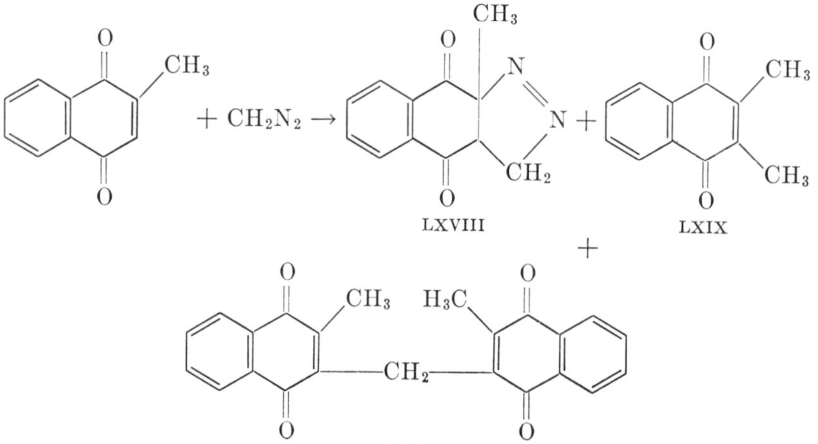

$+ CH_2N_2 \rightarrow$

LXVIII   LXIX

+

LXX

The only 1,4-quinone that has yielded products resulting from addition to the carbonyl group is 2,3,5,6-tetramethylbenzoquinone (LXXI),

[102] Fieser and Hartwell, *J. Am. Chem. Soc.*, **57**, 1479 (1935).
[103] Wallenfels, *Ber.*, **75**, 785 (1942).
[104] Spruit, *Rec. trav. chim.*, **66**, 655 (1947).
[105] Spruit, *Rec. trav. chim.*, **68**, 304 (1949).

which forms LXXII, LXXIII, and LXXV in the absence of methanol and LXXII, LXXIII, and LXXIV in the presence of methanol.[22] Pyrolysis of LXXII and LXXV yields nitrogen-free compounds for which seven- and eight-membered ring structures have been suggested.

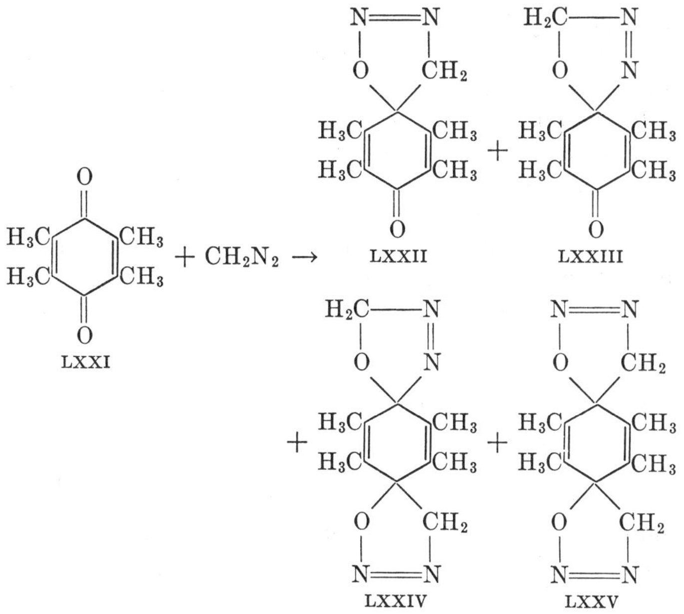

All 1,2-quinones that have been studied yield cyclic ethers of the type LXXVI. The reaction is catalyzed by methanol,[29, 102] and in the reaction between phenanthrenequinone and diazomethane the nature of the products is determined by the amount of methanol present. With large amounts of methanol the product corresponds to LXXVI (R = H), but with small amounts of methanol the product is the oxide

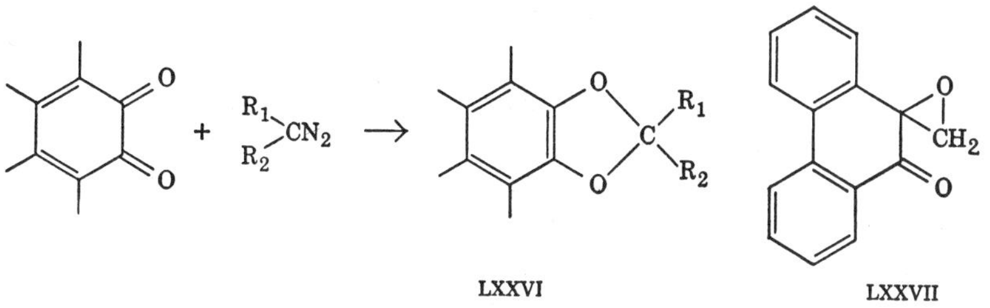

LXXVII.[29] With intermediate amounts of methanol, mixtures of the two compounds are obtained.

Methods of Isolation and Identification of Products

The diazoalkane remaining at the end of a reaction may be removed, particularly if it is of low molecular weight, by carefully distilling the solvent. Alternatively, it may be decomposed by the addition of acids such as dilute sulfuric or hydrochloric or by the addition of sodium bicarbonate solution. The product remaining is often a mixture of two or more compounds, and the problem of separation must be considered. One useful procedure involves a careful fractional distillation through an efficient column; the oxide often boils sufficiently below the carbonyl component to allow a clean separation. Another method, primarily of use where the carbonyl component is of major interest, involves the conversion of the oxide to the glycol by dilute acid hydrolysis; distillation then yields the carbonyl fraction as the lower-boiling material. Separation of the isomeric or closely related carbonyl products that often arise may occasionally be achieved by distillation, although the differences in boiling point are usually very small. More often, fractional crystallization of the carbonyl compounds themselves or of derivatives such as semicarbazones is employed. Advantage may also be taken of the fact that aldehydes, methyl ketones, and six- and seven-membered cyclic ketones (except those substituted in the 2 position) form bisulfite addition compounds, whereas most other carbonyl compounds do not.[30, 36, 38, 106, 107] Other methods that have been used include selective semicarbazone formation [108] and chromatographic separation.[51]

Analysis of the product without actual isolation of all the components of the mixture has been employed. The amount of oxide present can be measured by allowing the product to react with an amine such as piperidine and then weighing the acid-soluble material formed (amino alcohol). The amount of carbonyl product can be estimated through the use of Girard's reagent or other carbonyl reagents. The composition of the carbonyl fraction may be ascertained by quantitative infrared measurements.[33, 109]

The proof of structure of the products usually follows conventional lines. Oxides may be rearranged to aldehydes or ketones or may be converted to derivatives such as chlorohydrins, glycols, glycol diacetates, or amino alcohols; aldehydes and ketones may be converted to the usual carbonyl derivatives. In at least one instance, however,

[106] Mosettig and Jovanovic, *Monatsh.*, **54**, 427 (1929).
[107] Mousseron and Manon, *Compt. rend.*, **226**, 1989 (1948).
[108] Arndt, Eistert, and Partale, *Ber.*, **61**, 1107 (1928).
[109] C. D. Gutsche and J. M. Chang, unpublished observations.

semicarbazone formation proved to be an unsatisfactory means of characterization, for the carbocyclic ketones in the C_{16} to C_{19} region yield derivatives whose melting points are close together and show no significant depression in melting point upon admixture.[63]

ALIPHATIC DIAZO COMPOUNDS

In the following section a brief survey of the methods available for the preparation of aliphatic diazo compounds is given, and the properties of these compounds are briefly discussed.

Methods of Preparation

A. By the action of base on $RR'CHN(NO)Y$, where Y may be $CONH_2$, $CO_2C_2H_5$, $COCH_3$, COC_6H_5, $C(CH_3)_2CH_2COCH_3$, $C(NH)NHNO_2$, or $SO_2C_7H_7$. The two classical methods for preparing diazomethane make use of nitrosomethylurea ($Y = CONH_2$) and nitrosomethylurethan ($Y = CO_2C_2H_5$) as starting materials [110] which decompose in the presence of base as shown in the following equations.

$$CH_3N(NO)CONH_2 + KOH \rightarrow CH_2N_2 + KOCN + 2H_2O$$

$$CH_3N(NO)CO_2C_2H_5 + KOH \rightarrow$$

$$CH_2N_2 + K_2CO_3 + C_2H_5OH + H_2O \quad ex\ situ$$

$$CH_3N(NO)CO_2C_2H_5 + ROH \xrightarrow{K_2CO_3}$$

$$CH_2N_2 + O{=}C\begin{array}{l} \diagup OC_2H_5 \\ \diagdown OR \end{array} + H_2O \quad in\ situ$$

Nitrosomethylurea and nitrosomethylurethan each possess certain advantages and disadvantages.[110] The former is a non-toxic but relatively unstable solid most useful for the *ex situ* mode of reaction, whereas the latter is a fairly stable but highly irritating liquid most useful for the *in situ* mode of reaction. As a source of higher diazoalkanes, nitrosoalkylurethans are preferred and have been used, for instance, for the preparation of diazoethane, 1-diazopropane, diazopropene, phenyldiazomethane, and substituted phenyldiazomethanes. Among the older methods are also included the use of nitrosomethylacetamide ($Y = COCH_3$) and nitrosomethylbenzamide ($Y = COC_6H_5$).[111]

[110] Arndt, *Org. Syntheses*, Coll. Vol. 2, 461 (1943); Amstutz and Meyers, *ibid.*, 462; Hartman and Phillips, *ibid.*, 464; Arndt and Amende, *Z. angew. Chem.*, **43**, 444 (1930).
[111] v. Pechmann, *Ber.*, **27**, 1888 (1894).

More recently described methods involve the action of base on methyl nitrosomethylaminoisobutyl ketone $[Y = C(CH_3)_2CH_2COCH_3]$,[112-115] nitrosomethylnitroguanidine $[Y = C(NH)NHNO_2]$,[116, 117] and nitroso-methyl-p-toluenesulfonamide $(Y = SO_2C_7H_7)$.[118] These decompose to diazomethane according to the following equations.

$$CH_3N(NO)C(CH_3)_2CH_2COCH_3 \xrightarrow{RONa}$$

$$CH_2N_2 + (CH_3)_2C{=\!\!=}CHCOCH_3 + H_2O$$

$$CH_3N(NO)C(NH)NHNO_2 + KOH \rightarrow CH_2N_2 + K[NCNNO_2] + H_2O$$

$$CH_3N(NO)SO_2C_7H_7 + C_2H_5O^- \rightarrow CH_2N_2 + C_7H_7SO_2C_2H_5 + HO^-$$

All these methods claim the advantages of improved keeping qualities and relatively low toxicity of the nitroso compound and of high yields in the conversion to the diazo compound. As a source of higher diazo-alkanes, however, certain disadvantages appear. In the methyl nitro-soalkylaminoisobutyl ketone method the tendency of the α,β-unsatu-rated ketone to react with the diazoalkanes increases as the boiling points of the diazoalkanes increase. This tendency has been offset to some extent by substituting pulegone for mesityl oxide, and diazoal-kanes up to 1-diazoöctane have been prepared. Even for the prepara-tion of diazoethane, however, the nitrosoalkylurethan method has been preferred.[39] The nitrosoalkylnitroguanidine method has been applied to the preparation of higher diazoalkanes including diazoethane, 1-di-azopropane, 1-diazobutane, and phenyldiazomethane. The yields fall off in many cases, however, and the method appears to offer no advan-tage over the nitrosoalkylurethan procedure. The nitrosomethyl-p-tolu-enesulfonamide method has been described only for the preparation of diazomethane.

B. By the action of nitrous acid on amino compounds. Although aliphatic primary amines usually form complex mixtures of alcohols, olefins, and nitrites when treated with nitrous acid, compounds of the type $H_2NCH_2CR_3$ where the R groups are electron-withdrawing are often converted to the corresponding diazo compounds. Thus, sub-stances such as glycine ethyl ester [119] and β,β,β-trifluoroethylamine [120]

[112] Jones and Kenner, *J. Chem. Soc.*, **1933**, 363.
[113] Adamson and Kenner, *Nature*, **135**, 833 (1935).
[114] Adamson and Kenner, *J. Chem. Soc.*, **1935**, 286.
[115] Redemann, Rice, Roberts, and Ward, *Org. Syntheses*, **25**, 28 (1945).
[116] McKay, *J. Am. Chem. Soc.*, **70**, 1974 (1948).
[117] McKay, Ott, Taylor, Buchanan, and Crooker, *Can. J. Research*, **28B**, 683 (1950).
[118] Backer and de Boer, *Proc. Koninkl. Ned. Akad. Wetenschap.*, **54B**, 191 (1951) [*C. A.*, **46**, 1961 (1952)]; de Boer and Backer, *Org. Synthesis*, **34**, 96 (1954).
[119] Womack and Nelson, *Org. Syntheses*, **24**, 56 (1944).
[120] Gilman and Jones, *J. Am. Chem. Soc.*, **65**, 1458 (1943).

produce ethyl diazoacetate and trifluoromethyldiazomethane in good yield.

C. By oxidation of hydrazones. Disubstituted diazomethanes, particularly diaryl, are most conveniently prepared by this method. Diphenyldiazomethane, for instance, can be obtained in excellent yield by converting benzophenone to the hydrazone and allowing this to react with mercuric oxide.[121]

D. Miscellaneous methods for diazomethane. In addition to the methods already mentioned, diazomethane has been obtained in 20% yield from the reaction between hydrazine and chloroform in the presence of potassium hydroxide,[122] in comparable yield by the action of dichloromethylamine on hydroxylamine,[123] from the saponification of methyl-p-nitrophenylnitrosoamine,[124] from nitrosomethylhydrazine,[125] and by the reduction of methylnitramine.[125a]

E. Labeled diazomethane. C^{13}-Diazomethane [126] and C^{14}-diazomethane [127] can be prepared from C^{13}- and C^{14}-labeled sodium cyanide by reduction to methylamine followed by conversion to diazomethane via the nitrosomethylurea route. C^{13}-Methylamine has also been prepared in 98% yield from C^{13}-methyl iodide via the Gabriel synthesis.[128]

Properties

The lower diazoalkanes exist as gases at room temperature and are highly explosive, but the higher derivatives are liquid or solid and are much more stable. All the aliphatic diazo compounds are colored, the colors ranging from yellow to deep purple.[129] They have been arranged in the following order with reference to increasing stability (thermal) and decreasing reactivity (toward acetic acid): [130] R_2CN_2, $ArCHN_2$, Ar_2CN_2, $(RCO)_2CN_2$ or $(ArCO)_2CN_2$. Differences of reactivities within these groups have not been carefully studied, but with reference to the first group the higher homologs appear to be more reactive than diazomethane.

[121] Smith and Howard, *Org. Syntheses*, **24**, 53 (1944).

[122] Staudinger and Kupfer, *Ber.*, **45**, 501 (1912).

[123] Bamberger and Renauld, *Ber.*, **28**, 1682 (1895).

[124] Noelting, cited by Bamberger, *Ber.*, **33**, 101 (1900).

[125] Thiele, *Ann.*, **376**, 239 (1910).

[125a] Thiele and Meyer, *Ber.*, **29**, 961 (1896).

[126] Hershberg, Schwenk, and Stahl, *Arch. Biochem.*, **19**, 300 (1948).

[127] Heard, Jamieson, and Solomon, *J. Am. Chem. Soc.*, **73**, 4985 (1951).

[128] Cox and Warne, *J. Chem. Soc.*, **1951**, 1896.

[129] Staudinger, *Ber.*, **49**, 1884 (1916).

[130] Staudinger and Gaule, *Ber.*, **49**, 1897 (1916).

Safety Considerations

The nitroso compounds from which diazomethane can be derived are more or less toxic and should be handled with caution. Nitrosomethylurethan particularly should be manipulated with great care, for the vapor is toxic and direct contact of the liquid with the skin will cause painful and prolonged skin irritation. It is advisable when handling this compound to wear loose-fitting, heavy rubber gloves and to wash the hands thoroughly after the operation is completed. If any of the material is spilled on one's person the affected area should be washed immediately and thoroughly with ethanol. With due precaution, however, nitrosomethylurethan can be safely prepared and used by most people, although there seem to be wide differences in tolerance to this compound. Some persons are so sensitive that the presence of an open container of nitrosomethylurethan in the same room causes typical allergic symptoms, and continued exposure results in extensive rash and painful swelling of the eyes.[131] The other nitroso compounds used as sources of diazomethane are less dangerous but should also be handled carefully, for they may cause skin irritation.[116]

Diazomethane is generally recognized as a highly toxic substance, and several cases of diazomethane poisoning have been reported.[132-134] At least one of these [133] was fatal and is a stark example of the results of carelessness in the handling of this compound. The ill effects that have been noted after exposure to diazomethane are denudation of the skin and mucous membranes, irritation of the skin (particularly the finger tips), chest pains, fever, and asthmatic symptoms. Again there appear to be wide individual differences; some persons become hypersensitive to the compound and cannot work with it even under the most auspicious conditions, whereas others seem to be much less susceptible. With adequate hood facilities and with normal precaution, however, most people experience no difficulty in the use of diazomethane. Many of the higher diazoalkanes probably are toxic and should be handled with the same precautions.

Although liquid or gaseous diazomethane is highly explosive, the cold, dilute solutions usually employed in the reactions under discussion are fairly safe. In this connection, care should be taken not to reduce the quantity of ether used in generating diazomethane from the nitroso compound, and if a more concentrated solution is required it

[131] C. D. Gutsche, unpublished observations.
[132] Connor and Fields, *Am. J. Med. Sci.*, **195**, 469 (1938).
[133] LeWinn, *Am. J. Med. Sci.*, **218**, 556 (1949) [*C. A.*, **44**, 3615 (1950)].
[134] Braun, *Med. Monatsschr.*, **5**, 284 (1951) [*C. A.*, **45**, 5820 (1951)].

should be prepared by redistillation.[135] Also, one is warned against the use of calcium sulfate (Drierite) in drying tubes for systems containing diazomethane. Contact of the vapor with calcium sulfate results in an exothermic reaction and ultimately a detonation. Potassium hydroxide pellets should instead be used as the desiccant.[131] The various nitroso compounds are also dangerous with respect to explosiveness. Nitrosomethylurea [136–138] and methyl nitrosoaminoisobutyl ketone [114] have been reported to explode violently. As a precaution, these compounds should be stored in a refrigerator in smooth, brown, alkali-free bottles. Purification of nitroso compounds by distillation should be done very carefully and should not be attempted when the alkyl group is larger than propyl.

EXPERIMENTAL CONDITIONS AND SIDE REACTIONS

An attempt is made in the following discussion to suggest the most appropriate conditions for effecting the reactions of diazomethane and its derivatives with aldehydes and ketones.

Source of Diazoalkane

Solutions of diazomethane in an inert solvent (*ex situ* mode) can easily be prepared from nitrosomethylurea,[139] nitrosomethylurethan,[140] methyl nitrosomethylaminoisobutyl ketone,[115] nitrosomethylnitroguanidine,[116] or nitrosomethyl-*p*-toluenesulfonamide.[118] Such solutions contain, in addition to diazomethane, the other products of decomposition of the particular nitroso compound employed. The presence of water may be avoided by using a non-aqueous system in the decomposition of the nitroso compound or by drying the solution over potassium hydroxide pellets. Alcohols may be removed by allowing the diazomethane solution to stand over sodium ribbon for one to two hours followed by decantation and distillation.[141, 39] For many reactions the source of diazomethane appears to be immaterial, and considerations such as availability of starting materials, desirability of high stability of the nitroso compound, and personal preferences of the worker will determine the choice. In some instances, however, the side products from a given

[135] A. L. Wilds, private communication.
[136] Werner, *J. Chem. Soc.*, **115**, 1093 (1919).
[137] Arndt and Scholz, *Angew. Chem.*, **46**, 47 (1933).
[138] Arndt, Loewe, and Avan, *Ber.*, **73**, 606 (1940).
[139] Arndt, *Org. Syntheses*, Coll. Vol. 2, 165 (1943).
[140] Bachmann and Struve, *Org. Reactions*, **1**, 50 (1941).
[141] Fieser and Turner, *J. Am. Chem. Soc.*, **69**, 2338 (1947).

source may influence the course of the reaction [135] and thus determine its relative merits. Alcohols, as has already been indicated, may exert a catalytic effect on various reactions of diazoalkanes, and it is important, therefore, to specify the source of the diazoalkane and the extent of purification. For *in situ* reactions of diazomethane and its higher homologs and for the preparation, in general, of the higher homologs, the nitrosoalkylurethan method is probably the most satisfactory.

Reagents for the Decomposition of the Nitroso Compound

Strong, aqueous potassium hydroxide is invariably used to convert nitrosomethylurea to diazomethane, both in the *ex situ* and the *in situ* methods. For the preparation of diazomethane *ex situ* from nitrosomethylurethan, potassium hydroxide in methanol or sodium or potassium alkoxides in various alcohols have been used. For the *in situ* preparation from nitrosomethylurethan, potassium carbonate, sodium carbonate, barium hydroxide, and magnesium methoxide are satisfactory. Diazomethane has been generated *in situ* from methyl nitrosomethylaminoisobutyl ketone by the action of potassium carbonate and barium hydroxide, but sodium carbonate has been reported to be ineffective.[69]

Scale of Operation

In view of the poisonous and explosive nature of diazomethane and the nitroso precursors large-scale operation should be carried out with extreme caution. Descriptions have appeared in the literature of experiments with methyl nitrosomethylaminoisobutyl ketone on a 2-mole scale,[69] with nitrosomethylurea on a 2- to 4-mole scale,[64, 142] and with nitrosomethylurethan on a 4.5-mole scale.[32]

Method of Introduction of the Diazoalkane

There are two general methods for carrying out the reaction: (*a*) the *ex situ* method, in which a solution containing the diazoalkane is mixed with the carbonyl compound; (*b*) the *in situ* method, in which the diazoalkane is generated in the presence of the carbonyl compound. In the first method the diazoalkane can be derived from any source; in the second method the nitrosoalkylurethan is most satisfactory since in alcohol solution it requires only a catalytic amount of base for complete conversion to the diazoalkane and since it is usually a liquid and can be easily added dropwise to the reaction mixture. Although no exten-

---

[142] Lutz et al., *J. Am. Chem. Soc.*, **68**, 1813 (1946).

sive comparison of these two methods has been made, the *in situ* method appears to provide more favorable conditions for the less reactive carbonyl compounds and is the preferred method for carrying out ring-enlargement reactions. One attempt to use pure, liquid diazomethane at −50° has been reported.[38] The reaction, a ring enlargement of cyclooctanone, did not proceed, however, and requires the *in situ* method for success.[32]

Solvents and Catalysts

The reactions can be carried out in inert solvents such as ether or in solvents that exert a catalytic effect, such as water or alcohols. The choice is dependent on the reactivity of the carbonyl compound undergoing reaction and, in some cases, on the products desired. Ketones activated by adjacent electron-withdrawing groups and most aldehydes * usually do not require catalysis, whereas unactivated ketones do. Alcohol is sometimes included in the reaction mixture not to induce the reaction but to control the outcome, particularly in reactions in which aryl migration is sought.

Of the inert, non-catalytic solvents ether is the most often used. It is reported [26] to have some inhibiting effect on the reaction, however, and should be avoided where the additive power of the carbonyl group is low. Other inert solvents that have been employed occasionally, usually because of insufficient solubility of the carbonyl compound in ether, are petroleum ether, benzene, toluene, chloroform, 1,2-dichloroethane, and dioxane. Carbon tetrachloride was used as a solvent in a reaction of β-hydrindone with diazomethane which yielded an unidentified chlorine-containing product.[25] In the large-scale preparation of diazomethane, methylene dichloride has been used in place of ether to avoid the fire hazard, but in some cases it may have a deleterious effect on subsequent reactions.[142] Under certain conditions diazomethane may react with halogen-containing compounds such as chloroform or carbon tetrachloride [143] or with simple ethers,[144] but ordinarily this complication is unimportant.

Compounds that exert a catalytic effect on the reaction include water, alcohols, formamide, and metal salts such as lithium chloride. Protonic acids and Lewis acids usually decompose diazomethane. Zinc chloride,

* It is difficult to determine which aldehydes may require catalysis, however, because the degree of purification of the diazomethane solution usually is not sufficiently indicated in the literature. It is claimed [106] that piperonal in ether solution is practically inert to diazomethane if every trace of water and alcohol is removed. *p*-Nitrobenzaldehyde, on the other hand, does react with diazomethane in the strict absence of hydroxy compounds.[29]

[143] Urry and Eiszner, *J. Am. Chem. Soc.*, **74**, 5822 (1952).
[144] Meerwein, Rathjen, and Werner, *Ber.*, **75**, 1610 (1942).

for instance, acts on ethereal diazomethane to form zinc oxide, butane, ethylene dichloride, and nitrogen;[145] aluminum alkoxides and the *ortho* esters of boric acid and antimonous acid decompose diazomethane at an almost explosive rate with the formation of polymethylene and nitrogen.[146,147] The most useful catalysts are water and alcohols, and of these methanol appears to be most suitable; its catalytic activity is high,* it is a good solvent for most carbonyl compounds, and it does not undergo appreciable change during the reaction. Methanol mixed with other solvents such as ether, water, benzene, and chloroform is also useful, but since the rate of the reaction is dependent on the amount of methanol present,[24,64] unnecessary dilution with inert solvents should be avoided.

Temperature

The optimum temperature is usually dependent on the particular aliphatic diazo compound being used. Reactions involving alkyl- or aryl-substituted diazomethanes usually proceed exothermically at or below room temperature and may require moderation by external cooling. In one case studied, an increase in the reaction temperature from 0° to 50° increased the rate of reaction but did not influence the yield or the products formed.[32] Reactions involving acyl- or aroyl-substituted diazomethanes require higher temperatures.

Concentration of Reactants

In the reaction with cyclohexanone the concentration of diazomethane, as determined by the rate of addition of nitrosomethylurethan, influences the rate but not the nature or yield of product.[32] It is important, however, to avoid too rapid addition of nitrosomethylurethan, for, if the concentration of nitrogen-containing intermediates in the reaction mixture becomes too great, a violent explosion may result.[32]

Side Reactions

The replacement of acidic hydrogen atoms with alkyl groups from diazoalkanes has already been mentioned. Thus, alloxan undergoes N-methylation as well as carbonyl attack when treated with diazomethane;[53] 1-hydroxyisatin yields a 1-methoxyquinoline derivative;[29] compounds such as p-hydroxyacetophenone, o-hydroxybenzophenone,

* It has been shown that the catalytic activity of the alcohol decreases with increasing molecular weight and as the substitution at the carbinol carbon atom increases.[24,26]

[145] Caronna and Sansone, *Atti X° congr. intern. chim.*, **3**, 77 (1939) [*C. A.*, **34**, 980 (1940)].
[146] Meerwein, *Angew. Chem.*, **60**, 78 (1948).
[147] Buckley and Ray, *J. Chem. Soc.*, **1952**, 3701.

and 1,2-dihydroxyanthraquinone react only at the hydroxyl group to yield the corresponding methoxy derivatives.[148] Hydroxyl groups in the naphthoquinone nucleus are methylated if present in the 2 and 3 positions [149,150] but may escape attack if present in other positions. Alkylation of aliphatic hydroxyl groups usually proceeds more slowly than reaction at the carbonyl group. Diazomethane is also able to effect replacement of N- and O-acetyl groups with methyl, the first reaction being catalyzed by water or alcohols [151] and the second by piperidine.[152]

The cyclic acetals XLI (p. 381), LXXVIII ($R_1 = CH_3OCH_2$; $R_2 = CH_3$), and LXXVIII ($R_1 = CH_3OCH_2$; $R_2 = C_2H_5$) have been isolated from the reactions of diazomethane with cyclohexane-1,4-dione,[79] methoxyacetone,[25] and ethyl methoxymethyl ketone.[25] These may be the result of the stabilization of the labile intermediate III by an intermolecular route involving unreacted carbonyl compound, instead of the three usual routes of stabilization (cf. p. 368) involving intramolecular paths.

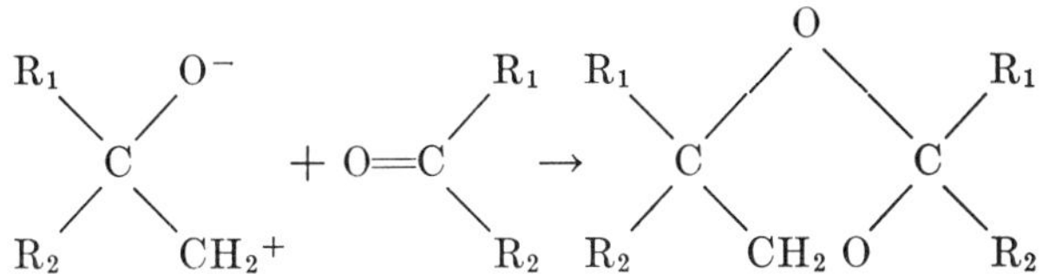

LXXVIII

The *in situ* method, involving a basic medium, may cause inversion of configuration at centers adjacent to the carbonyl group. Thus the ketone LXXIX, when treated with nitrosomethylurethan in ethanol solution in the presence of potassium carbonate or in ether-methanol solution in the presence of potassium hydroxide, yields an isomer of the starting ketone.[153] A different type of isomerizing action has been reported with the α,β-unsaturated ketone pulegone, which yields an addition product and the β,γ-unsaturated ketone isopulegone.[34]

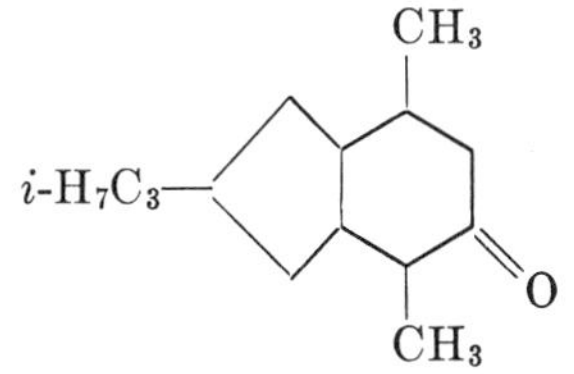

LXXIX

[148] Schönberg and Mustafa, *J. Chem. Soc.*, **1946**, 746.
[149] Fieser, *J. Am. Chem. Soc.*, **48**, 2922 (1926).
[150] Fieser, *J. Am. Chem. Soc.*, **50**, 439 (1928).
[151] Biltz, Loewe, and Pardon, *Ber.*, **64**, 1146 (1931).
[152] Nierenstein, *J. Am. Chem. Soc.*, **52**, 4012 (1930).
[153] Coats and Cook, *J. Chem. Soc.*, **1942**, 559.

When nitrosoalkylurethans are employed in the *in situ* method, one of the expected products is the alkyl carbonate derived from ethanol and the solvent alcohol. The alkyl carbonate can ordinarily be separated from the desired product by fractional distillation since it is usually a low-boiling liquid. In at least two instances a higher-molecular-weight carbonate has been formed as the major reaction product. From ω-hydroxyacetophenone the carbonate LXXX was obtained,[25] and from 2,3,4-trimethoxyphenyldiazomethane a 75% yield of the carbonate LXXXI was isolated under certain conditions.[87]

$$(C_6H_5COCH_2O)_2CO$$
LXXX

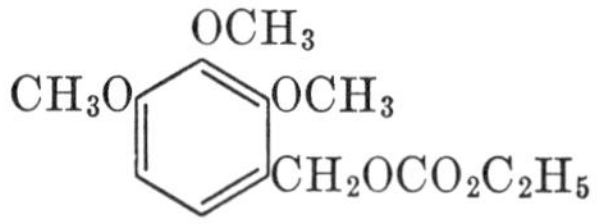

$$CH_3O \quad OCH_3 \quad OCH_3$$
$$CH_2OCO_2C_2H_5$$
LXXXI

Although the diazoalkanes themselves do not usually react with methanol to a significant extent,* the nitrosoalkylurethans, particularly those of the nitrosobenzylurethan class, may do so when used in the *in situ* method. Thus nitrosobenzylurethan treated with cyclohexanone, methanol, and potassium carbonate yields, in addition to 41% of 2-phenylcycloheptanone, 29% of methyl benzyl ether; the 2,3,4-trimethoxy and 2,4,6-trimethyl derivatives of nitrosobenzylurethan under similar conditions yield the ethers exclusively.[87]

A side reaction encountered in practically all reactions involving diazomethane is the formation of polymethylene; this is facilitated by metal alkoxides, copper powder, calcium chloride, and sharp objects such as boiling stones.

It is reported that diazomethane in the presence of catalysts reacts with ester and amide carbonyl groups,[26] but this type of reaction has not been carefully investigated.

EXPERIMENTAL PROCEDURES

Apparatus

An Erlenmeyer flask or round-bottomed flask often suffices for reactions effected by the *ex situ* method. The *in situ* reaction is most conveniently carried out in a round-bottomed flask equipped with a mechanical stirrer operating through a mercury seal or a close-fitting sleeve,

* It has been shown, however, that simple alcohols will react with diazomethane in the presence of certain catalysts.[154] 1-Butanol, for instance, forms methyl *n*-butyl ether with diazomethane in the presence of Lewis acids such as zinc chloride and ferric chloride. The same product is obtained in the presence of antimony *n*-butoxide or aluminum *n*-butoxide. In the last instance, the yield is 83%.

[154] Meerwein and Hinz, *Ann.*, **481**, 1 (1930).

an addition funnel, a condenser, and a thermometer reaching into the reaction mixture. To the top of the condenser may be attached a tube leading either to a bubbler or to a eudiometer tube, by means of which the progress of the reaction can be followed qualitatively or quantitatively. An ice-water bath should be available, although some reactions may require only occasional cooling or no cooling. The entire operation, to the point of decomposition of unreacted diazoalkane, should be carried out in a well-ventilated hood, and the precautions mentioned previously should be kept in mind.

Following are examples illustrating the *ex situ* method, with and without catalysis, and the *in situ* method. The diazo compounds included are diazomethane, 1-diazobutane, phenyldiazomethane, diphenyldiazomethane, and ethyl diazoacetate.

Ex Situ Method without Catalysis

Ethyl 2-Furyl Ketone (Aldehyde and a Higher Diazoalkane).[40] Nitrosoethylurea is prepared and converted to diazoethane by the same procedure that is used for diazomethane.[110, 139] The dry, alcohol-free solution of diazoethane (1.5 equivalents) in ether is added, with initial cooling, to a dry, alcohol-free solution of furaldehyde (1.0 equivalent) in ether. After the vigorous evolution of nitrogen has subsided, the cooling bath is removed and the reaction mixture is allowed to stand at room temperature until nitrogen is no longer formed (two to three days). Evaporation of the ether and excess diazoethane followed by distillation of the residue yields the product in almost quantitative amount; b.p. 182–183°, m.p. 28–30°.

3,4-Dibenzoyl-Δ^1-pyrazoline (Pyrazoline from an α,β-Unsaturated Ketone).[95] A solution of 2.7 g. (0.065 mole) of diazomethane (prepared from 10.3 g. of nitrosomethylurea) in 100 ml. of ether is cooled to $-10°$ and poured into a solution of 15.7 g. (0.065 mole) of *trans*-dibenzoylethylene in 100 ml. of chloroform also at $-10°$. An immediate reaction takes place, and within five minutes the product begins to separate. The mixture is allowed to stand at $-10°$ for thirty minutes, and the product is then removed by filtration and dried in a vacuum desiccator. The yield of the Δ^1-pyrazoline, m.p. 108°, is 18.0 g. (99%). This material cannot be purified by crystallization, however, for it changes to the Δ^2 isomer; after four crystallizations from aqueous ethanol the Δ^2-pyrazoline, m.p. 129–129.5°, is obtained.

3-Carbethoxy-*lin.*-naphthindazole-4,9-quinone (Pyrazoline from a 1,4-Quinone).[101] To a solution of 10 g. (0.0063 mole) of 1,4-naphthoquinone in benzene at room temperature is added a solution of 4 g.

(0.0035 mole) of ethyl diazoacetate in ether. The solution is warmed gently at first, boiled for thirty minutes, and then allowed to stand at room temperature overnight. By this time the solution is dark red, and the product has deposited as a hard crystalline crust. Digestion with chloroform dissolves the pyrazoline and leaves a residue consisting of almost pure 1,4-naphthalenediol. Evaporation of the chloroform extract yields 7.9 g. (47%) of solid which, by recrystallization from ethanol or benzene, is obtained as tufts of yellow microneedles of m.p. 186.5°.

6-Bromo-1,2-diphenylmethylenedioxynaphthalene (Methylenedioxy Derivative from a 1,2-Quinone).[102] A petroleum ether solution of diphenyldiazomethane prepared from 5.8 g. (0.032 mole) of benzophenone is added to a solution at room temperature of 5 g. (0.021 mole) of 6-bromo-1,2-naphthoquinone in 600 ml. of pure benzene. After fifteen hours the orange-yellow solution is concentrated to yield 7.8 g. (92%) of slightly colored but nearly pure product. Recrystallization from acetic acid yields material of m.p. 150.5–151°.

Ex Situ Method with Catalysis

1-Deoxy-keto-D-fructose Tetraacetate (Aldehyde and Diazomethane).[50] Diazomethane, generated by the action of methanolic potassium hydroxide[3] on 20 ml. (0.171 mole) of nitrosomethylurethan, is distilled directly * into an absolute chloroform solution of 24 g. (0.08 mole) of aldehydo-D-arabinose tetraacetate cooled to 0–5°. There is a steady, vigorous evolution of nitrogen as the reaction proceeds, and the yellow color of the diazomethane is quickly discharged until about three-fourths of the total quantity has been added. The solution then acquires a yellow tinge, but upon standing overnight at room temperature the mixture again becomes colorless. After removal by filtration of the amorphous polymethylenes, the solvent is evaporated. The syrupy residue is taken up in 50 ml. of absolute ethanol, and the solution is made opalescent by the addition of petroleum ether. The product crystallizes slowly on standing in an icebox to give 15.4 g. (62%) of beautiful cubic crystals; m.p. 75–77°. Pure material with m.p. 77–78° is obtained after four recrystallizations from 95% ethanol.

3,3,5-Trimethylcycloheptanone and 3,5,5-Trimethylcycloheptanone (Diazomethane Ring Enlargement).[64] To a solution of 180 g. (4.3 moles) of diazomethane (prepared from 620 g. of nitrosomethylurea) in 6 l. of ether is introduced 560 g. (2.5 moles) of 3,3,5-trimethylcyclohexanone (dihydroisophorone). No reaction is observed until a solution of 28 g.

* The distillate contains diazomethane, ether, methanol (from the methyl alcoholic potassium hydroxide), and ethanol (from the decomposition of the nitrosomethylurethan).

of lithium chloride in 1120 ml. of methanol is added, whereupon nitrogen is immediately evolved. The reaction mixture is allowed to stand at 0° for five days. The unused diazomethane is destroyed with a little sulfuric acid, and the ether solution is washed with sodium carbonate and water. Evaporation of the ether followed by fractional distillation of the residue yields 377 g. of material boiling at 60–70°/10 mm. and 160 g. boiling at 75–90°/10 mm. Re-treatment of the lower-boiling fraction with more diazomethane yields more higher-boiling material, bringing the final yield to 287 g. of lower-boiling fraction and 250 g. of higher-boiling fraction. By means of sodium bisulfite solution, the latter is separated into 66 g. (12%) of 3,3,5-trimethylcycloheptanone (which fails to form a bisulfite addition product) and 117 g. (21%) of 3,5,5-trimethylcycloheptanone (which forms a bisulfite addition product). The lower-boiling fraction contains 5% of unreacted starting material and 46% of 5,5,7-trimethyl-1-oxaspiro[2,5]octane.

2-Phenylcycloheptanone (Ring Enlargement with a Higher Diazoalkane).[88] A 7.4-g. (0.063-mole) sample of distilled phenyldiazomethane (prepared by mercuric oxide oxidation of benzaldehyde hydrazone) is added to a solution of 11.2 g. (0.11 mole) of cyclohexanone in 30 ml. of methanol. The mixture is allowed to stand at room temperature for twenty-four hours, the solvents are removed by evaporation, and the residue is distilled to yield 9.0 g. (76%) of 2-phenylcycloheptanone with b.p. 93–97°/0.2 mm., m.p. 18–23°.

The reaction may also be carried out with the crude petroleum ether solution of the phenyldiazomethane by filtering the mercury and treating the filtrate with methanol and cyclohexanone. By this procedure 100 g. of benzaldehyde can be converted to 60 g. of 2-phenylcycloheptanone. The product by either route is contaminated with a small amount of benzalazine. Pure material of m.p. 21–23° can be obtained by crystallization from petroleum ether.

In Situ Method

Cycloheptanone (Diazomethane Ring Enlargement).[32] A 2-l. three-necked flask fitted with an efficient stirrer, a thermometer, and a dropping funnel is charged with 475 g. (4.83 moles) of cyclohexanone, 500 ml. of methanol, and 1–2 g. of anhydrous sodium carbonate ground to an impalpable powder. About 10 ml. of nitrosomethylurethan is added, and, after a variable induction period, the reaction starts, as evidenced by a rise in the temperature. An additional 600 g. (4.55 moles) of nitrosomethylurethan is then added over a period of six hours at a rate of about 150 drops per minute. During this time the reaction temperature is maintained at 20–25° by external cooling with an ice-water bath. The solution becomes pale yellow; *green or red tones indicate an unsafe concentration of explosive intermediates.* After the addition has been completed the solution is stirred for an additional thirty minutes; then the reaction mixture is filtered and the filtrate is distilled. The lower-boiling fractions contain methanol, water, and methyl ethyl carbonate. Following these are 81 g. (15%) of 1-oxaspiro[2,5]octane with b.p. 148°, 340 g. (63%) of cycloheptanone with b.p. 175–182°, and a small amount of cyclooctanone with b.p. 195–197°.

2-[γ-(3′,4′,5′-Trimethoxyphenyl)propyl]cycloheptanone (Ring Enlargement with a Higher Diazoalkane).[87]   Ethyl N-[δ-(3,4,5-trimethoxyphenyl)butyl]carbamate is nitrosated for six hours at 15–20° following the general method described for the preparation of nitrosomethylurethan.[110] Since the nitroso compound detonates violently upon attempted distillation, it must be used without purification. In the apparatus described above for cycloheptanone are placed 20 g. (0.20 mole) of freshly distilled cyclohexanone, 50 ml. of absolute methanol, and 2 g. of anhydrous, finely powdered potassium carbonate. To the stirred mixture is added, over a period of forty-five minutes, 40 g. (0.12 mole) of the nitroso compound, the temperature being maintained at 25°. After four hours' standing at room temperature, the solids are separated by filtration and the methanol is removed under reduced pressure. The residue is distilled to give 5 g. of a forerun with b.p. 120–172° (mainly 120°)/0.2 mm. and 23 g. (61%) of the ketone as a colorless oil with b.p. 172–175°/0.2 mm., n_D^{25} 1.5290.

TABULAR SURVEY OF REACTIONS OF DIAZOMETHANE AND ITS DERIVATIVES WITH ALDEHYDES AND KETONES

Tables III to VIII include examples of reactions of diazomethane and its derivatives with aldehydes, acyclic ketones, carbocyclic ketones, heterocyclic ketones, α,β-unsaturated aldehydes and ketones, and quinones. The compounds are arranged in each table according to molecular formula, and the following information is given: diazo compound (source and mode of addition), solvent, temperature, time, products isolated, and reference. The literature has been reviewed through 1952.

The following abbreviations are employed for certain of the products formed:

"Oxide" refers to the ethylene oxide derivative formed from the starting compound in accordance with the following formulation.

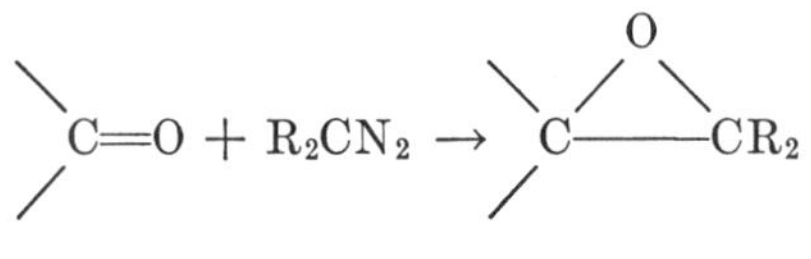

$$\begin{matrix} \diagdown \\ \diagup \end{matrix} C{=}O + R_2CN_2 \rightarrow \begin{matrix} & O & \\ & \diagup \diagdown & \\ \diagdown & & \\ \diagup & & \end{matrix} C{-\!\!-\!\!-}CR_2$$

"Enol ether" refers to the derivative formed from the starting compound in accordance with the following formulation.

$$\begin{array}{c} \diagdown \; \diagup \text{H} \\ \text{C} \\ \diagup \diagdown \\ \text{C}{=}\text{O} \\ | \end{array} \; + \; R_2CN_2 \; \rightarrow \; \begin{array}{c} \diagdown \\ \text{C} \\ \diagup \diagdown\!\!\diagdown \\ \text{COCHR}_2 \\ | \end{array}$$

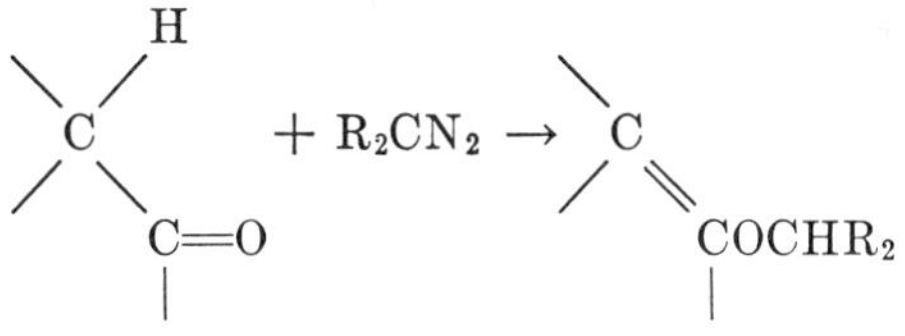

"Methylenedioxy derivative" refers to the derivative formed from the starting compound in accordance with the following formulation.

$$\begin{array}{c} \diagdown \\ \text{C}{=}\text{O} \\ | \\ \text{C}{=}\text{O} \\ \diagup \end{array} \; + \; R_2CN_2 \; \rightarrow \; \begin{array}{c} \diagdown \\ \text{C}{-}\text{O} \\ \| \quad\quad \diagdown \\ \quad\quad \text{CR}_2 \\ \| \quad\quad \diagup \\ \text{C}{-}\text{O} \\ \diagup \end{array}$$

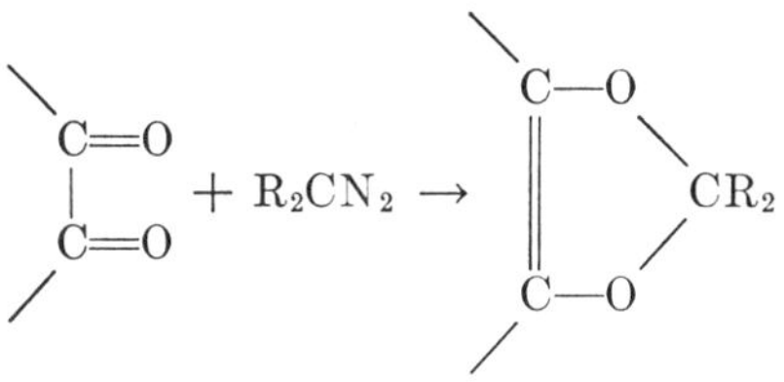

"Pyrazoline" refers to the product formed from the starting compound in accordance with the following formulation.

$$\begin{array}{c} \diagdown \\ \text{C}{=}\text{C}{-}\text{CO}{-} \\ \diagup \end{array} \; + \; R_2CN_2 \; \rightarrow \; \begin{array}{c} \diagdown \;\; 4 \quad\quad 3 \\ \text{C}\text{------}\text{C}{-}\text{CO}{-} \\ \diagup | \quad\quad \| \\ \text{H}_2\text{C} \quad\quad \text{N} \\ 5 \diagdown \quad\quad \diagup 2 \\ \text{N} \\ 1 \end{array}$$

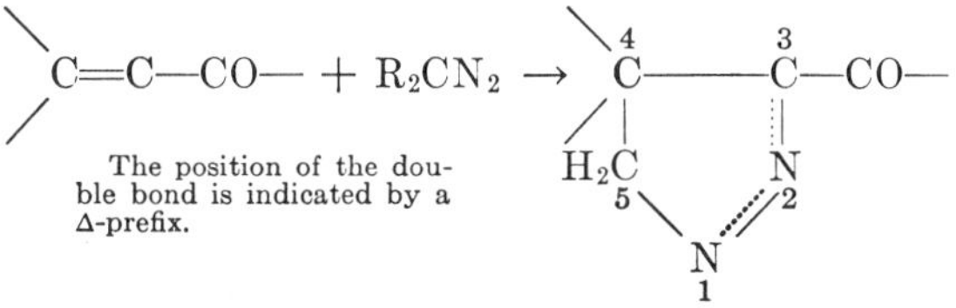

The position of the double bond is indicated by a Δ-prefix.

Structures for which there is some doubt on the part of the authors reporting them are enclosed in brackets. Entries in the solvent, temperature, and time columns that are estimates on the part of the author of this chapter are enclosed in parentheses.

The source of the diazoalkane employed is indicated by an italicized *A*, *B*, or *C*: *A* = Nitrosoalkylurea; *B* = nitrosoalkylurethan; *C* = methyl nitrosoalkylaminoisobutyl ketone.

The base used in the decomposition of the nitroso compound is indicated by an italicized *1*, *2*, or *3*: *1* = alkali metal hydroxide; *2* = alkali metal carbonate; *3* = alkali metal alkoxide.

Reactions in which the diazoalkane is generated *in situ* are indicated by the use of the subscript *is* after the diazoalkane source: thus, CH_2N_2-B_{is}, *2*, indicates that diazomethane was prepared *in situ* by the action of a carbonate on nitrosomethylurethan.

TABLE III

ALDEHYDES

Formula	Aldehyde Name or Structure	Diazo Compound	Solvent	Temperature, °C	Time	Products (% yield)	Reference *
CH_2O	Formaldehyde	CH_2N_2	H_2O		4 d.	CH_3COCH_3	53
		CH_2N_2-B, 3	$(C_2H_5)_2O$	10	24 hr.	CH_3NC	155
		CH_2N_2-B, 3	$(C_2H_5)_2O$	15	3 hr.	No reaction	156
		CH_2N_2-B, 3	$(C_2H_5)_2O$	20–60	2 d.	CH_3COCH_3 (28), CH_3NC, HCN	156
		$CH_3COC(N_2)CH_3$	H_2O			$CH_3COCH(CH_3)CHO$ (17–26), unidentified oil	157
C_2HBr_3O	Bromal	$N_2CHCO_2C_2H_5$	None			Oxide (42) a	55
C_2HCl_3O	Chloral	CH_2N_2	$(C_2H_5)_2O$	Cold	24 hr.	Oxide (54)	18, 29
		CH_2N_2	$(C_2H_5)_2O$		2 d.	Oxide, $Cl_3COCH_2CHOHCCl_3$ (37)	18
		CH_2N_2	$(C_2H_5)_2O$	20–40	2 hr.	Oxide (64), $Cl_2CHCO_2CH_3$ (trace)	52
		CH_2N_2	C_2H_5OH	0		Oxide (11), $Cl_3CCH(OCH_3)OC_2H_5$ (29), $CH_3OC_2H_5$ (29)	20
		CH_2N_2 b	C_2H_5OH	0		Oxide, $Cl_3CCH(OCH_3)OC_2H_5$, $CH_3OC_3H_7$ (46)	20
		CH_2N_2	n-C_3H_7-OH	0		Oxide: $Cl_3CCH(OCH_3)OC_3H_7$-n (1:8 ratio), $CH_3OC_3H_7$	20
		CH_2N_2	i-C_3H_7-OH	0		Oxide: $Cl_3CCH(OCH_3)OC_3H_7$-i (1:9.5 ratio), $CH_3OC_3H_7$	20
		CH_2N_2	n-C_4H_9OH	0		Oxide: $Cl_3CCH(OCH_3)OC_4H_9$-n (1:3.3 ratio), $CH_3OC_4H_9$	20
		CH_2N_2	t-C_4H_9OH	0		Oxide: $Cl_3CCH(OCH_3)OC_4H_9$-t (8:1 ratio)	20
		$N_2CHCO_2C_2H_5$		Heat	24 hr.	Oxide (72)	54, 55, 56, 158
$C_2H_2Cl_2O$	Dichloroacetaldehyde	$N_2CHCO_2C_2H_5$	None	20–warm	(16 hr.)	Oxide (72) a	55
$C_2H_2O_2$	Glyoxal	CH_2N_2	$(C_2H_5)_2O$		7 d.	$CH_3COCOCH_3$ (85)	53
C_2H_3ClO	Chloroacetaldehyde	$N_2CHCO_2C_2H_5$	$(C_2H_5)_2O$		Few min.	[Higher oxides, higher ketones]	29
		CH_2N_2	None			Oxide and/or $ClCH_2COCH_2CO_2C_2H_5$	55, 158
$C_2H_3Cl_3O_2$	Chloral hydrate	CH_2N_2	$(C_2H_5)_2O$	0		Oxide (47), $Cl_3CCH(OCH_3)_2$ (11), CH_3OH, $(CH_3)_2O$, unidentified product	20
C_2H_4O	Acetaldehyde	CH_2N_2		20	12 hr.	CH_3COCH_3 (28), oxide (28), $CH_3COCH_2CHOHCH_3$ (31)	24
	Acetaldehyde + acetone	CH_2N_2				$CH_3COCH_2CHOHCH_3$ (27)	24
$C_3H_4Br_2O$	α,β-Dibromopropionaldehyde	CH_2N_2				Oxide a	18
$C_3H_4Cl_2O$	α,β-Dichloropropionaldehyde	CH_2N_2	None			Oxide a	18
$C_4H_5Cl_3O$	α,α,β-Trichlorobutyraldehyde	$N_2CHCO_2C_2H_5$	None			Oxide (71) a	55
$C_3H_4O_2$	Methylglyoxal	CH_2N_2-B, 1	$(C_2H_5)_2O$		48 hr.	Biacetyl (poor)	159

Formula	Compound	Reagent	Solvent	Temp.	Time	Products	Ref.
$C_5H_4O_2$	2-Furaldehyde	CH_2N_2	CH_3OH	−10	7 d.	Methyl 2-furyl ketone (36)	160
		CH_2N_2		−10		Unidentified $C_7H_8O_2$ oxide	160
		CH_3CHN_2-A	$(C_2H_5)_2O$	20	12 d.	Methyl 2-furyl ketone (70–75)	40
		CH_3CHN_2-B	$(C_2H_5)_2O$	20	2–3 d.	Ethyl 2-furyl ketone (quant.)	40
$C_5H_{10}O$	Isovaleraldehyde		$(C_2H_5)_2O$	20	24 hr.	$CH_3COCH_2CH(CH_3)_2$ (33), unidentified isomeric carbonyl compound	1
$C_6H_6O_2$	5-Methyl-2-furaldehyde	CH_2N_2	$(C_2H_5)_2O$	20	21 d.	No reaction	40
		CH_3CHN_2-A	$(C_2H_5)_2O$	20	2–3 d.	Ethyl 2-(5-methylfuryl) ketone (quant.)	40
$C_6H_6O_3$	5-Hydroxymethyl-2-furaldehyde	CH_2N_2	$(C_2H_5)_2O$	20	14 d.	Methyl 2-(5-hydroxymethylfuryl) ketone (40)	40
$C_7H_3N_3O_7$	2,4,6-Trinitrobenzaldehyde	CH_2N_2	$(C_2H_5)_2O$			Product not isolated [2,4,6-Trinitroacetophenone]	4,159
		CH_2N_2	$(C_2H_5)_2O$			Unidentified product	161
C_5H_5ClO	p-Chlorobenzaldehyde	CH_2N_2				Unidentified product	29
		CH_2N_2				Unidentified product	4
$C_5H_5NO_3$	o-Nitrobenzaldehyde	CH_2N_2				Unidentified product	4
		CH_2N_2	$(C_2H_5)_2O$	−10 to 20	Several hours	Oxide (55–67), o-nitroacetophenone	162
		CH_2N_2				Oxide	163
		CH_2N_2				Oxide, o-nitroacetophenone, o-nitrophenylacetone	108,164
		CH_2N_2	$(C_2H_5)_2O$		36 hr.	Oxide (65), o-nitroacetophenone (16), o-nitrophenylacetone (trace), unidentified product	29
	m-Nitrobenzaldehyde	CH_2N_2	$(C_2H_5)_2O$-CH_3OH			Oxide (61), unidentified product (34)	29
		CH_2N_2	$(C_2H_5)_2O$-CH_3OH			Unidentified product	4
		CH_2N_2	$(C_2H_5)_2O$-CH_3OH			m-Nitroacetophenone (30)	29
	p-Nitrobenzaldehyde	CH_2N_2	$(C_2H_5)_2O$			Two unidentified products	4
		CH_2N_2	$(C_2H_5)_2O$		3–4 hr.	Oxide (35), p-nitroacetophenone (24), p-nitrophenylacetone (2.5), unidentified product (20)	19
		CH_2N_2	$(C_2H_5)_2O$-CH_3OH			Oxide (31), p-nitroacetophenone (24), p-nitrophenylacetone (5), unidentified product (26)	19
		CH_2N_2	$(C_2H_5)_2O$		2 d.	Oxide (46), p-nitroacetophenone (29), p-nitrophenylacetone (trace), unidentified product (9)	29
C_7H_6O	Benzaldehyde	$N_2CHCO_2C_2H_5$	None	60–80		Ethyl p-nitrobenzoylacetate (38)	55
		CH_2N_2				No reaction	4
		CH_2N_2-B	$(C_2H_5)_2O$		10 d.	$C_6H_5COCH_3$ (97), unidentified product	1
		CH_2N_2				$C_6H_5COCH_3$ (quant.)	53

* References 155–217 are on pp. 428–429.

a The product is formulated in ref. 55 as the ketone. By analogy to the product from chloral which has been shown to have the glycidic ester structure [29,55] it is probable that the ketone assignment is incorrect.

b This experiment differs from the preceding one with respect to the number of equivalents of diazomethane employed.

TABLE III—*Continued*

ALDEHYDES

Formula	Aldehyde Name or Structure	Diazo Compound	Solvent	Temperature, °C	Time	Products (% yield)	Reference*
C_7H_6O (*Cont.*)	Benzaldehyde (*Cont.*)	CH_2N_2	$(C_2H_5)_2O\text{-}CH_3OH$			$C_6H_5COCH_3$ (40–50)	41
		CH_3CHN_2-C	$(C_2H_5)_2O$		24 hr.	$C_6H_5COCH_2CH_3$ (94)	38
		$CH_3CH_2CHN_2$-C	$(C_2H_5)_2O$		48 hr.	$C_6H_5COCH_2CH_2CH_3$ (89)	38
		$CH_3CH_2CH_2CHN_2$	$(C_2H_5)_2O$		2 hr.	$C_6H_5CO(CH_2)_3CH_3$ (100)	38
		Diazocyclohexane-B	CH_3OH			Phenyl cyclohexyl ketone	165
		$N_2CHCO_2C_2H_5$	Toluene	110		$C_6H_5COCH_2CO_2C_2H_5$	2, 166
						$C_6H_5CH{\big<}\genfrac{}{}{0pt}{}{COC_6H_5\ ^c}{(CO_2C_2H_5)_2}$ α-form (40)	2
		$N_2CHCO_2C_2H_5$		170		$C_6H_5CH{\big<}\genfrac{}{}{0pt}{}{OCHC_6H_5}{OCHCO_2C_2H_5}$ β-form (40–60)	57
$C_7H_{14}O$	*n*-Heptaldehyde	CH_2N_2				No reaction	4
		CH_2N_2-B	$(C_2H_5)_2O$		6 d.	$CH_3CO(CH_2)_5CH_3$ (73)	1
		$N_2CHCO_2C_2H_5$		170		$C_6H_{13}CH{\big<}\genfrac{}{}{0pt}{}{OCHC_6H_{13}\text{-}n}{OCHCO_2C_2H_5}$	57
$C_8H_5NO_5$	*o*-Nitropiperonal	CH_2N_2	$(C_2H_5)_2O\text{-}CH_3OH$	20	18 hr.	Oxide (90), 6-nitro-3,4-methylenedioxyphenylacetone (10)	41
$C_8H_6O_3$	Piperonal	CH_3CHN_2	$(C_2H_5)_2O\text{-}C_2H_5OH$	20	18 hr.	Ethyl 6-nitro-3,4-methylenedioxyphenyl ketone (74)	41
		CH_2N_2-B, *1*	$(C_2H_5)_2O\text{-}CH_3OH$	20	2 d.	1,2-Epoxy-3-(3′,4′-methylenedioxy)propane (main product), 3,4-methylenedioxyacetophenone (6), piperonylacetone (18)	30
		CH_2N_2	$(C_2H_5)_2O$		14 d.	3,4-Methylenedioxyacetophenone (46)	30
		CH_2N_2-B ^{d}	$(C_2H_5)_2O$		14 d.	3,4-Methylenedioxyacetophenone (14), piperonylacetone (17), unidentified non-ketonic product (18)	30
		CH_2N_2	$(C_2H_5)_2O\text{-}CH_3OH$	−15	2–4 d.	1,2-Epoxy-3-(3′,4′-methylenedioxy)propane (7), 3,4-methylenedioxyacetophenone (7), piperonylacetone (21)	167

		CH_2CHN_2	$(C_2H_5)_2O$-C_2H_5OH	0–20	18 hr.	3,4-Methylenedioxypropiophenone (84)	41
$C_8H_7NO_3$	o-Nitrophenylacetaldehyde	CH_2N_2	$(C_2H_5)_2O$		3 hr.	o-Nitrophenylacetone	108
C_8H_8O	Phenylacetaldehyde	CH_2N_2	C_2H_5OH			$C_6H_5CH_2COCH_3$ (52)[c]	24
		CH_2N_2	$(C_2H_5)_2O$			$C_6H_5CH_2COCH_3$, $C_6H_5CH_2CH_2COCH_3$ (10 combined), unidentified fraction (35)	24
$C_9H_6O_2S$	2,3-Dihydro-2-ketothianaphthene-3-carboxaldehyde	CH_2N_2	$(C_2H_5)_2O$			2-Methoxythianaphthene-3-carboxaldehyde	168
						2-Methoxy-3-acetylthianaphthene	168
C_9H_7NO	α-Cyanophenylacetaldehyde[e]	CH_2N_2	$(C_2H_5)_2O$-CH_3OH			Enol ether	169
$C_9H_8O_3$	Methyl o-formylbenzoate	CH_2N_2	$(C_2H_5)_2O$-CH_3OH			[Methyl o-acetylbenzoate]	170
	3,4-Methylenedioxyphenylacetaldehyde	CH_2N_2	$(C_2H_5)_2O$-CH_3OH	Cold	24 hr.	Oxide (46), piperonylacetone (31)	41
$C_{13}H_{18}O_8$	aldehydo-D-Arabinose tetraacetate	CH_2N_2-B, 1	$(C_2H_5)_2O$-$CHCl_3$	0–20	18 hr.	1-Deoxy-keto-D-fructose tetraacetate (62), unidentified solid	50
	aldehydo-L-Arabinose tetraacetate	CH_2N_2-B, 1	$(C_2H_5)_2O$-$CHCl_3$	0–20	18 hr.	1-Deoxy-keto-L-fructose tetraacetate (62), unidentified solid	50
$C_{15}H_{10}O$	3-Hydroxy-4-phenanthrenealdehyde	CH_2N_2-A	$(C_2H_5)_2O$	20	3 d.	Oxide	171
$C_{15}H_{12}O_2$	2,3-Diphenyl-3-ketopropionaldehyde	CH_2N_2	$(C_2H_5)_2O$-$CHCl_3$			Enol ether	172
$C_{20}H_{28}O_3$	17α-Formyl-4-androsten-17-ol-3-one	CH_2N_2-A	$(C_2H_5)_2O$-dioxane	20	36 hr.	17α-Acetyl-4-androsten-17-ol-3-one (33)	51
	17β-Formyl-4-androsten-17-ol-3-one	CH_2N_2-A	$(C_2H_5)_2O$-dioxane	20	60 hr.	Oxide (30)	51
$C_{20}H_{32}O_3$	17α-Formylandrostane-3β,17β-diol	CH_2N_2-A	$(C_2H_5)_2O$	20	2 d.	17α-Acetylandrostane-3β,17β-diol (20)	51
$C_{26}H_{22}N_2O_5S_2$	$[(C_6H_5)_2NSO_2]_2CHCHO$	CH_2N_2	$(C_2H_5)_2O$			Enol ether (49)	43
$C_{34}H_{28}O_{10}$	aldehydo-D-Glucose tetrabenzoate	CH_2N_2	$(C_2H_5)_2O$		Several days	[1-Deoxy-keto-D-glucoheptulose tetrabenzoate]	173
		CH_2N_2	$CHCl_3$		1 hr.	[1-Deoxy-keto-D-glucoheptulose tetrabenzoate]	173

* References 155–217 are on pp. 428–429.

c This product is probably identical with the one shown in the following entry and, therefore, probably possesses the dioxolane structure.[57]

d This experiment differs from the preceding one in the method of mixing the aldehyde with the diazomethane. In the preceding experiment, ethereal solutions of diazomethane and piperonal were mixed; in this experiment, ethereal diazomethane was poured onto solid piperonal.

e Other examples of this same type of reaction with similar arylcyanoacetaldehydes are given in ref. 167.

TABLE IV
ACYCLIC KETONES

Formula	Acyclic Ketone Name or Structure	Diazo Compound	Solvent	Temperature, °C	Time	Products (% yield)	Reference *
CO	Carbon monoxide	CH_2N_2	$(C_2H_5)_2O$	400–500	85 hr. [a]	Ketene (2)	122
		$(C_6H_5)_2CN_2$	C_6H_6–$C_6H_5NH_2$		15 hr.	$(C_6H_5)_2C=NN=C(C_6H_5)_2$	89
$C_3H_3Cl_3O$	1,1,1-Trichloroacetone	CH_2N_2	$(C_2H_5)_2O$			Oxide (83)	29
C_3H_5ClO	Chloroacetone	CH_2N_2	$(C_2H_5)_2O$		12 hr.	Oxide (main product), [higher oxides]	29
C_3H_6O	Acetone	CH_2N_2-4, 3	$(C_2H_5)_2O$			No reaction	20
		CH_2N_2	H_2O			Oxide (29), methyl ethyl ketone, [higher ketones]	26
		CH_2N_2	H_2O-LiCl			Oxide (31), methyl ethyl ketone (2)	26
		CH_2N_2	n-C_4H_9OH			Oxide (37), methyl ethyl ketone (2.5), $CH_3OC_4H_9$-n, [higher ketones]	26
		CH_2N_2	$HCONH_2$		18 hr.	Oxide (13), methyl ethyl ketone (10)	20
		CH_2N_2	Cl_3CCH_2OH		18 hr.	Oxide (21), methyl ethyl ketone (18), $Cl_3CCH_2OCH_3$	20
		CH_2N_2-B_{18}, 9	n-C_4H_9OH		80 hr.	Oxide (33), methyl ethyl ketone (38)	31
		CH_2N_2-B_{18}	n-C_4H_9OH	0	20 hr.	Oxide (15), methyl ethyl ketone (19)	31
		CH_3CHN_2-C	H_2O	−50 to 0	5 hr.	Oxide (9), methyl isopropyl ketone (44)	38
$C_3H_6O_2$	Hydroxyacetone	CH_2N_2				$[CH_3COCH_2OCH_3]$ (0.5), $[CH_3CH_2COCH_2OH]$ (50)	154
$C_4H_6O_2$	Biacetyl	CH_2N_2			30 d.	No reaction	53
$C_4H_6O_3$	Methyl pyruvate	CH_2N_2-4	$(C_2H_5)_2O$		3 d.	Oxide (87)	58
C_4H_8O	Methyl ethyl ketone	CH_2N_2	H_2O			Oxide (38), methyl n-propyl ketone (15), diethyl ketone (13)	24
$C_4H_8O_2$	Methoxyacetone	CH_2N_2			12 d.	Oxide (39), $H_3C\text{-}C\!\!<\!\!{}^{O-CH_2OCH_3}_{O-CH_3}\!\!>\!\!CH_2OCH_3$ (20)	25
$C_5H_4N_2O$	1,1-Dicyanoacetone	CH_2N_2	$(C_2H_5)_2O$			Enol ether	174
$C_5H_8O_2$	Acetylacetone	CH_2N_2	$(C_2H_5)_2O$-CH_3OH			Enol ether (60) [b]	47
		$N_2CHCO_2C_2H_5$	1.5% NaOH	80	16 hr.	Ethyl 3-acetyl-4-methylpyrazole-5-carboxylate (50)	99
$C_5H_{10}O$	Diethyl ketone	CH_2N_2	H_2O			Oxide (37), ethyl n-propyl ketone (22)	24
	Methyl n-propyl ketone	CH_2N_2	H_2O			Oxide (58), methyl n-butyl ketone (5), ethyl n-propyl ketone (12)	24

Formula	Compound	Reagent	Solvent	Temp.	Time	Product	Ref.
$C_5H_{10}O_2$	Ethyl methoxymethyl ketone	CH_2N_2			7 d.	Oxide (38), $\begin{smallmatrix}CH_2OCH_3\\ H_5C_2C-OCH_2OCH_3\\ C\\ H_2C-OC_2H_5\end{smallmatrix}$ (15)	25
$C_6H_{10}O_2$	Acetonylacetone	CH_2N_2	1.3% NaOH	100	30 d.	No reaction	53
	Propionylacetone	$N_2CHCO_2C_2H_5$	$(C_2H_5)_2O$	20	0.5 hr.	Ethyl 3-propionyl-4-methylpyrazole-5-carboxylate	99
$C_6H_{10}O_3$	Ethyl acetoacetate	CH_2N_2-B	$(C_2H_5)_2O$		1–2 d.	Enol ether (37)	175
		CH_2N_2-A	$(C_2H_5)_2O$		3 d.	Enol ether (24), oxide (3)	60
		CH_2N_2-A	$(C_2H_5)_2O$-CH_3OH			Enol ether (4–8 parts), oxide (1 part) [c]	60
$C_6H_{10}O_6$	scyllo-ms-Inosose	CH_2N_2-A	$(C_2H_5)_2O$-H_2O	Cold	4–5 hr.	Oxide (79)	176
$C_7H_9NO_3$	Ethyl cyanoacetoacetate	CH_2N_2-A	$(C_2H_5)_2O$	–10		Enol ether	174
$C_7H_{10}O_3$	Heptane-2,4,6-trione	CH_2N_2				2,6-Dimethyl-γ-pyrone	177
$C_7H_{10}O_5$	Diethyl oxomalonate	CH_2N_2-B	$(C_2H_5)_2O$	20–40	2 hr.	Oxide (main product)	19
$C_7H_{12}O_3$	Ethyl methylacetoacetate	CH_2N_2-A	$(C_2H_5)_2O$		7 d.	No reaction	178
		CH_2N_2-A	$(C_2H_5)_2O$-CH_3OH		7–14 d.	Enol ether (30–44 parts), oxide (70–56 parts) (combined yield 13–45) [d]	178,174
$C_7H_{12}O_6$	Diethyl mesoxalate	CH_2N_2-B	$(C_2H_5)_2O$		2 hr.	Oxide (74)	19
C_8H_7ClO	ω-Chloroacetophenone	CH_2N_2	$(C_2H_5)_2O$-CH_3OH		12 hr.	Oxide (89)	38
$C_8H_7NO_3$	o-Nitroacetophenone	CH_2N_2	$(C_2H_5)_2O$-CH_3OH		Long	Unidentified product	29,19
	p-Nitroacetophenone	CH_2N_2	$(C_2H_5)_2O$-CH_3OH		Long	Unidentified product	29,19
C_8H_8O	Acetophenone	CH_2N_2	$(C_2H_5)_2O$-CH_3OH	20	3 d.	Oxide (12–16), phenylacetone (5.5)	106
$C_8H_8O_2$	ω-Hydroxyacetophenone	CH_2N_2	$CHCl_3$		10 d.	1-Benzyl-1-hydroxymethylethylene oxide (20)	25
		CH_2N_2-$B_{18,9}$				$(C_6H_5COCH_2O)_2CO$	25
		CH_2N_2	$CHCl_3$			$[C_6H_5COCH_2OCH_3]$ (low), $[C_6H_5CH_2COCH_2OH]$ (66)	154
$C_9H_7ClN_2O$	p-Chloro-α-diazopropiophenone	CH_2N_2	$(C_2H_5)_2O$			No reaction	39
		CH_3CHN_2	$(C_2H_5)_2O$			Unidentified solid	39
C_9H_7NO	Benzoylacetonitrile	CH_2N_2				Enol ether (100)	45
$C_9H_8O_3$	3,4-Methylenedioxyacetophenone	CH_2N_2-B, 3	$(C_2H_5)_2O$ and/or CH_3OH			No reaction	106
$C_9H_{10}O_2$	Phenylacetylcarbinol	CH_2N_2	$CHCl_3$		12 d.	Oxide (27)	25
	ω-Methoxyacetophenone	CH_2N_2				1-Benzyl-1-methoxymethylethylene oxide	25
$C_{10}H_6O_4$	Furil	CH_2N_2	$(C_2H_5)_2O$			Methylenedioxy derivative	53

* References 155–217 are on pp. 428–429.

[a] The reaction mixture was irradiated with a mercury-vapor lamp.

[b] The effect of experimental conditions on the course of the reaction is discussed in ref. 47.

[c] The ratio of enol ether to oxide increases as the amount of methanol employed increases.[60]

[d] The ratio of enol ether to oxide decreases as the amount of methanol employed increases.

TABLE IV—Continued
Acyclic Ketones

Formula	Acyclic Ketone Name or Structure	Diazo Compound	Solvent	Temperature, °C	Time	Products (% yield)	Reference*
$C_{10}H_9NO$	1-Cyano-1-phenylacetone[e]	CH_2N_2				Enol ether	169
$C_{10}H_{10}N_2O$	p-Methyl-α-diazopropiophenone	CH_3CHN_2				Unidentified solid	39
$C_{10}H_{10}O_3$	Methyl benzoylacetate	CH_2N_2				Enol ether	45
$C_{10}H_{12}O_3$	Piperonylacetone	CH_2N_2	$(C_2H_5)_2O$-CH_3OH		8 d.	Oxide (36)	106
$C_{10}H_{12}O_3$	3,4-Dimethoxyacetophenone	CH_2N_2	$(C_2H_5)_2O$-CH_3OH		8 d.	1,2-Epoxy-2-methyl-3-(3',4'-dimethoxyphenyl)propane (5), 3,4-dimethoxyphenylacetone (trace)[f]	106
$C_{10}H_{12}O_3S$	p-Toluenesulfonylacetone	CH_2N_2-A	$(C_2H_5)_2O$-H_2O		18 hr.	Enol ether (94)	43
$C_{11}H_{11}NO_3S$	1-(p-Toluenesulfonyl)-1-cyanoacetone	CH_2N_2-A	$(C_2H_5)_2O$	−10		Enol ethers (71), 1-(p-toluenesulfonyl)-1-cyano-1-methylacetone (trace)	174
$C_{11}H_{14}O_3$	3,4-Dimethoxyphenylacetone	CH_2N_2	$(C_2H_5)_2O$-CH_3OH		15 d.	Oxide (34)	106
$C_{11}H_{22}O$	Methyl n-nonyl ketone	CH_2N_2	C_2H_5OH		2 d.	Oxide (100)	24
$C_{14}H_8Br_2O_2$	p,p'-Dibromobenzil	CH_2N_2	$(C_2H_5)_2O$			Methylenedioxy derivative	53
$C_{14}H_{10}O_2$	Benzil	CH_2N_2	$(C_2H_5)_2O$			Methylenedioxy derivative	53
$C_{14}H_{12}O_2$	Benzoin	CH_2N_2	$CHCl_3$			No reaction	53
$C_{15}H_{10}O_3$	Diphenylpropanetrione	CH_2N_2	$(C_2H_5)_2O$			Methylenedioxy derivative (19)	62
$C_{15}H_{12}O_2$	Dibenzoylmethane	CH_2N_2				Enol ethers[g]	49
$C_{15}H_{14}O_3S$	ω-(p-Toluenesulfonyl)acetophenone	CH_2N_2	$(C_2H_5)_2O$-H_2O		18 hr.	Enol ether	43
$C_{16}H_{12}O_3$	Methyl 9-fluorenylglyoxylate	CH_2N_2-A				Enol ether	58
$C_{16}H_{20}O_{11}$	scyllo-ms-Inosose pentaacetate	CH_2N_2-A	$(C_2H_5)_2O$-$CHCl_3$	Cold-20	4-5 hr.	Oxide (84-88)	176
$C_{16}H_{22}O_{11}$	keto-D-Fructose pentaacetate	CH_2N_2	$CHCl_3$-CH_3OH			Oxide (75)	59
$C_{17}H_{16}N_2O_2$	7-Methoxy-2-diazoacetyl-1,2,3,4-tetrahydrophenanthrene	CH_2N_2	$(C_2H_5)_2O$			Unidentified 1:1 addition product	179
$C_{17}H_{18}O_5S_2$	$(CH_3C_6H_4SO_2CH_2)_2CO$	CH_2N_2	$(C_2H_5)_2O$		2 d.	Enol ether (100)	43
$C_{20}H_{16}O_7S_2$	$(C_6H_5OSO_2)_2CHCOC_6H_5$	CH_2N_2	C_6H_6	61	20 min.	Enol ether (60)	43
$C_{22}H_{20}O_5S_2$	$(CH_3C_6H_4SO_2)_2CHCOC_6H_5$	$N_2CHCO_2C_2H_5$	$CHCl_3$		3 hr.	Enol ether (45)	43
$C_{27}H_{34}N_4O_5S_2$	$[(C_6H_5)_2NSO_2]_2CHCOCH_3$	CH_2N_2-A	$(C_2H_5)_2O$-H_2O		2 d.	Enol ether (29)	43
$C_{29}H_{36}N_4O_7S_2$	$[(C_6H_5)_2NSO_2]_2CHCOCO_2C_2H_5$	CH_2N_2	C_6H_6 and/or $(C_2H_5)_2O$		20 min.	Enol ether (83); $[(C_6H_5)_2NSO_2]_2C(CH_3)COCO_2C_2H_5$ (54-60), enol ether (14-20)[h]	43
$C_{30}H_{28}N_2O_7S_2$	$[(C_6H_5)_2NSO_2]_2C(CH_3)COCO_2C_2H_5$	CH_2N_2	$(C_2H_5)_2O$		36 hr.	Oxide (68)	43

* References 155-217 are on pp. 428-429.

[e] Other examples of this same type of reaction with similar aryl cyano ketones are given in ref. 167.

[f] In this experiment 35-40% of starting material was recovered.

[g] The effect of experimental conditions on the course of the reaction is discussed in ref. 49.

[h] The higher yield was obtained with ether-benzene as the solvent.

STRUCTURES FOR TABLE V

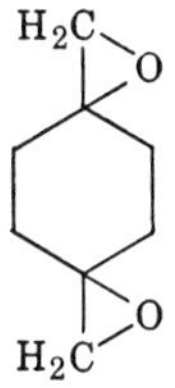

A

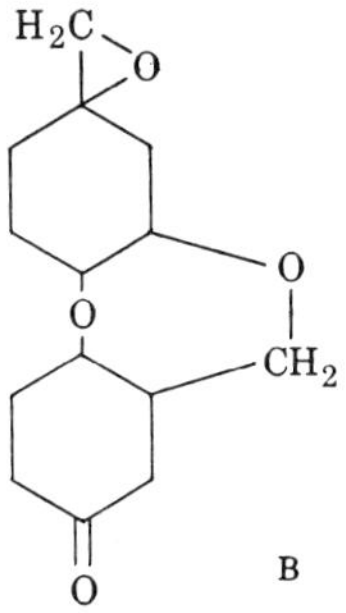

B

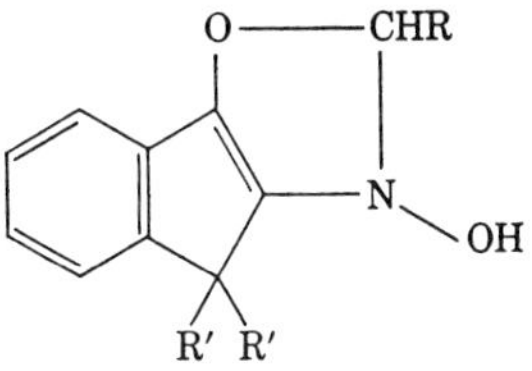

C

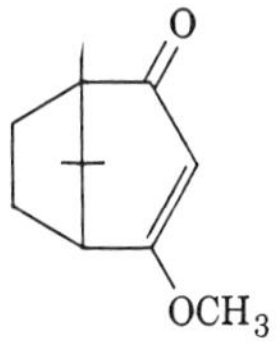

D

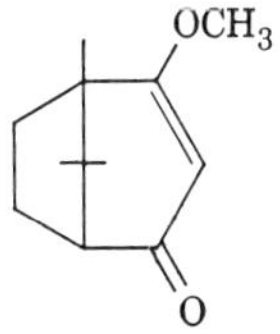

E

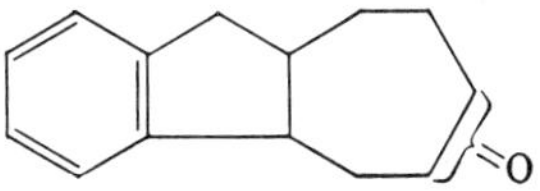

F

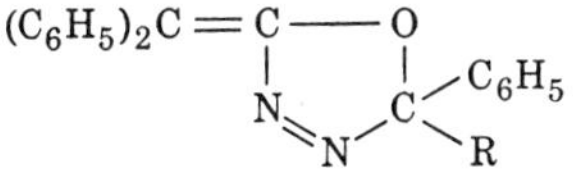

G

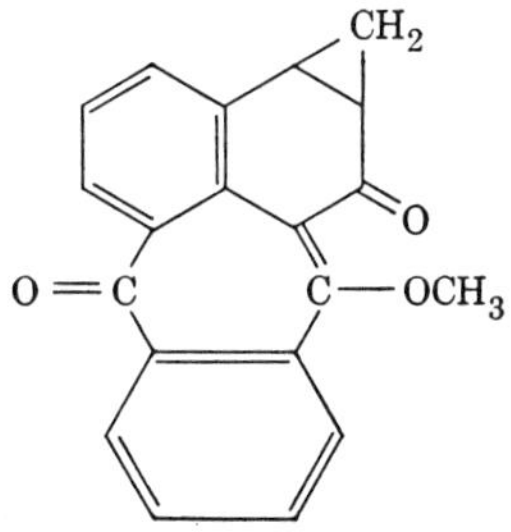

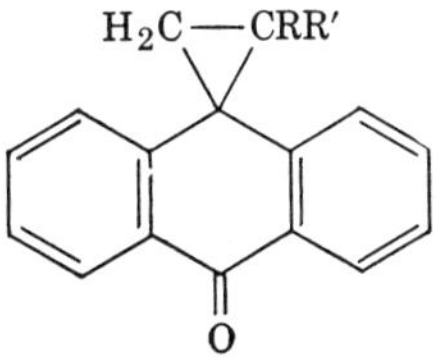

H

J

TABLE V
CARBOCYCLIC KETONES

Formula	Carbocyclic Ketone Name or Structure	Diazo Compound	Solvent	Temperature, °C	Time	Products (% yield)	Reference *
C_2H_6O	Ketene	CH_2N_2-B	$(C_2H_5)_2O$	20	1.5 hr.	Cyclobutanone (2)	68
		CH_2N_2	$(C_2H_5)_2O$	-15	40-60m.	Cyclobutanone (40)	67
		CH_2N_2-C	$(C_2H_5)_2O$	-70		Cyclobutanone (75)	69
		CH_2N_2	$(C_2H_5)_2O$-CH_3OH	0	2 hr.	Cyclopropanone methyl hemiacetal (13), cyclobutanone (trace)	67
		CH_2N_2-B, 3 or A	$(C_2H_5)_2O(H_2O)$ a			Cyclopropanone hydrate (32)	67
C_4H_6O	Dimethylketene	CH_2N_2-A	$(C_2H_5)_2O$	Cold		3,3-Dimethylcyclobutanone (18)	70
C_5H_7ClO	2-Chlorocyclopentanone	CH_2N_2				No reaction	34,107
C_5H_8O	Cyclopentanone	CH_2N_2				Cycloheptanone (main product), cyclohexanone	36
		CH_2N_2-B, 1	$(C_2H_5)_2O$-CH_3OH	0-20	3 d.	Cycloheptanone (45), [cyclooctanone], [oxides]	180
		CH_2N_2	H_2O		2 d.	Cycloheptanone (6), cyclooctanone (44), 1-oxaspiro[2,4]heptane and 1-oxaspiro[2,5]octane (24)	24
		CH_3CHN_2-B_{1s}, 2	(C_2H_5OH)	0 b		2-Methylcyclohexanone (8)	38
		CH_3CHN_2	$(C_2H_5)_2O$			2-Methylcyclohexanone (8)	38
		$CH_3CH_2CH_2CHN_2$-B_{1s}, 2	CH_3OH	25	18 hr.	2-n-Propylcyclohexanone (26), unidentified carbonyl compound (14)	88
		$C_6H_5CHN_2$-B_{1s}, 2	CH_3OH	25	18 hr.	2-Phenylcyclohexanone (5), methyl benzyl ether (20), stilbene (2)	88
		$C_6H_5CHN_2$-B_{1s}, 2	CH_3OH	65	18 hr.	Methyl benzyl ether (20), stilbene (20), unidentified oil (12)	88
$C_6H_8O_2$	Cyclohexane-1,3-dione	CH_2N_2	C_2H_5OH			Enol ether	46
	Cyclohexane-1,4-dione	CH_2N_2-B_{1s}, 2	$(C_2H_5)_2O$-CH_3OH			Compound A (8)	25
		CH_2N_2		0-20	24 hr.	Compound A (4.2), compound B (3.5), two unidentified oils (34, 9)	79
C_6H_9ClO	2-Chlorocyclohexanone	CH_2N_2	$(C_2H_5)_2O$-CH_3OH ?	20-30	7 hr.	2-Chlorocycloheptanone (quant.)	36
		CH_2N_2-B_{1s}, 2	CH_3OH	20-30	7 hr.	2-Chlorocycloheptanone (52), oxide (16)	181
		CH_2N_2-B_{1s}, 2	CH_3OH	20-30	7 hr.	2-Chlorocycloheptanone (11), oxide (14), unidentified compound (40)	33

		Reagent	Solvent	Temp.	Time	Products (yields)	Ref.
$C_6H_{10}O$	Cyclohexanone	CH_3CHN_2	$(C_2H_5)_2O\text{-}CH_3OH$?			?-Chloro-?-methylcycloheptanone (main product)	36
		$CH_2N_2\text{-}B, 1$	$(C_2H_5)_2O\text{-}CH_3OH$	0–20	3 d.	Cycloheptanone (52), cyclooctanone and oxide (21)	180
		$CH_2N_2\text{-}B_{1s}, 2$ ^{c}	C_2H_5OH		7 d.	Cycloheptanone (some), cyclooctanone (48), oxide (32)	31
		CH_2N_2	C_2H_5OH			Cycloheptanone (18), cyclooctanone (60), oxide (15)	24
		$CH_2N_2\text{-}B, 1$	$(C_2H_5)_2O\text{-}CH_3OH$	20	3 d.	Cycloheptanone (55), cyclooctanone (1–2), oxide (9)	23
		$CH_2N_2\text{-}B_{1s}, 2$	C_2H_5OH		2 d.	Cycloheptanone (40), cyclooctanone (8), oxide (23)	38
		$CH_2N_2\text{-}B_{1s}, 2$ ^{d}	CH_3OH	20–25	6–7 hr.	Cycloheptanone (63), oxide (15), higher ketones	32
		$CH_2N_2\text{-}C_{1s}, 2$	C_2H_5OH	30	5 d.	Cycloheptanone (61)	38
		$CH_2N_2\text{-}C_{1s}, 2$	CH_3OH	30	8 hr.	Cycloheptanone (60)	69
		CH_3CHN_2	$(C_2H_5)_2O\text{-}CH_3OH$?		24 hr.	2-Methylcycloheptanone	36, 86
		$CH_3CHN_2\text{-}B_{1s}, 2$	C_2H_5OH ^{e}			2-Methylcycloheptanone (39–47)	38
		$CH_3CHN_2\text{-}C_{1s}$				2-Methylcycloheptanone (39–47)	38
		$(CH_3)_2CHCHN_2\text{-}B_{1s}, 2$	CH_3OH			2-Isopropylcycloheptanone (31)	66
		$(CH_3)_2CHCHN_2\text{-}B_{1s}, 2$	CH_3OH	20–25		2-Isopropylcycloheptanone (51)	85
		$CH_3(CH_2)_6CHN_2\text{-}B_{1s}, 2$	CH_3OH			2-n-Heptylcycloheptanone (50)	38
		$N_2CH(CH_2)_4CO_2C_2H_5\text{-}B_{1s}, 2$	CH_3OH			2-(ω-Carbethoxybutyl)cycloheptanone (55)	38
		Diazocyclohexane-B	CH_3OH			[Spiro(5,6)dodecan-7-one], [1,1'-epoxy-bicyclohexyl]	165
		$C_6H_5CHN_2\text{-}B_{1s}, 2$	CH_3OH	25–30	23 hr.	2-Phenylcycloheptanone (26, 45), methyl benzyl ether (27)	33, 87
		$C_6H_5CHN_2$	CH_3OH			2-Phenylcycloheptanone (43, 76)	86, 88
		$o\text{-}CH_3C_6H_4CHN_2\text{-}B_{1s}, 2$	CH_3OH	25	48 hr.	2-(o-Tolyl)cycloheptanone (29), methyl o-methylbenzyl ether (37)	87
		$p\text{-}CH_3C_6H_4CHN_2\text{-}B_{1s}, 2$	CH_3OH	25	23 hr.	2-(p-Tolyl)cycloheptanone (26), methyl p-methylbenzyl ether (45)	87
		$2,4,6\text{-}(CH_3)_3C_6H_2CHN_2\text{-}B_{1s}, 2$	CH_3OH	25	23 hr.	Methyl 2,4,6-trimethylbenzyl ether (62)	87

* References 155–217 are on pp. 428–429.

^{a} After the addition of the ethereal solution of diazomethane the reaction mixture was evaporated in a stream of moist air.

^{b} The same results were obtained with a dilute ethereal solution of diazomethane at 0° and a concentrated ethereal diazomethane solution at $-50°$.[38]

^{c} With sodium carbonate in place of potassium carbonate 51% of cyclooctanone and 16% of oxide were obtained.

^{d} Variations in the temperature (0–50°), solvent (methanol, ethanol, 1-butanol), and base [Na_2CO_3, K_2CO_3, BaO, $Mg(OCH_3)_2$] affected the rate of the reaction but not the yield.

^{e} Similar results were obtained in ether solution.[38]

TABLE V—*Continued*

CARBOCYCLIC KETONES

Formula	Carbocyclic Ketone Name or Structure	Diazo Compound	Solvent	Temperature, °C	Time	Products (% yield)	Reference *
$C_6H_{10}O$ (*Cont.*)	Cyclohexanone (*Cont.*)	$o\text{-}CH_3OC_6H_4CHN_2\text{-}B_{18}$, 2	CH_3OH	25	23 hr.	2-(o-Anisyl)cycloheptanone (20), methyl o-methoxybenzyl ether (50)	87
		$p\text{-}CH_3OC_6H_4CHN_2\text{-}B_{18}$, 2	CH_3OH	25	23 hr.	2-(p-Anisyl)cycloheptanone (7), methyl p-methoxybenzyl ether (64)	87
		$2,3,4\text{-}(CH_3O)_3C_6H_2CHN_2\text{-}B_{18}$, 2	CH_3OH	25	23 hr.	Methyl 2,3,4-trimethoxybenzyl ether (72)	87
		$2,3,4\text{-}(CH_3O)_3C_6H_2CHN_2\text{-}B_{18}$, 2	$t\text{-}C_4H_9OH$	83	20 hr.	t-Butyl 2,3,4-trimethoxybenzyl ether (30), ethyl 2,3,4-trimethoxybenzyl carbonate (44)	87
		$2,3,4\text{-}(CH_3O)_3C_6H_2CHN_2\text{-}B_{18}$	Cyclohexanone	114	3 hr.	Ethyl 2,3,4-trimethoxybenzyl carbonate (76)	87
		$3,4,5\text{-}(CH_3O)_3C_6H_2(CH_2)_3\text{-}CHN_2\text{-}B_{18}$, 2	CH_3OH	25	23 hr.	2-(3',4',5'-Trimethoxyphenylpropyl)-cycloheptanone (61)	87
		$N_2CH(CH_2)_2CHN_2\text{-}B$				Unidentified compounds, $C_{10}H_{18}O$ and $C_{16}H_{26}O_2$	90b
$C_6H_{10}O_2$	2-Hydroxycyclohexanone	$CH_2N_2\text{-}B_{18}$				2-Methoxycyclohexanone (10), [oxide] (90)	34
C_7H_9NO	2-Cyanocyclohexanone	CH_2N_2	$(C_2H_5)_2O$		5 d.	[4-(2'-Ketocyclohexyl)triazole] (3)	34
$C_7H_{11}ClO$	2-Chlorocycloheptanone	$CH_2N_2\text{-}B_{18}$, 2	CH_3OH			2-Chlorocyclooctanone (13), oxide (12)	181
	(+)2-Chloro-5-methylcyclohexanone	$CH_2N_2\text{-}B_{18}$	CH_3OH		15 hr.	(−)2-Chloro-5-methylcycloheptanone (45), [oxide] (20)	34, 107
$C_7H_{12}O$	2-Methylcyclohexanone	CH_2N_2	$(C_2H_5)_2O$		10 d.	No ring enlargement	38
		$CH_2N_2\text{-}B_{18}$			5 d.	2-Methylcycloheptanone (10), 3-methylcycloheptanone (7), oxide (26) ^{f}	38
	3-Methylcyclohexanone	$CH_2N_2\text{-}A_{18}$, 1	CH_3OH	26-28	12 hr.	Methylcycloheptanones (82)	182
		CH_2N_2	$(C_2H_5)_2O\text{-}CH_3OH$		3 d.	3-Methylcycloheptanone	34
		$CH_2N_2\text{-}B$				Methylcycloheptanones (39), oxide (21)	38

Formula	Carbonyl compound	Diazoalkane	Solvent	Temp. (°)	Time	Products (yields)	Refs.
	(−)3-Methylcyclohexanone	CH_2N_2	$(C_2H_5)_2O$-CH_3OH			(−)3-Methylcycloheptanone (60), 3- or 4-methylcyclooctanone (12), oxide (13)	34, 107
	4-Methylcyclohexanone	CH_2N_2-Bis, 2	$(C_2H_5)_2O$-CH_3OH e		4 d.	4-Methylcycloheptanone (43), ?-methylcyclooctanone (4.5), oxide (18)	38
		CH_2N_2	$(C_2H_5)_2O$-CH_3OH	0–20	2 d.	4-Methylcycloheptanone (good)	86, 183
		CH_2N_2-Bis, 2	CH_3OH			4-Methylcycloheptanone	86
		CH_3CHN_2-Bis, 2	C_2H_5OH		2 d.	2,5-Dimethylcycloheptanone (52) e	38
		CH_2N_2				No reaction	36
	Cycloheptanone	CH_2N_2-Bis, 2	$(C_2H_5)_2O$-C_2H_5OH		6 d.	Cyclooctanone (32), oxide (30)	38
		CH_2N_2-Bis, 2	CH_3OH	30	20 hr.	Cyclooctanone (45), oxide (22), [higher ketones and oxides]	32
$C_7H_{12}O_2$	4-Methoxycyclohexanone	CH_2N_2-Cis, 2	CH_3OH	10–20	20 hr.	Cyclooctanone (30)	69
		CH_2N_2-Bis, 2	C_2H_5OH			4-Methoxycycloheptanone (42), oxide (23)	38
		$CH_3CH_2CH_2CHN_2$	CH_3OH	25	18 hr.	5-Methoxy-2-n-propylcycloheptanone (74)	87
$C_8H_{11}BrO_2$	2-Bromo-5,5-dimethylcyclohexane-1,3-dione	CH_2N_2				Enol ether	46
$C_8H_{12}O_2$	5,5-Dimethylcyclohexane-1,3-dione	CH_2N_2				Enol ether	46
$C_8H_{14}O$	2,2-Dimethylcyclohexanone	CH_2N_2-Bis, 2	CH_3OH	20–25	6 hr.	3,3-Dimethylcycloheptanone (27), ?,?-dimethylcyclooctanone (8)	34
	3,5-Dimethylcyclohexanone	CH_2N_2-Bis, 2	(C_2H_5OH) e			3,5-Dimethylcycloheptanone (39), oxide (18)	38
	4-Ethylcyclohexanone	CH_3CHN_2-Bis, 2	(C_2H_5OH)		5 d.	2,3,5-Trimethylcycloheptanone (45)	38
		CH_2N_2	$(C_2H_5)_2O$-CH_3OH			4-Ethylcycloheptanone (53), oxide (6)	38
		CH_3CHN_2	$(C_2H_5)_2O$			2-Methyl-4-ethylcycloheptanone (80)	38
	3-Methylcycloheptanone	CH_2N_2	$(C_2H_5)_2O$-CH_3OH		3 d.	3- or 4-Methylcyclooctanone (40)	34
	Cyclooctanone	CH_2N_2	CH_3OH	(−50)		No reaction	38
		CH_2N_2	CH_3OH	7		No reaction	38
		CH_2N_2-Bis, 2	CH_3OH	10–20	30 hr.	Cyclononanone (22), cyclodecanone (2)	32
		CH_2N_2-Cis, 2	CH_3OH	−50	60 hr.	Cyclononanone (15)	69
		CH_3CHN_2	$(C_2H_5)_2O$-CH_3OH			No reaction	38

* References 155–217 are on pp. 428–429.

e Similar results were obtained in ether solution.[38]

f The yields given in the experimental section in ref. 38 differ from those in the discussion, where a 37% yield of ketone and an equal amount of oxide are indicated.

TABLE V—*Continued*
CARBOCYCLIC KETONES

Formula	Carbocyclic Ketone Name or Structure	Diazo Compound	Solvent	Temperature, °C	Time	Products (% yield)	Reference*
$C_9H_6O_3$	Indan-1,2,3-trione	CH_2N_2	$(C_2H_5)_2O$	Cold	18 hr.	Methylenedioxy derivative (83)	184
$C_9H_5NO_3$	2-Oximinoindan-1,3-dione	CH_2N_2	$(C_2H_5)_2O$		6 hr.	Compound C (R = H, R'R' = O)	82
		CH_2CHN_2	$(C_2H_5)_2O$		6 hr.	Compound C (R = CH₃, R'R' = O)	82
C_9H_8O	α-Hydrindone	CH_2N_2	CCl_4			No reaction	107
	β-Hydrindone	CH_2N_2				Unidentified chlorine-containing product	25
$C_9H_{12}Br_2O_2$	5,5-Dibromo-1,1,2,2-tetramethylcyclopentane-3,4-dione	CH_2N_2	$(C_2H_5)_2O$			Methylenedioxy derivative	81
$C_9H_{14}O$	5-Ketohexahydroindan	CH_2N_2-$A$is, 1	CH_3OH-H_2O	0	3 d.	Bicyclo[6,3,0]undecanone, *cis*- and *trans*-bicyclo[5,3,0]decan-3-one (combined 21)	185
$C_9H_{16}O$	4-Isopropylcyclohexanone	CH_2N_2	$(C_2H_5)_2O$-CH_3OH	20	3 d.	Bicyclo[5,3,0]decan-3-one (59)	186
		CH_2N_2-$B$is, 2	CH_3OH	20–25	18 hr.	4-Isopropylcycloheptanone (70) g	66
		CH_2N_2-$B$is, 2	CH_3OH	24–26	2 d.	4-Isopropylcycloheptanone (54)	187
	3,5,5-Trimethylcyclohexanone	CH_2N_2-$A$is, 1	CH_3OH-H_2O	0–20	18 hr.	?,?,?-Trimethylcycloheptanone	188
		CH_2N_2-A, 1	$(C_2H_5)_2O$ CH_3OH-$LiCl$	0	5 d.	3,5,5-Trimethylcycloheptanone (12), 3,5,5-trimethylcycloheptanone (21), oxide (46)	64
		CH_2N_2-$A$is, 1	CH_3OH-H_2O	0–20	18 hr.	3,3,5-Trimethylcycloheptanone, 3,5,5-trimethylcycloheptanone	65
	Cyclononanone	CH_2N_2-$B$is, 2	CH_3OH	20	6 d.	Cyclodecanone (44) h	32
$C_{10}H_{10}O$	α-Tetralone	CH_2N_2	$(C_2H_5)_2O$			No reaction	35
		CH_2N_2-$B$is, 2	C_2H_5OH	Cold	Several days	[Oxide from ?-keto-5,6,7,8,9,10-hexahydrocyclooctabenzene] (32), unidentified ketone	25
		CH_2N_2-$B$is, 2	C_2H_5OH	10–15	28 d.	[2-Ketobenzocyclooctane] (6–7), unidentified non-ketonic fraction (7–8)	189
	β-Tetralone	CH_2N_2	$(C_2H_5)_2O$-CH_3OH	20	36 hr.	Oxide (56), unidentified oil (30)	35
		CH_3CHN_2				Unidentified products ‡	35
$C_{10}H_{14}O_2$	Camphorquinone	CH_2N_2-A	C_6H_6-CH_3OH	0–20	18 hr.	Compounds D and E (90) (26 of one isomer)	76, 77, 78
$C_{10}H_{18}O$	4-t-Butylcyclohexanone	CH_2N_2				4-t-Butylcycloheptanone (55)	190

Formula	Carbonyl compound	Diazo compound	Solvent	Temp.	Time	Products	Ref.
$C_{11}H_{12}O$	1-Benzosuberone	$N_2CHCO_2C_2H_5$	$(C_2H_5)_2O$			Enol ether	90
$C_{11}H_{15}NO_3$	3-Isonitroso-1,8,8-trimethylbicyclo[3.2.1]octane-2,4-dione	CH_2N_2				O-Methyl derivative (52)	84
$C_{12}H_{10}O_4$	2-Carbethoxyindan-1,3-dione	CH_2N_2 i	$(C_2H_5)_2O\text{-}CH_3OH$			Indan-1,3-dione	74
		CH_2N_2	$(C_2H_5)_2O\text{-}CH_3OH$			Ethyl 1-hydroxy-4-methoxynaphthalene-2-carboxylate, indan-1,3-dione (trace)	74,75
$C_{12}H_{14}O$	2-Phenylcyclohexanone	CH_2N_2-Bis, g	CH_3OH	25-30	12 hr.	2-Phenylcycloheptanone (37), 3-phenylcycloheptanone (12), oxide (21)	101
$C_{12}H_{20}O$	2-Cyclohexylcyclohexanone	CH_2N_2-B	$(C_2H_5)_2O$			?-Cyclohexylcycloheptanone (4-5)	34
$C_{13}H_6O_3$	Perinaphthindan-1,2,3-trione	CH_2N_2				Methylenedioxy derivative (84)	184
$C_{13}H_8O$	Fluorenone	CH_2N_2-Bis, g	$(C_2H_5)_2O\text{-}CH_3OH$	20	18 hr.	9-Methoxyphenanthrene (30), 9-phenanthrol (5)	71
$C_{13}H_{14}O$	3-Ketohexahydrofluorene	CH_2N_2	$(C_2H_5)_2O\text{-}CH_3OH$	15-16	3 d.	Compound F (53)	186
	Diphenylketene	$(C_6H_5)_2CN_2$	$(C_2H_5)_2O$	15-20	Several hours	Compound G (R = C_6H_5)	21
		$p\text{-}CH_3OC_6H_4C(N_2)C_6H_5$	$(C_2H_5)_2O$, pet. ether	15-20	1 d.	Compound G (R = $p\text{-}CH_3OC_6H_4$)	21
		$N_2CHCO_2CH_3$	$(C_2H_5)_2O$	15-20	Several hours	Oxide, methyl 1-hydroxy-3,3-diphenylcyclopropene-2-carboxylate	21
		$N_2CHCO_2C_2H_5$	$(C_2H_5)_2O$ or pet. ether	15-20	Several hours	Oxide (35-49), ethyl 1-hydroxy-3,3-diphenylcyclopropene-2-carboxylate (15-21), unidentified products	21
		$C_6H_5COC(N_2)C_6H_5$	None		1 d.	Unidentified compound, $C_{42}H_{30}N_2O_3$ (83)	21
$C_{13}H_{16}O_2$	2-(p-Anisyl)cyclohexanone	CH_2N_2-Bis, g	CH_3OH	25	2 d.	2-(p-Anisyl)cycloheptanone (50), 3-(p-anisyl)cycloheptanone (10), oxide (10)	109
$C_{14}H_{24}O$	4,7-Dimethyl-2-isopropyltetrahydro-indan-5-one	CH_2N_2-Bis, g	C_2H_5OH	0	5 d.	Isomer of starting material	153
		CH_2N_2-B, 1	$(C_2H_5)_2O\text{-}CH_3OH$		2 d.	Unidentified ketones	153
		CH_2N_2-B, 1	$(C_2H_5)_2O\text{-}CH_3OH$		5 d.	Isomer of starting material, [5- (or 6-)keto-4,8-dimethyl-2-isopropylperhydroazulene] k	153

* References 155-217 are on pp. 428-429.

g The product was isolated in two stereoisomeric forms; the nature of the isomerism is unknown.

h The yields given in the experimental section in ref. 32 differ from those in the discussion, where a 20% yield of ketone is indicated.

i In this reaction 50% of the starting material was recovered.

j In this experiment one equivalent of diazomethane was used; in the following experiment an excess was used.

k The azulene was identified after dehydrogenation of the reaction products.

TABLE V—Continued
CARBOCYCLIC KETONES

Formula	Carbocyclic Ketone Name or Structure	Diazo Compound	Solvent	Temperature, °C	Time	Products (% yield)	Reference*
$C_{15}H_{10}O$	Methyleneanthrone	CH_2N_2	$(C_2H_5)_2O\text{-}CH_3OH$	0	2 d.	Compound H (R and R' = H)	191
		CH_3CHN_2	$(C_2H_5)_2O\text{-}CH_3OH$	0	2 d.	Compound H (R = CH_3, R' = H)	191
		$(C_6H_5)_2CN_2$	C_6H_6	80	30 min.	Compound H (R and R' = C_6H_5)	191
$C_{15}H_{10}O_3$	2-Hydroxy-2-phenylindan-1,3-dione	CH_2N_2	$(C_2H_5)_2O$	11	12 hr.	2-Methoxy-2-phenylindan-1,3-dione	192
$C_{15}H_{28}O$	Cyclopentadecanone	$CH_2N_2\text{-}B_{18}, 2$	CH_3OH	11	7 hr.	Cyclohexadecanone (3), cycloheptadecanone (13), oxides (20) [l]	63
		$CH_2N_2\text{-}B_{18}, 2$	CH_3OH	11	7–8 hr.	Higher ketones (30), oxides (33) [m]	63
		$CH_2N_2\text{-}B_{18}, 2$	CH_3OH	12	15 hr.	Cyclohexadecanone (6), cycloheptadecanone (25), cyclooctadecanone (1.3), cyclononadecanone (1.9), [higher ketones] (3), oxides [n]	63
$C_{16}H_{10}O$	2-Benzylidenehydrindan-1,3-dione	$N_2CHCO_2C_2H_5$	$(C_2H_5)_2O$	110–115	2.5 hr.	3-Carbethoxy-2-phenylspiro[cyclopropane-1,2'-indan]-1',3'-dione	193
$C_{17}H_{10}O$	Chrysofluorenone	$N_2CHCO_2C_2H_5$	$(C_2H_5)_2O$	125	16 hr.	Unidentified solid	193
		CH_2N_2	$(C_2H_5)_2O\text{-}CH_3OH$	20	16 hr.	6-Methoxychrysene	73
$C_{17}H_{16}O_5$	2,3,4,7-Tetramethoxyfluorenone	CH_2N_2	$(C_2H_5)_2O\text{-}CH_3OH$	0–20	14 hr.	2,3,4,7(or 10)-Pentamethoxyphenanthrene (44)	72
$C_{18}H_{10}O_3$	1-Hydroxypleiadene-7,12-dione	$CH_2N_2\text{-}A$ or B	$C_2H_2Cl_4$ [o] $\text{-}(C_2H_5)_2O$	Cold	4–5 hr.	Compound J (35–39) [p], 1-methoxypleiadene-7,12-dione (1.3)	80
$C_{19}H_{12}O_3$	1-Methoxypleiadene-7,12-dione	CH_2N_2	$C_2H_2Cl_4$			No reaction	80
$C_{21}H_{15}NO_2$	2-Oximino-3,3-diphenylindan-1-one	CH_2N_2	$(C_2H_5)_2O$		6 hr.	Compound C (R = H, R' = C_6H_5)	82
		CH_3CHN_2	$(C_2H_5)_2O$		6 hr.	Compound C (R = CH_3, R' = C_6H_5)	82

* References 155–217 are on pp. 428–429.   This experiment differs from the previous one in that a greater excess of diazomethane was employed.

[l] In this reaction 60% of the starting material was recovered.

[m] In this reaction 34% of the starting material was recovered.

[n] In this reaction 20% of the starting material was recovered. The oxides isolated amounted to 45% and were identified as those derived from the starting material and the several ring-enlarged ketones listed.

[o] No reaction took place in ether solution.

[p] Other structures are also proposed in ref. 80.

TABLE VI
HETEROCYCLIC KETONES

In product column, $A = O=C$

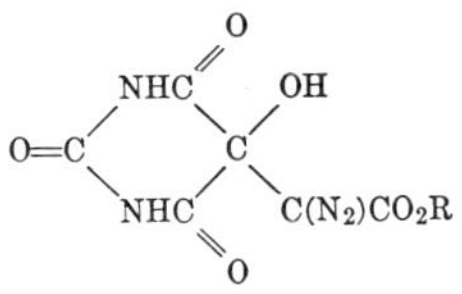

structure:
$$O=C \begin{array}{c} NHC=O \\ \diagdown C \diagup OH \\ \diagup \diagdown C(N_2)CO_2R \\ NHC=O \end{array}$$

Formula	Heterocyclic Ketone Name or Structure	Diazo Compound	Solvent	Temperature, °C	Time	Products (% yield)	Reference [*]
$C_4H_2N_2O_4$	Alloxan	CH_2N_2	$(C_2H_5)_2O$			Unidentified product	194
	Alloxan (monohydrate)	CH_2N_2				Oxide from N,N'-dimethylalloxan (quant.)	19, 53
	Alloxan (tetrahydrate)	$N_2CHCO_2CH_3$		Hot	5–8 hr.	Compound A (R = CH_3) (95)	93
		$N_2CHCO_2CH_3$		20	8 min.	Compound A (R = CH_3) (quant.)	93
		$N_2CHCO_2C_2H_5$		Hot	5 d.	Compound A (R = C_2H_5) (90–95)	93
		$N_2CHCO_2C_2H_5$		20	8 min.	Compound A (R = C_2H_5) (quant.)	93
$C_4H_2N_2O_3$	Isobarbituric acid	CH_2N_2			5 d.	Enol ether	53
$C_4H_4N_2O_4$	Isodialuric acid	CH_2N_2			24 hr.	Unidentified product	53
$C_5H_4N_2O_4$	N-Methylalloxan (dihydrate)	$N_2CHCO_2C_2H_5$		Hot	4 d.	N-Methyl derivative of compound A (R = C_2H_5) (90)	93
$C_5H_4O_4$	Acetonedicarboxylic anhydride	$N_2CHCO_2CH_3$	$(C_2H_5)_2O$	20 or hot		No product isolated	93
C_5H_5NO	γ-Pyridone	CH_2N_2-B				4,6-Dimethoxy-γ-pyrone (80)	195
		CH_2N_2				4-Methoxypyridine, N-methyl-γ-pyridone	196, 197
$C_6H_6N_2O_4$	N,N'-Dimethylalloxan (monohydrate)	CH_2N_2	$(C_2H_5)_2O$		5–8 hr.	Oxide	53, 19
		CH_2N_2	$(C_2H_5)_2O$		28 d.	Oxide (very low)	53
		CH_2N_2	$(C_2H_5)_2O$-H_2O			Oxide (higher than in previous example)	53
		$N_2CHCO_2CH_3$				No product isolated	93
		$N_2CHCO_2C_2H_5$				No product isolated	93
$C_6H_6O_4$	4-Hydroxy-6-methoxy-α-pyrone	CH_2N_2	$(C_2H_5)_2O$-CH_3OH			Enol ether	195
	α-Keto-β-acetylbutyrolactone	CH_2N_2				Enol ether	198
$C_7H_8ClN_2O_4$	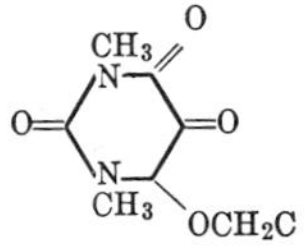 [structure]	CH_2N_2				Enol ether	53

* References 155–217 are on pp. 428–429.

TABLE VI—*Continued*

HETEROCYCLIC KETONES

Formula	Heterocyclic Ketone Name or Structure	Diazo Compound	Solvent	Temperature, °C	Time	Products (% yield)	Reference *
$C_8H_3BrClNO_2$	4-Chloro-5-bromoisatin	CH_2N_2	$(C_2H_5)_2O$			5-Chloro-6-bromo-2,3-dihydroxyquinoline	92
$C_8H_3Br_2NO_2$	5,7-Dibromoisatin	CH_2N_2	$(C_2H_5)_2O$		24 hr.	6,8-Dibromo-2,3-diketotetrahydroquinoline (67)	92
$C_8H_3Cl_2NO_2$	5,7-Dichloroisatin	CH_2N_2	$(C_2H_5)_2O$		24 hr.	6,8-Dichloro-2,3-diketotetrahydroquinoline	92
$C_8H_4BrNO_2$	5-Bromoisatin	CH_2N_2	$(C_2H_5)_2O$			6-Bromo-2,3-diketotetrahydroquinoline and an isomer	92
$C_8H_4ClNO_2$	5-Chloroisatin	CH_2N_2	$(C_2H_5)_2O$	0	24 hr.	6-Chloro-2,3-diketotetrahydroquinoline (69)	92
$C_8H_4O_2S$	2,3-Dihydrothianaphthene-2,3-dione	CH_2N_2	$(C_2H_5)_2O$	0	24 hr.	Methylenedioxy derivative	62
$C_8H_4O_3$	Coumaran-2,3-dione	CH_2N_2	$(C_2H_5)_2O$		24 hr.	Methylenedioxy derivative	62
$C_8H_5NO_2$	Isatin	CH_2N_2-B	$(C_2H_5)_2O$		24 hr.	2,3-Dihydroxyquinoline (60–90), 2-hydroxy-3-methoxyquinoline, oxide, unidentified products	91, 92
		CH_2N_2-B	$(C_2H_5)_2O\cdot H_2O$ or CH_3OH	−5	3–4 hr.	2,3-Dihydroxyquinoline (18–27), 2-hydroxy-3-methoxyquinoline (13–52), oxide (14–17)	19
$C_8H_5NO_3$	1-Hydroxyisatin	CH_2N_2	$(C_2H_5)_2O$		18 hr.	Unidentified product	199
		CH_2N_2	$(C_2H_5)_2O\cdot CH_3COCH_3$		18 hr.	3-Hydroxy-1-methoxycarbostyril (46) with 1 equiv. CH_2N_2, 1,3-dimethoxycarbostyril (46) with 2 equiv. CH_2N_2	29
$C_8H_4N_4O_8$	Alloxantin (dihydrate)	CH_2N_2				5,6-Dimethoxy-1,3-dimethyluracil (50–70), oxide from N,N'-dimethylalloxan (100)	53
$C_8H_6O_3S$	2,3-Dihydro-3-ketothianaphthene-1,1-dioxide	CH_2N_2	$(C_2H_5)_2O$		12 hr.	Enol ether (55)	43
$C_9H_5Br_2NO_2$	5,7-Dibromo-1-methylisatin	CH_2N_2	$[(C_2H_5)_2O]$	(20)		6,8-Dibromo-2,3-diketo-1-methyltetrahydroquinoline, unidentified solid	92
$C_9H_6ClNO_2$	5-Chloro-1-methylisatin	CH_2N_2	$[(C_2H_5)_2O]$	(20)	(24 hr.)	6-Chloro-2,3-diketo-1-methyltetrahydroquinoline	92
$C_9H_7NO_2$	7-Methylisatin	CH_2N_2	$(C_2H_5)_2O$	(20)	24 hr.	2,3-Dihydroxy-8-methylquinoline	92
	1-Methylisatin	CH_2N_2	$(C_2H_5)_2O$	(20)		3-Hydroxy-2-keto-1-methylquinoline	92
$C_{10}H_9NO_2$	5,7-Dimethylisatin	CH_2N_2-B	$(C_2H_5)_2O$	(20)	(24 hr.)	2,3-Dihydroxy-6,8-dimethylquinoline	91
	1,7-Dimethylisatin	CH_2N_2	$(C_2H_5)_2O$	(20)	24 hr.	2,3-Diketo-1,8-dimethyltetrahydroquinoline	92
$C_{11}H_{10}O_5S$	2-Carbethoxy-2,3-dihydro-3-keto-thianaphthene-1,1-dioxide	CH_2N_2	$(C_2H_5)_2O$			Enol ether (86)	43
		$N_2CHCO_2C_2H_5$	$CHCl_3$	Hot	4 hr.	Enol ether	43

Formula	Name	Diazo	Solvent	Yield	Time	Products	Reference[*]
$C_{11}H_{11}NO_2$	4,5,7-Trimethylisatin	CH_2N_2	$(C_2H_5)_2O$	(20)		2,3-Dihydroxy-5,6,8-trimethylquinoline	92
$C_{11}H_{14}N_4O_8$	Tetramethylalloxantin	CH_2N_2	$(C_2H_5)_2O$		1–2 d.	5,6-Dimethoxy-1,3-dimethyluracil (quant.)	53
$C_{12}H_6O_3$	4,5-Benzocoumaran-2,3-dione	CH_2N_2	$(C_2H_5)_2O$	0	24 hr.	Methylenedioxy derivative	62
$C_{12}H_6O_3$	6,7-Benzocoumaran-2,3-dione	CH_2N_2	$(C_2H_5)_2O$	0	24 hr.	Methylenedioxy derivative	62
$C_{12}H_7NO_2$	4,5-Benzoindoline-2,3-dione	CH_2N_2	$[(C_2H_5)_2O]$	(20)		Unidentified product	92
$C_{12}H_{13}NO_2$	1,4,5,7-Tetramethylisatin	CH_2N_2	$[(C_2H_5)_2O]$	(20)		Unidentified product (low)	92
$C_{13}H_9NO_2$	1-Methyl-4,5-benzoindoline-2,3-dione	CH_2N_2	$[(C_2H_5)_2O]$	(20)		Unidentified product	92
$C_{14}H_{12}O_3$	7-Phenyl-3a,4,5,6-tetrahydrocoumaran-2,3-dione	CH_2N_2	$(C_2H_5)_2O$	0		Enol ether (quant.)	200

TABLE VII

α,β-Unsaturated Aldehydes and Ketones

In product column, A = [structure], B = [structure], C = [structure]

Formula	α,β-Unsaturated Compound Name or Structure	Diazo Compound	Solvent	Temperature, °C	Time	Products (% yield)	Reference[*]
C_3H_2O	2-Propynal	CH_2N_2	$(C_2H_5)_2O$			Pyrazole-3-carboxaldehyde	201
		$N_2CHCO_2C_2H_5$				5-Carbethoxypyrazole-3-carboxaldehyde	201
C_3H_4O	Acrolein	CH_2N_2	$(C_2H_5)_2O$	0		Unidentified product	201
C_4H_5ClO	1-Chloro-3-keto-1-butene	CH_2N_2-A	$(C_2H_5)_2O$		1 hr.	Methyl 3-pyrazolyl ketone (67)	97, 98
		$N_2CHCO_2C_2H_5$-A		80		Ethyl 3-acetylpyrazole-5-carboxylate (34)	98
C_5H_7ClO	1-Chloro-3-keto-1-pentene	CH_2N_2-A	$(C_2H_5)_2O$	Cold	Several hours	Ethyl 3-pyrazolyl ketone (90)	98
C_6H_8O	Cyclohexenone	CH_2N_2	$(C_2H_5)_2O$			Unidentified addition products	34
C_6H_9ClO	1-Chloro-3-keto-1-hexene	CH_2N_2-A	$(C_2H_5)_2O$	Cold	Several hours	n-Propyl 3-pyrazolyl ketone (71)	98

* References 155–217 are on pp. 428–429.

TABLE VII—*Continued*

α,β-Unsaturated Aldehydes and Ketones

Formula	α,β-Unsaturated Compound Name or Structure	Diazo Compound	Solvent	Temperature, °C	Time	Products (% yield)	Reference*
$C_6H_{10}O$	Mesityl oxide	CH_2N_2				[Pyrazoline] [a]	38
		CH_3CHN_2				[Pyrazoline] [a]	38
		$(C_6H_5)_2CN_2$				No reaction	89
$C_7H_{11}ClO$	1-Chloro-3-keto-5-methyl-1-hexene	CH_2N_2-A	$(C_2H_5)_2O$	Cold	Several hours	Isobutyl 3-pyrazolyl ketone (73)	98
$C_{10}H_{10}O$	Benzalacetone	CH_2N_2-B	$(C_2H_5)_2O$		12 hr.	Δ²-Pyrazoline (58)	202
		CH_2N_2	$(C_2H_5)_2O$	−5 to 0	75 min.	Δ²-Pyrazoline (62) [b]	94
		CH_2N_2-A	$(C_2H_5)_2O$	0		Δ¹-Pyrazoline (85)	203
$C_{10}H_{16}O$	Pulegone	CH_2N_2				Isopulegone, unidentified addition product (30)	34
$C_{13}H_{16}O_2$	2,6,7-Trimethyl-1,4,4a,5,8,8a-hexahydronaphthalene-1,4-dione	CH_2N_2				Compound A	28
$C_{14}H_8O_3$	2-Furylideneindan-1,3-dione	CH_2N_2-A	$(C_2H_5)_2O$-CH_3OH	0	48 hr.	Compound B (R = furyl)	191
$C_{15}H_{12}O$	Benzalacetophenone	CH_2N_2-A	$(C_2H_5)_2O$	−14	1 hr.	Δ¹-Pyrazoline and Δ²-pyrazoline (100)	204
		CH_2N_2-A	$(C_2H_5)_2O$	0		Δ¹-Pyrazoline (67)	203
		$N_2CHCO_2C_2H_5$				Δ²-Pyrazoline	205
$C_{16}H_9ClO_2$	2-(p-Chlorobenzylidene)indan-1,3-dione	CH_2N_2-A	$(C_2H_5)_2O$-CH_3OH	0	48 hr.	Compound B (R = p-chlorophenyl)	191
$C_{16}H_9NO_4$	2-(o-Nitrobenzylidene)indan-1,3-dione	CH_2N_2-A	$(C_2H_5)_2O$-CH_3OH	0	48 hr.	Compound B (R = o-nitrophenyl)	191
	2-(p-Nitrobenzylidene)indan-1,3-dione	CH_2N_2-A	$(C_2H_5)_2O$-CH_3OH	0	48 hr.	Compound B (R = p-nitrophenyl)	191
$C_{16}H_{11}O_2$	2-Benzylideneindan-1,3-dione	CH_2N_2-A	$(C_2H_5)_2O$-$CHCl_3$	0	48 hr.	Compound B (R = phenyl)	191
$C_{16}H_{12}O_2$	trans-Dibenzoylethylene	CH_2N_2-A	$(C_2H_5)_2O$-$CHCl_3$	−10	30 min.	Δ¹-Pyrazoline (100)	95
		$C_6H_5CHN_2$	$CH_3CO_2C_2H_5$-$CHCl_3$		18 hr.	No identifiable products	95
		$(C_2H_5)_2CN_2$	Pet. ether-$CHCl_3$		18 hr.	Δ¹-Pyrazoline (47), 1,1-diphenyl-2,3-dibenzoylcyclopropane (20)	95
	cis-Dibenzoylethylene	CH_2N_2-A	$(C_2H_5)_2O$-$CHCl_3$	−10	30 min.	Δ²-Pyrazoline (80)	95
		$(C_6H_5)_2CN_2$	Pet. ether-$CHCl_3$		8 d.	Δ¹-Pyrazoline of trans-dibenzoylethylene (13)	95
$C_{17}H_{10}O_4$	2-(Piperonylidene)indan-1,3-dione	CH_2N_2-A	$(C_2H_5)_2O$-CH_3OH	0	48 hr.	Compound B (R = 3,4-methylenedioxyphenyl)	191
$C_{17}H_{12}O_3$	2-(p-Anisylidene)indan-1,3-dione	CH_2N_2-A	$(C_2H_5)_2O$-CH_3OH	0	48 hr.	Compound B (R = p-anisyl)	191
$C_{17}H_{14}O$	Dibenzalacetone	CH_2N_2-B			24 hr.	Mixture of bis-pyrazolines	202
		$(C_6H_5)_2CN_2$				No reaction	89

Formula	Compound	Diazoalkane	Solvent	Yield (%)	Time	Product	Ref.
$C_{18}H_{15}NO_2$	2-(p-Dimethylaminobenzylidene)in-dan-1,3-dione	CH_2N_2-A	$(C_2H_5)_2O$-CH_3OH	0	48 hr.	Compound B (R = p-dimethylaminophenyl)	191
$C_{18}H_{18}O_2$	6,7-Dimethyl-2-phenyl-1,4,4a,5,8,8a-hexahydronaphthalene-1,4-dione	CH_2N_2	$(C_2H_5)_2O$-CH_3OH		24 hr.	Unidentified $C_{19}H_{20}N_2O_2$ compound	28
$C_{20}H_{14}O_2$	2-Furylidene-3-phenylindan-1-one	CH_2N_2-A	$(C_2H_5)_2O$-CH_3OH	0	3 d.	Δ^2-Pyrazoline	206
$C_{20}H_{19}NO_2$	2-(p-Diethylaminobenzylidene)in-dan-1,3-dione	CH_2N_2-A	$(C_2H_5)_2O$-CH_3OH	0	48 hr.	Compound B (R = p-diethylaminophenyl)	189
$C_{21}H_{14}O$	2,3-Diphenylindan-1-one	CH_2N_2	$(C_2H_5)_2O$			No reaction	27
$C_{21}H_{28}O_2$	16-Dehydroprogesterone	CH_2N_2-A	$(C_2H_5)_2O$	20	18 hr.	Δ^1-Pyrazoline (cf. partial structure C)	96
$C_{21}H_{30}O_2$	5,16-Pregnadiene-3β-ol-20-one	CH_2N_2-A	$(C_2H_5)_2O$	20	24 hr.	Δ^1-Pyrazoline (cf. partial structure C)	96
	Progesterone	CH_2N_2-A	$(C_2H_5)_2O$	(20)		No reaction	96
$C_{22}H_{15}ClO$	2-(o-Chlorobenzylidene)-3-phenylin-dan-1-one	CH_2N_2-A	$(C_2H_5)_2O$-CH_3OH	0	3 d.	Δ^2-Pyrazoline	206
$C_{22}H_{15}NO_3$	2-(m-Nitrobenzylidene)-3-phenylin-dan-1-one	CH_2N_2-A	$(C_2H_5)_2O$-CH_3OH	0	3 d.	Δ^2-Pyrazoline	206
$C_{22}H_{16}O$	2-Benzylidene-3-phenylindan-1-one	CH_2N_2-A	$(C_2H_5)_2O$-CH_3OH	0	3 d.	Δ^2-Pyrazoline	206
$C_{23}H_{18}O$	2-(p-Methylbenzylidene)-3-phenyl-indan-1-one	CH_2N_2-A	$(C_2H_5)_2O$-CH_3OH	0	3 d.	Δ^2-Pyrazoline	206
$C_{23}H_{18}O_2$	2-(o-Methoxybenzylidene)-3-phenyl-indan-1-one	CH_2N_2-A	$(C_2H_5)_2O$-CH_3OH	0	3 d.	Δ^2-Pyrazoline	206
	2-(p-Methoxybenzylidene)-3-phenyl-indan-1-one	CH_2N_2-A	$(C_2H_5)_2O$-CH_3OH	0	3 d.	Δ^2-Pyrazoline	206
$C_{23}H_{32}O_3$	5,16-Pregnadiene-3β-ol-20-one-3-acetate	CH_2N_2-A	$(C_2H_5)_2O$	20	40 hr.	Δ^1-Pyrazoline (cf. partial structure C)	96

* References 155–217 are on pp. 428–429.

a The interaction of mesityl oxide with diazoalkanes, probably to give pyrazolines, has been observed as a side reaction in the preparation of diazoalkanes by the methyl nitrosoalkylamino-isobutyl ketone method.[38]

b In this reaction 46% of the starting material was recovered.

TABLE VIII

QUINONES

STRUCTURES FOR TABLE VIII

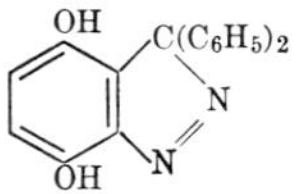

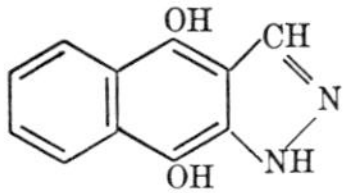

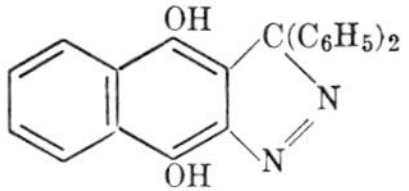

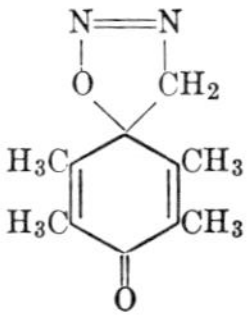

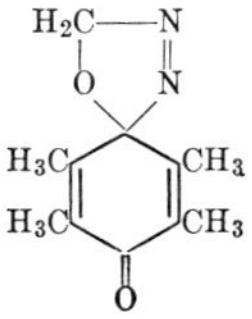

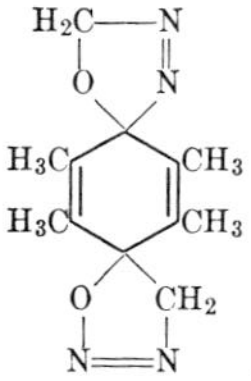

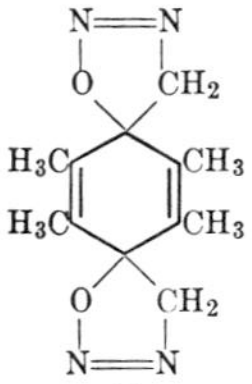

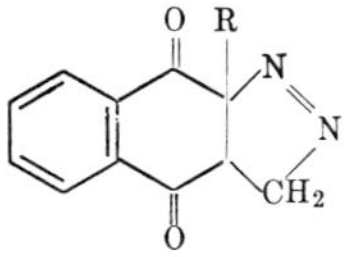

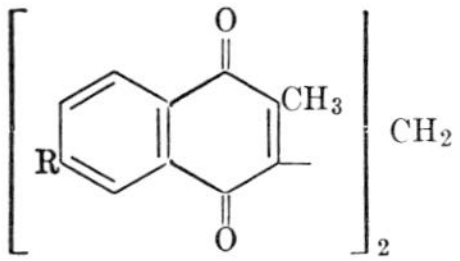

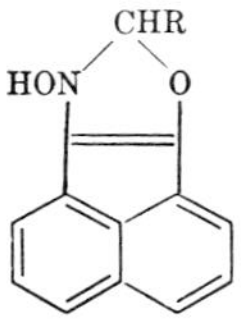

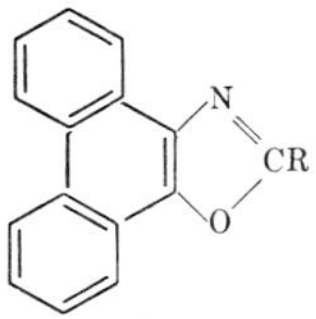

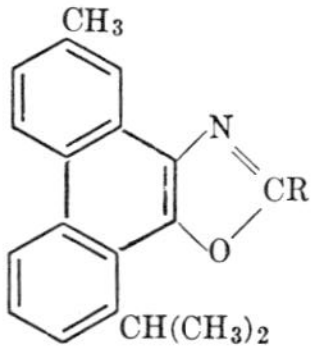

Formula	Quinone Name or Structure	Diazo Compound	Solvent	Temperature, °C	Time	Products (% yield)	Reference*
$C_6Br_4O_2$	Tetrabromo-1,2-benzoquinone	CH_2N_2-A	$(C_2H_5)_2O$	20		Methylenedioxy derivative (80)	207, 208
		$(C_6H_5)_2CN_2$	Pet. ether-C_6H_6			Methylenedioxy derivative (good)	207
		Diazofluorene	C_6H_6			Methylenedioxy derivative (86, quant.)	207, 209
		$N_2CHCO_2C_2H_5$	$(C_2H_5)_2O$-C_6H_6-CH_3OH	20–reflux	24 hr.	Methylenedioxy derivative	209
$C_6Cl_4O_2$	Tetrachloro-1,2-benzoquinone	CH_2N_2-A	$(C_2H_5)_2O$	20	90 min.	Methylenedioxy derivative (80)	207, 209
		$(C_6H_5)_2CN_2$	C_6H_6-CH_3OH	20	24 hr.	Methylenedioxy derivative (80)	207, 208
		Diazofluorene	C_6H_6	20–reflux	24 hr.	Methylenedioxy derivative (quant.)	207, 209
		$N_2CHCO_2C_2H_5$	$(C_2H_5)_2O$			Methylenedioxy derivative	209
$C_6H_4O_2$	1,4-Benzoquinone	CH_2N_2-B	$(C_2H_5)_2O$	Cold	1–2 d.	Di-Δ^2-pyrazoline (quinone form) (35)	3
		CH_2N_2	$(C_2H_5)_2O$			Unidentified addition product	53
		$(C_6H_5)_2CN_2$				Unidentified product	89
		$(C_6H_5)_2CN_2$	C_6H_6			Compound A (93)	101
$C_7H_6O_3$	Methoxy-1,4-benzoquinone	$N_2CHCO_2C_2H_5$	Pet. ether	80–100	2 hr.	Δ^2-Pyrazoline (3)	210
$C_8H_8O_2$	Xyloquinone	CH_2N_2	$(C_2H_5)_2O$			Unidentified $C_{10}H_{12}N_4O_2$ compound	211
$C_{10}H_4Cl_2O_2$	3,4-Dichloro-1,2-naphthoquinone	Diazofluorene	C_6H_6	20	4 d.	Methylenedioxy derivative (70)	209
$C_{10}H_5BrO_2$	6-Bromo-1,2-naphthoquinone	CH_2N_2	$(C_2H_5)_2O$			Δ^1-Pyrazoline (quinone form)	28
		CH_2N_2	$(C_2H_5)_2O$-C_6H_6-(CH_3OH)	Cold	24 hr.	Unidentified product	102
$C_{10}H_6O_2$	1,4-Naphthoquinone	$(C_6H_5)_2CN_2$	C_6H_6-pet. ether		15 hr.	Methylenedioxy derivative (92)	102
		$N_2CHCO_2C_2H_5$	Toluene	100	18 hr.	No reaction	102
		CH_2N_2-B	$(C_2H_5)_2O$	0–5		Δ^2-Pyrazoline (quinone form) (80)	212
		CH_2N_2-B	$(C_2H_5)_2O$			Compound B (93)	101
		$(C_6H_5)_2CN_2$	Pet. ether-C_6H_6	Heat	Several hours	Compound C (44)	101
		$N_2CHCO_2C_2H_5$	$(C_2H_5)_2O$-C_6H_6	20–reflux	18 hr.	1,4-Naphthalenediol (48), Δ^1-pyrazoline (quinone form) (47)	101
	1,2-Naphthoquinone	CH_2N_2	$(C_2H_5)_2O$			Unidentified compounds	213
		CH_2N_2	$(C_2H_5)_2O$			Methylenedioxy derivative	53
$C_{10}H_6O_3$	5-Hydroxy-1,4-naphthoquinone	CH_2N_2	$(C_2H_5)_2O$	20	1 hr.	Δ^2-Pyrazoline (quinone form)	105
$C_{10}H_6O_5$	5,6,8-Trihydroxy-1,4-naphthoquinone	CH_2N_2	$(C_2H_5)_2O$			Δ^2-Pyrazoline (quinone form)	103
$C_{10}H_{12}O_2$	2,3,5,6-Tetramethyl-1,4-benzoquinone	CH_2N_2-A	$(C_2H_5)_2O$-CH_3OH	−10 to −5	11 d.	Compounds D and E (47), compound F (53)	22

* References 155–217 are on pp. 428–429.

TABLE VIII—Continued

QUINONES

Formula	Quinone Name or Structure	Diazo Compound	Solvent	Temperature, °C	Time	Products (% yield)	Reference*
$C_{10}H_{12}O_2$	2,3,5,6-Tetramethyl-1,4-benzoquinone (Cont.)	CH_2N_2-A	$(C_2H_5)_2O$	-10 to -5	11 d.	Compounds D and E (35), compound G (57)	22
$C_{11}H_8O_2$	2-Methyl-1,4-naphthoquinone	CH_2N_2	$(C_2H_5)_2O$	0	24 hr.	2,3-Dimethyl-1,4-naphthoquinone, compound H (R = CH₃), compound J (R = H)	28
$C_{11}H_{14}N_2O_2$	Compound D	CH_2N_2-A	$(C_2H_5)_2O$-CH_3OH	5-10	3 d.	Compound F (27)	22
	Compound E	CH_2N_2	$(C_2H_5)_2O$	0-5	10 d.	Compound F (39)	22
$C_{12}Br_6O_4$	1,4,6,7,8,9-Hexabromodibenzo-p-dioxin-2,3-quinone	CH_2N_2	Dioxane		Several hours	Methylenedioxy derivative	207
		$(C_6H_5)_2CN_2$	Dioxane	100	2 hr.	Methylenedioxy derivative	207
		Diazofluorene	Dioxane		1 hr.	Unidentified product	207
$C_{12}Cl_6O_4$	1,4,6,7,8,9-Hexachlorodibenzo-p-dioxin-2,3-quinone	CH_2N_2	Dioxane		Several hours	Methylenedioxy derivative	207
$C_{12}H_7NO_2$	Acenaphthenequinone monoxime	CH_2N_2	$(C_2H_5)_2O$		6 hr.	Compound K (R = H)	82
		CH_2CHN_2	$(C_2H_5)_2O$		6 hr.	Compound K (R = CH₃)	82
$C_{12}H_8O_4$	6-Acetyl-5-hydroxy-1,4-naphthoquinone	CH_2N_2-A	$(C_2H_5)_2O$			Δ²-Pyrazoline (quinone form) a (98)	104
$C_{12}H_{10}O_2$	2,6-Dimethyl-1,4-naphthoquinone	CH_2N_2-B	$(C_2H_5)_2O$-C_6H_6	20-reflux	18 hr.	Compound J (R = CH₃) (40) b	214
		CH_2N_2		0	2 d.	Compound J (R = CH₃), [2,3,6-trimethyl-1,4-naphthoquinone], unidentified product	28
$C_{13}H_{12}O_2$	2,6,7-Trimethyl-1,4-naphthoquinone	CH_2N_2	CH_3OH	20	24 hr.	2,3,6,7-Tetramethyl-1,4-naphthoquinone	28
$C_{14}H_8O_2$	9,10-Phenanthrenequinone	CH_2N_2-B, 3	$(C_2H_5)_2O$	Cold-reflux	24 hr.	Methylenedioxy derivative	53, 213
		CH_2N_2	$(C_2H_5)_2O$-CH_3OH (trace)		18 hr.	Oxide (90), unidentified oil	29
		CH_2N_2	$(C_2H_5)_2O$-CH_3OH (20%)		15 min.	Methylenedioxy derivative	29
		CH_2N_2	$(C_2H_5)_2O$-CH_3OH (3-5%)			Oxide (49), methylenedioxy derivative (41)	29
		$C_6H_5CHN_2$	C_6H_6	20	24 hr.	Methylenedioxy derivative	148
		$(C_6H_5)(CH_3)CN_2$	C_6H_6	20	24 hr.	Methylenedioxy derivative	148
		$(C_6H_5)_2CN_2$	C_6H_6	20	24 hr.	Methylenedioxy derivative	148

		Diazofluorene	C6H6 or CHCl3				
$C_{14}H_9NO$	Anthraquinone	CH_2N_2	$(C_2H_5)_2O$-H_2O	20	7 d.	No reaction	209
	9,10-Phenanthrenequinone monoimine	CH_3CHN_2-A, 1	$(C_2H_5)_2O$	Cold	2 mo.	No reaction	53
$C_{14}H_9NO_2$	9,10-Phenanthrenequinone monoxime	CH_3CHN_2-A, 1	$(C_2H_5)_2O$	Cold		Compound L (R = H)	215
		CH_2N_2	$(C_2H_5)_2O$		6 hr.	Compound L (R = CH3)	215
		CH_3CHN_2	$(C_2H_5)_2O$		6 hr.	Compound L (R = H)	215
$C_{14}H_{10}O_6$	5,6-Diacetoxy-1,4-naphthoquinone	CH_2N_2-B	$CHCl_3$	0	2 d.	Compound L (R = CH3)	212
	5,8-Diacetoxy-1,4-naphthoquinone	CH_2N_2	$(C_2H_5)_2O$	20	1 hr.	Δ^2-Pyrazoline (quinone form) (50)	105
$C_{17}H_{18}O_4$	5,8-Dihydroxy-6-R-1,4-naphthoquinone R = $(CH_3)_2C=CHCH_2CH—$ OCH3	CH_2N_2	$(C_2H_5)_2O$-CH_3OH			Δ^2-Pyrazoline (quinone form) [Δ^1-Pyrazoline (quinone form)]	216
$C_{18}H_{10}O_2$	Chrysenequinone	CH_2N_2	$(C_2H_5)_2O$	0	16 hr.	Methylenedioxy derivative	148
		$(C_6H_5)_2CHN_2$	C_6H_6			Methylenedioxy derivative	148
$C_{18}H_{11}NO_2$	Chrysenequinone monoxime	CH_3CHN_2	$(C_2H_5)_2O$			Derivative similar to compound L (R = CH3)	82
$C_{18}H_{17}NO$	Retenequinone monoimine	CH_2N_2-A, 1	$(C_2H_5)_2O$	Cold	6 hr.	Compound M (R = H)	82
		CH_3CHN_2-A, 1	$(C_2H_5)_2O$	Cold		Compound M (R = CH3)	82
$C_{18}H_{17}NO_2$	Retenequinone monoxime	CH_2N_2	$(C_2H_5)_2O$		6 hr.	Compound M (R = H)	82
		CH_3CHN_2	$(C_2H_5)_2O$		6 hr.	Compound M (R = CH3)	82
$C_{19}H_{16}O_8$	Isoquercetone tetramethyl ether	CH_2N_2	$(C_2H_5)_2O$			Methylenedioxy derivative, unidentified product	217
$C_{23}H_{16}O_2$	2-Diphenylmethyl-1,4-naphthoquinone	CH_2N_2-B	$(C_2H_5)_2O$-C_6H_6	20–warm	1 hr.	Compound H, R = $(C_6H_5)_2CH—$ (89)	102
$C_{25}H_{17}BrO_2$	3-Bromo-5-triphenylmethyl-1,2-benzoquinone	Diazofluorene	C_6H_6		3 d.	Methylenedioxy derivative (70)	209
$C_{25}H_{18}O_2$	4-Triphenylmethyl-1,2-benzoquinone	$(C_6H_5)_2CN_2$	Pet. ether		16 hr.	No reaction	102
		$(C_6H_5)_2CN_2$	Pet. ether-C_2H_5OH		1 hr.	Methylenedioxy derivative (76)	102
		Diazofluorene	C_6H_6		3 d.	Methylenedioxy derivative (50)	209

* References 155–217 are on pp. 428–429.

a The quinone form of the product was obtained in high yield as a result of the addition of 1,4-benzoquinone to the reaction mixture. In the absence of benzoquinone, the quinone form was obtained only in low yield and as the N-methyl derivative.[104]

b In this reaction 60% of the starting material was recovered.

REFERENCES TO TABLES III–VIII

[155] Irrera, *Gazz. chim. ital.*, **62**, 30 (1932) [*C. A.*, **26**, 2963 (1932)].

[156] Caronna, *Gazz. chim. ital.*, **66**, 772 (1936) [*C. A.*, **31**, 3447 (1937)].

[157] Diels and Ilberg, *Ber.*, **49**, 158 (1916).

[158] Arndt and Rutz, footnote 15, p. 207, in Arndt, Amende, and Ender, *Monatsh.*, **59**, 202 (1932).

[159] Fischer and Taube, *Ber.*, **59**, 857 (1926).

[160] Yabuta and Tamura, *J. Agr. Chem. Soc. Japan*, **19**, 546 (1943) [*C. A.*, **46**, 965 (1952)].

[161] Sonn and Bülow, *Ber.*, **58**, 1691 (1925).

[162] Arndt and Partale, *Ber.*, **60**, 446 (1927).

[163] Tanasescu, *Bull. soc. chim. France*, [4], **43**, 1117 (1928).

[164] Arndt, Eistert, and Amende, *Ber.*, **61**, 1949 (1928).

[165] Bollinger, Hayes, and Siegel, *Abstracts*, p. 87M, A.C.S. Cleveland Meeting, April, 1951.

[166] Curtius, *J. prakt. Chem.*, [2], **38**, 396 (1888).

[167] Mosettig, *Ber.*, **62**, 1271 (1929).

[168] Glauert and Mann, *J. Chem. Soc.*, **1952**, 2127.

[169] Russell and Hitchings, *J. Am. Chem. Soc.*, **73**, 3763 (1951).

[170] Meyer, *Ber.*, **40**, 847 (1907).

[171] Cook and Thomson, *J. Chem. Soc.*, **1945**, 395.

[172] Blatt, *J. Am. Chem. Soc.*, **60**, 1164 (1938).

[173] Brigl, Mühlschlegel, and Schinle, *Ber.*, **64**, 2921 (1931).

[174] Arndt, Scholz, and Frobel, *Ann.*, **521**, 95 (1935).

[175] v. Pechmann, *Ber.*, **28**, 1624 (1895).

[176] Posternak, *Helv. Chim. Acta*, **27**, 457 (1944).

[177] Collie and Reilly, *J. Chem. Soc.*, **121**, 1984 (1922).

[178] Arndt, Loewe, and Beyer, *Ber.*, **74**, 1460 (1941).

[179] Dane and Höss, *Ann.*, **552**, 113 (1942).

[180] Mosettig and Burger, *J. Am. Chem. Soc.*, **52**, 3456 (1930).

[181] Steadman, *J. Am. Chem. Soc.*, **62**, 1606 (1940).

[182] Nozoe, Mukai, Kunori, Muroi, and Matsui, *Science Repts. Tohoku Univ.*, **35**, 242 (1952) [*C. A.*, **47**, 7475 (1953)].

[183] Qudrat-i-Khuda and Ghosh, *J. Indian Chem. Soc.*, **17**, 19 (1940).

[184] Moubasher, Awad, Ibrahim, and Othman, *J. Chem. Soc.*, **1950**, 1998.

[185] Plattner, Fürst, and Studer, *Helv. Chim. Acta*, **30**, 1091 (1947).

[186] Nunn and Rapson, *J. Chem. Soc.*, **1949**, 825.

[187] Nozoe, Seto, Kikuchi, Mukai, Matsumoto, and Murase, *Proc. Japan Acad.*, **26**, No. 7, 43 (1950) [*C. A.*, **45**, 7099 (1951)].

[188] Barbier, *Helv. Chim. Acta*, **23**, 519 (1940).

[189] Thompson, *J. Am. Chem. Soc.*, **66**, 156 (1944).

[190] Nozoe, Kishi, and Yoshikoshi, *Proc. Japan Acad.*, **27**, 149 (1951) [*C. A.*, **46**, 4523 (1952)].

[191] Mustafa and Hilmy, *J. Chem. Soc.*, **1952**, 1434.

[192] Moubasher, *J. Am. Chem. Soc.*, **73**, 3245 (1951).

[193] Rădulescu and Georgescu, *Bul. Soc. Stiinte Cluj*, **3**, 129 (1927) [*C. A.*, **21**, 3203 (1927)].

[194] Herzig, *Z. physiol. Chem.*, **117**, 13 (1921) [*C. A.*, **16**, 2678 (1922)].

[195] Lityński and Malachowski, *Roczniki Chem.*, **7**, 579 (1927) [*C. A.*, **22**, 4124 (1928)].

[196] Meyer, *Monatsh.*, **26**, 1311 (1905).

[197] Peratoner and Azzarello, *Atti accad. Lincei*, **15**, I, 139 (1906) [*Chem. Zentr.*, **1906**, I, 1439].

[198] Grove, *J. Chem. Soc.*, **1951**, 883.

[199] Arndt, Eistert, and Partale, *Ber.*, **60**, 1364 (1927).

[200] Bachmann, Fujimoto, and Wick, *J. Am. Chem. Soc.*, **72**, 1995 (1950).

[201] Hüttel, *Ber.*, **74**, 1680 (1941).

202 Azzarello, *Gazz. chim. ital.*, **36**, II, 50 (1906) [*Chem. Zentr.*, **1906**, II, 1130].
203 Ghate, Kaushal, and Deshapande, *J. Indian Chem. Soc.*, **27**, 633 (1950).
204 Smith and Pings, *J. Org. Chem.*, **2**, 23 (1937).
205 Kohler and Steele, *J. Am. Chem. Soc.*, **41**, 1093 (1919).
206 Mustafa and Hilmy, *J. Chem. Soc.*, **1951**, 3254.
207 Horner and Lingnau, *Ann.*, **573**, 30 (1951).
208 Schönberg, Awad, and Latif, *J. Chem. Soc.*, **1951**, 1368.
209 Schönberg and Latif, *J. Chem. Soc.*, **1952**, 446.
210 Bartels-Keith, Johnson, and Taylor, *J. Chem. Soc.*, **1951**, 2352.
211 Rotter and Schaudy, *Monatsh.*, **47**, 493 (1926).
212 v. Pechmann and Seel, *Ber.*, **32**, 2292 (1899).
213 Alessandri, *Atti accad. Lincei*, **22**, I, 517 (1913) [*C. A.*, **7**, 3494 (1913)].
214 Fieser and Seligman, *J. Am. Chem. Soc.*, **56**, 2690 (1934).
215 Schönberg and Awad, *J. Chem. Soc.*, **1947**, 651.
216 Raudnitz and Stein, *Ber.*, **68**, 1479 (1935).
217 Nierenstein, *J. Chem. Soc.*, **107**, 869 (1915).

INDEX

Numbers in **bold-face** type refer to experimental procedures.

Acetoacetic ester condensation, 67; *see also Vol. I*

Acetoacetylation of aromatic compounds, 105
  tabular survey, 187

3β-Acetoxy-5-cholen-24-al, **231**

Acetylacetone, **115, 122–124, 130**

Acetylation of ketones with ethyl acetate, 70–73

2-Acetylcyclohexanone, **122–124, 130–132**

2-Acetylcyclopentanone, **130–132**

Acetylenes, *Vol. V*

4-Acetyl-5-oxohexanoic acid, **332**

Acid anhydrides, self-condensation, 101
  use in acylating ketones, 98–106

Acid chlorides, use in acylating ketones, 95

Acids, α,β-unsaturated, preparation from β-lactones, 321–322, 324

1-Acyl-2-arylsulfonylhydrazines, conversion to aldehydes, 232–240

Acylation of ketones to β-diketones or β-ketonic aldehydes, 59–196
  comparison of methods, 106–110
  intramolecular, 79–85
  tabular survey, 134–187
  with basic reagents, 62–97
    condensing agents, 65–66
    effect of structure of reactants, 65–66
    experimental procedures, 111–128
    mechanism, 62–65
    related reactions, 97
    scope and limitations, 69–96
    side reactions, 66–69
  with boron fluoride, 98–106, 129–134
    experimental conditions, 129–130
    experimental procedures, 130–134
    mechanism, 99–101
    related reactions, 105–106
    scope and limitations, 102–105
    side reactions, 101–102

Acylhydrazines, oxidation to aldehydes, 233

Acyloins, *Vol. IV*

Alcohols, preparation by reductive desulfurization of thiol esters, 230

Aldehydes, preparation, 197–257
  by acid hydrolysis of Reissert's compounds, 220–224
  by method of Grundmann, 225–229
  by method of Hershberg, 225–226
  by method of Kalb-Gross, 233–234
  by method of McFadyen-Stevens, 232–240
  by method of Sonn and Müller, 240–246
  by method of Stephen, 246–252
  by reduction of amides and nitriles with lithium aluminum hydride, 252–257
  by reductive desulfurization of thiol esters, 229–233
  by Sommelet reaction, 197–217
  reaction with aliphatic diazo compounds, 372–375
  α,β-unsaturated, reaction with aliphatic diazo compounds, 384–385

Aliphatic diazo compounds, preparation, 389–391
  reaction with carbonyl compounds, 364–429
    experimental conditions, 393–398
    ex situ method, 394
    in situ method, 394
    experimental procedures, 398–402
    isolation and identification of products, 388–389
    mechanism, 367–371
    scope and limitations, 372–387
    side reactions, 396–398
    tabular survey, 402–427

Organolithium compounds, metalation with, 258–304

Organomagnesium compounds, use in preparation of ketones, 32–33
experimental procedures, 42

Organozinc compounds, preparation of, 31
use in preparation of ketones, 33–35
experimental procedures, 42–43

Oxalic esters, use in acylating ketones, 84–87

Pechmann reaction, *Vol. VII*

Periodic acid oxidation, *Vol. II*

Perkin reaction and related reactions, *Vol. I*

2-Phenanthraldehyde, **244**

3-Phenanthraldehyde, **244**

Phenylacetylpropionylmethane, **122–123, 125**

p-Phenylbenzoylacetone, **115–116**

1-Phenylbutane-1,3-dione, **130–132**

2-Phenylcycloheptanone, **401**

1-Phenyl-3-eicosanone, **44**

9-Phenylfluorene-9-carboxylic acid, **287**

1-Phenylhexane-1,3-dione, **130–132**

Phenyllithium, **286**

β-Phenylmercaptopropionic acid, **331**

9-Phenylnonatetraenal, **253**

1-Phenylpentane-1,3-dione, **130–132**

3-Phenylpentane-2,4-dione, **133–134**

α-Phenyltropic acid, **331**

Phosphonic and phosphinic acids, *Vol. VI*

Pictet-Gams synthesis of isoquinolines, *Vol. VI*

Pictet-Spengler synthesis of tetrahydroisoquinolines, *Vol. VI*

Pivaloylacetaldehyde, **122–123, 125**

Pivaloylacetone, **122–124, 126–128**

Polymetalation of diphenylmethane with ethyllithium, 266

Pomeranz-Fritsch synthesis of isoquinolines, *Vol. VI*

β-Propiolactone, **322–327**
tabular survey of reactions, 342–353

Propionylacetone, **122–124**

Propionylacetophenone, **122–123, 125**

Propionyl-*n*-butyrylmethane, **122–124**

2-Propionylcyclohexanone, **126–128, 130–132**

Propionylisovalerylmethane, **126–128**

Pyrazolines, from α,β-unsaturated carbonyl compounds and diazomethane, 384–386

Pyridine-3-carboxaldehyde, **211**

Pyridinium salts, conversion to aldehydes, 203

Quinodimethanes, 313–314

Quinolines, preparation by alkaline hydrolysis of Reissert's compounds, 222
Skraup synthesis of, *Vol. VII*

Quinones, reaction with diazomethane, 385–386

Raney nickel catalyst, use in reducing esters to alcohols, 23

Reissert's compounds, 220–223
acid hydrolysis to aldehydes, 220–223
alkaline hydrolysis to quinolines and isoquinolines, 220, 222

Rearrangements, carbonium ion following metalation of quaternary ammonium salts, 271–272
of carboxy-β-lactones to hydroxysuccinic anhydrides, 327–328
of esters of *o*-hydroxyacetophenones, 90
of β-lactones to acrylic acids, 328

Reduction, with aluminum alkoxides, *Vol. II*
with lithium aluminum hydride, *Vol. VI*

Reductive alkylation, *Vol. IV; see also Vol. V*

Reformatsky reaction, *Vol. I*

Replacement of aromatic primary amino group by hydrogen, *Vol. II*

Resolution of alcohols, *Vol. II*

Ring enlargement of cyclic ketones with diazomethane, 377–384

Rosenmund reduction, *Vol. IV*

Schiemann reaction, *Vol. V*

Schmidt reaction, *Vol. III*

Selenium dioxide oxidation, *Vol. V*

Skraup synthesis of quinolines, *Vol. VII*